ELDRIDGE
TIDE AND PILOT BOOK
2013

Our One Hundred Thirty-Ninth Year of Continuous Publication

CONTENTS

Publishers: **Robert Eldridge White, Jr. and Linda Foster White**
P.O. Box 775, Medfield, MA 02052   Tel. 617-482-8460
ebb2flood@gmail.com, www.eldridgetide.com   Fax: 617-482-8304

Copyright 2012 by Robert Eldridge White, Jr.

ISBN 978-1-883465-19-3

THE ORIGIN OF ELDRIDGE

In 1854 George Eldridge of Chatham, a celebrated cartographer, published "Eldridge's Pilot for Vineyard Sound and Monomoy Shoals." The book had 32 pages, a grey paper cover and no recorded price. Its pages were devoted to "Dangers," embellished with his personal observations, and to Compass Courses and Distances, etc. This volume was the precursor of the Tide and Pilot Book, which followed 21 years later.

In 1870 George Eldridge published another small book, called the "Compass Test," and asked his son, George W. Eldridge, to go to Vineyard Haven and sell it for him, along with the charts he produced.

Son George W. Eldridge was dynamic, restless, and inventive. He was glad to move to the Vineyard, for Vineyard Haven was at that time an important harbor for large vessels. The number of ships passing through Vineyard and Nantucket Sounds was second only to those plying the English Channel. As the ships came into the harbor (frequently as many as 100 schooners would anchor to await a fair current), George W. would go out to them in his catboat to sell his father's charts and the "Compass Test." He was constantly asked by mariners what time the current TURNED to run East or West in the Sound. He then began making observations, and one day, while in the ship chandlery of Charles Holmes, made the first draft of a current table. Shortly after, with the help of his father, he worked out the tables for places other than Vineyard Sound, and in 1875 the first Tide Book was published. It did not take long for mariners to realize the value of this information, and it soon became an indispensable book to all who sailed the Atlantic Coast from New York east. Gradually George W. added more important information, such as his explanation of the unusual currents which caused so many vessels to founder in the "Graveyard."

Captain George W. Eldridge based the tables on his own observations. In later years, knowing that the government's scientific calculations are the most accurate obtainable, the publishers have made use of them; some tables are directly taken from government figures and others, which the government does not give in daily schedules, are computed by the publishers from government predictions. Since the Captain's day there have been many changes and additions in the book to keep abreast of modern navigational aids.

In 1910 Captain George W. Eldridge transferred the management of the book to the next generation of his family, as he was interested in developing his chart business and inventing aids to navigation. At his death in 1914, his son-in-law became Publisher. Wilfrid O. White, an expert in marine navigation and President of Wilfrid O. White & Sons Co., compass manufacturers, served as Publisher until his death at 1955. Wilfrid's son Robert Eldridge White then became publisher, and with great help from his wife Molly he expanded the coverage of the book and significantly increased its readership. On Bob's death in 1990, Molly continued to expand the book's scope and circulation, with valuable assistance from her son Ridge and daughter-in-law Linda. On Molly's passing in 2004 the book moved once again into the hands of the next (fourth) generation. At every generational transfer the new Publisher was well prepared, each having apprenticed for years.

Whether new to ELDRIDGE or a longtime reader, we welcome you aboard! Please continue to offer your suggestions and, where necessary, corrections. Your sharp eyes keep us on course. We hope, as did Captain George W. Eldridge, that this book might ensure for you a "Fair Tide" and the safety of your ship.

Robert Eldridge White, Jr.
Linda Foster White
Publishers

Yours for a fair tide
Geo. W. Eldridge

3

About the 2013 ELDRIDGE, our 139th edition

☆ **NOTE:** *The information in this volume has been compiled from U. S. Government sources and others, and carefully checked. The Publishers cannot assume any liability for errors, omissions, or changes.*

Publishers: Robert Eldridge White, Jr. - Linda Foster White
Editorial and Advertising: Tel.: 617-482-8460, Fax: 617-482-8304
Email: ebb2flood@gmail.com, **Web:** www.eldridgetide.com
Mailing Address: P.O. Box 775, Medfield, MA 02052

Copyright 2012. All rights reserved. No part of this book may be reproduced in any form, by any means, without permission in writing from the Publishers.

New or Noteworthy Articles in the 2013 Edition

FREE SUPPLEMENT ON REQUEST - available after May 15, 2013
Changes and updates through May 1, 2013. To obtain a free Supplement:

1) Download a pdf from: www.eldridgetide.com *or*
   www.robertwhite.com (click on Eldridge)
2) Mail a stamped, self-addressed envelope, with your request, to:

ELDRIDGE TIDE & PILOT BOOK
P.O. Box 775
Medfield, MA 02052

I enclose a **stamped, self-addressed envelope**. Please send me a free Supplement, updating data through May 1, 2013.

Name   _____

Address   _____

City, State, Zip   _____

HOW TO USE THE TIDE AND CURRENT TABLES
AND CURRENT CHARTS

High and Low Water Tide Tables

In addition to presenting tide tables for nine reference ports, from Portland to Miami, we show the approximate time of High Water and the mean (average) height of high at some 350 substations.

- On pp. 12-20, find your harbor, or the nearest one to it, and note the time difference between it and the reference port.
- Apply this time difference to the reference table for that date. On average the Low Water will follow by about 6 hours, 12 minutes.
- When the height of High Water in the reference table is higher or lower than the average, it will be correspondingly higher or lower at your harbor.

Current Tables

There are eight current tables covering from Massachusetts to the Chesapeake. At over 300 other points, on pp. 22-29, we show the approximate time of current change, the directions of ebb and flood, and the average maximum velocities.

- Find the place you are concerned with, or the listed position nearest to it, and note the time difference between it and the reference location.
- Apply this time difference to the reference table for that date. On average, the current will change approximately every 6 hours, 12 minutes.
- When the velocity of the current in the reference table exceeds the average maximum, the current in your area will also exceed the average maximum.

Naming Currents

While it is traditional to name currents as Ebb or Flood, these terms can easily confuse. We recommend using the direction as the name of the current. It is more helpful to refer to an Easterly current, which means it is Eastbound or runs toward the East, than it is to name it as an Ebb or Flood Current, which leaves the listener guessing its direction.

Current Charts and Diagrams

- Find the appropriate current chart and note the table to which it is referenced. For instance, the Long Island Sound charts (pp. 92-97) reference the Race tables.
- Turn to this table, which shows the time of start of Flood and start of Ebb, and find the time of the start of the advantageous current for that day.
- The difference between having a fair current or a head current means hours and dollars to the slower moving vessel such as a trawler or auxiliary sailboat. See Smarter Boating, p. 36.

Effect of the Moon

It is wise to pay particular attention to the phase or position of the Moon. "Astronomical" tides and currents occur around the times of full and new moons, especially when the Moon is at Perigee, or closest to the Earth. Tides will be both higher and lower than average, and currents will run stronger than average. See pp. 234-236.

Why Tides and Currents Often Behave Differently

Frequently Asked Questions

We are often asked such questions as, **"Why are the times of high water and current change not the same?"** Shouldn't an ebb current begin right after a high tide? Although tides (vertical height of water) and currents (horizontal movement) are inextricably related, they often behave rather differently.

If the Earth had a uniform seabed and no land masses, it is likely that a high tide at one point would occur simultaneously with a change in the current direction. However, the existence of continents, a sea bottom which is anything but uniform, and the great ocean currents and different prevailing winds around the world, make the picture extremely complex.

As one example of how a time of high tide can differ greatly from the time of a current change, see the Relationship of High Water and Ebb Current, p. 155. Picture a fjord or long indentation into the coastline, with a narrow opening to the ocean. When a flood current is reaching its peak, or the tide is high outside the mouth of this fjord, the fjord is still filling, unable to keep pace with conditions on the outer coast.

Why do the heights of tides differ so much from one place to the next? Turn to Time of High Water at various ports, pp. 12-20, and compare the Rise in Feet of tides for Nova Scotia's outer coast (2.6 to 4.8 feet) to those for the Bay of Fundy (just below), with a range of up to 35.6 feet. Why the difference? The answer is geography, both above and below water. Tidal ranges of points out on the edge of an outer coast (Nantucket, for instance) tend to be moderate, while estuaries and deep bays with narrowing contours often experience a funneling effect which exaggerates the tidal range. Another explanation is proximity to the continental shelf: the closer a port is to the shelf, the more likely it is to experience a lower tidal range; the farther from the shelf, the more likely it is that a harbor is subject to surges, as when a wave crest hits the shallow water at a beach.

There are other anomalies between tides and currents. **Do stronger currents indicate higher tides?** Woods Hole, MA often has very strong currents through its narrow passage, sometimes as much as 7 knots, but the tidal range is less than 2 feet. Conversely, Boston Harbor has a mean tidal range of about 9.6 feet, but the average currents at the opening, between Deer Island and Hull, do not exceed 2 knots. There is no necessary correlation between current strength and range of tide.

Why did the tidal or current prediction in ELDRIDGE differ from what I saw? Unless there was an error in the Government tables we take our data from, the answer is either (1) weather-related, as when a storm either retards or advances a tidal event, or (2) the discrepancy is small enough to be explained by the approximate nature of tide and current predictions, and figures are sometimes rounded off. We appreciate hearing from readers of any observed discrepancies or errors. Call us at 617-482-8460, Monday to Friday, 9 a.m. to 5 p.m.

6

INLAND NAVIGATION RULES

Good Seamanship Rule (Rule 7): Every vessel shall use all available means appropriate to the prevailing circumstances and conditions to determine if risk of collision exists. If there is any doubt, such risk shall be deemed to exist.

General Prudential Rule (Rule 2b): Due regard shall be had to all dangers of navigation and collision, and to any special circumstances, including the limitations of the vessels involved, which may make a departure from these Rules necessary to avoid immediate danger.

General right-of-way (Rule 18): Vessel categories are listed in <u>decreasing</u> order of having the right-of-way:
- Vessel not under command (most right of way)
- Vessel restricted in ability to maneuver, in a narrow fairway or channel
- Vessel engaged in fishing with nets, lines, or trawls (but not trolling lines)
- Sailing vessel (sails only)
- Power-driven vessel (least right of way)

Vessels Under Power

Overtaking (Rule 13): A vessel overtaking another is the "give-way" vessel and must stay clear of the overtaken or "stand-on" vessel. The overtaking vessel is to sound one short blast if it intends to pass on the other vessel's starboard side, and two short blasts if it intends to pass on the other's port side. The overtaken vessel must respond with the identical sound signal if it agrees, and must maintain course and speed during the passing situation.

Meeting head-on (Rule 14): When two vessels are meeting approximately head-on, neither has right-of-way. Unless it is otherwise agreed, each vessel should turn to starboard and pass port to port. See poem, p. 11.

Crossing (Rule 15): When two vessels approaching each other are neither in an overtaking or meeting situation, they are deemed to be crossing. The power vessel which has the other on its starboard side is the give-way vessel and must change course, slow down, or stop. The vessel which is on the right, is in the right.

Vessels Under Sail

Port-Starboard (Rule 12): A vessel on the port tack shall keep clear of one on the starboard tack.

Windward-Leeward (Rule 12): When both vessels are on the same tack, the vessel to windward shall keep clear of a vessel to leeward.

Sail vs. Power (Rule 18): Generally, a sailboat has right of way over a power-boat. However: (1) a sailboat overtaking a powerboat must keep clear; (2) sail-boats operating in a narrow channel shall keep clear of a power vessel which can safely navigate only within a narrow channel; (3) sailboats must give way to a vessel which is fishing, a vessel restricted in its ability to maneuver, and a vessel not under command.

FEDERAL SAFETY EQUIPMENT REQUIREMENTS
(These are minimum requirements. Some states require additional equipment.)

Sound Signaling Devices

Under 39.4' or 12 meters:
> Must have some means of making an efficient sound signal

Over 39.4' or 12 meters:
> Whistle or horn, audible for 1/2 mile, and a bell at least 8" dia.

Visual Distress Signals (all with approval number)

Under 16' or 5 meters:
> Night: 1 electric SOS flashlight or 3 day/night red flares

Over 16' or 5 meters:
> Day only: 1 orange flag, 3 floating or hand-held orange smoke signals
> Day and night: 3 hand-held, or 3 pistol, or 3 hand-held rocket, or 3 pyrotechnic red flares

The following signals indicate distress or need of assistance:
see p. 239, Marine Emergency and Distress Calls

- A gun or other explosive signal fired at intervals of about 1 minute
- A continuous sounding with any fog-signaling apparatus
- Rockets or shells, fired one at a time or at short intervals
- SOS transmitted by any signaling method
- "Mayday" on the radiotelephone (channel 16)
- International Code Signal flags "NC"
- An orange square flag with a black square over a black ball
- Flames on the vessel
- Rocket parachute flare or hand-held flare
- Orange colored smoke
- Slowly and repeatedly raising and lowering outstretched arms
- Signals transmitted by EPIRB
- High intensity white light flashing 50-70 times per minute

Personal Flotation Devices (must be USCG approved)

Under 16' or 5 meters:
> 1 Type I, II, III, or V per person, USCG approved

Over 16' or 5 meters:
> 1 Type I, II, III, or V per person, and 1 Type IV per boat, USCG approved

Portable Fire Extinguishers (approved)

Under 26'   1 B-I, if no fixed extinguisher system in machinery space.
            (Not required on out-boards built so that vapor entrapment cannot occur.)

26-39'   2 B-I or 1 B-II & 1 B-I, if no fixed exting. system; 1 B-I, with a fixed exting. system.

40-65'   3 B-I or 1 B-II & 1 B-I, if no fixed exting. system; 2 B-I or 1 B-II with a fixed exting. system.

Back-Fire Flame Arrestor

One approved device per carburetor of all inboard gasoline engines.

At least 2 ventilator ducts fitted with cowls or their equivalent to ventilate efficiently the bilges of every engine and fuel tank compartment of boats using gasoline or other fuel with a flashpoint less than 110°F.

NAVIGATION LIGHTS

Definition of Lights

Masthead Light — a white light fixed over the centerline showing an unbroken light over an arc of 225°, from dead ahead to 22.5° abaft the beam on either side.

Sidelights — a green light on the starboard side and a red light on the port side showing an unbroken light over an arc of the horizon of 112.5°, from dead ahead to 22.5° abaft the beam on either side.

Sternlight — a white light placed as nearly as practicable at the stern showing an unbroken light over an arc of the horizon of 135°, 67.5° from dead aft to each side of the vessel.

All-round Light — an unbroken light over an arc of the horizon of 360°.

Towing Light — a yellow light with same characteristics as the sternlight.

Note: R . and Y. Flashing Lights are now authorized for vessels assigned to Traffic Control, Medical Emergencies, Search and Rescue, Fire-Fighting, Salvage and Disabled Vessels.

When under way, in all weathers from sunset to sunrise, every vessel shall carry and exhibit the following lights

When Under Power Alone or When Under Power and Sail Combined

Under 39.4' or 12 meters:
Masthead light visible 2 miles
Sidelights visible 1 mile
Stern light visible 2 miles (may be combined with masthead light)

Over 39.4' or 12 meters to 65' or 20 meters::
Masthead light visible 3 miles
Sidelights visible 2 miles
Stern light visible 2 miles (or in lieu of separate masthead and stern lights, an all-round white light visible 2 miles)

Sailing Vessels Under Way (Sail Only)

Under 22' or 7 meters:
Either the lights listed below for sailing vessels under 65'; or a white light to be exhibited (for example, by shining it on the sail) in sufficient time to prevent collision
Under 65' or 20 meters: *may be combined in one tricolor light carried near top of mast*
Sidelights visible 2 miles
Stern light visible 2 miles

At Anchor

Vessels under 50 meters (165') must show an all-round white light visible 2 miles.
Vessels under 7 meters (22') need no light unless they are near a channel, a fairway, an anchorage or area where other vessels navigate.

Fishing

Vessels Trawling shall show, in addition to the appropriate lights above, 2 all-round lights in a vertical line, the upper green and the lower white.
Vessels Fishing (other than trawling) shall show, in addition to the appropriate lights above, 2 all-round lights, the upper red and the lower white.

When Towing or Being Towed

Towing Vessel: 2 masthead lights (if tow is less than 200 meters); 3 masthead lights in a vertical line forward (if tow exceeds 200 meters); sidelights; sternlight; a yellow tow light in vertical line above sternlight; a diamond shape where it can best be seen (if tow exceeds 200 meters).
Vessel Being Towed: sidelights; sternlight; a diamond shape where it can best be seen (if tow exceeds 200 meters).

SOUND SIGNALS FOR FOG

Ask your Chart Dealer for the latest Navigation Rules—Inland/International

All signals prescribed by this article for vessels under way shall be given:
>**First:** By Power-driven Vessels – On the Whistle or Horn.
>**Second:** By Sailing Vessels or Vessels being Towed – On the Fog Horn.

A prolonged blast shall mean a blast of 4 to 6 seconds' duration.

A power-driven vessel having way upon her shall sound at intervals of no more than 2 minutes, a prolonged blast.

A power-driven vessel under way, but stopped and having no way upon her, shall sound at intervals of no more than 2 minutes, 2 prolonged blasts with about 2 seconds between them.

A sailing vessel under way, shall sound at intervals of not more than 2 minutes, 1 prolonged blast followed by 2 short blasts, regardless of tack.

A fishing vessel or a power-driven vessel towing or pushing another vessel, shall sound every 2 minutes, 1 prolonged blast followed by 2 short blasts. A vessel being towed shall sound 1 prolonged blast followed by 3 short blasts.

A vessel at anchor shall ring a bell rapidly for about 5 seconds at intervals of not more than 1 minute and may in addition sound 3 blasts, 1 short, 1 prolonged, 1 short, to give warning of her position to an approaching vessel. Vessels under 20 meters (65') shall not be required to sound these signals when anchored in a special anchorage area.

A vessel aground shall give the bell signal and shall, in addition, give 3 separate and distinct strokes of the bell.

PASSING SIGNALS

Inland Rules:

>1 short blast: I intend to direct my course to Starboard.

>2 short blasts: I intend to direct my course to Port.

International Rules:

>1 short blast: I am directing my course to Starboard.

>2 short blasts: I am directing my course to Port.

>2 long, 1 short blast: I am overtaking you on your Starboard side.

>2 long, 2 short blasts: I am overtaking you on your Port side.

Response: long blast, short blast, long blast, short blast if agreeable.

Frequently, in fog, small sail or power boats cannot be heard or picked up by other vessels' radar. The Coast Guard strongly recommends that, to avoid collisions, all vessels carry Radar Reflectors mounted as high as possible.

A Cautionary Word on Using Tide and Current Data
The Budget Crunch at NOAA/NOS, and How It Affects You

As some of our readers may have noticed, a number of subordinate stations for tides and currents have been omitted from the usual listing beginning on p. 12. The reason is that in 2000, NOAA/NOS began a complete review of substations to check the times of change for tides and currents, the heights of tides, and strength of currents. Some of the data they found were over 100 years old, and deemed not reliable. As a result, quite a number of tide substations have been dropped from government tables. As for currents, the publication of current charts ceased a number of years ago.

Given severe budgetary restraints, NOAA/NOS says that it is not likely that the tidal and current data recently dropped will be reintroduced anytime soon.

In the interest of caution, the Publishers initially decided to follow suit and de-list the stations NOAA no longer supports. We hoped that readers would find harbors close by the place they were interested in, and use that information to make an estimate.

However, recognizing that old, somewhat suspect data – in the absence of anything else - may still be of some use to the mariner, the Publishers decided to reintroduce a number of the substations we dropped previously. These locations are clearly identified by an asterisk (*). We have done so with the obvious cautions that (1) no single source of information, even this publication, should be relied upon completely, and that (2) experience, vigilance, and prudence should govern the decisions of the navigator. Furthermore, experience shows that tide and current predictions are approximate to begin with, as weather can have an effect on both.

We warn our readers to note the asterisk (*) in our list of substations for tides and currents (p. 12 and following) and to exercise a greater than usual degree of caution in relying on the data which is given for these relisted stations.

Memorized for generations by mariners, the verse below tells what to do when power vessels meet at night. See p. 7 for Inland Navigation Rules.

The Rule of the Road

When all three lights I see ahead,
I turn to **Starboard** and show my **Red:**
Green to Green, Red to Red,
Perfect Safety – **Go Ahead.**

But if to **Starboard Red appear,**
It is my duty to keep clear –
To act as judgment says is proper:
To **Port** or **Starboard, Back** or **Stop** her.

And if upon my **Port** is seen
A Steamer's **Starboard** light of **Green,**
I hold my course and watch to see *
That **Green** to **Port** keeps Clear of me.

Both in safety and in doubt
Always keep a good look out.
In danger, with no room to turn,
Ease her, **Stop** her, **Go Astern.**

* "There's nought for me to do but see" is the original version

TIME OF HIGH WATER

Time figures shown are the *average* differences throughout the year. Rise in feet is mean range.
(Low Water times are given *only* when they vary more than 20 min. from High Water times.)

NOTE: *Asterisk indicates that NOAA has recently dropped these substations from its listing because the data are judged to be of questionable accuracy. We have published NOAA's most recently available figures with this warning: Mariners are cautioned that the starred information is only approximate and not supported by NOAA or the Publishers of Eldridge.

See NOAA Article p. 11, *A Cautionary Word on Using Tide and Current Data.*

---

*For **Canadian Ports**, if your watch is set for Atlantic Time, use the time differences listed here; if your watch is set for Eastern Time, subtract one hour from these time differences.*

NOVA SCOTIA, Outer Coast	Hr.	Min.			Rise in feet
Guysborough	3	05	before	PORTLAND	3.8
Whitehaven Harbour	3	20	"	"	3.7
Liscomb Harbour	3	20	"	"	4.2
Sheet Harbour	3	20	"	"	4.2
Ship Harbour	3	20	"	"	4.2
Jeddore Harbour	3	15	"	"	4.3
Halifax	3	10	"	"	4.4
Sable Island, northside	3	15	"	"	2.6
Sable Island, southside	3	10	"	"	3.9
Chester, Mahone Bay	3	10	"	"	4.4
Mahone Harbour, Mahone Bay	3	10	"	"	4.5
Lunenburg	3	05	"	"	4.2
Riverport, La Have River	3	00	"	"	4.5
Liverpool Bay	2	55	"	"	4.3
Lockeport	2	40	"	"	4.6
Shelburne	2	40	"	"	4.8

NOVA SCOTIA & NEW BRUNSWICK, Bay of Fundy					
Lower E. Pubnico	1	10	before	PORTLAND	8.7
Yarmouth Harbour	0	20	"	"	11.5
Annapolis Royal, Annapolis R.	0	50	after	"	22.6
Parrsboro, Minas Basin, Partridge Is.	1	35	"	"	34.4
Burntcoat Head, Minas Basin	1	50	"	"	38.4
Amherst Point, Cumberland Basin	1	20	"	"	35.6
Grindstone Is, Petitcodiac River.	1	05	"	"	31.1
Hopewell Cape, Petitcodiac River	1	00	"	"	33.2
Saint John	0	45	"	"	20.8
Indiantown, Saint John River	2	15	"	"	1.2
L'Etang Harbor	0	45	"	"	18.4

REVERSING FALLS, SAINT JOHN, N.B.

The most turbulence in the gorge occurs on days when the tides are largest. On largest tides the outward fall is between 15 and 16 1/2 feet and is accompanied by a greater turbulence than the inward fall which is between 11 and 12 1/2 feet. The outward fall is at its greatest between two hours before and one hour after low water at St. John; the inward fall is greater just before the time of high water. For complete tidal information of Canadian ports see Tide Tables of the Atlantic Coast of Canada. (Purchase tables from nautical dealers in Canadian ports or from the Queen's Printer, Department of Public Printing, Ottawa).

PORTLAND Tables, pp. 30-35

When a high tide exceeds avg. ht., the *following* low tide will be lower than avg.
*Times and Hts. are approximate. *Important*: See NOTE, top p. 12, and NOAA Article, p. 11.

TIME OF HIGH WATER

Time figures shown are the *average* differences throughout the year. Rise in feet is mean range.
(Low Water times are given *only* when they vary more than 20 min. from High Water times.)

U.S. ATLANTIC COAST, from Maine southward

MAINE	Hr. Min.			Rise in feet
Eastport	0 15	before	PORTLAND	18.4
Cutler, Little River	0 25	"	"	13.5
Shoppee Pt., Englishman Bay	0 20	"	"	12.1
Steele Harbor Island	0 30	"	"	11.6
*Jonesport	0 20	"	"	11.5
Green Island, Petit Manan Bar	0 30	"	"	10.6
Prospect Harbor	0 25	"	"	10.5
Winter Harbor, Frenchman Bay	0 20	"	"	10.1
Bar Harbor, Mt. Desert Island	0 20	"	"	10.6
Southwest Harbor, Mt. Desert Island	0 20	"	"	10.2
Bass Harbor	**high 0 15** before, low..0 45	"	"	9.9
Blue Hill Harbor, Blue Hill Bay	0 10	"	"	10.1
Burnt Coat Harbor, Swans Island	0 20	"	"	9.5
Penobscot Bay				
Center Harbor, Eggemoggin Reach	0 10	"	"	10.1
Little Deer Isle, Eggemoggin Reach	0 05	"	"	10.0
Isle Au Haut	0 20	"	"	9.3
Stonington, Deer Isle	0 10	"	"	9.7
Matinicus Harbor, Wheaton Is.	0 15	"	"	9.0
Vinalhaven	0 10	"	"	9.3
North Haven	0 05	"	"	9.7
Pulpit Harbor, North Haven Is.	0 10	"	"	9.9
Castine	0 05	"	"	10.1
Bucksport, Penobscott River	0 25	"	"	10.8
Bangor, Penobscot River	**high 0 25** before, low..same as		"	13.4
Belfast	0 10	before	"	10.2
*Camden	0 10	"	"	9.6
Rockland	0 10	"	"	9.8
MAINE, Outer Coast				
Tenants Harbor	0 10	before	PORTLAND	9.3
Monhegan Island	0 15	"	"	8.8
Port Clyde, St. George River	0 10	"	"	8.9
Thomaston, St. George River	0 05	"	"	9.4
New Harbor, Muscongus Bay	0 10	"	"	8.8
Friendship Harbor	0 20	"	"	9.0
Waldoboro, Medomak River	0 15	"	"	9.5
East Boothbay, Damariscotta River	same as		"	8.9
Boothbay Harbor	0 05	before	"	8.8
Wiscasset, Sheepscot River	0 15	after	"	9.4
Robinhood, Sasanoa River	0 15	"	"	8.8
Phippsburg, Kennebec River	0 25	"	"	8.0
Bath, Kennebec River	1 00	"	"	6.4
Casco Bay				
*Small Point Harbor	0 10	before	"	8.8
Cundy Harbor, New Meadows River	same as		"	8.9
South Harpswell, Potts Harbor	same as		"	8.9
South Freeport	0 10	after	"	9.0

PORTLAND Tables, pp. 30-35

When a high tide exceeds avg. ht., the *following* low tide will be lower than avg.
*Times and Hts. are approximate. *Important*: See NOTE, top p. 12, and NOAA Article, p. 11.

TIDE STATIONS

TIME OF HIGH WATER

Time figures shown are the *average* differences throughout the year. Rise in feet is mean range.
(Low Water times are given *only* when they vary more than 20 min. from High Water times.)

	Hr. Min.			Rise in feet
MAINE, Cont.				
Falmouth Foreside	same as		PORTLAND	9.1
Great Chebeague Island	same as		"	9.1
Portland Head Light	same as		"	8.9
Cape Porpoise	0 10	after	"	8.7
Kennebunkport	0 05	"	"	8.8
York Harbor	0 05	"	"	8.6
NEW HAMPSHIRE				
Portsmouth	0 20	after	PORTLAND	7.8
Gosport Harbor, Isles of Shoals	same as		"	8.5
Hampton Harbor	0 15	after	"	8.3
MASSACHUSETTS, Outer Coast				
Newburyport, Merrimack River.. **high 0 30** *after, low*	1 10	after	PORTLAND	7.8
Plum Island Sound, S. End .... **high 0 10** *after, low*	0 35	"	"	8.6
Annisquam, Lobster Cove	0 10	"	"	8.8
Rockport	0 05	"	"	8.7
Gloucester Harbor	same as		BOSTON	8.8
*Manchester	same as		"	8.8
Salem	same as		"	8.9
*Marblehead	same as		"	9.1
Lynn, Lynn Harbor	same as		"	9.2
Neponset, Neponset R.	same as		"	9.5
Weymouth, Fore River Bridge	0 10	after	"	9.5
Hingham	0 10	"	"	9.5
Hull	0 05	"	"	9.3
Cohasset Harbor (White Head)	0 05	"	"	8.8
Scituate, Scituate Harbor	0 05	"	"	8.9
Cape Cod Bay				
Duxbury Harbor	**high 0 05** *after, low*	0 35	"	"	9.9
Plymouth	0 05	"	"	9.8
Cape Cod Canal, East Entrance	same as		"	8.7
Barnstable Harbor, Beach Point	0 10	after	"	9.5
Wellfleet	0 15	"	"	10.0
Provincetown	0 15	"	"	9.1
Cape Cod				
Stage Harbor, Chatham	0 45	"	"	4.0
Chatham Hbr, Aunt Lydias Cove **high 1 10** *after, low*	1 55	"	"	4.6
Pleasant Bay, Chatham.............. **high 2 30** *after, low*	3 25	"	"	3.2
Nantucket Sound				
Wychmere Harbor **high 0 50** *after, low*	0 25	"	"	3.7
Dennisport **high 1 05** *after, low*	0 40	"	"	3.4
South Yarmouth, Bass River	1 50	"	"	2.8
Hyannis Port **high 1 00** *after, low*	0 25	"	"	3.2
Cotuit Highlands **high 1 15** *after, low*	0 45	"	"	2.5
Falmouth Heights	0 15	before	"	1.3
Nantucket Island				
Nantucket	1 05	after	"	3.0
Great Point	0 45	"	"	3.1
Muskeget Island, North side	0 25	"	"	2.0

PORTLAND Tables, pp. 30-35, BOSTON Tables, pp. 38-43
When a high tide exceeds avg. ht., the *following* low tide will be lower than avg.
*Times and Hts. are approximate. *Important*: See NOTE, top p. 12, and NOAA Article, p. 11.

TIME OF HIGH WATER

Time figures shown are the *average* differences throughout the year. Rise in feet is mean range.
(Low Water times are given *only* when they vary more than 20 min. from High Water times.)

	Hr.	Min.			Rise in feet
MASSACHUSETTS, Martha's Vineyard					
Edgartown (Caution: new data needed but not yet available)					
Oak Bluffs.................................... **high 0 30** *after, low* ...0	10		*before*	*BOSTON*	1.7
Vineyard Haven .... **high 0 25** *after, low* .. *same as*				"	1.7
Lake Tashmoo (inside)...2	30		*before*	"	2.0
Cedar Tree Neck .... **high 0 10** *after, low* 1	30		*after*	*NEWPORT*	2.2
Menemsha Bight....................... **high** *same as, low* ...0	35		"	"	2.7
Gay Head...................................... **high 0 05** *before, low*..0	45		"	"	2.9
Squibnocket Point....................... **high 0 45** *before, low* *same as*			"	"	2.9
Wasque Point, Chappaquiddick.. **high 2 00** *after, low* 3	20		*after*	"	1.1
Nomans Land............................... **high 0 20** *before, low*..0	20		"	"	3.0
Vineyard Sound					
Little Hbr., Woods Hole................ **high 0 30** *after, low* 2	20		"	"	1.4
Quick's Hole, N. side 0	10		*before*	"	3.5
Cuttyhunk..1	20		*after*	"	3.4
Buzzards Bay					
Cuttyhunk Pond Entr....................................*same as*				"	3.4
W. Falmouth Harbor, Chappaquoit Pt. 0	05		*after*	"	3.8
Pocasset Hbr., Barlows Landing 0	25		"	"	4.0
Monument Beach 0	15		"	"	4.0
Wareham River..0	20		"	"	4.1
Great Hill...0	10		"	"	4.0
Marion, Sippican Harbor...0	10		"	"	4.0
Mattapoisett Harbor..0	10		"	"	3.9
Clarks Point..0	15		"	"	3.6
New Bedford..0	05		"	"	3.7
South Dartmouth..0	25		"	"	3.7
Westport Harbor, Westport River. **high 0 10** *after, low* 0	35		*after*	"	3.0
RHODE ISLAND & MASS, Narragansett Bay					
Sakonnet, Sakonnet River......................................0	10		*before*	*NEWPORT*	3.2
Beavertail Point, Conanicut Island 0	05		"	"	3.3
Conanicut Point, Conanicut Island 0	05		*after*	"	3.8
Prudence Island (south end)..0	10		"	"	3.8
Bristol Harbor 0	15		"	"	4.1
Fall River, MA..0	20		"	"	4.4
Bay Spring, Bullock Cove..0	10		"	"	4.3
Providence, State Pier no. 1..0	15		"	"	4.4
Pawtucket, Seekonk River 0	20		"	"	4.6
East Greenwich..0	15		"	"	4.0
Wickford..0	05		"	"	3.7
Narragansett Pier....................... **high 0 10** *before, low*..0	10		*after*	"	3.2
RHODE ISLAND, Outer Coast					
Pt. Judith, Harbor of Refuge....... **high** *same as, low* 0	35		*after*	*NEWPORT*	3.0
Block Island, Old Harbor........... **high 0 15** *before, low*..0	15		"	"	2.9
Watch Hill Pt. .... **high 0 40** *after, low* 1	15		"	"	2.6
CONNECTICUT, L.I. Sound					
Stonington 2	15		*before*	*BRIDGEPORT*	2.7
Noank...2	05		"	"	2.3
New London, Thames River (State Pier) 1	45		"	"	2.6
Norwich, Thames River..1	20		"	"	3.0

BOSTON Tables, pp. 38-43, NEWPORT Tables, pp. 78-83, BRIDGEPORT Tables, pp. 98-103
When a high tide exceeds avg. ht., the *following* low tide will be lower than avg.
*Times and Hts. are approximate. *Important*: See NOTE, top p. 12, and NOAA Article, p. 11.

TIDE STATIONS

TIME OF HIGH WATER

Time figures shown are the *average* differences throughout the year. Rise in feet is mean range.
(Low Water times are given *only* when they vary more than 20 min. from High Water times.)

	Hr.	Min.				Rise in feet
CONNECTICUT, L.I. Sound, Cont.						
Saybrook Jetty, Connecticut River	0	35	before	BRIDGEPORT		3.5
Essex, Connecticut River	0	05	"	"		3.0
Madison	0	20	"	"		4.9
Branford, Branford River	0	05	"	"		5.9
New Haven Harbor, New Haven Reach	same as			"		6.2
Milford Harbor	same as			"		6.3
Sniffens Point, Housatonic River	0	10	after	"		6.4
South Norwalk	0	10	"	"		7.1
Stamford	0	05	"	"		7.2
Cos Cob Harbor	0	05	"	"		7.2
*Greenwich	same as			"		7.4
NEW YORK, Long Island Sound, North Side						
Rye Beach	0	20	before	KINGS POINT		7.3
New Rochelle	0	15	"	"		7.3
Throgs Neck	0	10	after	"		7.0
Whitestone, East River	0	05	"	"		7.1
College Point, Flushing Bay	0	15	"	"		6.8
Hunts Point, East River	0	15	"	"		7.0
North Brother Island, East River	0	20	"	"		6.6
Port Morris, Stony Pt., East River	0	05	"	"		6.2
NEW YORK, Long Island, North Shore						
Willets Point	same as			KINGS POINT		7.2
Port Washington, Manhasset Bay	0	10	before	"		7.3
Glen Cove, Hempstead Harbor	0	20	"	"		7.3
Oyster Bay Harbor, Oyster Bay	0	05	after	BRIDGEPORT		7.3
Cold Spring Harbor, Oyster Bay	0	05	before	"		7.3
Eatons Neck Point	same as			"		7.1
Lloyd Harbor, Huntington Bay	same as			"		7.0
Northport, Northport Bay	0	05	before	"		7.3
Port Jefferson Harbor Entrance	same as			"		6.6
Mattituck Inlet	0	05	after	"		5.2
Shelter Island Sound						
Orient	1	10	before	"		2.5
Greenport	0	40	"	"		2.4
Southold	same as			"		2.3
Sag Harbor	0	45	before	"		2.5
New Suffolk, Peconic Bay	0	40	after	"		2.6
South Jamesport, Peconic Bay	0	40	"	"		2.8
Threemile Harbor, Entr., Gardiners Bay	1	05	before	"		2.5
Montauk Harbor Entr.	2	10	"	"		2.0
Long Island, South Shore						
Shinnecock Inlet, Ocean ... **high 0 40** before, low	1	05	before	SANDY HOOK		3.3
Moriches Inlet	1	00	"	"		2.9
Democrat Point, Fire Island Inlet	0	40	"	"		2.6
Patchogue, Great South Bay	3	15	after	"		1.1
Bay Shore, Watchogue Creek Entrance	2	15	"	"		1.0
Jones Inlet (Point Lookout)	0	20	before	"		3.6
Bellmore, Hempstead Bay ... **high 1 30** after, low	2	00	after	"		2.0

BRIDGEPORT Tables, pp. 98-103, KINGS POINT Tables, pp. 104-109, SANDY HOOK Tables, pp. 134-139

When a high tide exceeds avg. ht., the *following* low tide will be lower than avg.

*Times and Hts. are approximate. *Important*: See NOTE, top p. 12, and NOAA Article, p. 11.

TIME OF HIGH WATER

Time figures shown are the *average* differences throughout the year. Rise in feet is mean range.
(Low Water times are given *only* when they vary more than 20 min. from High Water times.)

	Hr. Min.			Rise in feet
NEW YORK, Long Island, South Shore, Cont.				
Freeport, Baldwin Bay 0 40	after	SANDY HOOK		3.0
E. Rockaway Inlet.......................................0 10	before	"		4.1
Barren Is., Rockaway Inlet, Jamaica Bay ....same as		"		5.0
NEW YORK & NEW JERSEY				
New York Harbor				
Coney Island.......................................0 05	before	SANDY HOOK		4.7
Fort Hamilton, The Narrows ....same as		"		4.7
Tarrytown, Hudson River 1 50	after	BATTERY		3.2
Poughkeepsie, Hudson River.......................................4 35	"	"		3.1
Kingston, Hudson River.......................................5 20	"	"		3.7
NY & NJ, the Kills and Newark Bay				
Constable Hook, Kill Van Kull.......................................0 20	before	"		4.6
Port Elizabeth.......................................same as		"		5.1
Bellville, Passaic River .... **high 0 10** *after, low* 0 50	after	"		5.6
Kearny Pt., Hackensack River........................................0 10	"	"		5.2
Hackensack, Hackensack River........................................1 05	"	"		6.0
Lower NY Bay, Raritan Bay				
Great Kills Harbor 0 05	after	SANDY HOOK		4.7
South Amboy, Raritan River.......................................0 05	before	"		5.1
New Brunswick, Raritan River.......................................0 30	after	"		5.7
Keyport.......................................0 05	before	"		5.0
Atlantic Highlands, Sandy Hook Bay 0 10	"	"		4.7
Highlands, Shrewsbury R., Rte. 36 bridge, Sandy Hook .0 15	after	"		4.2
Red Bank, Navesink River, Sandy Hook Bay.......................1 20	"	"		3.5
Sea Bright, Shrewsbury River, Sandy Hook Bay.............1 15	"	"		3.2
NEW JERSEY, Outer Coast				
Shark River, R.R. Bridge, Shark River Island 0 15	before	"		4.3
Manasquan Inlet, USCG Station 0 10	"	"		4.0
Brielle, Rte. 35 bridge, Manasquan River.......................0 05	"	"		3.9
Barnegat Inlet,USCG Station, Barnegat Bay.................0 10	"	"		2.2
Manahawkin Drawbridge.......... **high 2 50** *after, low* 3 40	after	"		1.3
Beach Haven, USCG Station, Little Egg Harbor...............1 20	"	"		2.2
Absecon Creek, Rte. 30 bridge 1 05	"	"		3.9
Atlantic City, Ocean........................................0 25	before	"		4.0
Beesleys Pt., Great Egg Hbr. Bay **high 0 30** *after, low* 1 05	after	"		3.6
Townsends Inlet, Ocean Dr. bridge 0 10	"	"		3.9
Stone Harbor, Great Channel, Hereford Inlet 0 35	"	"		4.0
Cape May Harbor, Cape May Inlet 0 10	"	"		4.5
NEW JERSEY & DELAWARE BAY				
Delaware Bay, Eastern Shore				
Brandywine Shoal Light............. **high 0 30** *after, low* 1 00	after	BATTERY		4.9
Cape May Point, Sunset Beach 0 15	"	"		4.8
Dennis Creek, 2.5 mi. above Entr..... **high 1 15** *after, low* 2 05	"	"		5.2
Mauricetown, Maurice R........................................2 40	"	"		4.4
Millville, Maurice R........................................3 55	"	"		5.0

SANDY HOOK Tables, pp. 134-139, BATTERY Tables, pp. 122-127

When a high tide exceeds avg. ht., the *following* low tide will be lower than avg.
*Times and Hts. are approximate. *Important*: See NOTE, top p. 12, and NOAA Article, p. 11.

TIDE STATIONS

TIME OF HIGH WATER

Time figures shown are the *average* differences throughout the year. Rise in feet is mean range.
(Low Water times are given *only* when they vary more than 20 min. from High Water times.)

	Hr. Min.			Rise in feet
NEW JERSEY & DELAWARE BAY, Cont.				
Delaware Bay, Western Shore				
*Cape Henlopen...0 10		after	BATTERY	4.1
Lewes (Breakwater Harbor)........ **high 0 20** *after, low* 0 45		"	"	4.1
*St. Jones River Ent.................... **high 1 10** *after, low* 1 55		"	"	4.8
Delaware River				
*Liston Point, Delaware......................................2 05		"	"	5.7
Salem, Salem River, NJ 3 55		"	"	4.2
Reedy Point, Delaware .... **high 3 05** *after, low* 3 25		"	"	5.3
C&D Summit Bridge, Delaware......................2 35		"	"	3.5
Chesapeake City, MD..2 20		"	"	2.9
New Castle, Delaware .... **high 3 35** *after, low* 4 05		"	"	5.2
Wilmington Marine Terminal..... **high 3 55** *after, low* 4 30		"	"	5.3
Philadelphia, PA, USCG Station **high 5 30** *after, low* 5 50		"	"	6.0
Burlington, NJ .... **high 6 25** *after, low* 7 05		"	"	7.2
Trenton, NJ................................ **high 6 45** *after, low* 7 45		"	"	8.2
DELAWARE, MARYLAND & VIRGINIA				
Indian River Inlet, USCG Station, Delaware 0 55		after	SANDY HOOK	2.5
Ocean City Fishing Pier...............................0 20		before	"	3.4
Harbor of Refuge, Chincoteague Bay.......................0 10		after	"	2.4
Chincoteague Channel, south end 0 20		"	"	2.2
Chincoteague Island, USCG Station..................0 40		"	"	1.6
Metompkin Inlet 0 40		"	"	3.6
Wachapreague, Wachapreague Channel...................0 50		"	"	4.0
*Quinby Inlet Entrance...............................0 05		"	"	4.0
Great Machipongo Inlet, inside 0 45		"	"	3.9
Chesapeake Bay, Eastern Shore				
Cape Charles Harbor 0 40		after	BATTERY	2.3
Crisfield, Little Annemessex River.....................4 30		"	"	1.9
Salisbury, Wicomico River 7 15		"	"	3.0
Middle Hooper Island 4 40		before	BALTIMORE	1.5
Taylors Island, Little Choptank River...................3 15		"	"	1.3
*Sharps Is. Lt...3 50		"	"	1.3
Cambridge, Choptank River 2 40		"	"	1.6
Dover Bridge, Choptank River........................0 20		"	"	1.7
Oxford, Tred Avon River.................................2 50		"	"	1.4
Easton Pt., Tred Avon River............................2 45		"	"	1.6
St. Michaels, Miles River..............................2 10		"	"	1.4
Kent Island Narrows...................................1 30		"	"	1.2
*Bloody Pt. Bar Lt...2 40		"	"	1.1
Worton Creek Entrance 1 20		after	"	1.3
Town Point Wharf, Elk River 3 20		"	"	2.2
Chesapeake Bay, Western Shore				
Havre de Grace, Susquehanna River...................3 15		after	"	1.9
*Pooles Is..0 55		"	"	1.2
Annapolis, Severn River (US Naval Academy) 1 30		before	"	1.0
*Sandy Point 1 20		"	"	0.8
Thomas Pt. Shoal Lt...1 55		"	"	0.9
*Drum Point, Pawtuxent River...........................4 50		"	"	1.2
Solomons Island, Pawtuxent River......................4 40		"	"	1.2
Point Lookout..5 30		"	"	1.2

BATTERY Tables, pp. 122-127, SANDY HOOK Tables, pp. 134-139, BALTIMORE Tables, pp. 156-159

When a high tide exceeds avg. ht., the *following* low tide will be lower than avg.

*Times and Hts. are approximate. *Important*: See NOTE, top p. 12, and NOAA Article, p. 11.

TIME OF HIGH WATER

Time figures shown are the *average* differences throughout the year. Rise in feet is mean range.
(Low Water times are given *only* when they vary more than 20 min. from High Water times.)

	Hr.	Min.			Rise in feet
DELAWARE, MARYLAND & VIRGINIA, Cont.					
Sunnybank, Little Wicomico River	6	35	after	BATTERY	0.8
Glebe Point, Great Wicomico River	4	10	"	"	1.2
Windmill Point, Rappahannock River	2	45	"	"	1.2
*Orchard Point, Rappahannock River	3	20	"	"	1.4
*New Point Comfort, Mobjack Bay	0	45	"	"	2.3
Tue Marshes Light, York River	0	55	"	"	2.2
*Perrin River, York River	1	05	"	"	2.3
Yorktown, Goodwin Neck, York River	1	10	"	"	2.2
Hampton Roads, Sewells Pt........ **high 0 50** after, low 0		40	"	"	2.4
Norfolk, Elizabeth River	1	15	"	"	2.8
Newport News, James River	1	20	"	"	2.6
Jamestown Is., James River........ **high 3 55** after, low 4		15	"	"	2.0
*Windmill Pt., James River .... **high 6 15** after, low 6		30	"	"	2.3
Chesapeake Bay Br. Tunnel......... **high 0 05** before, low ..0		20	before	"	2.6
Cape Henry	0	05	"	"	3.1
NORTH CAROLINA					
Roanoke Sound Channel	1	10	after	BATTERY	0.5
Oregon Inlet Marina................... **high 0 20** before, low ..0		10	before	"	0.9
Oregon Inlet, USCG Station....... **high 0 40** before, low ..1		00	"	"	1.9
Oregon Inlet Channel	0	30	"	"	1.2
Cape Hatteras Fishing Pier	1	00	"	"	3.0
Hatteras Inlet	0	50	"	"	2.0
Ocracoke Inlet	0	50	"	"	2.0
Beaufort Inlet Channel Range	0	55	"	"	3.2
Morehead City	0	35	"	"	3.1
Bogue Inlet	0	45	"	"	2.2
New River Inlet	0	45	"	"	3.0
New Topsail Inlet................... **high 0 40** before, low ..0		10	"	"	3.0
Bald Head, Cape Fear River	1	15	"	"	4.5
Wilmington............... **high 1 20** after, low 1		45	after	"	4.3
Lockwoods Folly Inlet	0	55	"	"	4.2
SOUTH CAROLINA					
Little River Neck, north end	1	20	after	BATTERY	4.7
Hog Inlet Pier	0	45	"	"	5.0
Myrtle Beach, Springmaid Pier	0	50	"	"	5.0
Pawleys Island Pier (ocean)	0	55	"	"	4.9
Winyah Bay Entrance, south jetty	0	45	before	"	4.6
South Island Plantation, C.G. Station	0	10	after	"	3.8
Georgetown, Sampit River.......... **high 1 00** after, low 1		40	"	"	3.7
North Santee River Inlet	0	35	before	"	4.5
Charleston (Custom House Wharf)	0	25	"	"	5.2
Folly River, north, Folly Island ... **high** same as, low 0		35	"	"	5.4
Rockville, Bohicket Creek, North Edisto River	0	05	"	"	5.8
Edisto Marina, Big Bay Creek entr., South Edisto River .0		20	"	"	6.0
Harbor River Bridge, St. Helena Sound	0	10	"	"	6.0
Hutchinson Island, Ashepoo River, St. Helena Sound......0		15	after	"	6.0
Fripps Inlet, Hunting Island Bridge, St. Helena Sound...0		25	before	"	6.1
Port Royal Plantation, Hilton Head Is.	0	15	"	"	6.1
Battery Creek, Beaufort River Port Royal Sd, 4 mi. above entr. .... **high 1 00** after, low 0		15	after	"	7.6

BATTERY Tables, pp. 122-127

When a high tide exceeds avg. ht., the *following* low tide will be lower than avg.

*Times and Hts. are approximate. *Important*: See NOTE, top p. 12, and NOAA Article, p. 11.

TIME OF HIGH WATER

Time figures shown are the *average* differences throughout the year. Rise in feet is mean range.
(Low Water times are given *only* when they vary more than 20 min. from High Water times.)

	Hr. Min.			Rise in feet
SOUTH CAROLINA, Cont.				
Beaufort, Beaufort River .... **high 0 55** *after, low* 0 30	*after*	BATTERY	7.4
Braddock Point, Hilton Head Island, Calibogue Sd. 0 10	*before*	"	6.7
GEORGIA				
Savannah River Entrance, Fort Pulaski 0 15	*before*	BATTERY	6.9
Tybee Creek Entrance..0 25	"	"	6.8
Wilmington River, north entrance......................................0 25	*after*	"	7.6
Isle of Hope, Skidaway River ...... **high 0 35** *after, low* 0 10	"	"	7.8
Egg Islands, Ossabaw Sound 0 10	*before*	"	7.2
Walburg Creek Entr., St. Catherines Sd..........................same as		"	7.1
Blackbeard Island...0 05	*after*	"	6.9
Blackbeard Creek, Blackbeard Island.............................0 05	"	"	6.5
Old Tower, Sapelo Island, Doboy Sound ....same as		"	6.8
Threemile Cut Entrance, Darien River.............................0 30	*after*	"	7.1
St. Simons Sound Bar..0 15	*before*	"	6.5
Frederica River, St. Simons Sound..................................0 35	*after*	"	7.2
Brunswick, East River, St. Simons Sound 0 45	"	"	7.2
Jekyll Is. Marina, Jekyll Creek, St. Andrew Sound 0 30	"	"	6.8
Cumberland Wharf, Cumberland River 0 30	*after*	"	6.8
FLORIDA, East Coast				
St. Marys Entrance, north jetty, Cumberland Sd..............0 10	*before*	BATTERY	5.8
Fernandina Beach, Amelia R...... **high 0 30** *after, low* 0 05	*after*	"	6.0
Nassau River Entrance .... **high 0 10** *after, low* 0 50	"	"	5.1
Amelia City, South Amelia River.......................................0 50	"	"	5.4
Mayport, (Bar Pilot Dock) .... **high 0 15** *after, low* 0 15	*before*	"	4.6
St. Augustine, City Dock...0 10	*after*	"	4.5
Ponce Inlet, Halifax River .... **high 0 05** *after, low* ..0 30	*after*	MIAMI	2.8
Cape Canaveral.......................... **high 1 05** *before, low* ..0 45	*before*	"	3.5
Port Canaveral, Trident Pier..same as		"	3.5
Sebastian Inlet bridge................ **high 0 50** *before, low* ..0 25	*before*	"	2.2
St. Lucie, Indian River .... **high 0 40** *after, low* 1 45	*after*	"	1.0
Vero Beach, ocean 0 55	*before*	"	3.4
Fort Pierce Inlet, south jetty...0 30	"	"	2.6
Stuart, St. Lucie River .... **high 2 15** *after, low* 3 30	*after*	"	0.9
Jupiter Inlet, south jetty..0 10	*before*	"	2.5
North Palm Beach, Lake Worth .. **high 0 15** *before, low* ..0 15	*after*	"	2.8
Port of Palm Beach, Lake Worth . **high 0 20** *before, low* ..0 05	"	"	2.7
Lake Worth Pier, ocean .... **high 0 45** *before, low* ..0 20	*before*	"	2.7
Hillsboro Inlet, C.G. Light Station 0 15	"	"	2.5
Hillsboro Inlet Marina............... **high 0 05** *before, low* ..0 25	*after*	"	2.5
Lauderdale-by-the-Sea, fish pier. **high 0 35** *before, low* ..0 15	*before*	"	2.6
Bahia Mar Yacht Club .... **high 0 05** *before, low* ..0 35	*after*	"	2.4
Port Everglades, Turning Basin.. **high 0 30** *before, low* ..0 10	*before*	"	2.5
North Miami Beach, fishing pier **high 0 20** *before, low*...same as		"	2.5
Miami, Miamarina, Biscayne Bays **high 0 20** *after, low* 0 50	*after*	"	2.2
Dinner Key Marina, Biscayne Bay **high 0 55** *after, low* 1 50	"	"	1.9
Key Biscayne Yt. Club, Biscayne B **high 0 45** *after low*....1 30	"	"	2.0
Ocean Reef Hbr., Key Largo .... **high 0 10** *before, low* ..0 15	"	"	2.3
Tavernier Harbor, Hawk Ch........ **high 0 05** *after, low* 0 25	"	"	2.0
Key West...0 50	*before*	BOSTON	1.3

BATTERY Tables, pp. 122-127, MIAMI Tables, pp. 160-163, BOSTON Tables, pp. 38-43

When a high tide exceeds avg. ht., the *following* low tide will be lower than avg.
*Times and Hts. are approximate. *Important*: See NOTE, top p. 12, and NOAA Article, p. 11.

Piloting in a Cross Current

When we are piloting in a body of water with an active current from ahead or astern, our course is not affected and the arithmetic for speed is easy. (See p. 36.) When the current comes at an angle to the bow or stern, unless our speed is far greater than the current, we need to alter course to compensate.

First, what not to do. When in a cross current it is a major mistake simply to steer toward our destination. The current will carry us more and more off course, with the heading or bearing to our destination changing all the time. We may finally get there, but we will have traveled considerably farther, on what is termed a hooked course, and possibly have entered dangerous water while doing so.

By GPS: With GPS it's all too easy to find the new heading. We enter our destination waypoint and press GoTo. There are several screens to choose from. First, carefully check the Map screen to see if there are any hazards or obstructions between us and our destination. The Highway screen, considered perhaps the most useful display, will show if we are on course by displaying the highway as straight ahead. The screen will also indicate how far to the left or right of our course we are. This is crosstrack error. We steer to that side which brings us back onto the center of the highway, and then continue to steer in such a way that we stay in the middle. We have changed our heading to achieve the desired COG, course over ground. Now the Course and Bearing numbers should be the same, and we have compensated for cross current.

By eye: Without the help of electronics but with good visibility, we know we need to alter course toward the current until a foreground object, let's say a point on the shore, remains steady in relation to an object farther away, perhaps a distant steeple. This alignment is called a range. Once we find the corrected heading, we can use our compass to maintain it, checking those objects periodically in case current or wind conditions change.

By a chart: With compromised visibility and again without electronics, the problem is solved the traditional way with a paper chart. First, consult the proper current table to determine the speed and direction of the current for the hour(s) in question. (Keep in mind that speeds and times are predictions only. They are approximate and can be altered by weather.) Plot the course, let's say 090°, as if there is no current. Then construct a one-hour vector diagram. From the departure point, construct a line in the direction of the current, let's say 180°, whose length is the distance the current would carry an object in one hour. If the predicted current is 2 knots, that's 2 n.m. Now we set our dividers for a distance which represents how far our boat speed will take us through the water in one hour, let's say 8 n.m. We will put one point of the dividers on the far end of the line representing current, and then swing the dividers until the second point intercepts the line of our intended course. The direction of that third line represents what our boat's heading needs to be (the course to steer) to maintain the original course we drew. The intercept point represents about where our boat will be along the intended course line (COG) at the end of one hour. If this leg is longer or shorter than one hour, it doesn't matter. The course to steer is the same as we determined in our one-hour vector plot, until conditions change.

TIME OF CURRENT CHANGE

(See Note at bottom of Boston Tables, pp. 38-43: Rule-of-Thumb for Current Velocities.)

NOTE: NOAA has recently dropped many substations from its listing because the data are judged to be of questionable accuracy.

See NOAA Article p. 11,

CURRENTS IN THE GULF OF MAINE - In the Gulf of Maine, on the western side, the Flood Current splits at Cape Ann, Mass., and floods north and east along the shore towards the Bay of Fundy. At the same time, on the eastern side of the Gulf, at the southern tip of Nova Scotia, the Flood Current runs to the west and then north and eastwards along the shore into the Bay of Fundy. The Ebb Current is just the reverse. In addition to these large principal currents, along the Maine Coast, at least at the mouths of principal bays, there is a shoreward set during the Flood and an offshore set during the Ebb, although this set is of considerably less velocity.

West of Mount Desert, the average along-shore current is rarely more than a knot but the farther east one goes, the greater are the average velocities to be expected, up to 2 knots or more. When heading west, therefore, start off at the time shown for High Water in your area (see p. 13) and have a fair Ebb current for 6 hours. Headed east, start at the time for Low Water in your area (about 6 ½ hours after High Water) and carry the beneficial Flood current. East of Schoodic Point, the average currents are up to 2 knots and taking advantage of them will save considerable time and fuel.

Off shore, in the Gulf of Maine, unlike the along-shore currents that come to dead slack and *reverse*, there are so-called *rotary* currents. These currents constantly change direction in a clockwise flow completing the circle in about 12 ½ hours. The maximum currents are when it is flooding in the northeasterly direction or ebbing in a southwesterly direction; minimum currents occur halfway between. There is no slack water.

Entering the Bay of Fundy through Grand Manan Channel, one finds that the average velocities are from 1-2 ½ knots, although in the narrower channels off the Bay, velocities are higher (Friar Roads at Eastport has average velocities of 3 knots of more). The Current in the Bay Floods to the Northeast and Ebbs to the Southwest.

In using this table, bear in mind that **actual times of Slack or Maximum occasionally differ from the predicted times** by as much as half an hour and in rare instances as much as an hour. Referring the Time of Current Change at the subordinate stations listed below, to the predicted Current Change at the reference station gives the *approximate* time only. Therefore, to make make sure of getting the full advantage of a favorable current or slack water, the navigator should reach the entrance or strait at least half an hour before the predicted time. (This is basically the same precautionary note found in the U.S. Tidal Currents Table Book.)

Figures shown below are **average maximum** velocities in knots. We have omitted places having an average maximum velocity of less than 1 knot. To find the Time of Current Change (Start of Flood and Start of Ebb) at a selected point, refer to the table heading that particular section (in bold type) and add or subtract the time listed.

TIME DIFFERENCES Flood Starts; Ebb Starts Hr. Min.	MAXIMUM FLOOD Dir.(true) in degrees	Avg. Max. in knots	MAXIMUM EBB Dir.(true) in degrees	Avg. Max. in knots
MAINE COAST – based on Boston, pp. 38-43				
(Flood starts at Low Water; Ebb starts at High Water)				
Isle Au Haut, 0.8 mi. E of Richs Pt. .... -0 05	336	1.4	139	1.5
Damariscotta R., off Cavis Pt. .... F+1 30, E+0 00	350	0.6	215	1.0
Sheepscot R., off Barter Is. .... F+1 25, E+0 05	005	0.8	200	1.1
Lowe Pt., NE of, Sasanoa R. .... F+1 25, E+0 35	327	1.7	152	1.8
Lower Hell Gate, Knubble Bay* F+1 50, E+0 35	290	3.0	155	3.5

*Velocities up to 9.0 kts. have been observed in the vicinity of the Boilers.

Important: See NOTE, bottom p. 29 and NOAA Article, p. 11.

TIME OF CURRENT CHANGE

(See Note at bottom of Boston Tables, pp. 38-43: Rule-of-Thumb for Current Velocities.)

	TIME DIFFERENCES Flood Starts; Ebb Starts Hr. Min.	MAXIMUM FLOOD Dir.(true) in degrees	MAXIMUM FLOOD Avg. Max. in knots	MAXIMUM EBB Dir.(true) in degrees	MAXIMUM EBB Avg. Max. in knots
KENNEBEC RIVER – based on Boston, pp. 38-43					
(Fl. starts at Low Water; Ebb starts at High Water)					
Hunniwell Pt., NE of .... F+2 20, E+1 25		332	2.4	151	2.9
Bald Head, 0.3 mi. SW of .... F+2 40, E+1 20		321	1.6	153	2.3
Bluff Head, W of .... F+2 50, E+1 50		014	2.3	184	3.4
Fiddler Ledge, N of .... F+3 00, E+1 45		267	1.9	113	2.6
Doubling Pt., S of........................ F+1 45, E+1 45		300	2.6	127	3.0
Lincoln Ledge, E. of..................... F+2 45, E+1 45		359	1.9	174	2.8
Bath, 0.2 mi. S of bridge.............. F+2 45, E+2 05		003	1.0	177	1.5
CASCO BAY – based on Boston, pp. 38-43					
(Flood starts at Low Water; Ebb starts at High Water)					
Broad Sound, W. of Eagle Is. .... F+1 00, E-0 05		010	0.9	168	1.3
Hussey Sound, SW of Overset Is. F+0 45, E+0 25		316	1.1	153	1.2
Portland Hbr. entr.,					
SW of Cushing Is......................... F+0 30, E-0 00		322	1.0	154	1.1
Portland Bridge, Center of draw F+1 10, E+0 45		225	0.9	050	1.0
PORTSMOUTH HARBOR – based on Boston, pp. 38-43					
(Flood starts at Low Water; Ebb starts at High Water)					
Kitts Rocks, 0.2 mi. WSW of........ F+2 05, E+1 30		314	0.7	133	0.8
Portsmouth Hbr. entr. .... F+2 05, E+1 30		342	1.2	194	1.5
Fort Point.................................... F+2 10, E+1 35		328	1.6	098	2.0
Clark Is., S of .... +2 15		270	1.6	085	2.3
Henderson Pt., W of .... F+2 35, E+2 00		285	2.4	138	2.8
MASSACHUSETTS COAST – based on Boston, pp. 38-43					
(Flood starts at Low Water; Ebb starts at High Water)					
Merrimack River entr. .... +1 35		285	2.2	105	1.4
Newburyport, Merrimack R. ...... F+1 25, E+2 05		288	1.5	098	1.4
Plum Is. Sound entr. .... F+0 30, E+1 10		316	1.6	184	1.5
Gloucester Hbr., Blynman Canal entr. .... -0 05		310	3.0	130	3.3
Hypocrite Channel........................ F+0 10, E+1 10		262	0.9	070	1.0
BOSTON HARBOR – based on Boston, pp. 38-43					
(Flood starts at Low Water; Ebb starts at High Water)					
Pt. Allerton, 0.4 mi. NW. .... F-0 15, E+0 35		265	0.7	080	0.8
Deer Island Lt................................. F-0 05, E+0 18		254	1.1	111	1.2
Nantasket Rds					
Hull Gut .... +0 15		163	1.2	350	1.8
West Head (W. Gut) 0.2mi. SW F-0 10, E+1 25		167	1.4	322	1.4
Weir R. entr., Worlds End, N of.. F+0 15, E+1 05		076	0.7	272	0.8
Bumkin Is., 0.4mi. W. of .... F-0 20, E+0 45		195	0.5	303	0.3
Weymouth Back R., betw. Grape I.					
and Lower Neck.......................... F-0 20, E+0 30		094	0.7	281	0.9
CAPE COD BAY – based on Boston, pp. 38-43					
(Flood starts at Low Water; Ebb starts at High Water)					
Race Point, 7 mi. N of .... F-0 05, E+0 20		290	1.5	–	1.5
Race Point, 1 mi. NW of................ F-0 10, E+0 15		226	1.0	061	0.9
Barnstable Harbor........................ F+0 15, E+0 40		192	1.2	004	1.4
Manomet Point.............................. F+0 00, E+0 25		155	1.1	010	0.9
Gurnet Point, 1 mi. E of .... F-0 10, E+0 15		250	1.4	–	1.0
Farnham Rock, 1 mi. E of.............. F-0 25, E-0 00		180	1.1	010	0.9

CURRENT STATIONS

Important: **See NOTE, bottom p. 29 and NOAA Article, p. 11**

TIME OF CURRENT CHANGE

(See Note at bottom of Boston Tables, pp. 38-43: Rule-of-Thumb for Current Velocities.)

	TIME DIFFERENCES Flood Starts; Ebb Starts Hr. Min.	MAXIMUM FLOOD Dir.(true) in degrees	Avg. Max. in knots	MAXIMUM EBB Dir.(true) in degrees	Avg. Max. in knots
NANTUCKET SOUND – based on Pollock Rip Channel, pp. 60-65					
Pollock Rip Channel, E end .... -0 20		053	2.0	212	1.8
*POLLOCK RIP CHANNEL at Butler Hole - See table, pp. 60-65					
Monomoy Point, 0.2 mi. W of .... +0 10		170	1.7	346	2.0
Halfmoon Shoal, 3.5 mi. E of .... +1 10		088	1.1	295	1.0
Great Point, 0.5 mi. W of .... F+0 25, E+1 15		029	1.1	195	1.2
Tuckernuck Shoal, off E end .... +1 15		113	0.9	287	0.9
Nantucket Hbr. entr. chan........... F+3 20, E+2 45		171	1.2	350	1.5
Muskeget Is. chan., 1 mi. NE of . F+1 30, E+1 00		108	1.1	295	1.5
Muskeget Rock, 1.3 mi. SW of .... +1 05		024	1.3	192	1.0
Muskeget Channel...................................... +1 35		021	3.8	200	3.3
Betw. Long Shoal-Norton Shoal .... +1 30		100	1.4	260	1.1
Cape Poge Lt., 1.7 mi. SSE of .... +0 55		025	1.6	215	1.3
Cross Rip Channel....................................... +1 50		091	1.3	272	0.9
Cape Poge, 3.2 mi. NE of .... +2 35		095	1.6	300	1.2
Betw. Broken Gr.-Horseshoe Sh.F+1 45, E+1 15		107	1.1	276	0.9
Point Gammon, 1.2 mi. S of........................ +1 10		105	1.1	260	1.0
Lewis Bay entr. chan. .... +2 45		004	0.9	184	1.3
Betw. Wreck Shoal-Eldridge Shoal .... +1 45		062	1.7	245	1.4
Hedge Fence Lighted Gong Buoy 22 .... +2 45		108	1.4	268	1.2
Betw. E. Chop-Squash Meadow F+2 10, E+1 45		131	1.4	329	1.8
East Chop, 1 mi. N of .... F+2 40, E+2 20		116	2.2	297	2.2
West Chop, 0.8 mi. N of .... F+2 50, E+2 20		096	3.1	282	3.0
Betw. Hedge Fence-L'hommedieu Shoal . +2 15		106	2.1	276	2.2
Waquoit Bay entr. .... F+3 20, E+3 40		348	1.5	203	1.4
L'hommedieu Shoal, N of W end .... +2 20		080	2.3	268	2.3
Nobska Point, 1.8 mi. E of............................ +2 05		063	2.3	240	1.7
VINEYARD SOUND – based on Pollock Rip Channel, pp. 60-65					
West Chop, 0.2 mi. W of .... F+1 20, E+1 50		059	2.7	241	1.4
Nobska Point, 1 mi. SE of .... +2 30		071	2.6	259	2.4
Norton Point, 0.5 mi. N of............................ +2 00		050	3.4	240	2.4
Tarpaulin Cove, 1.5 mi. E of .... F+2 50, E+2 10		055	1.9	232	2.3
Robinsons Hole, 1.2 mi. SE of .... F+2 30, E+2 10		060	1.9	240	2.1
Gay Head, 3 mi. N of.................................... +2 05		074	1.1	255	1.2
Gay Head, 1.5 mi. NW of.............................. +1 35		012	2.0	249	2.0
VINEYARD SOUND-BUZZARDS BAY – based on Woods Hole, pp. 52-57					
Robinsons Hole, Naushon Pt. .... +0 40		151	3.0	332	2.9
Quicks Hole, S end...................... F+1 20, E+0 30		140	1.9	300	2.0
Quicks Hole, Middle.................... F+1 30, E+1 00		157	2.3	327	1.8
Quicks Hole, N end .... F+1 40, E+0 55		165	2.0	002	2.6
Canapitsit Channel .... F+1 00, E+0 14		131	1.7	312	1.7
BUZZARDS BAY – based on Woods Hole, pp. 52-57					
Westport River entr.. -1 20		290	2.2	108	2.5
Gooseberry Nk., 2 mi. SSE of (41°27'N- 71°01'W) *rotary current, no slack water. Avg. max. 0.6 kts, approx. dir. 52° true at 3 1/2 hrs. after Flood starts at Poll. Rip. Avg. max. 0.5 kts, approx. dir. 232° true 2 1/2 hrs. after Ebb starts at Poll. Rip.*					
Betw. Ribbon Reef-Sow &Pigs Rf.F-1 45, E-3 45		062	0.8	237	1.2
Penikese Is., 0.8 mi. NW of...........F-3 00, E-1 55		050	1.2	254	1.1
Betw. Gull Is.-Nashawena Is......F-3 39, E-3 00		091	0.9	247	1.1
Dumpling Rocks, 0.2 mi. SE of F-3 10, E-2 30		066	0.8	190	1.1
BUZZARDS BAY – based on Cape Cod Canal, pp. 46-51					
Abiels Ledge, 0.4 mi. S of .... F+0 13, E-0 15		069	1.3	236	1.8
CAPE COD CANAL - table, pp. 46-51		070	4.0	250	4.5

*See Tidal Current Chart Buzzards Bay, Vineyard and Nantucket Sounds, pp. 66-77

Important: **See NOTE, bottom p. 29 and NOAA Article, p. 11.**

TIME OF CURRENT CHANGE

(See Note at bottom of Boston Tables, pp. 38-43: Rule-of-Thumb for Current Velocities.)

	TIME DIFFERENCES Flood Starts; Ebb Starts Hr. Min.	MAXIMUM FLOOD Dir.(true) in degrees	Avg. Max. in knots	MAXIMUM EBB Dir.(true) in degrees	Avg. Max. in knots
**NARRAGANSETT BAY – based on Pollock Rip Channel, pp. 60-65					
Tiverton, Stone Bridge, Sakonnet	F-3 00, E-2 25	010	2.7	190	2.7
Tiverton, RR Bridge, Sakonnet R.	F-3 25, E-2 50	000	2.3	180	2.4
Castle Hill, W of East Passage	F-0 05, E-1 05	013	0.7	237	1.2
Bull Point, E of	-1 10	001	1.2	206	1.5
Rose Is., NE of	F-1 55, E-1 15	310	0.8	124	1.0
Rose Is., W of	F-0 40, E-1 20	001	0.7	172	1.0
Dyer Is., W of	-1 00	023	0.8	216	1.0
Mount Hope Bridge	-1 15	047	1.1	230	1.4
Kickamuit R., Mt. Hope Bay	F-2 05, E-1 20	000	1.4	191	1.7
Warren R., Warren	-0 20	358	1.0	171	0.9
Beavertail Point, 0.8 mi NW of	F-0 10, E-1 30	003	0.5	188	1.0
Betw. Dutch Is.-Beaver Head	-1 55	030	1.0	233	1.0
Dutch Is., W of	-1 25	014	1.3	206	1.2
India Pt. RR Bridge, Seekonk R.	-1 40	020	1.0	180	1.4
BLOCK ISLAND SOUND – based on The Race, pp. 86-91					
Pt. Judith Pond entr.	-3 10	351	1.8	186	1.5
Sandy Pt., Block Is. 1.5 mi N of	F-0 25, E-1 05	315	1.9	063	2.1
Lewis Pt., 1.0 mi. SW of	F-1 30, E-0 25	298	1.9	136	1.8
Lewis Pt., 1.5 mi. W of	F-1 35, E-0 50	318	1.4	170	1.7
Southwest Ledge	-0 25	321	1.5	141	2.1
Watch Hill Pt., 2.2 mi. E of	F-0 30, E+0 45	260	1.2	086	0.7
Montauk Pt., 1.2 mi. E of	F-1 20, E-0 40	346	2.8	162	2.8
Montauk Pt., 1 mi. NE of	F-2 05, E-1 15	356	2.4	145	1.9
Betw. Shagwong Reef-Cerberus Shoal	-0 30	241	1.9	056	1.8
Betw. Cerberus Sh.-Fishers Is.	F-1 00, E+0 05	264	1.3	096	1.3
Gardiners Is., 3 mi. NE of	-0 35	305	0.9	138	1.0
GARDINERS BAY etc. – based on The Race, pp. 86-91					
Goff Point, 0.4 mi. NW of	-1 35	225	1.2	010	1.6
Acabonack Hbr. entr., 0.6 mi. ESE of	F-1 35, E-1 05	345	1.4	140	1.2
Gardiners Pt. Ruins, 1.1 mi. N of	-0 10	270	1.2	066	1.8
Betw. Gardiners Point-Plum Is.	-0 25	288	1.4	100	1.6
Jennings Pt., 0.2 mi. NNW of	+0 35	290	1.6	055	1.5
Cedar Pt., 0.2 mi. W of	F-0 10, E+0 30	195	1.8	005	1.6
North Haven Peninsula, N of	F+0 10, E+0 40	230	2.4	035	2.1
Paradise Pt., 0.4 mi. E of	+0 35	145	1.5	345	1.5
Little Peconic Bay entr.	+0 45	240	1.6	015	1.5
Robins Is., 0.5 mi. S of	F+0 30, E+0 55	245	1.7	065	0.6
FISHERS ISLAND SOUND – based on The Race, pp. 86-91					
Napatree Point, 0.7 mi. SW of	-0 50	284	1.7	113	2.2
Little Narragansett Bay entr.	-2 05	092	1.3	268	1.3
Ram Island Reef, S of	-0 50	255	1.3	088	1.6
LONG ISLAND SOUND – based on The Race, pp. 86-91					
*THE RACE (near Valiant Rock) – See pp. 86-91		290	3.3	106	4.2
Race Point, 0.4 mi. SW of	-0 25	288	2.6	135	3.5
Little Gull Is., 1.1 mi. ENE of	+0 05	301	4.0	130	4.7
Little Gull Is., 0.8 mi. NNW of	F+0 25, E-2 20	258	1.9	043	2.9
Great Gull Is., SW of	-0 40	320	2.3	147	3.3
New London St. Pier, Thames R.	-1 30	358	0.4	178	0.4
Goshen Pt., 1.9 mi. SSE of	-0 55	285	1.2	062	1.6
Bartlett Reef, 0.2 mi. S of	F-2 05, E-1 05	255	1.4	090	1.3
Twotree Is. Channel	F-1 00, E-0 35	267	1.2	099	1.6

*See Tidal Current Chart Long Is. and Block Is. Sounds, pp. 92-97
**Floods somewhat unstable. Flood currents differing from predicted should be expected.

Important: See NOTE, bottom p. 29 and NOAA Article, p. 11

CURRENT STATIONS

TIME OF CURRENT CHANGE

(See Note at bottom of Boston Tables, pp. 38-43: Rule-of-Thumb for Current Velocities.)

	TIME DIFFERENCES Flood Starts; Ebb Starts Hr. Min.	MAXIMUM FLOOD Dir.(true) in degrees	Avg. Max. in knots	MAXIMUM EBB Dir.(true) in degrees	Avg. Max. in knots
LONG ISLAND SOUND – based on The Race, pp. 86-91					
Black Point, 0.8 mi. S of F-0 40, E-0 15		260	1.3	073	1.4
Betw. Black Pt.-Plum Is. ....+0 35		236	2.1	076	2.4
Plum Is., 0.8 mi. NNW of..............F+0 10,E-1 05		247	1.7	065	2.4
Plum Gut ....-1 00		306	1.9	116	3.0
Hatchett Pt., 1.1 mi. WSW of F-2 30, E-0 40		240	1.3	045	1.2
Saybrook Bkwtr., 1.5 mi. SE of......F-1 20, E-0 45		260	1.9	070	2.0
Conn. River I-95 Bridge...............F+1 15, E+0 20		356	0.9	166	1.8
Mulford Pt., 3.1 mi. NW of ....+0 05		269	1.9	066	2.3
Cornfield Point, 2.8 mi. SE of........F-1 30, E-0 30		249	1.9	085	1.4
Cornfield Point, 1.1 mi. S of ....-0 50		293	1.4	108	1.6
Kelsey Point, 1 mi. S of...................F-1 35, E-1 05		249	2.0	118	1.5
Six Mile Reef, 2 mi. E of...............F-0 30, E+0 05		235	1.6	040	2.1
Sachem Head, 1 mi. SSE of ....-0 30		255	1.1	065	1.0
New Haven Harbor entr. ....-0 05		277	0.7	122	0.5
Housatonic R., Milford Pt., 0.2 mi. W of ... +0 15		330	1.2	135	1.2
Point No Point, 2.1 mi. S of...........................-0 10		251	1.3	074	1.2
Port Jefferson Harbor entr. ....-0 10		150	1.6	336	1.0
Crane Neck Point, 0.5 mi. NW of .F-0 45, E-1 40		256	1.3	016	1.5
Eatons Neck Pt., 1.3 mi. N of ....+0 20		283	1.4	075	1.4
Lloyd Point, 1.3 mi. NNW of......................+1 30		255	1.0	055	0.9
EAST RIVER – based on Hell Gate, pp. 110-115					
Cryders Pt., 0.4 mi. NNW of ....-0 30		110	1.3	285	1.1
College Pt. Rf., .25 mi. NW of ....-0 30		074	1.5	261	1.4
Rikers Is. Chann. off La Guardia Field ..... +0 05		088	1.1	261	1.3
Hunts Point, SW of...0 00		108	1.7	280	1.3
S. Brother Is. NW of .... - 0 10		054	1.5	252	1.2
Off Winthrop Ave., Astoria 0 00		040	3.4	220	2.5
Mill Rock, NE of...-0 25		103	2.3	288	0.6
Mill Rock, W of F-0 25, E-0 00		000	1.2	180	1.0
HELL GATE (off Mill Rock) – table, pp. 110-115		050	3.4	230	4.6
Roosevelt Is., W of, off 75th St. ....-0 05		037	3.8	215	4.7
Roosevelt Is., E of, off 36th Ave. ....-0 10		030	3.5	210	3.4
Roosevelt Is., W of, off 67th St. ....+0 10		011	3.6	230	4.0
Off 19th St. (Pier 67) ....-0 10		355	1.8	179	1.9
Williamsburg Br., 0.3 mi. N of ....-0 05		020	2.7	220	2.9
Brooklyn Bridge, 0.1 mi. SW of ....-0 10		046	2.9	222	3.5
Buttermilk Channel **Caution** ....F-0 30, E+0 05		050	1.8	221	2.6
LONG ISLAND, South Coast – based on The Narrows, pp. 116-121					
Shinnecock Inlet ....F+0 05, E-0 40		350	2.5	170	2.3
Fire Is. Inlet, 0.5 mi. S. of Oak Bch. .... +0 15		082	2.4	244	2.4
Jones Inlet F-1 15, E-0 50		035	3.1	217	2.6
East Rockaway Inlet F-1 35, E-1 10		042	2.2	227	2.3
JAMAICA BAY – based on The Narrows, pp. 116-121					
Rockaway Inlet entr. ....-1 45		085	1.8	244	2.7
Barren Is., E of F-1 50, E-0 10		004	1.2	192	1.7
Beach Channel (bridge) F-1 40, E-0 05		062	1.9	225	2.0
Grass Hassock Channel ....-1 10		052	1.0	228	1.0

Caution- During the first two hours of flood in the channel north of Governers Island, the current in the Hudson River is still ebbing while during the first 1 1/2 hours of ebb in this channel, the current in the Hudson River is still flooding.

Important: **See NOTE, bottom p. 29 and NOAA Article, p. 11.**

TIME OF CURRENT CHANGE
(See Note at bottom of Boston Tables, pp. 38-43: Rule-of-Thumb for Current Velocities.)

	TIME DIFFERENCES Flood Starts; Ebb Starts Hr. Min.	MAXIMUM FLOOD Dir.(true) in degrees	Avg. Max. in knots	MAXIMUM EBB Dir.(true) in degrees	Avg. Max. in knots
NEW YORK HARBOR ENTRANCE – based on The Narrows, pp. 116-121					
Ambrose Channel .... -0 40		303	1.6	123	1.7
Norton Pt., WSW of.................................... +0 10		341	1.0	166	1.2
THE NARROWS (mid-ch.) – table, pp. 116-121		336	1.6	164	1.9
NEW YORK HARBOR, Upper Bay – based on The Narrows, pp. 116-121					
Bay Ridge, W of............................ F+0 00, E+0 35		354	1.4	185	1.5
Red Hook Channel.........................F-0 55, E-0 15		353	1.0	170	0.7
Robbins Reef Light, E of ....F+0 25, E-0 05		016	1.3	204	1.6
Red Hook, 1 mi. W of .... +0 45		024	1.3	206	2.3
Statue of Liberty, E of .... +0 55		031	1.4	205	1.9
HUDSON RIVER, Midchannel – based on The Narrows, pp. 116-121					
George Washington Bridge .... +1 35		010	1.8	203	2.5
Spuyten Duyvil .... +1 35		020	1.6	–	2.1
Riverdale .... F+2 25, E+1 50		015	1.4	200	2.0
Dobbs Ferry .... F+2 45, E+2 10		010	1.3	–	1.7
Tarrytown... +2 40		000	1.1	–	1.5
West Point, off Duck Is............................... +3 40		010	1.0	–	1.1
NEW YORK HARBOR, Lower Bay – based on The Narrows, pp. 116-121					
Sandy Hook Channel.................................... -1 20		286	1.6	094	1.9
Sandy Hook Channel, 0.4 mi. W of N. tip .-1 40		235	2.0	050	1.6
Coney Is. Lt., 1.5 mi. SSE of.......................-1 10		310	1.1	125	1.3
Rockaway Inlet Jetty, 1 mi. SW of F-2 05, E-1 35		287	1.2	142	1.4
Coney Is. Channel, W end F-1 15, E-0 30		293	1.1	102	1.2
SANDY HOOK BAY – based on The Narrows, pp. 116-121					
Highlands Bridge, Shrewsbury R.............. +0 25		170	2.6	–	2.5
Sea Bright Br., Shrewsbury R. ...F+1 05, E+0 45		185	1.4	–	1.7
RARITAN RIVER – based on The Narrows, pp. 116-121					
Washington Canal, N entr. F-1 00, E-1 40		240	1.5	060	1.5
South River entr. F-1 45, E-0 35		180	1.1	000	1.0
*ARTHUR KILL & KILL VAN KULL – based on The Narrows, pp. 116-121					
Tottenville, Arthur Kill River....................... -0 50		023	1.0	211	1.1
Tufts Pt.-Smoking Pt. .... -0 35		109	1.2	267	1.2
Elizabethport... +0 20		090	1.4	262	1.1
Bergen Pt., East Reach .... -1 35		274	1.1	094	1.2
New Brighton... -1 35		262	1.3	072	1.9
NEW JERSEY COAST – based on Del. Bay Entr., pp. 140-145					
Manasquan Inlet F-0 45, E-1 10		300	1.7	120	1.8
Manasquan R. Hwy. Br. Main Ch.F-0 40, E-1 15		230	2.2	050	2.1
**Pt. Pleasant Canal,					
north bridge................................ F+1 45, E+0 50		170	1.8	350	2.0
Barnegat Inlet................................ F+1 00, E+0 15		270	2.2	090	2.5
Manahawkin Drawbridge........................... +2 30		030	1.1	210	0.9
McCrie Shoal... -0 35		280	1.3	100	1.4
Cape May Harbor entr. .... -1 35		324	1.6	142	1.7
Cape May Canal, E end................................ -1 50		310	1.9	130	1.9

CURRENT STATIONS

* *Tidal flow erratic due to dredging.*

***Waters are extremely turbulent. Currents of 6 to 7 knots have been reported near the bridges.*

Important: **See NOTE, bottom p. 29 and NOAA Article, p. 11**

TIME OF CURRENT CHANGE

(See Note at bottom of Boston Tables, pp. 38-43: Rule-of-Thumb for Current Velocities.)

	TIME DIFFERENCES Flood Starts; Ebb Starts Hr. Min.	MAXIMUM FLOOD Dir.(true) in degrees	Avg. Max. in knots	MAXIMUM EBB Dir.(true) in degrees	Avg. Max. in knots
DELAWARE BAY & RIVER – based on Del. Bay Entr., pp. 140-145					
Cape May Channel	-1 10	306	1.5	150	2.3
DELAWARE BAY ENTR. – table, pp. 140-145		327	1.4	147	1.3
Cape Henlopen, 0.7 mi. ESE of	F- 0 05, E- 040	331	1.8	139	2.4
Cape Henlopen, 2 mi. NE of	F+0 20, E-0 05	315	2.0	145	2.3
Cape Henlopen, 5 mi. N of	+0 30	344	2.0	173	1.9
Mispillion River Mouth	F+2 35, E+1 50	025	1.5	190	1.0
Bay Shore chan., City of Town Bank	- 0 40	006	0.9	183	1.0
Fourteen Ft. Bk., Lt., 1.2 mi. E of	+0 10	339	1.3	174	1.5
Maurice River entr.	+1 00	012	1.1	192	1.0
Kelly Island, 1.5 mi. E of	+0 50	348	0.9	164	1.2
Miah Maull rge. at Cross Ledge rge	+1 25	335	1.5	160	1.8
False Egg Is. Pt., 2 mi. off	+0 20	342	1.1	158	1.3
Ben Davis Pt. Shoal., SW of	+1 40	321	1.8	147	1.9
Cohansey R., 0.5 mi. above entr.	+1 30	074	1.2	254	1.4
Arnold Point, 2.2 mi. WSW of	+2 25	324	2.1	145	1.9
Smyrna River entr.	+1 55	250	1.2	070	1.5
Stony Point chan., W of	F+3 25, E+2 30	324	1.5	151	1.9
Appoquinimink R. entr.	+2 25	231	1.0	048	1.2
Reedy Is., off end of pier	+2 55	027	2.4	194	2.6
Alloway Creek entr., 0.2 mi. above	+2 15	129	2.1	325	2.1
Reedy Point, 0.85 mi. NE of	F+3 35, E+2 50	341	1.6	163	2.2
Salem River entr.	+3 40	062	1.5	245	1.6
Bulkhead Sh. chan., off Del. City	F+3 15, E+2 55	308	2.1	138	2.1
Pea Patch Is., chan., E of	+3 30	319	2.3	148	2.3
New Castle, chan., abreast of	F+3 35, E+3 00	051	1.9	230	2.4
CHESAPEAKE BAY – based on The Race, pp. 86-91					
(over 90% correlation within 15 min. throughout year)					
Cape Henry Light, 2.0 mi. N of	+0 40	289	1.2	110	1.1
Chesapeake Bay entr.	F+0 20, E-0 20	300	0.8	129	1.2
Cape Henry Light, 4.6 mi. N of	F-0 25, E-0 05	294	1.3	104	1.3
Cape Henry Light, 8.3 mi. NW of	+0 30	329	1.0	133	1.1
Tail of the Horseshoe	F+0 20, E-0 05	300	0.9	110	1.0
Chesapeake Channel (Bridge Tunnel)	+0 15	335	1.8	145	1.5
Fisherman Is., 1.7 mi. S of	F-0 00, E-0 35	297	1.0	126	1.4
York Spit Channel N buoy "26"	F+1 50, E+1 05	010	0.8	195	1.1
Old Plantation Flats Lt., 0.5 mi. W of	+1 40	005	1.2	175	1.3
Wolf Trap Lt., 0.5 mi. W of	F+2 00, E+1 15	015	1.0	190	1.2
Stingray Point, 5.5 mi. E of	+2 50	343	1.0	179	0.9
Stingray Point, 12.5 mi. E of	F+2 35, E+1 50	030	1.0	175	0.8
Smith Point Lt., 6.0 mi. N of	+4 45	350	0.4	135	1.0
Cove Point - See Chesapeake Bay Current Diagram, p. 154					
Pooles Island - See Chesapeake Bay Current Diagram, p. 154					
Worton Point - See Chesapeake Bay Current Diagram, p. 154					
CHESAPEAKE & DELAWARE CANAL - table, pp. 148-153					
HAMPTON ROADS – based on The Race, pp. 86-91					
(over 90% correlation within 15 min. throughout year)					
Thimble Shoal Channel (West End)	+0 05	293	0.9	116	1.2
Old Point Comfort, 0.2 mi. S of	F-0 20, E-1 15	240	1.7	075	1.4
Willoughby Spit, 0.8 mi. NW of	F-1 15, E-2 00	260	0.7	040	1.0
Sewells Point, chan., W of	F-0 25, E-1 50	195	0.9	000	1.2
Newport News, chan., middle	F-0 25, E -0 32	244	1.1	076	1.1
C&D CANAL POINTS – based on C&D Canal, pp. 148-153					
Back Creek, 0.3 mi. W of Sandy Pt.	-0 05	057	1.2	244	1.4
Reedy Point Radio Tower, S of	F-1 00, E-0 05	078	1.9	263	1.3

Important: **See NOTE, bottom p. 29 and NOAA Article, p. 11.**

TIME OF CURRENT CHANGE

(See Note at bottom of Boston Tables, pp. 38-43: Rule-of-Thumb for Current Velocities.)

	TIME DIFFERENCES Flood Starts; Ebb Starts Hr. Min.	MAXIMUM FLOOD		MAXIMUM EBB	
		Dir.(true) in degrees	Avg. Max. in knots	Dir.(true) in degrees	Avg. Max. in knots

VA, NC, SC, GA & FL, outer coast – based on Hell Gate, pp. 110-115
(over 90% correlation within 15 min. throughout year)

Hatteras Inlet	F+1 00, E+0 40	307	2.1	148	2.0
Ocracoke Inlet chan. entr.	F+1 10, E+0 45	000	1.7	145	2.4
Beaufort Inlet Approach	F+0 25, E-1 00	358	0.3	161	1.4
Cape Fear R. Bald Head	F-1 25, E-1 30	034	2.2	190	2.9
Winyah Bay entr.	+0 05	320	1.9	140	2.0
North Santee R. entr.	F-0 40, E-1 35	010	1.5	165	1.8
South Santee R. entr.	F-1 20, E-1 15	045	1.5	240	1.6
Charleston Hbr. entr., betw. jetties	-1 40	320	1.8	121	1.8
Charleston Hbr., off Ft. Sumter	-1 40	313	1.7	127	2.0
Charleston Hbr. S. ch. 0.8 mi. ENE of Ft. Johnson	F-0 55, E-1 40	275	0.8	115	2.6
Charleston Hbr., Drum Is., E of (bridge)	-1 20	020	1.2	183	2.0
North Edisto River entr.	-0 35	332	2.9	142	3.7
South Edisto River entr.	F-1 20, E-1 50	350	1.8	146	2.2
Ashepoo R. off Jefford Cr. entr.	-0 40	016	1.5	197	1.6
Port Royal Sd., SE chan. entr.	F-2 10, E-1 50	310	1.3	150	1.6
Hilton Head	-1 20	324	1.8	146	1.8
Beaufort River entr.	-1 20	010	1.3	195	1.4
Savannah River entr.	F-1 00, E-0 50	286	2.0	110	2.0
Vernon R. 1.2 mi. S of Possum Pt.	F-1 25, E-1 00	324	1.1	166	1.7
Raccoon Key & Egg Is. Shoal bet.	F-0 40, E -1 15	254	1.6	129	2.0
St. Catherines Sound entr.	F-1 40, E-0 35	291	1.8	126	1.7
Sapelo Sound entr.	F-1 30, E-0 55	290	1.7	118	2.2
Doboy Sound entr.	-1 25	289	1.6	106	1.8
Altamaha Sd., 1 mi. SE of Onemile Cut	F-0 15, E-2 00	272	1.0	092	1.9
St. Simons Sound Bar Channel	F-1 15, E-0 40	308	0.8	119	1.7
St. Andrews Sound entr.	F-1 20, E-0 50	268	2.1	103	2.2
Cumberland Sd., St. Mary's River, Ft. Clinch, 0.3 mi. N	F-1 25, E-1 00	275	1.4	087	1.6
Drum Point Is., rge. D chan	-0 50	350	1.1	170	1.5
Nassau Sd., midsound, 1 mi. N of Sawpit Cr. entr.	F-0 15, E-0 40	312	1.7	135	1.7

FLORIDA EAST COAST – based on The Narrows, pp. 116-121
(over 90% correlation within 15 min. throughout year)

St. Johns R. entr. betw. jetties	+0 20	262	2.0	081	2.0
Mayport	+0 30	211	2.2	026	3.3
St. Johns Bluff	F+0 50, E+0 05	244	1.6	059	2.4

FLORIDA EAST COAST – based on Hell Gate, pp. 110-115
(over 90% correlation within 15 min. throughout year)

Fort Pierce Inlet entr.	+0 40	258	2.7	080	2.8
Lake Worth Inlet, entr.	F-1 05, E-0 45	267	1.6	086	1.3
Miami Hbr., Bakers Haulover Cut	-0 05	270	2.9	090	2.5
Miami Hbr. entr.	-0 15	293	2.2	113	2.4

CURRENT STATIONS

NOTE: Velocities shown are from U.S. Gov't. figures. It is obvious, however, to local mariners and other observers, that coastal inlets may have far greater velocities than indicated here. Strong winds and opposing tides can cause even more dangerous conditions, and great caution should be used. Separate times for Flood and Ebb are given only when the times are more than 20 minutes apart.

Important: **See NOTE, bottom p. 29 and NOAA Article, p. 11**

2013 HIGH & LOW WATER
PORTLAND, ME
43°39.6'N, 70°14.8'W

Standard Time   Standard Time

JANUARY

Day of Month	Day of Week	HIGH a.m.	Ht.	HIGH p.m.	Ht.	LOW a.m.	LOW p.m.
1	T	1 11	8.9	1 16	9.6	7 06	7 34
2	W	1 49	9.0	1 58	9.4	7 49	8 14
3	T	2 32	9.1	2 46	9.2	8 36	9 00
4	F	3 17	9.2	3 37	9.0	9 27	9 49
5	S	4 08	9.4	4 35	8.8	10 25	10 44
6	S	5 05	9.6	5 38	8.7	11 28	11 44
7	M	6 05	9.9	6 45	8.8	...	12 33
8	T	7 07	10.3	7 51	9.0	12 47	1 38
9	W	8 09	10.8	8 53	9.4	1 49	2 39
10	T	9 08	11.2	9 50	9.8	2 49	3 36
11	F	10 04	11.5	10 45	10.1	3 47	4 30
12	S	10 58	11.6	11 37	10.3	4 42	5 22
13	S	11 50	11.4	...	...	5 35	6 12
14	M	12 27	10.4	12 42	11.1	6 28	7 01
15	T	1 17	10.2	1 34	10.5	7 20	7 50
16	W	2 08	10.0	2 26	9.9	8 14	8 40
17	T	2 58	9.7	3 20	9.2	9 09	9 31
18	F	3 51	9.3	4 17	8.6	10 06	10 24
19	S	4 45	9.0	5 17	8.1	11 06	11 20
20	S	5 41	8.8	6 18	7.8	...	12 08
21	M	6 38	8.8	7 18	7.8	12 18	1 07
22	T	7 32	8.8	8 12	7.8	1 14	2 02
23	W	8 22	9.0	9 01	8.0	2 06	2 51
24	T	9 08	9.2	9 44	8.3	2 53	3 34
25	F	9 49	9.5	10 23	8.5	3 35	4 12
26	S	10 27	9.7	10 58	8.8	4 14	4 47
27	S	11 03	9.8	11 32	9.0	4 50	5 21
28	M	11 38	9.9	...	...	5 26	5 54
29	T	12 06	9.2	12 15	9.9	6 04	6 29
30	W	12 42	9.4	12 54	9.8	6 43	7 06
31	T	1 20	9.5	1 36	9.6	7 26	7 47

FEBRUARY

Day of Month	Day of Week	HIGH a.m.	Ht.	HIGH p.m.	Ht.	LOW a.m.	LOW p.m.
1	F	2 02	9.7	2 22	9.4	8 12	8 32
2	S	2 48	9.7	3 15	9.1	9 04	9 22
3	S	3 41	9.8	4 14	8.7	10 03	10 20
4	M	4 39	9.8	5 19	8.6	11 06	11 22
5	T	5 43	9.9	6 29	8.6	...	12 15
6	W	6 51	10.1	7 38	8.8	12 29	1 23
7	T	7 57	10.4	8 42	9.2	1 36	2 26
8	F	8 58	10.8	9 39	9.7	2 39	3 24
9	S	9 55	11.0	10 31	10.1	3 37	4 16
10	S	10 47	11.1	11 19	10.3	4 31	5 05
11	M	11 36	11.0	...	...	5 21	5 52
12	T	12 06	10.4	12 24	10.7	6 10	6 37
13	W	12 51	10.3	1 11	10.2	6 58	7 21
14	T	1 35	10.0	1 58	9.6	7 46	8 05
15	F	2 20	9.7	2 46	9.0	8 35	8 51
16	S	3 07	9.3	3 37	8.4	9 26	9 40
17	S	3 56	8.9	4 33	7.9	10 21	10 32
18	M	4 50	8.6	5 32	7.6	11 20	11 30
19	T	5 49	8.5	6 34	7.5	...	12 21
20	W	6 48	8.5	7 32	7.6	12 29	1 20
21	T	7 43	8.7	8 23	7.9	1 26	2 12
22	F	8 33	9.0	9 08	8.3	2 18	2 57
23	S	9 17	9.3	9 48	8.6	3 03	3 37
24	S	9 57	9.6	10 25	9.0	3 44	4 13
25	M	10 36	9.8	11 00	9.4	4 23	4 48
26	T	11 13	10.0	11 35	9.8	5 01	5 23
27	W	11 52	10.1	...	...	5 40	6 00
28	T	12 12	10.1	12 33	10.0	6 21	6 40

Dates when Ht. of **Low** Water is below Mean Lower Low with Ht. of lowest given for each period and Date of lowest in ( ):

8th - 16th: -1.9' (12th)   6th - 14th: -1.6' (10th)
27th - 31st: -0.4' (29th - 30th)   25th - 28th: -0.6' (27th - 28th)

Average Rise and Fall 9.1 ft.

When a high tide exceeds avg. ht., the *following* low tide will be lower than avg.

2013 HIGH & LOW WATER
PORTLAND, ME
43°39.6'N, 70°14.8'W

*Daylight Time starts March 10 at 2 a.m.

Daylight Saving Time

DATE OF MONTH	DAY OF WEEK	MARCH						DAY OF MONTH	DAY OF WEEK	APRIL					
		HIGH				LOW				HIGH				LOW	
		a.m.	Ht.	p.m.	Ht.	a.m.	p.m.			a.m.	Ht.	p.m.	Ht.	a.m.	p.m.
1	F	12 53	10.2	1 17	9.8	7 06	7 23	1	M	3 08	10.7	3 50	9.4	9 34	9 50
2	S	1 37	10.3	2 06	9.5	7 54	8 10	2	T	4 06	10.4	4 52	9.1	10 34	10 52
3	S	2 26	10.2	3 01	9.2	8 48	9 04	3	W	5 11	10.0	6 01	9.0	11 40	...
4	M	3 20	10.1	4 00	8.8	9 46	10 02	4	T	6 19	9.8	7 09	9.0	12 01	12 48
5	T	4 21	9.9	5 08	8.6	10 51	11 09	5	F	7 31	9.7	8 15	9.3	1 12	1 54
6	W	5 29	9.8	6 19	8.6	...	12 01	6	S	8 37	9.8	9 14	9.6	2 20	2 55
7	T	6 40	9.8	7 28	8.9	12 19	1 10	7	S	9 37	9.9	10 07	10.0	3 22	3 50
8	F	7 48	10.1	8 30	9.4	1 29	2 13	8	M	10 31	10.0	10 54	10.3	4 16	4 39
9	S	8 50	10.3	9 25	9.8	2 32	3 09	9	T	11 19	10.0	11 36	10.4	5 05	5 23
10	S	*10 44	10.5	*11 14	10.2	*4 28	*4 59	10	W	...	...	12 03	9.9	5 50	6 04
11	M	11 34	10.6	11 59	10.2	5 19	5 46	11	T	12 16	10.4	12 45	9.7	6 32	6 43
12	T	...	...	12 20	10.5	6 07	6 29	12	F	12 54	10.2	1 25	9.4	7 12	7 21
13	W	12 42	10.4	1 04	10.2	6 52	7 10	13	S	1 31	10.0	2 04	9.1	7 52	7 59
14	T	1 22	10.3	1 47	9.8	7 35	7 51	14	S	2 09	9.7	2 45	8.8	8 32	8 39
15	F	2 02	10.0	2 30	9.4	8 18	8 31	15	M	2 49	9.4	3 28	8.4	9 13	9 21
16	S	2 43	9.7	3 14	8.9	9 02	9 13	16	T	3 32	9.1	4 14	8.2	9 58	10 08
17	S	3 25	9.3	4 00	8.4	9 47	9 58	17	W	4 20	8.8	5 04	8.0	10 46	10 59
18	M	4 11	8.9	4 51	8.0	10 36	10 47	18	T	5 12	8.6	5 57	8.0	11 38	11 55
19	T	5 02	8.6	5 46	7.7	11 30	11 42	19	F	6 08	8.5	6 52	8.1	...	12 32
20	W	5 58	8.4	6 45	7.6	...	12 29	20	S	7 05	8.5	7 45	8.4	12 53	1 25
21	T	6 58	8.4	7 43	7.7	12 41	1 27	21	S	8 01	8.7	8 34	8.9	1 50	2 16
22	F	7 56	8.5	8 37	8.0	1 41	2 22	22	M	8 54	9.0	9 20	9.4	2 43	3 04
23	S	8 50	8.8	9 24	8.5	2 36	3 10	23	T	9 44	9.4	10 05	10.1	3 33	3 50
24	S	9 38	9.1	10 06	9.0	3 25	3 53	24	W	10 32	9.7	10 49	10.6	4 20	4 35
25	M	10 23	9.5	10 46	9.5	4 10	4 33	25	T	11 20	10.0	11 33	11.1	5 07	5 20
26	T	11 05	9.8	11 24	10.0	4 52	5 12	26	F	...	...	12 07	10.2	5 54	6 06
27	W	11 46	10.1	...	...	5 34	5 51	27	S	12 19	11.4	12 57	10.3	6 42	6 54
28	T	12 03	10.5	12 29	10.2	6 16	6 32	28	S	1 08	11.5	1 48	10.2	7 33	7 46
29	F	12 44	10.8	1 14	10.2	7 01	7 16	29	M	2 00	11.4	2 43	10.0	8 26	8 40
30	S	1 28	10.9	2 02	10.0	7 48	8 03	30	T	2 55	11.1	3 41	9.7	9 22	9 39
31	S	2 16	10.9	2 54	9.7	8 39	8 54								

Dates when Ht. of **Low** Water is below Mean Lower Low with Ht. of lowest given for each period and Date of lowest in ( ):

1st - 4th: -0.7' (1st)	1st - 3rd: -0.8' (1st)
7th - 15th: -1.0' (11th)	7th - 13th: -0.6' (10th - 11th)
26th - 31st: -1.2' (30th)	24th - 30th: -1.5' (27th - 28th)

Average Rise and Fall 9.1 ft.

When a high tide exceeds avg. ht., the *following* low tide will be lower than avg.

2013 HIGH & LOW WATER
PORTLAND, ME
43°39.6'N, 70°14.8'W

Daylight Saving Time   Daylight Saving Time

D A Y O F M O N T H	D A Y O F W E E K	MAY HIGH a.m.	Ht.	HIGH p.m.	Ht.	LOW a.m.	LOW p.m.	D A Y O F M O N T H	D A Y O F W E E K	JUNE HIGH a.m.	Ht.	HIGH p.m.	Ht.	LOW a.m.	LOW p.m.
1	W	3 55	10.6	4 44	9.5	10 22	10 43	1	S	5 49	9.8	6 30	9.8	...	12 06
2	T	4 59	10.2	5 48	9.4	11 26	11 52	2	S	6 54	9.4	7 29	9.8	12 42	1 06
3	F	6 08	9.8	6 55	9.5	...	12 31	3	M	7 58	9.1	8 26	9.9	1 47	2 05
4	S	7 16	9.6	7 56	9.7	1 01	1 33	4	T	8 57	9.0	9 17	9.9	2 45	2 57
5	S	8 21	9.5	8 53	9.9	2 06	2 32	5	W	9 50	8.9	10 04	10.0	3 39	3 47
6	M	9 20	9.4	9 44	10.1	3 06	3 26	6	T	10 39	8.9	10 47	10.0	4 27	4 32
7	T	10 13	9.4	10 30	10.2	4 00	4 14	7	F	11 23	8.8	11 26	10.0	5 11	5 13
8	W	11 01	9.4	11 12	10.3	4 48	4 58	8	S	...	...	12 03	8.8	5 52	5 52
9	T	11 44	9.3	11 51	10.2	5 32	5 39	9	S	12 04	10.0	12 42	8.8	6 29	6 29
10	F	...	...	12 25	9.2	6 12	6 17	10	M	12 40	9.9	1 18	8.7	7 06	7 06
11	S	12 28	10.1	1 03	9.1	6 51	6 54	11	T	1 16	9.8	1 55	8.7	7 41	7 44
12	S	1 04	10.0	1 41	8.9	7 28	7 31	12	W	1 54	9.7	2 32	8.7	8 17	8 23
13	M	1 41	9.8	2 20	8.7	8 06	8 10	13	T	2 33	9.5	3 11	8.7	8 54	9 04
14	T	2 19	9.6	3 00	8.5	8 44	8 51	14	F	3 14	9.3	3 51	8.8	9 33	9 49
15	W	3 00	9.3	3 42	8.4	9 25	9 34	15	S	3 58	9.1	4 35	8.9	10 15	10 38
16	T	3 45	9.1	4 27	8.4	10 08	10 22	16	S	4 46	9.0	5 21	9.1	11 01	11 30
17	F	4 32	8.9	5 14	8.4	10 53	11 14	17	M	5 38	8.9	6 11	9.4	11 50	...
18	S	5 23	8.7	6 03	8.6	11 42	...	18	T	6 35	8.8	7 04	9.8	12 27	12 43
19	S	6 18	8.7	6 54	8.9	12 08	12 33	19	W	7 34	8.9	7 59	10.3	1 26	1 39
20	M	7 14	8.8	7 46	9.4	1 05	1 25	20	T	8 35	9.1	8 55	10.8	2 25	2 36
21	T	8 11	9.0	8 36	9.9	2 02	2 18	21	F	9 35	9.4	9 51	11.2	3 24	3 33
22	W	9 07	9.2	9 27	10.5	2 57	3 09	22	S	10 33	9.7	10 46	11.6	4 20	4 29
23	T	10 01	9.6	10 17	11.1	3 50	4 01	23	S	11 29	10.1	11 42	11.8	5 15	5 25
24	F	10 54	9.9	11 07	11.5	4 42	4 52	24	M	...	...	12 24	10.3	6 09	6 20
25	S	11 47	10.1	11 58	11.8	5 33	5 43	25	T	12 37	11.9	1 19	10.4	7 03	7 16
26	S	...	...	12 40	10.3	6 25	6 36	26	W	1 32	11.7	2 14	10.5	7 56	8 13
27	M	12 51	11.8	1 35	10.3	7 18	7 31	27	T	2 28	11.3	3 10	10.4	8 50	9 12
28	T	1 46	11.6	2 31	10.2	8 13	8 28	28	F	3 26	10.8	4 06	10.2	9 45	10 12
29	W	2 43	11.3	3 29	10.1	9 09	9 28	29	S	4 25	10.2	5 03	10.1	10 40	11 13
30	T	3 42	10.8	4 28	10.0	10 07	10 31	30	S	5 25	9.6	6 00	9.9	11 37	...
31	F	4 45	10.3	5 29	9.9	11 06	11 36								

Dates when Ht. of **Low** Water is below Mean Lower Low with Ht. of lowest given for each period and Date of lowest in ( ):

1st - 2nd: -0.7' (1st)   21st - 29th: -1.8' (25th)
8th - 10th: -0.3' (9th)
23rd - 31st: -1.7' (26th - 27th)

Average Rise and Fall 9.1 ft.

When a high tide exceeds avg. ht., the *following* low tide will be lower than avg.

2013 HIGH & LOW WATER
PORTLAND, ME
43°39.6'N, 70°14.8'W

Daylight Saving Time · · · Daylight Saving Time

DATE OF MONTH	DAY OF WEEK	JULY						DAY OF MONTH	DAY OF WEEK	AUGUST					
		HIGH				LOW				HIGH				LOW	
		a.m.	Ht.	p.m.	Ht.	a.m.	p.m.			a.m.	Ht.	p.m.	Ht.	a.m.	p.m.
1	M	6 27	9.1	6 57	9.7	12 16	12 34	1	T	7 55	8.1	8 11	9.2	1 44	1 52
2	T	7 29	8.7	7 53	9.6	1 18	1 31	2	F	8 51	8.1	9 03	9.3	2 41	2 45
3	W	8 29	8.5	8 47	9.6	2 19	2 27	3	S	9 43	8.2	9 52	9.4	3 33	3 36
4	T	9 23	8.4	9 35	9.6	3 13	3 17	4	S	10 28	8.4	10 35	9.6	4 18	4 20
5	F	10 13	8.4	10 20	9.7	4 03	4 04	5	M	11 09	8.6	11 14	9.7	4 59	5 01
6	S	10 58	8.5	11 02	9.8	4 47	4 48	6	T	11 46	8.8	11 52	9.8	5 36	5 39
7	S	11 39	8.6	11 40	9.8	5 28	5 27	7	W	...	...	12 21	9.0	6 10	6 15
8	M	...	...	12 17	8.7	6 06	6 05	8	T	12 27	9.8	12 55	9.1	6 43	6 52
9	T	12 17	9.8	12 52	8.7	6 41	6 42	9	F	1 03	9.8	1 29	9.3	7 16	7 29
10	W	12 53	9.8	1 27	8.8	7 14	7 18	10	S	1 40	9.7	2 05	9.5	7 51	8 09
11	T	1 29	9.7	2 02	8.9	7 48	7 56	11	S	2 20	9.6	2 44	9.7	8 29	8 53
12	F	2 06	9.6	2 38	9.0	8 23	8 36	12	M	3 03	9.4	3 27	9.8	9 11	9 41
13	S	2 46	9.5	3 17	9.2	9 00	9 19	13	T	3 51	9.2	4 15	9.9	9 58	10 34
14	S	3 28	9.3	3 59	9.4	9 41	10 07	14	W	4 44	9.0	5 08	10.0	10 50	11 33
15	M	4 15	9.1	4 45	9.6	10 26	10 59	15	T	5 44	8.8	6 08	10.1	11 48	...
16	T	5 07	8.9	5 36	9.8	11 16	11 56	16	F	6 49	8.8	7 12	10.3	12 37	12 51
17	W	6 05	8.8	6 31	10.0	...	12 11	17	S	7 56	8.9	8 17	10.5	1 43	1 56
18	T	7 07	8.8	7 31	10.4	12 57	1 10	18	S	9 01	9.3	9 21	10.9	2 47	3 01
19	F	8 11	9.0	8 32	10.7	2 01	2 11	19	M	10 02	9.7	10 20	11.2	3 48	4 02
20	S	9 15	9.3	9 33	11.1	3 03	3 13	20	T	10 57	10.2	11 16	11.3	4 43	4 59
21	S	10 16	9.7	10 31	11.5	4 03	4 13	21	W	11 49	10.5	...	...	5 35	5 53
22	M	11 13	10.0	11 28	11.7	4 59	5 10	22	T	12 09	11.3	12 39	10.7	6 25	6 45
23	T	...	...	12 08	10.4	5 53	6 06	23	F	1 00	11.1	1 27	10.7	7 13	7 35
24	W	12 23	11.7	1 01	10.6	6 45	7 01	24	S	1 50	10.7	2 15	10.5	8 00	8 26
25	T	1 17	11.5	1 53	10.6	7 36	7 56	25	S	2 40	10.1	3 03	10.2	8 47	9 18
26	F	2 10	11.1	2 44	10.5	8 27	8 51	26	M	3 30	9.5	3 52	9.8	9 35	10 11
27	S	3 04	10.5	3 37	10.3	9 18	9 47	27	T	4 23	8.9	4 43	9.4	10 26	11 06
28	S	3 59	9.9	4 29	10.0	10 10	10 44	28	W	5 19	8.4	5 37	9.1	11 19	...
29	M	4 56	9.3	5 24	9.7	11 03	11 44	29	T	6 17	8.1	6 34	8.9	12 05	12 16
30	T	5 55	8.7	6 19	9.4	11 58	...	30	F	7 16	7.9	7 32	8.8	1 05	1 14
31	W	6 55	8.3	7 16	9.2	12 44	12 55	31	S	8 13	8.0	8 27	8.9	2 02	2 10

Dates when Ht. of **Low** Water is below Mean Lower Low with Ht. of lowest given for each period and Date of lowest in ( ):

20th - 27th: -1.6' (23rd - 24th) · · · 18th - 25th: -1.3' (21st - 22nd)

Average Rise and Fall 9.1 ft.

When a high tide exceeds avg. ht., the *following* low tide will be lower than avg.

33

2013 HIGH & LOW WATER
PORTLAND, ME
43°39.6'N, 70°14.8'W

Daylight Saving Time   Daylight Saving Time

DAY OF MONTH	DAY OF WEEK	SEPTEMBER HIGH a.m.	Ht.	HIGH p.m.	Ht.	LOW a.m.	LOW p.m.	DAY OF MONTH	DAY OF WEEK	OCTOBER HIGH a.m.	Ht.	HIGH p.m.	Ht.	LOW a.m.	LOW p.m.
1	S	9 05	8.1	9 17	9.1	2 55	3 02	1	T	9 09	8.6	9 25	9.1	2 56	3 12
2	M	9 52	8.4	10 03	9.4	3 41	3 48	2	W	9 51	9.0	10 08	9.4	3 38	3 56
3	T	10 34	8.7	10 45	9.6	4 23	4 31	3	T	10 30	9.4	10 50	9.6	4 18	4 38
4	W	11 10	9.0	11 22	9.7	5 00	5 09	4	F	11 06	9.9	11 29	9.8	4 55	5 16
5	T	11 45	9.3	11 59	9.8	5 34	5 46	5	S	11 44	10.2	...	...	5 32	5 57
6	F	...	...	12 19	9.6	6 08	6 24	6	S	12 09	9.9	12 22	10.5	6 11	6 39
7	S	12 36	9.9	12 55	9.9	6 43	7 03	7	M	12 51	9.9	1 04	10.7	6 52	7 23
8	S	1 15	9.8	1 33	10.1	7 20	7 45	8	T	1 37	9.8	1 49	10.7	7 37	8 11
9	M	1 57	9.7	2 14	10.2	8 01	8 30	9	W	2 26	9.7	2 39	10.6	8 25	9 04
10	T	2 42	9.5	3 00	10.2	8 46	9 20	10	T	3 19	9.4	3 34	10.4	9 19	10 01
11	W	3 33	9.3	3 51	10.2	9 35	10 15	11	F	4 18	9.2	4 35	10.2	10 18	11 03
12	T	4 29	9.0	4 49	10.1	10 31	11 16	12	S	5 23	9.1	5 42	10.0	11 24	...
13	F	5 31	8.9	5 52	10.0	11 33	...	13	S	6 30	9.2	6 52	9.9	12 10	12 33
14	S	6 39	8.9	7 00	10.1	12 22	12 40	14	M	7 36	9.4	7 59	9.9	1 16	1 42
15	S	7 47	9.1	8 08	10.2	1 30	1 48	15	T	8 37	9.8	9 02	10.1	2 18	2 46
16	M	8 50	9.5	9 12	10.5	2 34	2 53	16	W	9 33	10.2	9 59	10.2	3 16	3 44
17	T	9 48	9.9	10 10	10.7	3 33	3 53	17	T	10 23	10.5	10 51	10.2	4 07	4 36
18	W	10 41	10.4	11 04	10.8	4 26	4 48	18	F	11 09	10.7	11 38	10.1	4 55	5 24
19	T	11 30	10.7	11 54	10.8	5 16	5 39	19	S	11 52	10.7	...	...	5 40	6 10
20	F	...	...	12 16	10.8	6 02	6 27	20	S	12 23	9.9	12 33	10.5	6 22	6 53
21	S	12 41	10.5	1 00	10.7	6 47	7 14	21	M	1 06	9.7	1 14	10.3	7 03	7 35
22	S	1 28	10.2	1 43	10.4	7 31	8 00	22	T	1 49	9.3	1 54	9.9	7 44	8 18
23	M	2 14	9.7	2 27	10.1	8 15	8 47	23	W	2 32	8.9	2 36	9.6	8 26	9 01
24	T	3 01	9.2	3 13	9.7	9 00	9 35	24	T	3 16	8.6	3 21	9.2	9 10	9 47
25	W	3 49	8.7	4 01	9.3	9 47	10 26	25	F	4 04	8.3	4 10	8.9	9 58	10 36
26	T	4 41	8.3	4 53	8.9	10 38	11 21	26	S	4 54	8.1	5 03	8.6	10 50	11 28
27	F	5 36	8.0	5 49	8.7	11 34	...	27	S	5 47	8.1	5 58	8.5	11 46	...
28	S	6 34	7.9	6 47	8.6	12 18	12 32	28	M	6 41	8.2	6 55	8.5	12 22	12 43
29	S	7 30	8.0	7 44	8.7	1 15	1 30	29	T	7 32	8.4	7 50	8.6	1 14	1 39
30	M	8 22	8.2	8 37	8.9	2 08	2 23	30	W	8 20	8.8	8 41	8.8	2 03	2 30
								31	T	9 05	9.3	9 29	9.1	2 49	3 18

Dates when Ht. of **Low** Water is below Mean Lower Low with Ht. of lowest given for each period and Date of lowest in ( ):

8th - 9th: -0.2'   5th - 10th: -0.8' (7th)
16th - 22nd: -1.0' (20th)   16th - 21st: -0.8' (18th - 19th)

Average Rise and Fall 9.1 ft.

When a high tide exceeds avg. ht., the *following* low tide will be lower than avg.

34

2013 HIGH & LOW WATER
PORTLAND, ME
43°39.6'N, 70°14.8'W

Standard Time starts Nov. 3 at 2 a.m.   **Standard Time**

DATE OF MONTH	DAY OF WEEK	NOVEMBER						DAY OF MONTH	DAY OF WEEK	DECEMBER					
		HIGH				LOW				HIGH				LOW	
		a.m.	Ht.	p.m.	Ht.	a.m.	p.m.			a.m.	Ht.	p.m.	Ht.	a.m.	p.m.
1	F	9 47	9.8	10 14	9.4	3 33	4 03	1	S	8 55	10.6	9 32	9.5	2 39	3 20
2	S	10 29	10.3	10 59	9.7	4 15	4 47	2	M	9 43	11.1	10 22	9.8	3 28	4 09
3	S	*10 12	10.8	*10 45	9.9	*3 59	*4 32	3	T	10 33	11.4	11 13	10.0	4 19	4 59
4	M	10 55	11.1	11 31	10.0	4 42	5 17	4	W	11 23	11.6	...	...	5 08	5 49
5	T	11 41	11.2	...	...	5 28	6 05	5	T	12 04	10.1	12 15	11.5	6 00	6 41
6	W	12 19	10.0	12 30	11.2	6 17	6 56	6	F	12 57	10.1	1 10	11.3	6 55	7 35
7	T	1 12	9.9	1 23	11.0	7 09	7 50	7	S	1 53	10.1	2 08	10.8	7 53	8 31
8	F	2 07	9.7	2 21	10.7	8 06	8 48	8	S	2 52	9.9	3 09	10.3	8 54	9 30
9	S	3 08	9.5	3 23	10.3	9 07	9 49	9	M	3 52	9.8	4 14	9.8	9 59	10 31
10	S	4 11	9.5	4 30	9.9	10 14	10 53	10	T	4 55	9.7	5 21	9.3	11 07	11 33
11	M	5 16	9.5	5 39	9.7	11 24	11 58	11	W	5 57	9.7	6 28	9.1	...	12 14
12	T	6 20	9.7	6 47	9.5	...	12 32	12	T	6 57	9.8	7 31	8.9	12 35	1 18
13	W	7 20	9.9	7 49	9.5	12 59	1 35	13	F	7 53	9.9	8 28	8.9	1 32	2 15
14	T	8 14	10.2	8 45	9.6	1 56	2 32	14	S	8 44	10.0	9 20	8.9	2 26	3 07
15	F	9 04	10.4	9 36	9.5	2 47	3 23	15	S	9 30	10.0	10 06	8.9	3 14	3 54
16	S	9 49	10.4	10 23	9.5	3 35	4 10	16	M	10 12	10.0	10 48	8.9	3 58	4 36
17	S	10 31	10.4	11 06	9.4	4 18	4 53	17	T	10 50	10.0	11 27	8.9	4 39	5 15
18	M	11 10	10.3	11 46	9.2	4 59	5 33	18	W	11 27	9.9	...	...	5 17	5 51
19	T	11 48	10.1	...	...	5 38	6 12	19	T	12 03	8.8	12 03	9.8	5 53	6 27
20	W	12 26	9.0	12 26	9.8	6 17	6 51	20	F	12 39	8.7	12 40	9.6	6 30	7 02
21	T	1 05	8.8	1 06	9.6	6 56	7 30	21	S	1 15	8.7	1 18	9.4	7 08	7 38
22	F	1 45	8.6	1 47	9.3	7 37	8 11	22	S	1 53	8.6	1 58	9.1	7 48	8 15
23	S	2 28	8.4	2 31	9.0	8 21	8 54	23	M	2 32	8.6	2 40	8.8	8 31	8 56
24	S	3 12	8.3	3 19	8.7	9 09	9 39	24	T	3 14	8.6	3 27	8.6	9 18	9 40
25	M	4 00	8.3	4 10	8.5	10 00	10 28	25	W	4 00	8.7	4 18	8.4	10 09	10 28
26	T	4 49	8.4	5 04	8.4	10 54	11 18	26	T	4 49	8.9	5 13	8.3	11 04	11 20
27	W	5 39	8.6	6 00	8.4	11 50	...	27	F	5 41	9.2	6 13	8.3	...	12 03
28	T	6 29	9.0	6 55	8.5	12 09	12 46	28	S	6 36	9.6	7 13	8.5	12 16	1 02
29	F	7 19	9.5	7 49	8.8	1 00	1 39	29	S	7 32	10.1	8 12	8.9	1 13	2 00
30	S	8 07	10.0	8 41	9.2	1 50	2 30	30	M	8 27	10.6	9 08	9.3	2 09	2 56
								31	T	9 21	11.2	10 03	9.8	3 05	3 49

Dates when Ht. of **Low** Water is below Mean Lower Low with Ht. of lowest given for each period and Date of lowest in ( ):

2nd - 9th: -1.3' (5th)   1st - 9th: -1.7' (4th - 5th)
14th - 19th: -0.5' (16th - 17th)   15th - 17th: -0.3' (15th - 16th)
                                        29th - 31st: -1.4' (31st)

Average Rise and Fall 9.1 ft.

When a high tide exceeds avg. ht., the *following* low tide will be lower than avg.

Smarter Boating in Currents

If your vessel is a sailboat or a displacement powerboat your normal cruising speed is probably under 10 knots. In this range, current can become a significant factor. (See the Current Tables for the Cape Cod Canal and the Race, and the Current Diagrams for Vineyard Sound, showing some currents of 4 to 5 knots.) You can save a remarkable amount of time and, if under power, a great deal of fuel expense by using the current for maximum efficiency.

SAIL: Slow vs. Flow

The arithmetic is simple. If your 35' sailboat has a boat speed (BS) through the water of 5 knots under power or sail, then a 2-knot current directly against you means your speed made good (SMG) is 3 knots, and the same current going with you boosts that to 7 knots. Tacking into or with a current changes the simple arithmetic shown here. (See Coping With Currents, p. 21) The time difference can be great: a destination 10 miles away is 3 hours 20 minutes against the current, but only 1 hour 26 minutes with the current. Leaving earlier or later to go with the current leaves more time (almost 2 hours) to relax either at your departure point or destination. Of course if you're just out for a sail on a beautiful day, the arithmetic may not matter! If your sailboat is under power, keep reading.

POWER: Ego vs. Eco

As long as speed thrills, as we know it does, some boaters will demand it. But the trend is headed the other way. Today it is more about being economical, not egomaniacal. By far the most dramatic saving in fuel cost, or nautical miles per gallon (NMPG), comes from cutting back on the throttle; however, there are further savings from using the current to your advantage, especially with slower vessels.

Consider a trawler that burns 10 gallons of fuel per hour at a speed of 8 knots. If the cost of fuel is, say, $4 per gallon, that's $40 per hour. For a destination 24 nautical miles away, going directly against a current of 2 knots, her SMG is only 6 knots, requiring 4 hours for the trip, and costing her owner $160. If the skipper had gone with a current of 2 knots, then her SMG would be 10 knots, her transit time 2 hours 24 minutes, with a fuel expense of only $96. The time saved, 1 hour 36 minutes, allows more time for relaxation (TFR) either before departure or after arrival, and the $64 saved could buy a nice meal ashore. That's smarter boating

Consult the table below for SMG and time/fuel consequences in currents.

SMG *WITH* CURRENT, and Time/Fuel GAINS

Current Speed Kts *With* +		+1 kt	+2 kts	+3 kts	+4 kts
Boat Speed: 4 kts	SMG =	5 kts	6 kts	7 kts	8 kts
Time/Fuel **Gain**		20%	33%	43%	50%
Boat Speed: 6 kts	SMG =	7 kts	8 kts	9 kts	10 kts
Time/Fuel **Gain**		14%	25%	33%	40%
Boat Speed: 8 kts	SMG =	9 kts	10 kts	11 kts	12 kts
Time/Fuel **Gain**		11%	20%	28%	33%
Boat Speed: 10 kts	SMG =	11 kts	12 kts	13 kts	14 kts
Time/Fuel **Gain**		9%	17%	24%	29%

SMG *AGAINST* CURRENT, and Time/Fuel LOSSES

Current Speed Kts *Against* -		-1 kt	-2 kts	-3 kts	-4 kts
Boat Speed: 4 kts	SMG =	3 kts	2 kts	1 kts	0 kts
Time/Fuel **Loss**		33%	100%	300%	---
Boat Speed: 6 kts	SMG =	5 kts	4 kts	3 kts	2 kts
Time/Fuel **Loss**		20%	50%	100%	200%
Boat Speed: 8 kts	SMG =	7 kts	6 kts	5 kts	4 kts
Time/Fuel **Loss**		14%	33%	60%	100%
Boat Speed: 10 kts	SMG =	9 kts	8 kts	7 kts	6 kts
Time/Fuel **Loss**		11%	25%	43%	67%

Boston Harbor Currents

This diagram shows the direction of the Flood Currents in Boston Harbor at the Maximum* Flood velocity, generally 3.5 hours after Low Water at Boston.

The Ebb Currents flow in precisely the opposite direction (note one exception, shown by dotted arrow east of Winthrop), and reach these maximum velocities about 4 hours after High Water at Boston.

The velocities of the Ebb Currents are about the same as those of the Flood Currents. Where the Ebb Current differs by .2 kts., the velocity of the Ebb is shown in parentheses.

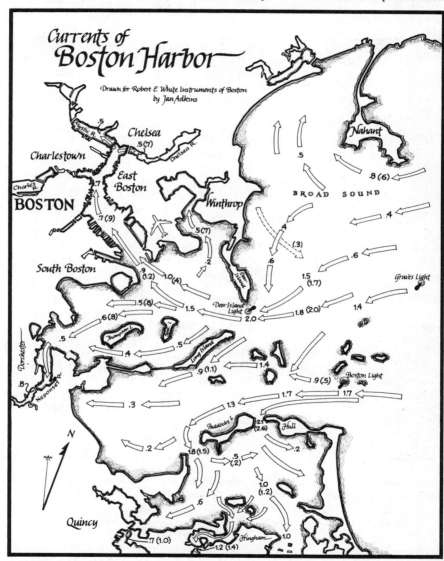

*The Velocities shown on this Current Diagram are the **maximums** normally encountered each month at Full Moon and at New Moon. At other times the velocities will be lower. As a rule of thumb, the velocities shown are those found on days when High Water at Boston is 11.0' to 11.5' (see Boston High Water Tables pp. 38-43). When the height of High Water is 10.5', subtract 10% from the velocities shown; at 10.0', subtract 20%; at 9.0', 30%; at 8.0', 40%; below 7.5', 50%.

2013 HIGH & LOW WATER
BOSTON, MA
42°21.3'N, 71°03.1'W

Standard Time   Standard Time

D A Y O F M O N T H	D A Y O F W E E K	JANUARY HIGH a.m.	Ht.	HIGH p.m.	Ht.	LOW a.m.	LOW p.m.	D A Y O F M O N T H	D A Y O F W E E K	FEBRUARY HIGH a.m.	Ht.	HIGH p.m.	Ht.	LOW a.m.	LOW p.m.
1	T	1 27	9.3	1 35	10.0	7 27	7 55	1	F	2 21	10.1	2 42	9.8	8 35	8 56
2	W	2 07	9.4	2 19	9.8	8 12	8 37	2	S	3 07	10.2	3 34	9.5	9 27	9 46
3	T	2 51	9.5	3 07	9.6	9 00	9 24	3	S	4 00	10.2	4 32	9.2	10 24	10 43
4	F	3 37	9.6	3 58	9.4	9 51	10 13	4	M	4 56	10.3	5 34	9.0	11 24	11 42
5	S	4 28	9.8	4 54	9.2	10 48	11 08	5	T	5 58	10.4	6 39	9.0	...	12 28
6	S	5 22	10.1	5 55	9.1	11 47	...	6	W	7 01	10.6	7 44	9.2	12 45	1 31
7	M	6 20	10.4	6 57	9.2	12 05	12 49	7	T	8 04	10.9	8 47	9.6	1 47	2 32
8	T	7 20	10.8	8 00	9.4	1 05	1 50	8	F	9 05	11.2	9 44	10.0	2 47	3 29
9	W	8 19	11.2	9 00	9.8	2 04	2 48	9	S	10 01	11.5	10 37	10.4	3 44	4 22
10	T	9 17	11.6	9 58	10.2	3 02	3 45	10	S	10 54	11.6	11 27	10.7	4 37	5 11
11	F	10 13	11.9	10 53	10.5	3 58	4 38	11	M	11 44	11.5	...	...	5 28	5 58
12	S	11 07	12.0	11 45	10.7	4 52	5 30	12	T	12 13	10.8	12 32	11.2	6 17	6 43
13	S	...	...	12 01	11.9	5 45	6 20	13	W	12 58	10.7	1 18	10.7	7 05	7 28
14	M	12 36	10.8	12 51	11.5	6 36	7 08	14	T	1 43	10.5	2 05	10.1	7 52	8 13
15	T	1 25	10.7	1 42	11.0	7 28	7 57	15	F	2 28	10.1	2 53	9.5	8 40	8 58
16	W	2 15	10.4	2 33	10.4	8 19	8 45	16	S	3 14	9.7	3 43	8.9	9 30	9 46
17	T	3 04	10.1	3 26	9.7	9 12	9 35	17	S	4 03	9.3	4 36	8.4	10 23	10 38
18	F	3 55	9.8	4 20	9.0	10 07	10 26	18	M	4 56	9.0	5 33	8.0	11 19	11 32
19	S	4 48	9.4	5 17	8.5	11 04	11 20	19	T	5 52	8.9	6 32	7.9	...	12 18
20	S	5 42	9.2	6 17	8.2	...	12 03	20	W	6 50	8.9	7 30	8.0	12 29	1 15
21	M	6 38	9.1	7 16	8.1	12 15	1 02	21	T	7 45	9.1	8 24	8.2	1 25	2 09
22	T	7 32	9.2	8 11	8.1	1 10	1 58	22	F	8 36	9.4	9 11	8.6	2 17	2 56
23	W	8 23	9.4	9 01	8.3	2 02	2 48	23	S	9 23	9.7	9 54	9.0	3 05	3 39
24	T	9 11	9.6	9 47	8.6	2 51	3 33	24	S	10 06	10.0	10 34	9.5	3 50	4 20
25	F	9 54	9.9	10 28	8.8	3 36	4 13	25	M	10 47	10.3	11 12	9.9	4 33	5 00
26	S	10 35	10.1	11 07	9.1	4 19	4 52	26	T	11 27	10.5	11 50	10.2	5 15	5 39
27	S	11 14	10.3	11 44	9.4	5 00	5 30	27	W	...	...	12 08	10.6	5 57	6 19
28	M	11 52	10.4	...	...	5 41	6 08	28	T	12 29	10.5	12 50	10.5	6 41	7 01
29	T	12 21	9.6	12 32	10.4	6 22	6 47								
30	W	12 58	9.8	1 12	10.3	7 04	7 27								
31	T	1 38	10.0	1 55	10.1	7 48	8 10								

Dates when Ht. of **Low** Water is below Mean Lower Low with Ht. of lowest given for each period and Date of lowest in ( ):

8th - 16th: -2.0' (12th)   1st: -0.2'
27th - 31st: -0.5' (29th - 30th)   6th - 14th: -1.6' (10th)
                        25th - 28th: -0.7' (27th - 28th)

Average Rise and Fall 9.5 ft.

When a high tide exceeds avg. ht., the *following* **low tide will be lower than avg.** Since there is a high degree of correlation between the height of High Water and the velocities of the Flood and Ebb Currents for that same day, we offer a rough rule of thumb for estimating the current velocities, for ALL the Current Charts and Diagrams in this book. **Rule of Thumb:** Refer to Boston High Water. If the height of High Water is 11.0' or over, use the Current Chart velocities as shown. When the height is 10.5', subtract 10%; at 10.0', subtract 20%; at 9.0', 30%; at 8.0', 40%; below 7.5', 50%.

2013 HIGH & LOW WATER
BOSTON, MA
42°21.3'N, 71°03.1'W

*Daylight Time starts March 10 at 2 a.m.　　　**Daylight Saving Time**

D A Y O F M O N T H	D A Y O F W E E K	MARCH						D A Y O F M O N T H	D A Y O F W E E K	APRIL					
		HIGH				LOW				HIGH				LOW	
		a.m.	Ht.	p.m.	Ht.	a.m.	p.m.			a.m.	Ht.	p.m.	Ht.	a.m.	p.m.
1	F	1 10	10.7	1 35	10.3	7 26	7 45	1	M	3 25	11.2	4 04	9.9	9 50	10 08
2	S	1 55	10.8	2 24	10.0	8 15	8 33	2	T	4 21	10.9	5 03	9.6	10 48	11 07
3	S	2 44	10.7	3 18	9.6	9 08	9 26	3	W	5 23	10.5	6 08	9.4	11 50	...
4	M	3 37	10.6	4 15	9.3	10 04	10 23	4	T	6 28	10.3	7 13	9.4	12 11	12 53
5	T	4 37	10.4	5 19	9.1	11 06	11 25	5	F	7 35	10.1	8 18	9.6	1 16	1 57
6	W	5 41	10.3	6 26	9.1	...	12 10	6	S	8 41	10.2	9 17	9.9	2 21	2 57
7	T	6 48	10.3	7 32	9.3	12 29	1 15	7	S	9 41	10.3	10 10	10.3	3 22	3 51
8	F	7 53	10.5	8 33	9.7	1 34	2 16	8	M	10 35	10.4	10 58	10.6	4 17	4 41
9	S	8 54	10.7	9 29	10.1	2 35	3 12	9	T	11 24	10.4	11 41	10.7	5 07	5 26
10	S	*10 49	10.9	*11 19	10.5	*4 31	*5 03	10	W	...	...	12 08	10.3	5 52	6 08
11	M	11 40	11.0	...	...	5 23	5 50	11	T	12 22	10.7	12 50	10.1	6 35	6 49
12	T	12 05	10.7	12 27	10.9	6 11	6 34	12	F	1 01	10.6	1 31	9.9	7 17	7 29
13	W	12 48	10.8	1 11	10.7	6 57	7 17	13	S	1 40	10.5	2 11	9.6	7 58	8 10
14	T	1 30	10.7	1 54	10.3	7 41	7 58	14	S	2 20	10.2	2 53	9.2	8 40	8 52
15	F	2 11	10.5	2 37	9.8	8 25	8 40	15	M	3 02	9.9	3 38	8.9	9 23	9 36
16	S	2 52	10.2	3 21	9.3	9 09	9 24	16	T	3 47	9.6	4 25	8.6	10 09	10 24
17	S	3 36	9.8	4 08	8.9	9 55	10 09	17	W	4 35	9.3	5 15	8.4	10 58	11 15
18	M	4 22	9.4	4 58	8.4	10 44	10 59	18	T	5 28	9.0	6 08	8.4	11 50	...
19	T	5 13	9.1	5 52	8.1	11 37	11 52	19	F	6 23	8.9	7 02	8.5	12 10	12 44
20	W	6 08	8.9	6 49	8.0	...	12 32	20	S	7 19	9.0	7 54	8.9	1 06	1 37
21	T	7 06	8.8	7 46	8.1	12 48	1 29	21	S	8 13	9.2	8 44	9.3	2 01	2 28
22	F	8 03	9.0	8 40	8.4	1 45	2 23	22	M	9 06	9.5	9 31	9.9	2 54	3 17
23	S	8 56	9.2	9 29	8.9	2 40	3 13	23	T	9 56	9.9	10 17	10.5	3 44	4 05
24	S	9 46	9.6	10 14	9.4	3 31	4 00	24	W	10 45	10.2	11 02	11.1	4 33	4 52
25	M	10 32	10.0	10 56	9.9	4 18	4 43	25	T	11 33	10.5	11 48	11.5	5 21	5 38
26	T	11 17	10.3	11 37	10.5	5 04	5 26	26	F	...	...	12 21	10.7	6 09	6 25
27	W	...	...	12 01	10.6	5 48	6 08	27	S	12 35	11.8	1 11	10.8	6 58	7 14
28	T	12 18	10.9	12 44	10.7	6 33	6 52	28	S	1 23	11.9	2 02	10.7	7 48	8 04
29	F	1 01	11.2	1 30	10.7	7 19	7 36	29	M	2 15	11.8	2 55	10.5	8 40	8 57
30	S	1 45	11.4	2 18	10.5	8 07	8 23	30	T	3 09	11.5	3 52	10.2	9 35	9 53
31	S	2 33	11.4	3 09	10.2	8 57	9 14								

Dates when Ht. of **Low** Water is below Mean Lower Low with Ht. of lowest given for each period and Date of lowest in ( ):

1st - 4th: -0.8' (1st)　　　　　　　　1st - 3rd: -0.9' (1st)
8th - 15th: -0.9' (10th - 12th)　　　8th - 13th: -0.6' (10th - 11th)
26th - 31st: -1.3' (29th - 30th)　　24th - 30th: -1.7' (27th - 28th)

Average Rise and Fall 9.5 ft.
When a high tide exceeds avg. ht., the *following* **low tide will be lower than avg.**
Since there is a high degree of correlation between the height of High Water and the velocities of the Flood and Ebb Currents for that same day, we offer a rough rule of thumb for estimating the current velocities, for ALL the Current Charts and Diagrams in this book. **Rule of Thumb:** Refer to Boston High Water. If the height of High Water is 11.0' or over, use the Current Chart velocities as shown. When the height is 10.5', subtract 10%; at 10.0', subtract 20%; at 9.0', 30%; at 8.0', 40%; below 7.5', 50%.

2013 HIGH & LOW WATER
BOSTON, MA
42°21.3'N, 71°03.1'W

Daylight Saving Time   **Daylight Saving Time**

D A Y O F M O N T H	D A Y O F W E E K	MAY						D A Y O F M O N T H	D A Y O F W E E K	JUNE					
		HIGH			LOW					HIGH			LOW		
		a.m.	Ht.	p.m.	Ht.	a.m.	p.m.			a.m.	Ht.	p.m.	Ht.	a.m.	p.m.
1	W	4 07	11.1	4 52	10.0	10 32	10 53	1	S	5 55	10.1	6 33	10.2	...	12 09
2	T	5 09	10.6	5 54	9.8	11 32	11 57	2	S	6 58	9.7	7 32	10.1	12 42	1 07
3	F	6 15	10.2	6 58	9.8	...	12 34	3	M	8 01	9.4	8 28	10.2	1 45	2 04
4	S	7 20	10.0	7 58	10.0	1 02	1 34	4	T	8 59	9.3	9 18	10.2	2 44	2 57
5	S	8 24	9.8	8 55	10.2	2 06	2 33	5	W	9 53	9.2	10 05	10.3	3 38	3 46
6	M	9 23	9.8	9 46	10.4	3 06	3 26	6	T	10 41	9.2	10 49	10.3	4 27	4 32
7	T	10 16	9.8	10 33	10.5	4 00	4 15	7	F	11 25	9.2	11 30	10.3	5 11	5 15
8	W	11 04	9.7	11 16	10.6	4 48	5 00	8	S	...	...	12 06	9.2	5 51	5 56
9	T	11 48	9.7	11 55	10.6	5 32	5 42	9	S	12 09	10.3	12 46	9.2	6 31	6 36
10	F	...	...	12 29	9.6	6 14	6 22	10	M	12 48	10.3	1 25	9.2	7 10	7 17
11	S	12 34	10.5	1 08	9.5	6 54	7 02	11	T	1 28	10.2	2 04	9.1	7 49	7 58
12	S	1 13	10.4	1 48	9.3	7 33	7 42	12	W	2 08	10.1	2 44	9.1	8 28	8 40
13	M	1 52	10.2	2 28	9.2	8 14	8 24	13	T	2 49	9.9	3 25	9.2	9 09	9 24
14	T	2 33	10.0	3 10	9.0	8 55	9 07	14	F	3 32	9.7	4 08	9.2	9 52	10 11
15	W	3 16	9.7	3 54	8.9	9 38	9 53	15	S	4 18	9.5	4 52	9.3	10 36	11 00
16	T	4 02	9.5	4 41	8.8	10 24	10 42	16	S	5 07	9.3	5 40	9.5	11 24	11 53
17	F	4 51	9.3	5 29	8.9	11 12	11 34	17	M	6 00	9.2	6 29	9.9	...	12 14
18	S	5 43	9.1	6 19	9.1	...	12 02	18	T	6 55	9.3	7 21	10.2	12 48	1 07
19	S	6 37	9.1	7 09	9.4	12 28	12 53	19	W	7 52	9.4	8 15	10.7	1 45	2 01
20	M	7 32	9.2	8 00	9.8	1 23	1 45	20	T	8 50	9.6	9 09	11.2	2 42	2 56
21	T	8 27	9.5	8 50	10.4	2 18	2 37	21	F	9 47	9.9	10 04	11.7	3 38	3 52
22	W	9 21	9.8	9 40	11.0	3 12	3 28	22	S	10 44	10.2	10 59	12.1	4 33	4 46
23	T	10 14	10.1	10 30	11.5	4 04	4 19	23	S	11 40	10.5	11 53	12.3	5 27	5 41
24	F	11 07	10.4	11 21	11.9	4 56	5 10	24	M	...	...	12 35	10.8	6 20	6 35
25	S	...	...	12 01	10.6	5 47	6 01	25	T	12 48	12.3	1 29	10.9	7 13	7 29
26	S	12 12	12.2	12 52	10.8	6 39	6 53	26	W	1 43	12.1	2 23	10.9	8 05	8 24
27	M	1 05	12.3	1 46	10.8	7 31	7 46	27	T	2 38	11.7	3 17	10.8	8 58	9 19
28	T	1 59	12.1	2 41	10.7	8 24	8 41	28	F	3 34	11.2	4 12	10.7	9 50	10 16
29	W	2 54	11.7	3 37	10.6	9 18	9 38	29	S	4 32	10.5	5 07	10.5	10 44	11 15
30	T	3 53	11.2	4 35	10.4	10 13	10 37	30	S	5 30	9.9	6 03	10.2	11 39	...
31	F	4 53	10.7	5 34	10.3	11 10	11 39								

Dates when Ht. of **Low** Water is below Mean Lower Low with Ht. of lowest given for each period and Date of lowest in ( ):

1st - 2nd: -0.7' (1st)   21st - 29th: -1.9' (24th - 25th)
9th - 10th: -0.2'
23rd - 31st: -1.9' (27th)

Average Rise and Fall 9.5 ft.
When a high tide exceeds avg. ht., the *following* **low tide will be lower than avg.**
Since there is a high degree of correlation between the height of High Water and the velocities of the Flood and Ebb Currents for that same day, we offer a rough rule of thumb for estimating the current velocities, for ALL the Current Charts and Diagrams in this book. **Rule of Thumb:** Refer to Boston High Water. If the height of High Water is 11.0' or over, use the Current Chart velocities as shown. When the height is 10.5', subtract 10%; at 10.0', subtract 20%; at 9.0', 30%; at 8.0', 40%; below 7.5', 50%.

2013 HIGH & LOW WATER
BOSTON, MA
42°21.3'N, 71°03.1'W

Daylight Saving Time   Daylight Saving Time

DAY OF MONTH	DAY OF WEEK	JULY						DAY OF MONTH	DAY OF WEEK	AUGUST					
		HIGH				LOW				HIGH				LOW	
		a.m.	Ht.	p.m.	Ht.	a.m.	p.m.			a.m.	Ht.	p.m.	Ht.	a.m.	p.m.
1	M	6 30	9.4	6 59	10.1	12 15	12 35	1	T	7 55	8.4	8 11	9.5	1 41	1 49
2	T	7 31	9.0	7 54	9.9	1 16	1 30	2	F	8 51	8.4	9 04	9.6	2 38	2 43
3	W	8 30	8.8	8 47	9.9	2 17	2 25	3	S	9 44	8.5	9 53	9.7	3 31	3 34
4	T	9 24	8.7	9 36	9.9	3 11	3 15	4	S	10 30	8.7	10 37	9.9	4 16	4 20
5	F	10 14	8.7	10 22	10.0	4 01	4 03	5	M	11 12	8.9	11 20	10.1	4 58	5 03
6	S	11 00	8.8	11 05	10.1	4 46	4 48	6	T	11 52	9.2	...	...	5 37	5 45
7	S	11 42	8.9	11 45	10.2	5 27	5 30	7	W	12 01	10.2	12 29	9.4	6 15	6 26
8	M	...	...	12 21	9.1	6 06	6 11	8	T	12 39	10.2	1 06	9.6	6 53	7 06
9	T	12 25	10.2	12 59	9.2	6 44	6 52	9	F	1 17	10.2	1 43	9.8	7 31	7 48
10	W	1 04	10.2	1 37	9.3	7 22	7 33	10	S	1 57	10.1	2 21	10.0	8 10	8 30
11	T	1 43	10.1	2 15	9.4	8 01	8 14	11	S	2 38	10.0	3 02	10.1	8 51	9 15
12	F	2 23	10.0	2 54	9.5	8 40	8 57	12	M	3 23	9.8	3 46	10.2	9 34	10 04
13	S	3 05	9.9	3 34	9.6	9 20	9 42	13	T	4 11	9.6	4 34	10.3	10 22	10 57
14	S	3 49	9.7	4 17	9.8	10 04	10 30	14	W	5 05	9.4	5 27	10.4	11 14	11 54
15	M	4 37	9.5	5 04	10.0	10 50	11 22	15	T	6 03	9.2	6 25	10.5	...	12 11
16	T	5 29	9.3	5 55	10.2	11 41	...	16	F	7 05	9.2	7 26	10.7	12 55	1 11
17	W	6 25	9.2	6 49	10.5	12 18	12 35	17	S	8 08	9.4	8 28	11.0	1 57	2 13
18	T	7 25	9.3	7 46	10.8	1 17	1 33	18	S	9 10	9.7	9 29	11.3	2 57	3 13
19	F	8 25	9.4	8 45	11.2	2 17	2 31	19	M	10 09	10.2	10 27	11.6	3 55	4 12
20	S	9 26	9.7	9 44	11.6	3 16	3 30	20	T	11 04	10.6	11 23	11.7	4 50	5 07
21	S	10 25	10.1	10 41	11.9	4 13	4 27	21	W	11 56	11.0	...	...	5 42	6 01
22	M	11 22	10.5	11 37	12.1	5 08	5 23	22	T	12 16	11.7	12 46	11.2	6 31	6 52
23	T	...	...	12 16	10.8	6 02	6 18	23	F	1 07	11.5	1 34	11.2	7 19	7 43
24	W	12 32	12.1	1 09	10.8	6 53	7 11	24	S	1 57	11.1	2 22	11.0	8 06	8 33
25	T	1 26	11.9	2 01	11.1	7 43	8 04	25	S	2 47	10.5	3 09	10.7	8 53	9 23
26	F	2 19	11.5	2 52	11.0	8 33	8 57	26	M	3 37	9.9	3 58	10.3	9 41	10 14
27	S	3 12	10.9	3 43	10.8	9 23	9 51	27	T	4 29	9.3	4 48	9.9	10 30	11 07
28	S	4 06	10.3	4 34	10.4	10 14	10 46	28	W	5 23	8.8	5 41	9.5	11 22	...
29	M	5 01	9.6	5 27	10.1	11 06	11 43	29	T	6 19	8.5	6 37	9.3	12 03	12 17
30	T	5 58	9.1	6 22	9.8	11 59	...	30	F	7 17	8.3	7 33	9.2	1 01	1 13
31	W	6 56	8.7	7 17	9.6	12 42	12 54	31	S	8 14	8.3	8 28	9.3	1 58	2 08

Dates when Ht. of **Low** Water is below Mean Lower Low with Ht. of lowest given for each period and Date of lowest in ( ):

19th - 27th: -1.8' (24th)   18th - 25th: -1.4' (21st - 22nd)

Average Rise and Fall 9.5 ft.
When a high tide exceeds avg. ht., the *following* **low tide will be lower than avg.**
Since there is a high degree of correlation between the height of High Water and the velocities of the Flood and Ebb Currents for that same day, we offer a rough rule of thumb for estimating the current velocities, for ALL the Current Charts and Diagrams in this book. **Rule of Thumb:** Refer to Boston High Water. If the height of High Water is 11.0' or over, use the Current Chart velocities as shown. When the height is 10.5', subtract 10%; at 10.0', subtract 20%; at 9.0', 30%; at 8.0', 40%; below 7.5', 50%.

2013 HIGH & LOW WATER
BOSTON, MA
42°21.3'N, 71°03.1'W
Daylight Saving Time   **Daylight Saving Time**

DAY OF MONTH	DAY OF WEEK	SEPTEMBER HIGH a.m.	Ht.	HIGH p.m.	Ht.	LOW a.m.	LOW p.m.	DAY OF MONTH	DAY OF WEEK	OCTOBER HIGH a.m.	Ht.	HIGH p.m.	Ht.	LOW a.m.	LOW p.m.
1	S	9 06	8.5	9 19	9.5	2 51	3 00	1	T	9 13	9.0	9 30	9.6	2 57	3 15
2	M	9 54	8.8	10 06	9.8	3 39	3 49	2	W	9 57	9.5	10 15	9.8	3 42	4 02
3	T	10 38	9.2	10 51	10.0	4 23	4 35	3	T	10 39	9.9	11 00	10.1	4 26	4 47
4	W	11 17	9.5	11 31	10.2	5 03	5 17	4	F	11 18	10.3	11 41	10.3	5 06	5 29
5	T	11 55	9.8	...	...	5 42	5 58	5	S	11 58	10.7	...	...	5 47	6 13
6	F	12 11	10.3	12 32	10.1	6 21	6 40	6	S	12 24	10.4	12 38	11.0	6 29	6 57
7	S	12 51	10.3	1 10	10.4	7 00	7 22	7	M	1 08	10.4	1 21	11.2	7 13	7 43
8	S	1 32	10.3	1 50	10.6	7 40	8 05	8	T	1 53	10.3	2 07	11.2	7 58	8 31
9	M	2 15	10.1	2 32	10.7	8 23	8 52	9	W	2 42	10.1	2 56	11.1	8 47	9 23
10	T	3 01	9.9	3 18	10.7	9 09	9 42	10	T	3 35	9.8	3 51	10.9	9 39	10 18
11	W	3 51	9.7	4 09	10.6	9 58	10 36	11	F	4 33	9.6	4 50	10.7	10 37	11 17
12	T	4 47	9.4	5 06	10.6	10 53	11 35	12	S	5 34	9.5	5 53	10.4	11 38	...
13	F	5 47	9.3	6 07	10.5	11 53	...	13	S	6 38	9.6	6 59	10.3	12 19	12 42
14	S	6 51	9.3	7 11	10.6	12 36	12 56	14	M	7 42	9.8	8 04	10.3	1 21	1 47
15	S	7 55	9.5	8 16	10.7	1 39	1 59	15	T	8 42	10.2	9 06	10.4	2 22	2 49
16	M	8 56	9.9	9 17	10.9	2 40	3 01	16	W	9 37	10.6	10 03	10.5	3 18	3 46
17	T	9 53	10.4	10 15	11.1	3 37	3 59	17	T	10 27	10.9	10 55	10.5	4 10	4 39
18	W	10 46	10.8	11 09	11.2	4 31	4 53	18	F	11 14	11.1	11 43	10.5	4 58	5 28
19	T	11 36	11.1	...	...	5 20	5 44	19	S	11 58	11.1	...	...	5 44	6 14
20	F	12 01	11.1	12 22	11.2	6 08	6 33	20	S	12 28	10.3	12 40	11.0	6 27	6 58
21	S	12 48	10.9	1 07	11.1	6 53	7 20	21	M	1 12	10.0	1 21	10.7	7 10	7 41
22	S	1 34	10.6	1 51	10.9	7 38	8 06	22	T	1 55	9.7	2 03	10.4	7 52	8 24
23	M	2 20	10.1	2 35	10.6	8 22	8 53	23	W	2 39	9.3	2 47	10.1	8 36	9 09
24	T	3 07	9.6	3 21	10.1	9 08	9 41	24	T	3 24	9.0	3 32	9.7	9 21	9 55
25	W	3 55	9.1	4 09	9.7	9 55	10 31	25	F	4 12	8.7	4 22	9.3	10 10	10 44
26	T	4 47	8.7	5 00	9.4	10 45	11 24	26	S	5 02	8.5	5 14	9.1	11 01	11 36
27	F	5 41	8.4	5 55	9.1	11 39	...	27	S	5 55	8.5	6 09	8.9	11 55	...
28	S	6 37	8.3	6 52	9.0	12 19	12 35	28	M	6 48	8.6	7 04	8.9	12 29	12 51
29	S	7 33	8.4	7 48	9.1	1 14	1 31	29	T	7 40	8.9	7 58	9.1	1 21	1 46
30	M	8 25	8.7	8 41	9.3	2 07	2 25	30	W	8 29	9.3	8 50	9.3	2 11	2 38
								31	T	9 15	9.7	9 39	9.6	2 59	3 27

Dates when Ht. of **Low** Water is below Mean Lower Low with Ht. of lowest given for each period and Date of lowest in ( ):

    7th - 10th: -0.3' (8th - 9th)   4th - 11th: -0.9' (7th - 8th)
    16th - 22nd: -1.0' (19th - 20th)   16th - 21st: -0.8' (18th - 19th)

Average Rise and Fall 9.5 ft.
When a high tide exceeds avg. ht., the *following* **low tide will be lower than avg.**
Since there is a high degree of correlation between the height of High Water and the velocities of the Flood and Ebb Currents for that same day, we offer a rough rule of thumb for estimating the current velocities, for ALL the Current Charts and Diagrams in this book. **Rule of Thumb:** Refer to Boston High Water. If the height of High Water is 11.0' or over, use the Current Chart velocities as shown. When the height is 10.5', subtract 10%; at 10.0', subtract 20%; at 9.0', 30%; at 8.0', 40%; below 7.5', 50%.

2013 HIGH & LOW WATER
BOSTON, MA
42°21.3'N, 71°03.1'W

Standard Time starts Nov. 3 at 2 a.m.   Standard Time

DAY OF MONTH	DAY OF WEEK	NOVEMBER HIGH a.m.	Ht.	HIGH p.m.	Ht.	LOW a.m.	LOW p.m.	DAY OF MONTH	DAY OF WEEK	DECEMBER HIGH a.m.	Ht.	HIGH p.m.	Ht.	LOW a.m.	LOW p.m.
1	F	9 59	10.3	10 26	9.9	3 45	4 15	1	S	9 09	11.1	9 44	9.9	2 57	3 34
2	S	10 42	10.8	11 12	10.1	4 31	5 01	2	M	9 58	11.5	10 35	10.2	3 47	4 24
3	S	*10 27	11.2	*10 59	10.3	*4 17	*4 48	3	T	10 48	11.9	11 27	10.4	4 37	5 15
4	M	11 10	11.6	11 46	10.4	5 01	5 34	4	W	11 37	12.1	...	...	5 27	6 04
5	T	11 57	11.7	...	...	5 48	6 23	5	T	12 17	10.6	12 29	12.0	6 18	6 55
6	W	12 35	10.4	12 46	11.7	6 37	7 13	6	F	1 10	10.6	1 23	11.8	7 11	7 48
7	T	1 26	10.3	1 39	11.5	7 28	8 06	7	S	2 05	10.5	2 20	11.3	8 07	8 42
8	F	2 21	10.1	2 35	11.2	8 23	9 01	8	S	3 01	10.4	3 19	10.8	9 05	9 38
9	S	3 19	10.0	3 35	10.7	9 21	9 59	9	M	4 00	10.2	4 21	10.2	10 05	10 36
10	S	4 20	9.9	4 39	10.3	10 23	11 00	10	T	5 00	10.1	5 25	9.7	11 09	11 35
11	M	5 22	9.9	5 45	10.0	11 28	...	11	W	6 00	10.1	6 30	9.4	...	12 13
12	T	6 24	10.0	6 50	9.9	12 01	12 33	12	T	6 59	10.1	7 33	9.2	12 34	1 16
13	W	7 23	10.3	7 52	9.8	1 00	1 35	13	F	7 55	10.2	8 31	9.1	1 31	2 15
14	T	8 18	10.5	8 48	9.8	1 56	2 32	14	S	8 46	10.3	9 23	9.1	2 24	3 08
15	F	9 07	10.7	9 40	9.8	2 48	3 24	15	S	9 32	10.3	10 09	9.1	3 13	3 54
16	S	9 53	10.8	10 26	9.7	3 36	4 11	16	M	10 15	10.4	10 52	9.1	3 58	4 37
17	S	10 36	10.8	11 10	9.6	4 20	4 55	17	T	10 55	10.4	11 31	9.1	4 40	5 17
18	M	11 16	10.7	11 51	9.5	5 03	5 37	18	W	11 34	10.3	...	...	5 21	5 55
19	T	11 56	10.5	...	...	5 44	6 17	19	T	12 09	9.1	12 13	10.2	6 01	6 33
20	W	12 32	9.3	12 36	10.3	6 26	6 58	20	F	12 48	9.1	12 52	10.0	6 42	7 12
21	T	1 12	9.1	1 17	10.0	7 07	7 40	21	S	1 26	9.1	1 32	9.8	7 23	7 52
22	F	1 55	9.0	2 00	9.7	7 51	8 23	22	S	2 06	9.0	2 14	9.6	8 06	8 33
23	S	2 39	8.8	2 46	9.4	8 36	9 08	23	M	2 48	9.0	2 59	9.3	8 51	9 16
24	S	3 25	8.7	3 35	9.1	9 25	9 55	24	T	3 32	9.0	3 47	9.0	9 39	10 02
25	M	4 13	8.7	4 26	8.9	10 16	10 44	25	W	4 18	9.1	4 38	8.8	10 31	10 51
26	T	5 03	8.8	5 20	8.8	11 10	11 35	26	T	5 08	9.3	5 32	8.7	11 25	11 43
27	W	5 53	9.1	6 14	8.8	...	12 05	27	F	5 59	9.6	6 29	8.8	...	12 22
28	T	6 43	9.5	7 08	9.0	12 26	12 59	28	S	6 53	10.0	7 27	9.0	12 38	1 19
29	F	7 32	9.9	8 02	9.3	1 17	1 52	29	S	7 47	10.6	8 24	9.3	1 33	2 15
30	S	8 21	10.5	8 54	9.6	2 07	2 44	30	M	8 41	11.1	9 20	9.7	2 28	3 10
								31	T	9 35	11.6	10 14	10.2	3 22	4 03

Dates when Ht. of **Low** Water is below Mean Lower Low with Ht. of lowest given for each period and Date of lowest in ( ):

2nd - 10th: -1.5' (5th)   1st - 9th: -1.9' (4th - 5th)
15th - 19th: -0.5' (16th - 17th)   16th - 17th: -0.2'
30th: -0.2'   29th - 31st: -1.5' (31st)

Average Rise and Fall 9.5 ft.

When a high tide exceeds avg. ht., the *following* **low tide will be lower than avg.** Since there is a high degree of correlation between the height of High Water and the velocities of the Flood and Ebb Currents for that same day, we offer a rough rule of thumb for estimating the current velocities, for ALL the Current Charts and Diagrams in this book. **Rule of Thumb:** Refer to Boston High Water. If the height of High Water is 11.0' or over, use the Current Chart velocities as shown. When the height is 10.5', subtract 10%; at 10.0', subtract 20%; at 9.0', 30%; at 8.0', 40%; below 7.5', 50%.

CAPE COD CANAL

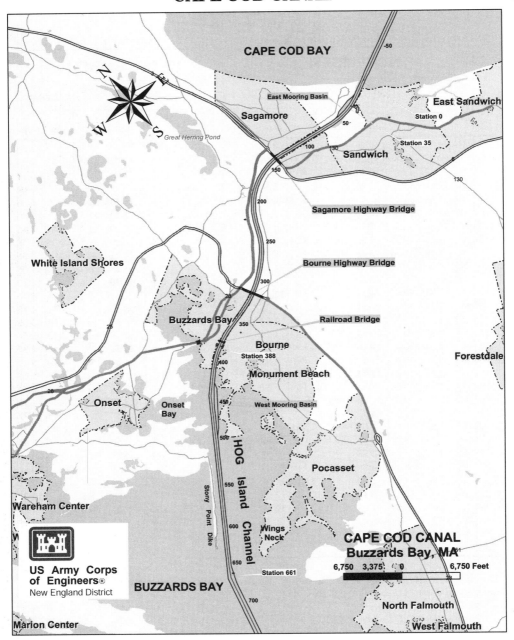

SMALL BOAT BASINS ON EITHER END OF THE CANAL: On E. end, 13-ft. mean low water, on S. side of Sandwich, available for mooring small boat traffic; On W. end, channel 13-ft. at mean low water, 100 ft. wide leads from NE side of Hog Is. Ch. abreast of Hog Is. to harbor in Onset Bay. Fuel, supplies and phone services at both locations.

See Cape Cod Canal Currents pp. 46-51.

CAPE COD CANAL REGULATIONS
For complete regulations see 33 USC, Part 207 and 36 CFR, Part 327

No excessive wake – Speed Limit 10 m.p.h. (8.7 kts.)

Vessels going *with* the current have right of way over those going *against* it.

Clearance under all bridges: 135 feet at mean high water. Buzzards Bay Railroad Bridge is maintained in up, or open position, except when lowered for trains or maintenance.

Obtaining Clearance
Vessels 65 feet and over shall not enter the Canal until clearance has been given by radio from the Marine Traffic Controller.

Vessels of any kind unable to make a through transit of the Canal against a head current of 6 kts. within a time limit of 2-1/2 hrs. are required to obtain helper tug assistance or wait for a fair current prior to receiving clearance from the Controller.

Two-way traffic through the Canal for all vessels is allowed when Controller on duty considers conditions suitable.

Communications
Direct communications are available at all hours by VHF radio or by phoning 978-318-8500. Call on Channel 13 to establish contact. Transmissions may then be switched to Channel 14 as the working channel. Channel 16 is also available but should be limited to emergency situations. Vessels shall maintain a radio guard on Channel 13 during the entire passage.

Traffic Lights
Traffic Lights are at Eastern End at Sandwich (Cape Cod Bay entrance) and at Western End near Wings Neck (Buzzards Bay entrance). When traffic lights are extinguished: all vessels over 65 feet are cautioned not to enter Canal until clearance given, as above.

Entering From EASTERN END: (Lights on South side of entrance to Canal.)
> RED LIGHT: Any type of vessel 65 feet in length and over must stop clear of the Cape Cod Bay entrance channel.
> YELLOW LIGHT: Vessels 65 feet in length and over and drawing less than 25 feet may proceed as far as the East Mooring Basin where they must stop.
> GREEN LIGHT: Vessels may proceed westward through the Canal.

Entering From WESTERN END: (Lights near Wings Neck at West Entrance to Hog Is. Channel)
> RED LIGHT: Vessels 65 feet and over in length and drawing less than 25 feet must keep southerly of Hog Island Channel Entrance Buoys Nos. 1 and 2 and utilize the general anchorage areas adjacent to the improved channel. Vessel traffic drawing 25 feet and over are directed not to enter the Canal channel at the Cleveland Ledge Light entrance and shall lay to or anchor in Buzzards Bay until clearance is granted by the Marine Traffic Controller or a green traffic light at Wings Neck is displayed.
> YELLOW LIGHT: Vessels may proceed through Hog Island Channel as far as the West Mooring Basin where they must stop.
> GREEN LIGHT: Vessels may proceed eastward through the Canal.

Prohibited Activities
Jet skis, sea planes, paddle-driven craft and sailing vessels not under power are prohibited from transiting the Canal.

Fishing from a vessel within the channel limits of the Canal is prohibited.

Anchoring within the channel limits of the Canal, except in emergencies with notice given to the Traffic Controller, is prohibited.

CAPE COD CANAL
41°44.5'N, 70°36.8'W at R.R. Bridge

| Standard Time | | | | | | | | Standard Time | | | | | | |

JANUARY / FEBRUARY

DAY OF MONTH	DAY OF WEEK	CURRENT TURNS TO						DAY OF MONTH	DAY OF WEEK	CURRENT TURNS TO					
		EAST Flood Starts			WEST Ebb Starts					EAST Flood Starts			WEST Ebb Starts		
		a.m.	p.m.	Kts.	a.m.	p.m.	Kts.			a.m.	p.m.	Kts.	a.m.	p.m.	Kts.
1	T	5 37	5 59	p4.3	11 49	...	4.5	1	F	6 36	7 00	p4.3	12 42	12 53	p4.5
2	W	6 18	6 41	p4.2	12 33	12 30	p4.4	2	S	7 25	7 50	a4.2	1 25	1 46	a4.4
3	T	7 04	7 27	p4.1	1 14	1 16	p4.3	3	S	8 21	8 48	a4.1	2 16	2 48	a4.3
4	F	7 53	8 17	p4.0	2 00	2 10	p4.2	4	M	9 22	9 51	a4.0	3 13	3 58	a4.3
5	S	8 49	9 14	p4.0	2 51	3 12	4.1	5	T	10 30	10 59	a4.0	4 18	5 10	a4.3
6	S	9 50	10 15	p4.0	3 47	4 19	a4.2	6	W	11 38	...	4.2	5 24	6 17	a4.4
7	M	10 54	11 19	4.0	4 46	5 28	a4.3	7	T	12 07	12 42	p4.4	6 27	7 19	a4.6
8	T	11 57	...	4.2	5 46	6 32	a4.5	8	F	1 09	1 41	p4.6	7 26	8 14	a4.8
9	W	12 22	12 58	p4.5	6 44	7 32	a4.7	9	S	2 05	2 34	p4.8	8 20	9 05	a5.0
10	T	1 22	1 54	p4.7	7 40	8 28	a4.9	10	S	2 57	3 24	p4.9	9 11	9 52	a5.1
11	F	2 18	2 48	p4.9	8 33	9 21	a5.1	11	M	3 45	4 11	p4.9	10 00	10 38	a5.1
12	S	3 11	3 39	p5.0	9 24	10 11	a5.2	12	T	4 31	4 55	p4.8	10 47	11 21	a5.1
13	S	4 01	4 28	p5.0	10 14	10 59	a5.2	13	W	5 15	5 39	4.6	11 33	...	4.9
14	M	4 50	5 16	p4.9	11 04	11 47	a5.1	14	T	5 59	6 22	4.4	12 04	12 20	4.7
15	T	5 39	6 04	p4.7	11 54	...	5.0	15	F	6 44	7 06	a4.2	12 48	1 09	a4.5
16	W	6 28	6 52	p4.5	12 35	12 45	p4.8	16	S	7 31	7 54	a4.0	1 33	2 00	a4.3
17	T	7 18	7 41	4.2	1 23	1 38	4.5	17	S	8 22	8 45	a3.7	2 21	2 57	a4.1
18	F	8 10	8 34	3.9	2 14	2 35	a4.3	18	M	9 19	9 43	a3.5	3 15	3 58	a3.9
19	S	9 06	9 29	3.7	3 06	3 35	a4.1	19	T	10 21	10 46	a3.4	4 13	5 01	a3.8
20	S	10 06	10 28	a3.6	4 01	4 37	a4.0	20	W	11 23	11 47	a3.5	5 13	6 01	a3.8
21	M	11 06	11 28	a3.6	4 58	5 39	a3.9	21	T	...	12 20	3.7	6 10	6 55	a3.9
22	T	...	12 04	3.7	5 53	6 36	a3.9	22	F	12 43	1 11	p3.9	7 02	7 43	a4.1
23	W	12 24	12 57	p3.8	6 45	7 28	a4.1	23	S	1 31	1 56	p4.1	7 48	8 26	a4.3
24	T	1 15	1 44	p4.0	7 33	8 14	a4.2	24	S	2 14	2 37	p4.3	8 30	9 06	a4.5
25	F	2 01	2 26	p4.1	8 17	8 57	a4.4	25	M	2 54	3 15	p4.4	9 10	9 43	a4.6
26	S	2 43	3 06	p4.2	8 57	9 37	a4.5	26	T	3 31	3 53	p4.5	9 48	10 19	a4.8
27	S	3 21	3 43	p4.3	9 36	10 14	a4.6	27	W	4 09	4 31	p4.6	10 27	10 55	a4.8
28	M	3 58	4 20	p4.4	10 12	10 50	a4.7	28	T	4 47	5 10	p4.6	11 06	11 32	a4.8
29	T	4 35	4 56	p4.4	10 49	11 26	a4.7								
30	W	5 13	5 35	p4.4	11 27	...	4.7								
31	T	5 52	6 15	p4.4	12 02	12 08	p4.6								

The Kts. (knots) columns show the **maximum** predicted velocities of the stronger one of the Flood Currents and the stronger one of the Ebb Currents for each day.

The letter "a" means the velocity shown should occur **after** the **a.m.** Current Change. The letter "p" means the velocity shown should occur **after** the **p.m.** Current Change (even if next morning). No "a" or "p" means a.m. and p.m. velocities are the same for that day.

Avg. Max. Velocity: Flood 4.0 Kts., Ebb 4.5 Kts.

Max. Flood 3 hrs. after Flood Starts, ±20 min.

Max. Ebb 3 hrs. after Ebb Starts, ±20 min.

Average rise and fall: canal east end, 8.7 ft. (time of high water same as Boston); west end, at Monument Beach, 4.0 ft. (time of high water 15 min. after Newport).

See pp. 22-29 for Current Change at other points.

2013 CURRENT TABLE
CAPE COD CANAL
41°44.5'N, 70°36.8'W at R.R. Bridge

*Daylight Time starts Mar. 10 at 2 a.m.   Daylight Saving Time

		MARCH CURRENT TURNS TO									APRIL CURRENT TURNS TO					
D A Y O F M O N T H	D A Y O F W E E K	EAST Flood Starts			WEST Ebb Starts			D A Y O F M O N T H	D A Y O F W E E K	EAST Flood Starts			WEST Ebb Starts		
		a.m.	p.m.	Kts.	a.m.	p.m.	Kts.			a.m.	p.m.	Kts.	a.m.	p.m.	Kts.
1	F	5 28	5 52	4.5	11 49	...	4.7	1	M	7 45	8 14	a4.5	1 35	2 20	a4.7
2	S	6 13	6 38	a4.5	12 12	12 37	4.6	2	T	8 43	9 14	a4.4	2 30	3 23	a4.6
3	S	7 03	7 30	a4.4	12 57	1 31	a4.6	3	W	9 47	10 23	a4.2	3 32	4 31	a4.5
4	M	7 58	8 28	a4.2	1 49	2 34	a4.4	4	T	10 55	11 33	a4.1	4 41	5 40	a4.4
5	T	9 02	9 34	a4.1	2 49	3 44	a4.4	5	F	...	12 04	4.2	5 51	6 44	a4.4
6	W	10 11	10 45	a4.1	3 57	4 55	a4.3	6	S	12 40	1 08	p4.3	6 57	7 42	a4.5
7	T	11 21	11 54	a4.2	5 07	6 03	a4.4	7	S	1 41	2 06	p4.4	7 57	8 34	a4.6
8	F	...	12 27	4.3	6 13	7 03	a4.5	8	M	2 34	2 58	p4.5	8 51	9 21	a4.7
9	S	12 57	1 25	p4.5	7 12	7 56	a4.7	9	T	3 22	3 44	4.5	9 40	10 04	4.7
10	S	1 52	*3 18	p4.7	*9 07	*9 45	a4.9	10	W	4 05	4 27	4.5	10 26	10 45	4.7
11	M	3 41	4 06	p4.7	9 57	10 30	a4.9	11	T	4 46	5 07	a4.5	11 10	11 23	p4.7
12	T	4 26	4 50	p4.7	10 44	11 12	a4.9	12	F	5 25	5 45	a4.5	11 52	...	4.5
13	W	5 09	5 32	4.6	11 29	11 53	a4.9	13	S	6 03	6 23	a4.3	12 01	12 33	a4.6
14	T	5 50	6 12	a4.6	...	12 12	4.7	14	S	6 42	7 02	a4.2	12 39	1 16	a4.5
15	F	6 30	6 52	a4.4	12 32	12 56	a4.7	15	M	7 23	7 44	a4.0	1 18	2 00	a4.3
16	S	7 11	7 33	a4.2	1 12	1 41	a4.5	16	T	8 08	8 32	a3.9	2 01	2 49	a4.2
17	S	7 55	8 16	a4.0	1 53	2 28	a4.3	17	W	8 57	9 25	a3.7	2 49	3 43	a4.0
18	M	8 42	9 06	a3.8	2 38	3 21	a4.1	18	T	9 52	10 24	a3.6	3 45	4 41	a3.9
19	T	9 35	10 02	a3.6	3 30	4 19	a3.9	19	F	10 51	11 25	a3.6	4 46	5 39	a3.8
20	W	10 35	11 04	a3.5	4 28	5 21	a3.8	20	S	11 50	...	3.7	5 47	6 33	a3.9
21	T	11 37	...	3.5	5 31	6 22	a3.8	21	S	12 23	12 46	p3.8	6 44	7 23	4.0
22	F	12 07	12 37	p3.6	6 31	7 17	a3.9	22	M	1 15	1 37	p4.0	7 37	8 09	p4.3
23	S	1 05	1 31	p3.8	7 26	8 06	4.0	23	T	2 03	2 24	p4.2	8 26	8 51	p4.5
24	S	1 56	2 19	p4.1	8 15	8 50	a4.3	24	W	2 48	3 10	p4.4	9 12	9 33	p4.7
25	M	2 40	3 02	p4.3	8 59	9 30	a4.5	25	T	3 32	3 54	p4.6	9 57	10 14	p4.9
26	T	3 22	3 44	p4.4	9 42	10 08	4.6	26	F	4 16	4 39	a4.7	10 43	10 56	p5.0
27	W	4 02	4 24	p4.6	10 23	10 46	4.8	27	S	5 01	5 25	a4.8	11 31	11 39	p5.0
28	T	4 42	5 05	4.6	11 04	11 24	4.9	28	S	5 48	6 14	a4.8	...	12 20	4.8
29	F	5 23	5 47	a4.7	11 47	...	4.9	29	M	6 38	7 05	a4.8	12 27	1 13	a5.0
30	S	6 07	6 32	a4.7	12 04	12 34	a4.9	30	T	7 31	8 01	a4.7	1 18	2 10	a4.9
31	S	6 54	7 20	a4.7	12 47	1 24	a4.8								

The Kts. (knots) columns show the **maximum** predicted velocities of the stronger one of the Flood Currents and the stronger one of the Ebb Currents for each day.

The letter "a" means the velocity shown should occur **after** the **a.m.** Current Change. The letter "p" means the velocity shown should occur **after** the **p.m.** Current Change (even if next morning). No "a" or "p" means a.m. and p.m. velocities are the same for that day.

Avg. Max. Velocity: Flood 4.0 Kts., Ebb 4.5 Kts.

Max. Flood 3 hrs. after Flood Starts, ±20 min.

Max. Ebb 3 hrs. after Ebb Starts, ±20 min.

Average rise and fall: canal east end, 8.7 ft. (time of high water same as Boston); west end, at Monument Beach, 4.0 ft. (time of high water 15 min. after Newport).

See pp. 22-29 for Current Change at other points.

2013 CURRENT TABLE
CAPE COD CANAL
41°44.5'N, 70°36.8'W at R.R. Bridge

Daylight Saving Time   Daylight Saving Time

MAY

DAY OF MONTH	DAY OF WEEK	CURRENT TURNS TO					
		EAST Flood Starts			WEST Ebb Starts		
		a.m.	p.m.	Kts.	a.m.	p.m.	Kts.
1	W	8 29	9 02	a4.5	2 15	3 11	a4.7
2	T	9 31	10 08	a4.3	3 17	4 15	a4.6
3	F	10 38	11 16	a4.2	4 25	5 19	a4.4
4	S	11 43	...	4.2	5 33	6 20	a4.4
5	S	12 20	12 45	p4.2	6 38	7 16	a4.4
6	M	1 19	1 42	p4.3	7 37	8 07	4.4
7	T	2 12	2 33	p4.3	8 32	8 54	p4.5
8	W	2 59	3 20	4.3	9 21	9 37	p4.6
9	T	3 43	4 02	a4.4	10 07	10 17	p4.6
10	F	4 23	4 41	a4.4	10 50	10 56	p4.6
11	S	5 01	5 19	a4.3	11 32	11 33	p4.5
12	S	5 39	5 57	a4.3	...	12 12	4.2
13	M	6 17	6 35	a4.2	12 10	12 53	a4.5
14	T	6 57	7 17	a4.1	12 49	1 35	a4.4
15	W	7 39	8 02	a4.0	1 30	2 20	a4.2
16	T	8 24	8 51	a3.9	2 15	3 08	a4.1
17	F	9 14	9 45	a3.8	3 06	4 00	a4.0
18	S	10 08	10 41	a3.7	4 02	4 53	a3.9
19	S	11 04	11 38	a3.8	5 01	5 46	3.9
20	M	...	12 01	3.9	6 01	6 37	p4.1
21	T	12 33	12 55	p4.0	6 58	7 26	p4.3
22	W	1 26	1 47	p4.2	7 52	8 13	p4.6
23	T	2 16	2 38	p4.4	8 44	8 59	p4.8
24	F	3 05	3 27	a4.6	9 34	9 45	p5.0
25	S	3 54	4 17	a4.8	10 25	10 31	p5.1
26	S	4 43	5 06	a4.9	11 15	11 19	p5.1
27	M	5 32	5 58	a4.9	...	12 07	4.8
28	T	6 24	6 51	a4.9	12 10	1 01	a5.1
29	W	7 17	7 47	a4.8	1 03	1 56	a5.0
30	T	8 13	8 46	a4.6	2 00	2 53	a4.9
31	F	9 12	9 48	a4.4	3 00	3 53	a4.7

JUNE

DAY OF MONTH	DAY OF WEEK	CURRENT TURNS TO					
		EAST Flood Starts			WEST Ebb Starts		
		a.m.	p.m.	Kts.	a.m.	p.m.	Kts.
1	S	10 14	10 51	a4.3	4 05	4 52	a4.5
2	S	11 16	11 54	a4.1	5 10	5 50	a4.3
3	M	...	12 18	4.1	6 14	6 46	p4.3
4	T	12 52	1 14	p4.1	7 14	7 37	p4.3
5	W	1 46	2 06	a4.1	8 09	8 25	p4.4
6	T	2 35	2 53	a4.2	9 00	9 09	p4.4
7	F	3 19	3 37	a4.2	9 47	9 51	p4.5
8	S	4 00	4 17	a4.2	10 30	10 30	p4.5
9	S	4 39	4 55	a4.2	11 11	11 08	p4.5
10	M	5 17	5 33	a4.2	11 51	11 46	p4.5
11	T	5 54	6 11	a4.2	...	12 30	4.1
12	W	6 33	6 51	a4.1	12 24	1 10	a4.4
13	T	7 12	7 33	a4.1	1 03	1 51	a4.3
14	F	7 54	8 18	a4.0	1 44	2 34	a4.2
15	S	8 40	9 07	a4.0	2 30	3 19	a4.2
16	S	9 29	10 00	a3.9	3 22	4 08	a4.1
17	M	10 22	10 56	a3.9	4 19	5 00	4.0
18	T	11 19	11 54	3.9	5 20	5 53	p4.2
19	W	...	12 16	4.0	6 22	6 46	p4.4
20	T	12 52	1 14	4.1	7 22	7 39	p4.6
21	F	1 48	2 10	4.3	8 20	8 30	p4.8
22	S	2 42	3 05	a4.6	9 15	9 21	p5.0
23	S	3 35	3 58	a4.8	10 08	10 12	p5.1
24	M	4 26	4 50	a4.9	11 00	11 03	p5.2
25	T	5 18	5 42	a5.0	11 52	11 54	p5.2
26	W	6 09	6 34	a4.9	...	12 44	4.8
27	T	7 01	7 28	a4.8	12 47	1 36	a5.1
28	F	7 54	8 23	a4.7	1 42	2 29	a4.9
29	S	8 49	9 20	a4.4	2 40	3 24	a4.7
30	S	9 45	10 20	a4.2	3 40	4 20	a4.5

The Kts. (knots) columns show the **maximum** predicted velocities of the stronger one of the Flood Currents and the stronger one of the Ebb Currents for each day.
The letter "a" means the velocity shown should occur **after** the a.m. Current Change. The letter "p" means the velocity shown should occur **after** the p.m. Current Change (even if next morning). No "a" or "p" means a.m. and p.m. velocities are the same for that day.
Avg. Max. Velocity: Flood 4.0 Kts., Ebb 4.5 Kts.
Max. Flood 3 hrs. after Flood Starts, ±20 min.
Max. Ebb 3 hrs. after Ebb Starts, ±20 min.
Average rise and fall: canal east end, 8.7 ft. (time of high water same as Boston); west end, at Monument Beach, 4.0 ft. (time of high water 15 min. after Newport).

See pp. 22-29 for Current Change at other points.

2013 CURRENT TABLE
CAPE COD CANAL
41°44.5'N, 70°36.8'W at R.R. Bridge

Daylight Saving Time   Daylight Saving Time

		JULY							AUGUST					
		CURRENT TURNS TO								CURRENT TURNS TO				
DAY OF MONTH	DAY OF WEEK	EAST Flood Starts			WEST Ebb Starts			DAY OF MONTH	DAY OF WEEK	EAST Flood Starts			WEST Ebb Starts	
		a.m.	p.m.	Kts.	a.m.	p.m.	Kts.			a.m.	p.m.	Kts.	a.m.	p.m.	Kts.
1	M	10 44	11 21	a4.0	4 43	5 16	4.2	1	T	...	12 07	3.5	6 17	6 31	p4.0
2	T	11 44	...	3.9	5 46	6 12	p4.2	2	F	12 43	1 05	a3.7	7 16	7 25	p4.1
3	W	12 22	12 43	3.8	6 47	7 05	p4.2	3	S	1 39	1 59	a3.8	8 09	8 15	p4.2
4	T	1 17	1 36	a3.9	7 44	7 55	p4.2	4	S	2 27	2 45	a4.0	8 57	9 00	p4.3
5	F	2 08	2 26	a4.0	8 36	8 42	p4.3	5	M	3 11	3 28	a4.1	9 41	9 42	p4.4
6	S	2 55	3 11	a4.1	9 24	9 26	p4.4	6	T	3 51	4 07	a4.2	10 21	10 22	p4.5
7	S	3 37	3 53	a4.1	10 07	10 07	p4.5	7	W	4 29	4 44	a4.3	10 59	10 59	p4.6
8	M	4 17	4 32	a4.2	10 48	10 46	p4.5	8	T	5 05	5 20	a4.3	11 35	11 36	p4.6
9	T	4 54	5 10	a4.2	11 27	11 23	p4.5	9	F	5 41	5 56	a4.4	...	12 10	4.4
10	W	5 31	5 47	a4.2	...	12 05	4.2	10	S	6 18	6 34	a4.3	12 12	12 45	a4.6
11	T	6 08	6 24	a4.2	12 01	12 42	a4.5	11	S	6 57	7 15	a4.3	12 51	1 22	a4.5
12	F	6 45	7 04	a4.2	12 37	1 19	a4.5	12	M	7 38	8 01	a4.2	1 34	2 02	a4.4
13	S	7 25	7 46	a4.2	1 17	1 58	a4.4	13	T	8 25	8 52	a4.1	2 22	2 48	a4.3
14	S	8 08	8 32	a4.1	2 00	2 39	a4.3	14	W	9 18	9 51	4.0	3 19	3 42	p4.2
15	M	8 54	9 23	a4.0	2 48	3 26	a4.2	15	T	10 18	10 55	p4.0	4 25	4 43	p4.2
16	T	9 47	10 20	a4.0	3 44	4 17	4.1	16	F	11 24	...	3.9	5 35	5 49	p4.4
17	W	10 44	11 21	3.9	4 48	5 14	p4.2	17	S	12 02	12 31	a4.1	6 43	6 53	p4.5
18	T	11 46	...	3.9	5 54	6 13	p4.4	18	S	1 07	1 35	a4.3	7 46	7 54	p4.7
19	F	12 24	12 49	4.1	7 00	7 12	p4.6	19	M	2 08	2 34	a4.5	8 43	8 50	p4.9
20	S	1 25	1 50	a4.3	8 01	8 09	p4.8	20	T	3 03	3 27	a4.7	9 35	9 43	p5.1
21	S	2 23	2 47	a4.6	8 59	9 04	p5.0	21	W	3 55	4 17	a4.9	10 24	10 33	p5.2
22	M	3 18	3 42	a4.8	9 52	9 56	p5.1	22	T	4 44	5 05	a4.9	11 11	11 22	p5.1
23	T	4 11	4 34	a4.9	10 44	10 48	p5.2	23	F	5 31	5 51	a4.9	11 56	...	4.9
24	W	5 02	5 24	a5.0	11 33	11 39	p5.2	24	S	6 17	6 38	a4.7	12 11	12 41	a5.0
25	T	5 51	6 14	a4.9	...	12 22	4.9	25	S	7 02	7 24	a4.5	1 00	1 26	a4.8
26	F	6 40	7 04	a4.8	12 30	1 10	a5.1	26	M	7 49	8 13	a4.2	1 50	2 13	a4.5
27	S	7 30	7 55	a4.6	1 22	1 59	a4.9	27	T	8 37	9 05	3.9	2 43	3 03	4.2
28	S	8 20	8 48	a4.4	2 16	2 50	a4.7	28	W	9 30	10 02	p3.7	3 40	3 57	4.0
29	M	9 13	9 44	a4.1	3 12	3 43	a4.4	29	T	10 29	11 03	p3.5	4 41	4 55	p3.9
30	T	10 08	10 43	a3.8	4 12	4 38	4.1	30	F	11 31	...	3.3	5 44	5 55	p3.9
31	W	11 07	11 44	p3.7	5 15	5 35	p4.0	31	S	12 05	12 32	a3.6	6 43	6 52	p3.9

The Kts. (knots) columns show the **maximum** predicted velocities of the stronger one of the Flood Currents and the stronger one of the Ebb Currents for each day.

The letter "a" means the velocity shown should occur **after** the **a.m.** Current Change. The letter "p" means the velocity shown should occur **after** the **p.m.** Current Change (even if next morning). No "a" or "p" means a.m. and p.m. velocities are the same for that day.

Avg. Max. Velocity: Flood 4.0 Kts., Ebb 4.5 Kts.

Max. Flood 3 hrs. after Flood Starts, ±20 min.

Max. Ebb 3 hrs. after Ebb Starts, ±20 min.

Average rise and fall: canal east end, 8.7 ft. (time of high water same as Boston); west end, at Monument Beach, 4.0 ft. (time of high water 15 min. after Newport).

See pp. 22-29 for Current Change at other points.

2013 CURRENT TABLE
CAPE COD CANAL
41°44.5'N, 70°36.8'W at R.R. Bridge

Daylight Saving Time   Daylight Saving Time

SEPTEMBER							OCTOBER						
DAY OF MONTH	DAY OF WEEK	CURRENT TURNS TO						DAY OF MONTH	DAY OF WEEK	CURRENT TURNS TO			
		EAST Flood Starts			WEST Ebb Starts					EAST Flood Starts			WEST Ebb Starts
		a.m.	p.m.	Kts.	a.m.	p.m.	Kts.			a.m.	p.m.	Kts.	a.m.	p.m.	Kts.
1	S	1 03	1 27	a3.7	7 37	7 45	p4.1	1	T	1 15	1 41	a3.8	7 49	7 59	p4.2
2	M	1 54	2 16	a3.9	8 26	8 32	p4.3	2	W	2 02	2 25	4.0	8 33	8 44	p4.4
3	T	2 40	3 00	a4.0	9 09	9 15	p4.4	3	T	2 46	3 07	4.2	9 13	9 26	p4.5
4	W	3 21	3 38	a4.2	9 49	9 55	p4.6	4	F	3 26	3 44	p4.4	9 50	10 06	p4.7
5	T	3 59	4 15	4.3	10 26	10 33	p4.7	5	S	4 05	4 23	p4.5	10 27	10 46	4.7
6	F	4 36	4 51	4.4	11 01	11 10	p4.7	6	S	4 44	5 02	p4.6	11 03	11 27	a4.8
7	S	5 13	5 28	4.4	11 36	11 49	p4.7	7	M	5 24	5 43	p4.6	11 40	...	4.8
8	S	5 50	6 07	4.4	...	12 11	4.6	8	T	6 06	6 28	p4.6	12 10	12 21	p4.8
9	M	6 30	6 49	4.4	12 29	12 49	4.6	9	W	6 53	7 17	p4.5	12 58	1 06	p4.7
10	T	7 13	7 36	4.3	1 13	1 30	4.5	10	T	7 44	8 11	p4.4	1 51	1 57	p4.6
11	W	8 02	8 29	p4.2	2 04	2 19	p4.4	11	F	8 42	9 12	p4.2	2 51	2 57	p4.5
12	T	8 57	9 29	p4.1	3 03	3 16	p4.3	12	S	9 47	10 19	p4.2	3 57	4 05	p4.4
13	F	10 00	10 36	p4.1	4 10	4 21	p4.3	13	S	10 57	11 28	p4.2	5 06	5 16	p4.4
14	S	11 10	11 45	p4.1	5 21	5 31	p4.4	14	M	...	12 06	3.9	6 11	6 24	p4.5
15	S	...	12 19	3.9	6 28	6 39	p4.5	15	T	12 34	1 08	a4.3	7 10	7 26	p4.6
16	M	12 52	1 23	a4.3	7 30	7 40	p4.7	16	W	1 34	2 04	4.4	8 04	8 22	p4.7
17	T	1 52	2 20	a4.5	8 25	8 37	p4.9	17	T	2 28	2 55	4.5	8 53	9 14	p4.8
18	W	2 47	3 12	a4.7	9 15	9 29	p5.0	18	F	3 18	3 41	4.6	9 38	10 03	4.8
19	T	3 37	3 59	a4.8	10 02	10 18	p5.0	19	S	4 03	4 24	4.6	10 21	10 48	a4.8
20	F	4 24	4 44	a4.8	10 46	11 05	p5.0	20	S	4 45	5 05	p4.6	11 02	11 33	a4.8
21	S	5 08	5 28	4.7	11 29	11 51	a4.9	21	M	5 26	5 46	p4.5	11 41	...	4.7
22	S	5 51	6 11	4.5	...	12 10	4.8	22	T	6 06	6 26	p4.3	12 16	12 21	p4.6
23	M	6 33	6 54	4.3	12 37	12 52	4.6	23	W	6 46	7 08	p4.1	1 00	1 01	p4.4
24	T	7 17	7 39	4.1	1 24	1 35	4.4	24	T	7 30	7 53	p3.9	1 46	1 45	p4.2
25	W	8 02	8 27	p3.9	2 14	2 22	p4.2	25	F	8 17	8 42	p3.7	2 35	2 34	p4.0
26	T	8 52	9 21	p3.6	3 07	3 14	p4.0	26	S	9 10	9 37	p3.6	3 28	3 30	p3.9
27	F	9 49	10 20	p3.5	4 05	4 13	p3.8	27	S	10 09	10 35	p3.6	4 25	4 31	p3.8
28	S	10 51	11 22	p3.5	5 06	5 15	p3.8	28	M	11 10	11 34	p3.6	5 23	5 32	p3.8
29	S	11 54	...	3.3	6 06	6 15	p3.9	29	T	...	12 08	3.4	6 17	6 29	p3.9
30	M	12 21	12 51	a3.6	7 00	7 10	p4.0	30	W	12 29	1 00	a3.8	7 07	7 22	p4.1
								31	T	1 20	1 48	a4.0	7 52	8 10	p4.3

The Kts. (knots) columns show the **maximum** predicted velocities of the stronger one of the Flood Currents and the stronger one of the Ebb Currents for each day.

The letter "a" means the velocity shown should occur **after** the **a.m.** Current Change. The letter "p" means the velocity shown should occur **after** the **p.m.** Current Change (even if next morning). No "a" or "p" means a.m. and p.m. velocities are the same for that day.

Avg. Max. Velocity: Flood 4.0 Kts., Ebb 4.5 Kts.

Max. Flood 3 hrs. after Flood Starts, ±20 min.

Max. Ebb 3 hrs. after Ebb Starts, ±20 min.

Average rise and fall: canal east end, 8.7 ft. (time of high water same as Boston); west end, at Monument Beach, 4.0 ft. (time of high water 15 min. after Newport).

See pp. 22-29 for Current Change at other points.

2013 CURRENT TABLE
CAPE COD CANAL
41°44.5'N, 70°36.8'W at R.R. Bridge

*Standard Time starts Nov. 3 at 2 a.m.   Standard Time

NOVEMBER

DAY OF MONTH	DAY OF WEEK	EAST Flood Starts a.m.	p.m.	Kts.	WEST Ebb Starts a.m.	p.m.	Kts.
1	F	2 07	2 32	p4.2	8 34	8 55	p4.5
2	S	2 51	3 14	p4.4	9 14	9 39	4.6
3	S	*2 35	*2 57	p4.6	*8 53	*9 23	a4.8
4	M	3 17	3 39	p4.7	9 33	10 08	a4.9
5	T	4 01	4 23	p4.8	10 14	10 55	a5.0
6	W	4 47	5 11	p4.8	10 59	11 45	a5.0
7	T	5 36	6 02	p4.7	11 47	...	4.9
8	F	6 29	6 57	p4.5	12 40	12 41	p4.8
9	S	7 28	7 57	p4.4	1 38	1 42	p4.6
10	S	8 32	9 01	p4.3	2 41	2 49	p4.5
11	M	9 40	10 08	p4.2	3 45	3 58	p4.4
12	T	10 47	11 12	p4.2	4 48	5 06	p4.4
13	W	11 49	...	4.1	5 46	6 08	4.4
14	T	12 13	12 45	4.3	6 40	7 06	4.5
15	F	1 07	1 36	p4.4	7 29	7 58	a4.6
16	S	1 57	2 22	p4.5	8 14	8 47	a4.7
17	S	2 42	3 04	p4.5	8 57	9 32	a4.7
18	M	3 23	3 45	p4.4	9 37	10 15	a4.7
19	T	4 03	4 24	p4.4	10 16	10 56	a4.6
20	W	4 41	5 02	p4.3	10 54	11 38	a4.6
21	T	5 20	5 42	p4.1	11 33	...	4.4
22	F	6 01	6 23	p4.0	12 20	12 14	p4.3
23	S	6 45	7 08	p3.9	1 04	12 59	p4.1
24	S	7 33	7 56	p3.8	1 51	1 48	p4.0
25	M	8 26	8 49	p3.7	2 42	2 44	p3.9
26	T	9 22	9 44	p3.7	3 35	3 43	p3.9
27	W	10 20	10 40	p3.8	4 28	4 43	p3.9
28	T	11 15	11 35	p3.9	5 20	5 41	4.0
29	F	...	12 08	3.9	6 08	6 35	4.2
30	S	12 27	12 57	p4.2	6 54	7 26	4.4

DECEMBER

DAY OF MONTH	DAY OF WEEK	EAST Flood Starts a.m.	p.m.	Kts.	WEST Ebb Starts a.m.	p.m.	Kts.
1	S	1 17	1 45	p4.4	7 39	8 15	a4.7
2	M	2 06	2 32	p4.7	8 23	9 03	a4.9
3	T	2 54	3 20	p4.8	9 08	9 51	a5.0
4	W	3 41	4 07	p4.9	9 54	10 41	a5.1
5	T	4 30	4 56	p4.9	10 42	11 32	a5.1
6	F	5 21	5 48	p4.8	11 33	...	5.1
7	S	6 15	6 42	p4.7	12 25	12 27	p4.9
8	S	7 11	7 39	p4.5	1 20	1 26	p4.8
9	M	8 12	8 39	p4.3	2 19	2 30	p4.6
10	T	9 16	9 42	p4.2	3 19	3 36	p4.4
11	W	10 21	10 46	p4.1	4 19	4 43	4.3
12	T	11 24	11 47	p4.1	5 17	5 47	a4.3
13	F	...	12 22	4.1	6 12	6 46	a4.3
14	S	12 44	1 15	p4.2	7 03	7 40	a4.4
15	S	1 35	2 02	p4.3	7 50	8 29	a4.5
16	M	2 21	2 46	p4.3	8 34	9 15	a4.5
17	T	3 03	3 26	p4.3	9 15	9 57	a4.6
18	W	3 42	4 04	p4.3	9 54	10 36	a4.6
19	T	4 20	4 41	p4.3	10 32	11 15	a4.6
20	F	4 57	5 18	p4.2	11 09	11 54	a4.5
21	S	5 35	5 56	p4.1	11 48	...	4.4
22	S	6 15	6 36	p4.1	12 33	12 28	p4.3
23	M	6 58	7 19	p4.0	1 14	1 12	p4.2
24	T	7 45	8 06	p3.9	1 58	2 00	p4.0
25	W	8 36	8 58	p3.8	2 45	2 56	3.9
26	T	9 32	9 54	p3.8	3 36	3 56	3.9
27	F	10 30	10 52	p3.8	4 30	4 59	4.0
28	S	11 29	11 50	p4.0	5 24	6 01	a4.2
29	S	...	12 25	4.1	6 17	6 59	a4.4
30	M	12 47	1 19	p4.4	7 08	7 53	a4.6
31	T	1 41	2 11	p4.7	7 59	8 45	a4.9

The Kts. (knots) columns show the **maximum** predicted velocities of the stronger one of the Flood Currents and the stronger one of the Ebb Currents for each day.

The letter "a" means the velocity shown should occur **after** the a.m. Current Change. The letter "p" means the velocity shown should occur **after** the p.m. Current Change (even if next morning). No "a" or "p" means a.m. and p.m. velocities are the same for that day.

Avg. Max. Velocity: Flood 4.0 Kts., Ebb 4.5 Kts.

Max. Flood 3 hrs. after Flood Starts, ±20 min.

Max. Ebb 3 hrs. after Ebb Starts, ±20 min.

Average rise and fall: canal east end, 8.7 ft. (time of high water same as Boston); west end, at Monument Beach, 4.0 ft. (time of high water 15 min. after Newport).

See pp. 22-29 for Current Change at other points.

2013 CURRENT TABLE
WOODS HOLE, MA, The Strait
41°31.16'N, 70°40.97'W

Standard Time		Standard Time	

JANUARY

DAY OF MONTH	DAY OF WEEK	CURRENT TURNS TO					
		SOUTHEAST Flood Starts			NORTHWEST Ebb Starts		
		a.m.	p.m.	Kts.	a.m.	p.m.	Kts.
1	T	6 41	7 12	p2.3	12 50	12 55	p3.5
2	W	7 26	7 54	p2.3	1 32	1 38	p3.5
3	T	8 17	8 42	p2.4	2 16	2 26	p3.5
4	F	9 12	9 34	p2.4	3 03	3 18	p3.4
5	S	10 13	10 29	p2.4	3 53	4 16	a3.3
6	S	11 13	11 26	p2.4	4 47	5 18	a3.3
7	M	...	12 13	2.1	5 45	6 22	a3.2
8	T	12 24	1 13	a2.4	6 46	7 25	a3.3
9	W	1 22	2 11	a2.3	7 45	8 25	a3.4
10	T	2 20	3 08	p2.5	8 42	9 21	a3.5
11	F	3 17	4 02	p2.7	9 37	10 15	a3.6
12	S	4 13	4 55	p2.8	10 30	11 08	a3.6
13	S	5 08	5 46	p2.8	11 23	...	3.6
14	M	6 01	6 36	p2.7	12 01	12 15	p3.5
15	T	6 55	7 26	p2.6	12 51	1 06	p3.4
16	W	7 49	8 16	p2.5	1 41	1 57	p3.1
17	T	8 46	9 08	p2.3	2 31	2 48	2.9
18	F	9 45	10 01	2.1	3 21	3 40	2.6
19	S	10 41	10 52	1.9	4 11	4 33	a2.4
20	S	11 35	11 41	a1.8	5 02	5 27	a2.3
21	M	...	12 26	1.8	5 53	6 21	a2.3
22	T	12 29	1 15	p1.8	6 44	7 14	a2.4
23	W	1 16	2 01	p1.9	7 33	8 03	a2.4
24	T	2 01	2 45	p1.9	8 19	8 49	a2.5
25	F	2 45	3 26	p1.9	9 01	9 32	a2.7
26	S	3 27	4 05	2.0	9 42	10 14	a2.9
27	S	4 08	4 43	2.2	10 22	10 55	a3.2
28	M	4 48	5 21	2.3	11 02	11 36	a3.4
29	T	5 29	5 58	2.4	11 43	...	3.6
30	W	6 11	6 37	2.5	12 17	12 27	p3.7
31	T	6 56	7 18	p2.5	1 00	1 13	p3.8

FEBRUARY

DAY OF MONTH	DAY OF WEEK	CURRENT TURNS TO					
		SOUTHEAST Flood Starts			NORTHWEST Ebb Starts		
		a.m.	p.m.	Kts.	a.m.	p.m.	Kts.
1	F	7 46	8 06	p2.5	1 45	2 03	p3.7
2	S	8 43	9 01	p2.4	2 33	2 57	a3.6
3	S	9 48	10 03	p2.4	3 25	3 56	a3.5
4	M	10 52	11 05	p2.3	4 22	4 59	a3.3
5	T	11 55	...	2.0	5 23	6 03	a3.2
6	W	12 07	12 57	a2.2	6 26	7 07	a3.1
7	T	1 09	1 57	p2.3	7 28	8 08	a3.2
8	F	2 08	2 54	p2.6	8 26	9 04	a3.3
9	S	3 05	3 48	p2.8	9 21	9 57	a3.4
10	S	4 00	4 38	p2.9	10 14	10 48	a3.5
11	M	4 53	5 26	p2.9	11 05	11 38	a3.5
12	T	5 44	6 13	p2.7	11 54	...	3.4
13	W	6 34	6 58	2.5	12 27	12 44	p3.3
14	T	7 24	7 44	2.3	1 14	1 32	3.1
15	F	8 17	8 33	a2.2	2 02	2 21	a2.9
16	S	9 12	9 24	a2.0	2 49	3 11	a2.7
17	S	10 08	10 16	a1.8	3 37	4 02	a2.4
18	M	11 02	11 07	a1.7	4 26	4 54	a2.2
19	T	11 53	11 56	a1.6	5 16	5 46	a2.1
20	W	...	12 41	1.6	6 07	6 39	a2.1
21	T	12 44	1 27	1.6	6 56	7 29	2.2
22	F	1 30	2 11	1.7	7 44	8 15	2.4
23	S	2 14	2 51	1.9	8 28	8 59	2.7
24	S	2 56	3 30	2.1	9 10	9 40	3.0
25	M	3 37	4 08	2.3	9 51	10 21	3.3
26	T	4 19	4 46	2.5	10 33	11 03	a3.6
27	W	5 01	5 24	2.6	11 17	11 46	a3.8
28	T	5 44	6 05	p2.7	...	12 03	3.9

See the Woods Hole Current Diagram inset on pp. 66-77.

Mariners should exercise great caution when transiting Woods Hole Passage as velocities have been reported to exceed NOAA's predictions.

To hold longest fair current from Buzzards Bay headed East through Vineyard and Nantucket Sounds go through Woods Hole 2 1/2 hrs. after flood starts SE in Woods Hole. (Any earlier means adverse currents in the Sounds.)

2013 CURRENT TABLE
WOODS HOLE, MA, The Strait

41°31.16'N, 70°40.97'W

*Daylight Time starts Mar. 10 at 2 a.m.   Daylight Saving Time

DAY OF MONTH	DAY OF WEEK	CURRENT TURNS TO						DAY OF MONTH	DAY OF WEEK	CURRENT TURNS TO					
		SOUTHEAST Flood Starts			NORTHWEST Ebb Starts					SOUTHEAST Flood Starts			NORTHWEST Ebb Starts		
		a.m.	p.m.	Kts.	a.m.	p.m.	Kts.			a.m.	p.m.	Kts.	a.m.	p.m.	Kts.
1	F	6 31	6 49	2.6	12 30	12 52	3.9	1	M	9 02	9 20	2.3	2 47	3 26	a3.8
2	S	7 22	7 39	p2.5	1 17	1 44	a3.9	2	T	10 08	10 28	2.2	3 44	4 25	a3.6
3	S	8 21	8 38	p2.4	2 08	2 40	a3.8	3	W	11 18	11 38	2.1	4 44	5 26	a3.3
4	M	9 25	9 42	p2.3	3 03	3 40	a3.6	4	T	...	12 22	2.2	5 46	6 27	a3.0
5	T	10 34	10 50	p2.2	4 02	4 42	a3.3	5	F	12 42	1 23	p2.3	6 49	7 29	a2.8
6	W	11 39	11 54	p2.1	5 04	5 46	a3.1	6	S	1 44	2 20	p2.5	7 51	8 27	2.8
7	T	...	12 42	2.2	6 08	6 49	a3.0	7	S	2 41	3 14	p2.7	8 49	9 22	p3.0
8	F	12 57	1 41	p2.5	7 10	7 49	a3.0	8	M	3 35	4 03	p2.8	9 43	10 12	p3.1
9	S	1 56	2 37	p2.7	8 09	8 44	a3.1	9	T	4 26	4 48	2.8	10 33	11 00	p3.2
10	S	*3 52	*4 28	p2.9	*10 03	*10 36	3.2	10	W	5 14	5 32	a2.8	11 22	11 46	p3.2
11	M	4 45	5 16	p2.9	10 55	11 25	a3.3	11	T	6 01	6 15	a2.7	...	12 09	3.0
12	T	5 35	6 01	2.8	11 44	...	3.3	12	F	6 46	6 57	a2.5	12 31	12 55	a3.1
13	W	6 23	6 45	a2.7	12 13	12 32	3.2	13	S	7 31	7 40	a2.3	1 15	1 41	a3.0
14	T	7 11	7 28	a2.5	1 00	1 20	a3.2	14	S	8 17	8 25	a2.0	1 59	2 27	a2.9
15	F	7 58	8 12	a2.3	1 45	2 07	a3.1	15	M	9 05	9 12	a1.9	2 42	3 12	a2.8
16	S	8 47	8 58	a2.1	2 30	2 54	a2.9	16	T	9 55	10 03	a1.7	3 26	3 59	a2.6
17	S	9 39	9 48	a1.9	3 16	3 42	a2.7	17	W	10 46	10 56	a1.7	4 11	4 45	a2.5
18	M	10 32	10 40	a1.7	4 02	4 30	a2.5	18	T	11 35	11 47	1.7	4 57	5 33	a2.4
19	T	11 26	11 32	1.6	4 49	5 20	a2.3	19	F	...	12 22	1.7	5 45	6 22	a2.4
20	W	...	12 16	1.5	5 37	6 10	a2.2	20	S	12 36	1 07	1.8	6 34	7 11	2.4
21	T	12 23	1 04	1.6	6 27	7 01	2.1	21	S	1 23	1 50	p2.0	7 25	7 59	p2.7
22	F	1 11	1 49	1.7	7 17	7 51	p2.3	22	M	2 10	2 33	p2.2	8 16	8 47	p3.0
23	S	1 57	2 32	1.8	8 06	8 38	2.5	23	T	2 56	3 16	p2.3	9 07	9 33	p3.4
24	S	2 42	3 13	2.0	8 53	9 23	2.8	24	W	3 41	3 58	p2.5	9 56	10 18	p3.7
25	M	3 25	3 53	2.2	9 38	10 06	p3.2	25	T	4 28	4 42	p2.6	10 45	11 04	p3.9
26	T	4 08	4 32	2.4	10 22	10 48	p3.5	26	F	5 15	5 28	p2.7	11 35	11 52	p4.0
27	W	4 51	5 12	p2.6	11 07	11 32	p3.8	27	S	6 04	6 17	2.7	...	12 27	p3.8
28	T	5 36	5 54	2.7	11 54	...	3.8	28	S	6 55	7 09	2.6	12 43	1 21	a4.1
29	F	6 22	6 38	2.7	12 16	12 44	a4.0	29	M	7 49	8 05	2.4	1 35	2 15	a4.0
30	S	7 11	7 26	2.6	1 04	1 35	a4.0	30	T	8 48	9 07	a2.3	2 30	3 11	a3.8
31	S	8 03	8 19	p2.5	1 54	2 29	a4.0								

See the Woods Hole Current Diagram inset on pp. 66-77.

Mariners should exercise great caution when transiting Woods Hole Passage as velocities have been reported to exceed NOAA's predictions.

CAUTION: Going *from* Buzzards Bay *into* Vineyard Sound, whether through Woods Hole, or Robinsons Hole or Quicks Hole, *Red* Buoys must be kept on the LEFT or PORT hand, *Green* Buoys kept on the RIGHT or STARBOARD hand. You are considered to be proceeding seaward and should thus follow the rules for LEAVING a harbor.

See pp. 22-29 for Current Change at other points.

2013 CURRENT TABLE
WOODS HOLE, MA, The Strait
41°31.16'N, 70°40.97'W

Daylight Saving Time   Daylight Saving Time

MAY

DAY OF MONTH	DAY OF WEEK	SOUTHEAST Flood Starts a.m.	**p.m.**	Kts.	NORTHWEST Ebb Starts a.m.	**p.m.**	Kts.
1	W	9 52	10 15	a2.2	3 27	4 09	a3.5
2	T	10 59	11 23	a2.3	4 26	5 08	a3.2
3	F	...	12 03	2.3	5 27	6 07	a2.9
4	S	12 27	1 00	p2.4	6 28	7 06	a2.7
5	S	1 27	1 55	p2.5	7 28	8 03	p2.8
6	M	2 23	2 46	p2.6	8 26	8 56	p3.0
7	T	3 16	3 33	2.6	9 20	9 46	p3.1
8	W	4 05	4 19	a2.7	10 10	10 33	p3.1
9	T	4 52	5 02	a2.7	10 58	11 18	p3.1
10	F	5 37	5 45	a2.6	11 44	...	2.8
11	S	6 21	6 27	a2.4	12 01	12 30	a3.0
12	S	7 04	7 10	a2.2	12 44	1 14	a3.0
13	M	7 47	7 53	a2.0	1 27	1 58	a2.9
14	T	8 31	8 38	a1.9	2 09	2 42	a2.9
15	W	9 16	9 26	a1.8	2 51	3 26	a2.8
16	T	10 03	10 17	1.8	3 33	4 10	a2.8
17	F	10 51	11 09	a1.9	4 17	4 55	a2.7
18	S	11 38	11 59	a2.0	5 04	5 42	a2.7
19	S	...	12 23	2.1	5 53	6 30	2.7
20	M	12 49	1 09	p2.2	6 47	7 20	p2.9
21	T	1 38	1 54	p2.3	7 42	8 11	p3.2
22	W	2 28	2 41	p2.4	8 38	9 02	p3.5
23	T	3 18	3 29	p2.5	9 33	9 51	p3.7
24	F	4 08	4 18	p2.6	10 26	10 41	p3.9
25	S	4 58	5 09	p2.6	11 18	11 33	p4.0
26	S	5 50	6 01	2.6	...	12 12	3.6
27	M	6 43	6 56	2.5	12 25	1 06	a4.0
28	T	7 37	7 54	a2.4	1 20	2 00	a3.9
29	W	8 34	8 55	a2.4	2 15	2 55	a3.7
30	T	9 34	10 00	a2.4	3 10	3 51	a3.5
31	F	10 37	11 06	a2.4	4 07	4 47	a3.2

JUNE

DAY OF MONTH	DAY OF WEEK	SOUTHEAST Flood Starts a.m.	**p.m.**	Kts.	NORTHWEST Ebb Starts a.m.	**p.m.**	Kts.
1	S	11 37	...	2.4	5 05	5 43	a2.9
2	S	12 08	12 32	p2.4	6 04	6 39	2.6
3	M	1 07	1 26	p2.4	7 02	7 35	p2.8
4	T	2 01	2 15	2.3	8 00	8 28	p2.9
5	W	2 53	3 03	a2.4	8 54	9 18	p2.9
6	T	3 42	3 48	a2.5	9 45	10 05	p3.0
7	F	4 28	4 32	a2.5	10 33	10 49	p2.9
8	S	5 12	5 15	a2.4	11 18	11 32	p2.9
9	S	5 55	5 57	a2.3	...	12 02	2.7
10	M	6 36	6 39	a2.1	12 14	12 46	a3.0
11	T	7 17	7 21	2.0	12 55	1 28	a3.0
12	W	7 57	8 04	a2.0	1 35	2 10	a3.0
13	T	8 37	8 48	a2.0	2 15	2 51	a3.1
14	F	9 20	9 36	2.0	2 56	3 34	a3.1
15	S	10 05	10 28	a2.1	3 39	4 17	a3.1
16	S	10 52	11 22	a2.2	4 26	5 03	a3.0
17	M	11 40	...	2.2	5 17	5 52	3.0
18	T	12 15	12 30	p2.3	6 13	6 44	p3.1
19	W	1 09	1 20	p2.4	7 13	7 39	p3.2
20	T	2 03	2 13	p2.4	8 14	8 35	p3.5
21	F	2 57	3 06	p2.5	9 13	9 30	p3.7
22	S	3 51	4 00	p2.5	10 08	10 23	p3.8
23	S	4 45	4 54	p2.6	11 03	11 17	p3.9
24	M	5 38	5 49	2.6	11 57	...	3.5
25	T	6 31	6 45	a2.6	12 10	12 50	a3.9
26	W	7 24	7 41	a2.6	1 04	1 43	a3.8
27	T	8 18	8 39	a2.6	1 58	2 36	a3.7
28	F	9 13	9 41	a2.5	2 52	3 29	a3.4
29	S	10 10	10 44	a2.4	3 46	4 23	a3.1
30	S	11 07	11 45	a2.3	4 41	5 16	a2.8

See the Woods Hole Current Diagram inset on pp. 66-77.

Mariners should exercise great caution when transiting Woods Hole Passage as velocities have been reported to exceed NOAA's predictions.

To hold longest fair current from Buzzards Bay headed East through Vineyard and Nantucket Sounds go through Woods Hole 2 1/2 hrs. after flood starts SE in Woods Hole. (Any earlier means adverse currents in the Sounds.)

WOODS HOLE, MA, The Strait

41°31.16'N, 70°40.97'W

Daylight Saving Time   Daylight Saving Time

		JULY									AUGUST					
		CURRENT TURNS TO									CURRENT TURNS TO					
		SOUTHEAST Flood Starts			NORTHWEST Ebb Starts						SOUTHEAST Flood Starts			NORTHWEST Ebb Starts		
DAY OF MONTH	DAY OF WEEK	a.m.	p.m.	Kts.	a.m.	p.m.	Kts.	DAY OF MONTH	DAY OF WEEK	a.m.	p.m.	Kts.	a.m.	p.m.	Kts.
1	M	...	12 02	2.2	5 38	6 11	2.5	1	T	1 08	1 12	a1.9	7 01	7 25	p2.4
2	T	12 42	12 53	2.1	6 34	7 05	p2.6	2	F	1 59	2 01	a2.0	7 56	8 16	p2.5
3	W	1 37	1 44	2.1	7 31	7 58	p2.7	3	S	2 48	2 49	a2.0	8 47	9 05	p2.5
4	T	2 28	2 31	a2.2	8 26	8 48	p2.7	4	S	3 32	3 33	a2.0	9 35	10 02	p2.6
5	F	3 16	3 18	a2.2	9 18	9 36	p2.8	5	M	4 14	4 15	a2.1	10 19	10 31	p2.8
6	S	4 02	4 02	a2.3	10 05	10 20	p2.8	6	T	4 54	4 57	2.0	11 00	11 11	p3.0
7	S	4 45	4 45	a2.3	10 50	11 02	p2.8	7	W	5 32	5 37	p2.2	11 41	11 50	p3.2
8	M	5 26	5 27	a2.2	11 33	11 43	p3.0	8	T	6 08	6 17	p2.3	...	12 21	3.1
9	T	6 06	6 08	2.1	...	12 14	2.8	9	F	6 44	6 57	2.4	12 30	1 01	a3.4
10	W	6 44	6 49	2.1	12 22	12 55	a3.1	10	S	7 21	7 39	2.4	1 11	1 41	a3.6
11	T	7 21	7 30	2.2	1 02	1 36	a3.2	11	S	7 59	8 24	a2.4	1 54	2 23	a3.6
12	F	7 58	8 12	2.2	1 42	2 16	a3.3	12	M	8 42	9 15	a2.4	2 40	3 07	3.6
13	S	8 37	8 58	2.2	2 23	2 58	a3.4	13	T	9 31	10 15	a2.4	3 30	3 56	3.5
14	S	9 20	9 49	a2.3	3 06	3 41	a3.4	14	W	10 29	11 18	a2.4	4 26	4 50	p3.4
15	M	10 08	10 46	a2.3	3 55	4 27	a3.3	15	T	11 32	...	2.3	5 26	5 49	p3.2
16	T	11 01	11 45	a2.4	4 48	5 18	3.2	16	F	12 22	12 34	p2.3	6 30	6 51	p3.2
17	W	11 57	...	2.4	5 47	6 13	p3.2	17	S	1 24	1 36	p2.2	7 34	7 55	p3.2
18	T	12 43	12 53	p2.3	6 49	7 13	p3.2	18	S	2 24	2 36	p2.3	8 36	8 55	p3.3
19	F	1 42	1 51	p2.3	7 53	8 13	p3.4	19	M	3 22	3 35	2.4	9 34	9 52	p3.4
20	S	2 40	2 49	p2.4	8 54	9 12	p3.5	20	T	4 17	4 31	a2.7	10 28	10 46	p3.5
21	S	3 37	3 46	p2.4	9 52	10 08	p3.6	21	W	5 08	5 25	a2.8	11 20	11 38	p3.6
22	M	4 32	4 42	2.5	10 46	11 02	p3.7	22	T	5 58	6 17	a2.9	...	12 11	3.4
23	T	5 25	5 38	a2.7	11 40	11 55	p3.7	23	F	6 46	7 09	a2.8	12 29	1 01	a3.5
24	W	6 17	6 32	a2.8	...	12 32	3.4	24	S	7 33	8 00	a2.6	1 20	1 50	a3.4
25	T	7 07	7 26	a2.7	12 48	1 24	a3.7	25	S	8 20	8 53	a2.4	2 10	2 38	a3.2
26	F	7 57	8 21	a2.7	1 40	2 14	a3.6	26	M	9 10	9 49	a2.2	3 00	3 27	a3.0
27	S	8 48	9 18	a2.5	2 31	3 05	a3.3	27	T	10 02	10 47	2.0	3 51	4 16	a2.7
28	S	9 41	10 18	a2.4	3 23	3 56	a3.1	28	W	10 57	11 43	p1.9	4 43	5 07	a2.4
29	M	10 35	11 17	a2.2	4 16	4 47	a2.8	29	T	11 50	...	1.6	5 35	5 58	a2.2
30	T	11 30	...	2.0	5 10	5 39	a2.5	30	F	12 36	12 41	1.5	6 29	6 50	p2.2
31	W	12 14	12 22	a2.0	6 05	6 32	p2.4	31	S	1 26	1 30	a1.8	7 22	7 41	p2.3

See the Woods Hole Current Diagram inset on pp. 66-77.

Mariners should exercise great caution when transiting Woods Hole Passage as velocities have been reported to exceed NOAA's predictions.

CAUTION: Going *from* Buzzards Bay *into* Vineyard Sound, whether through Woods Hole, or Robinsons Hole or Quicks Hole, *Red* Buoys must be kept on the LEFT or PORT hand, *Green* Buoys kept on the RIGHT or STARBOARD hand. You are considered to be proceeding seaward and should thus follow the rules for LEAVING a harbor.

See pp. 22-29 for Current Change at other points.

2013 CURRENT TABLE
WOODS HOLE, MA, The Strait
41°31.16'N, 70°40.97'W

Daylight Saving Time   Daylight Saving Time

SEPTEMBER

DAY OF MONTH	DAY OF WEEK	CURRENT TURNS TO					
		SOUTHEAST Flood Starts			NORTHWEST Ebb Starts		
		a.m.	p.m.	Kts.	a.m.	p.m.	Kts.
1	S	2 13	2 17	a1.8	8 13	8 30	p2.3
2	M	2 57	3 02	1.8	9 01	9 15	p2.5
3	T	3 39	3 45	1.9	9 45	9 58	p2.8
4	W	4 17	4 26	p2.1	10 26	10 38	p3.1
5	T	4 54	5 06	p2.3	11 06	11 18	p3.3
6	F	5 31	5 46	p2.5	11 46	...	3.4
7	S	6 08	6 27	2.5	12 01	12 26	3.6
8	S	6 46	7 10	a2.6	12 43	1 08	3.7
9	M	7 26	7 57	a2.6	1 30	1 52	3.8
10	T	8 12	8 49	a2.5	2 19	2 39	p3.8
11	W	9 04	9 50	a2.4	3 12	3 31	p3.7
12	T	10 07	10 57	a2.3	4 09	4 28	p3.5
13	F	11 14	...	2.2	5 09	5 29	p3.2
14	S	12 03	12 20	p2.2	6 12	6 33	p3.1
15	S	1 07	1 23	p2.2	7 15	7 37	p3.0
16	M	2 07	2 24	2.3	8 17	8 38	p3.1
17	T	3 04	3 22	2.5	9 15	9 35	p3.2
18	W	3 57	4 17	a2.8	10 08	10 28	p3.3
19	T	4 47	5 09	a2.9	10 59	11 19	p3.4
20	F	5 35	6 00	2.8	11 48	...	3.4
21	S	6 21	6 49	2.7	12 09	12 36	3.3
22	S	7 06	7 38	2.5	12 58	1 23	3.2
23	M	7 52	8 27	p2.3	1 47	2 10	a3.1
24	T	8 39	9 19	p2.1	2 36	2 57	2.8
25	W	9 29	10 14	p1.9	3 24	3 44	2.6
26	T	10 23	11 08	p1.8	4 14	4 33	2.4
27	F	11 17	...	1.5	5 04	5 22	2.2
28	S	12 01	12 09	a1.7	5 55	6 12	2.1
29	S	12 49	12 57	1.6	6 45	7 02	p2.1
30	M	1 35	1 44	p1.7	7 35	7 51	p2.3

OCTOBER

DAY OF MONTH	DAY OF WEEK	CURRENT TURNS TO					
		SOUTHEAST Flood Starts			NORTHWEST Ebb Starts		
		a.m.	p.m.	Kts.	a.m.	p.m.	Kts.
1	T	2 18	2 29	p1.8	8 23	8 38	p2.5
2	W	2 59	3 13	p2.0	9 08	9 23	p2.8
3	T	3 39	3 56	p2.2	9 50	10 06	p3.1
4	F	4 16	4 36	p2.4	10 31	10 49	p3.4
5	S	4 54	5 18	2.5	11 11	11 34	3.6
6	S	5 34	6 01	2.6	11 54	...	3.8
7	M	6 15	6 47	a2.7	12 21	12 38	p4.0
8	T	7 00	7 36	a2.6	1 10	1 26	p4.0
9	W	7 50	8 30	a2.5	2 02	2 17	p3.9
10	T	8 46	9 31	a2.4	2 56	3 12	p3.7
11	F	9 51	10 38	a2.3	3 54	4 10	p3.5
12	S	11 00	11 45	a2.2	4 53	5 12	p3.2
13	S	...	12 07	2.1	5 54	6 15	p3.0
14	M	12 48	1 11	a2.2	6 56	7 18	p2.9
15	T	1 47	2 11	a2.4	7 56	8 19	p2.9
16	W	2 42	3 08	2.6	8 53	9 15	3.0
17	T	3 34	4 01	2.7	9 46	10 09	a3.2
18	F	4 23	4 52	2.8	10 35	10 59	a3.2
19	S	5 09	5 41	p2.8	11 23	11 48	a3.3
20	S	5 54	6 28	p2.6	...	12 10	3.2
21	M	6 39	7 14	p2.5	12 36	12 56	p3.1
22	T	7 23	8 01	p2.3	1 24	1 41	p3.0
23	W	8 09	8 49	p2.1	2 11	2 26	2.8
24	T	8 57	9 39	p1.9	2 57	3 11	p2.7
25	F	9 48	10 30	p1.7	3 44	3 57	2.5
26	S	10 41	11 20	p1.7	4 31	4 44	p2.4
27	S	11 33	...	1.6	5 19	5 31	p2.3
28	M	12 07	12 22	1.7	6 06	6 20	p2.3
29	T	12 52	1 10	1.8	6 54	7 09	p2.4
30	W	1 35	1 55	1.9	7 42	7 59	p2.6
31	T	2 16	2 40	p2.1	8 28	8 48	p2.9

See the Woods Hole Current Diagram inset on pp. 66-77.

Mariners should exercise great caution when transiting Woods Hole Passage as velocities have been reported to exceed NOAA's predictions.

To hold longest fair current from Buzzards Bay headed East through Vineyard and Nantucket Sounds go through Woods Hole 2 1/2 hrs. after flood starts SE in Woods Hole. (Any earlier means adverse currents in the Sounds.)

41°31.16'N, 70°40.97'W
*Standard Time starts Nov. 3 at 2 a.m.   Standard Time

D A Y O F M O N T H	D A Y O F W E E K	CURRENT TURNS TO						D A Y O F M O N T H	D A Y O F W E E K	CURRENT TURNS TO					
		SOUTHEAST Flood Starts			NORTHWEST Ebb Starts					SOUTHEAST Flood Starts			NORTHWEST Ebb Starts		
		a.m.	**p.m.**	Kts.	a.m.	**p.m.**	Kts.			a.m.	**p.m.**	Kts.	a.m.	**p.m.**	Kts.
NOVEMBER								**DECEMBER**							
1	F	2 58	3 25	2.2	9 13	9 36	3.1	1	S	2 06	2 45	a2.4	8 26	9 01	a3.5
2	S	3 39	4 09	2.4	9 57	10 23	3.4	2	M	2 53	3 34	a2.5	9 15	9 52	a3.8
3	S	*3 22	*3 55	2.5	*9 41	*10 12	a3.7	3	T	3 43	4 24	a2.6	10 05	10 45	a4.0
4	M	4 05	4 40	a2.7	10 26	11 02	a3.9	4	W	4 33	5 14	a2.7	10 57	11 38	a4.0
5	T	4 51	5 29	a2.7	11 15	11 54	a4.1	5	T	5 26	6 07	a2.6	11 50	...	4.0
6	W	5 41	6 20	a2.6	...	12 06	4.1	6	F	6 22	7 01	a2.5	12 31	12 44	p3.9
7	T	6 34	7 15	a2.5	12 47	1 00	p3.9	7	S	7 20	7 59	p2.4	1 26	1 40	p3.7
8	F	7 32	8 15	2.3	1 42	1 55	p3.7	8	S	8 23	9 00	p2.4	2 20	2 36	p3.4
9	S	8 37	9 20	2.2	2 38	2 54	p3.5	9	M	9 30	10 01	p2.4	3 16	3 34	3.1
10	S	9 46	10 25	p2.3	3 36	3 54	p3.2	10	T	10 36	11 00	p2.3	4 13	4 33	2.8
11	M	10 53	11 25	p2.3	4 35	4 55	2.9	11	W	11 37	11 55	p2.3	5 09	5 33	a2.7
12	T	11 55	...	2.2	5 34	5 56	2.7	12	T	...	12 35	2.3	6 06	6 32	a2.7
13	W	12 22	12 54	a2.4	6 32	6 56	2.7	13	F	12 49	1 30	p2.4	7 02	7 30	a2.8
14	T	1 16	1 50	2.5	7 29	7 54	a2.9	14	S	1 40	2 22	p2.5	7 55	8 24	a3.0
15	F	2 07	2 43	p2.7	8 21	8 47	a3.1	15	S	2 28	3 11	p2.6	8 45	9 14	a3.0
16	S	2 56	3 32	p2.7	9 11	9 37	a3.1	16	M	3 15	3 57	p2.6	9 31	10 01	a3.0
17	S	3 42	4 20	p2.7	9 57	10 26	a3.1	17	T	4 00	4 41	p2.5	10 16	10 47	a3.0
18	M	4 27	5 06	p2.6	10 43	11 13	a3.1	18	W	4 43	5 24	p2.3	10 59	11 31	a3.0
19	T	5 11	5 50	p2.4	11 28	11 59	a3.0	19	T	5 26	6 05	p2.1	11 42	...	3.0
20	W	5 55	6 34	p2.2	...	12 12	3.0	20	F	6 09	6 45	p2.0	12 14	12 23	p3.0
21	T	6 39	7 18	p2.0	12 44	12 55	p2.9	21	S	6 52	7 25	p2.0	12 57	1 04	p3.0
22	F	7 25	8 02	p1.9	1 28	1 38	p2.8	22	S	7 36	8 06	p2.0	1 38	1 45	p3.0
23	S	8 12	8 49	p1.8	2 12	2 21	p2.7	23	M	8 22	8 49	p2.0	2 20	2 26	p3.0
24	S	9 03	9 36	p1.8	2 56	3 05	p2.6	24	T	9 12	9 34	p2.1	3 02	3 10	p2.9
25	M	9 54	10 22	p1.9	3 41	3 50	p2.6	25	W	10 04	10 21	p2.2	3 45	3 58	p2.9
26	T	10 44	11 07	p2.0	4 26	4 37	p2.6	26	T	10 56	11 08	p2.2	4 31	4 50	2.8
27	W	11 33	11 50	p2.1	5 12	5 27	p2.6	27	F	11 47	11 57	p2.3	5 19	5 47	a2.9
28	T	...	12 21	2.0	6 00	6 20	2.7	28	S	...	12 39	2.1	6 12	6 46	a3.1
29	F	12 35	1 09	a2.2	6 49	7 15	2.9	29	S	12 47	1 32	a2.3	7 07	7 45	a3.3
30	S	1 20	1 57	a2.3	7 38	8 09	a3.2	30	M	1 39	2 25	a2.4	8 01	8 41	a3.5
								31	T	2 32	3 17	a2.5	8 55	9 35	a3.7

See the Woods Hole Current Diagram inset on pp. 66-77.

Mariners should exercise great caution when transiting Woods Hole Passage as velocities have been reported to exceed NOAA's predictions.

CAUTION: Going *from* Buzzards Bay *into* Vineyard Sound, whether through Woods Hole, or Robinsons Hole or Quicks Hole, *Red* Buoys must be kept on the LEFT or PORT hand, *Green* Buoys kept on the RIGHT or STARBOARD hand. You are considered to be proceeding seaward and should thus follow the rules for LEAVING a harbor.

See pp. 22-29 for Current Change at other points.

My dear Captain and M. Mate,

As I cannot talk with you, I will do the next best thing. I will write you a letter.

Do you know, Captain and M. Mate of a place on the Atlantic Coast that is called "The Graveyard"? I propose to tell you something about it; and do what I can to keep vessels out of it. "The Graveyard" so called, is that part of the coast which lies — between Sow and Pigs Rocks and Naushon Island. This place has been called "The Graveyard" for many years, — because many a good craft has laid her bones there, and many a captain has lost his reputation there also. If a vessel gets into this graveyard, there must be a cause for it. Did it ever occur to you that seldom does a vessel go ashore on Gay Head, or on the south side of the Sound? but that hundreds of them have been piled up in "The Graveyard", or on the north side of the Sound? I will explain why this is so. If you are bound into Vineyard Sound in thick weather, you will probably refer to the "Gay Head and Cross Rip" table in this book, to see when the tide turns in or out. You will notice at the — head of each table that it says, "This table shows the time that the current turns Easterly and —. Westerly, off Gay Head in ship channel." That — means off Gay Head when it bears about South. Now, as a rule, captains figure on the current; after they leave the Lightship, as running East-erly into the Sound, when as a matter of fact the first of the flood between the Lightship and Gay Head runs nearly North; and the current does not begin to run to the eastward until you are well into the Sound, as shewn by the chart on the opposite page. Vessels bound into — Vineyard Sound from the Westward will have the current of ebb on the starboard bow. (see arrows on the hulls in the chart on the opposite page)

I have explained this matter, and I leave the rest to your judgment and careful consideration; and thus you will undoubtedly keep your vessel out of "The Graveyard". Yours for a fair tide,

Geo. W. Eldridge.

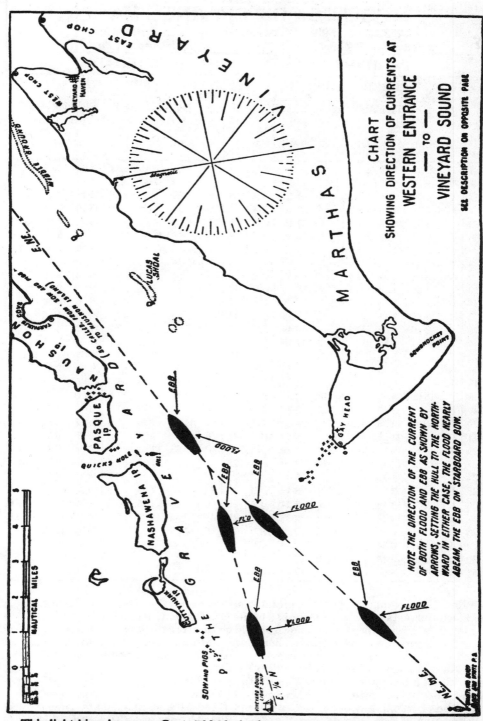

CHART
SHOWING DIRECTION OF CURRENTS AT
WESTERN ENTRANCE
— to —
VINEYARD SOUND

SEE DESCRIPTION ON OPPOSITE PAGE

NOTE THE DIRECTION OF THE CURRENT
OF BOTH FLOOD AND EBB AS SHOWN BY
ARROWS, SETTING THE HULL TO THE NORTH-
WARD IN EITHER CASE, THE FLOOD NEARLY
ABEAM, THE EBB ON STARBOARD BOW.

This lightship, shown on Capt. Eldridge's chart, on the western edge, was replaced many years ago by a buoy.

2013 CURRENT TABLE
POLLOCK RIP CHANNEL, MA
41°33'N, 69°59'W SE of Monomoy Pt. at Butler Hole
Standard Time Standard Time

DAY OF MONTH	DAY OF WEEK	NORTHEAST Flood Starts			SOUTHWEST Ebb Starts			DAY OF MONTH	DAY OF WEEK	NORTHEAST Flood Starts			SOUTHWEST Ebb Starts		
		a.m.	**p.m.**	Kts.	a.m.	**p.m.**	Kts.			a.m.	**p.m.**	Kts.	a.m.	**p.m.**	Kts.
		JANUARY								**FEBRUARY**					
1	T	5 31	**5 40**	p2.2	11 53	...	1.9	1	F	6 21	**6 40**	2.1	12 36	**12 55**	2.0
2	W	6 11	**6 23**	p2.1	12 27	**12 37**	1.9	2	S	7 09	**7 31**	2.0	1 22	**1 48**	a1.9
3	T	6 56	**7 10**	p2.1	1 10	**1 25**	1.9	3	S	8 02	**8 29**	a1.9	2 13	**2 47**	a1.8
4	F	7 43	**8 00**	p2.0	1 57	**2 18**	1.8	4	M	9 01	**9 33**	a1.9	3 10	**3 51**	a1.7
5	S	8 35	**8 56**	p1.9	2 47	**3 15**	a1.8	5	T	10 06	**10 42**	a1.8	4 11	**4 58**	a1.7
6	S	9 32	**9 57**	1.8	3 41	**4 16**	a1.7	6	W	11 13	**11 51**	a1.9	5 16	**6 04**	a1.6
7	M	10 31	**11 00**	a1.9	4 37	**5 18**	a1.7	7	T	...	**12 18**	2.0	6 19	**7 06**	a1.7
8	T	11 32	...	2.0	5 36	**6 19**	a1.7	8	F	12 56	**1 19**	p2.2	7 18	**8 03**	a1.8
9	W	12 04	**12 31**	p2.1	6 33	**7 19**	a1.8	9	S	1 55	**2 15**	p2.3	8 14	**8 55**	a1.9
10	T	1 06	**1 29**	p2.2	7 30	**8 15**	a1.9	10	S	2 48	**3 07**	p2.4	9 06	**9 44**	a2.0
11	F	2 04	**2 24**	p2.3	8 24	**9 08**	a2.0	11	M	3 37	**3 55**	p2.4	9 56	**10 30**	a2.0
12	S	2 58	**3 17**	p2.4	9 17	**9 59**	a2.0	12	T	4 23	**4 42**	p2.3	10 44	**11 15**	a2.0
13	S	3 50	**4 08**	p2.4	10 08	**10 49**	a2.1	13	W	5 08	**5 28**	2.2	11 32	...	2.0
14	M	4 41	**4 58**	p2.4	11 00	**11 38**	a2.0	14	T	5 54	**6 14**	2.1	12 01	**12 21**	a1.9
15	T	5 31	**5 49**	p2.3	11 52	...	2.0	15	F	6 40	**7 02**	a2.0	12 47	**1 11**	a1.8
16	W	6 22	**6 40**	p2.2	12 28	**12 45**	1.9	16	S	7 29	**7 54**	a1.9	1 35	**2 05**	a1.7
17	T	7 14	**7 34**	2.0	1 19	**1 41**	a1.8	17	S	8 22	**8 49**	a1.8	2 26	**3 01**	a1.6
18	F	8 08	**8 30**	1.9	2 11	**2 39**	a1.7	18	M	9 17	**9 48**	a1.8	3 20	**3 59**	a1.5
19	S	9 04	**9 28**	a1.9	3 05	**3 38**	a1.6	19	T	10 15	**10 47**	a1.8	4 16	**4 57**	a1.5
20	S	10 02	**10 28**	a1.9	4 00	**4 38**	a1.6	20	W	11 11	**11 44**	a1.9	5 12	**5 52**	a1.5
21	M	10 58	**11 26**	a1.9	4 55	**5 35**	a1.6	21	T	...	**12 04**	2.0	6 05	**6 43**	a1.6
22	T	11 52	...	2.0	5 49	**6 29**	a1.6	22	F	12 35	**12 52**	p2.1	6 54	**7 30**	a1.7
23	W	12 20	**12 41**	p2.1	6 39	**7 19**	a1.6	23	S	1 21	**1 35**	p2.2	7 40	**8 12**	a1.9
24	T	1 10	**1 26**	p2.2	7 26	**8 04**	a1.7	24	S	2 02	**2 15**	p2.2	8 21	**8 51**	a1.9
25	F	1 54	**2 08**	p2.2	8 10	**8 45**	a1.8	25	M	2 40	**2 53**	p2.3	9 01	**9 29**	a2.0
26	S	2 35	**2 46**	p2.2	8 50	**9 24**	1.8	26	T	3 16	**3 30**	p2.3	9 39	**10 05**	2.0
27	S	3 12	**3 22**	p2.3	9 29	**10 01**	1.9	27	W	3 52	**4 07**	p2.3	10 18	**10 43**	2.1
28	M	3 48	**3 58**	p2.3	10 07	**10 37**	a2.0	28	T	4 29	**4 47**	p2.3	10 59	**11 22**	2.1
29	T	4 23	**4 34**	p2.3	10 45	**11 15**	2.0								
30	W	5 00	**5 13**	p2.3	11 25	**11 54**	a2.1								
31	T	5 39	**5 54**	p2.2	...	**12 08**	2.0								

The Kts. (knots) columns show the **maximum** predicted velocities of the stronger one of the Flood Currents and the stronger one of the Ebb Currents for each day.

The letter "a" means the velocity shown should occur **after** the a.m. Current Change. The letter "p" means the velocity shown should occur **after** the p.m. Current Change (even if next morning). No "a" or "p" means a.m. and p.m. velocities are the same for that day.

Avg. Max. Velocity: Flood 2.0 Kts., Ebb 1.8 Kts.

Max. Flood 3 hrs. 20 min. after Flood Starts, ±15 min.

Max. Ebb 2 hrs. 45 min. after Ebb Starts, ±15 min.

Gay Head (1 1/2 mi. NW of): avg. max velocity, Flood 2.0 kts., Ebb 2.0 kts. Time of Flood and Ebb 1 hr. 35 min. after Pollock Rip. Cross Rip: avg. max. velocity, Flood 1.3 kts., Ebb 0.9 kts. Time of Flood and Ebb 1 hr. 50 min. after Pollock Rip. Use POLLOCK RIP tables with current charts on pp. 66-77. See pp. 22-29 for Current Change at other points.

2013 CURRENT TABLE
POLLOCK RIP CHANNEL, MA
41°33'N, 69°59'W SE of Monomoy Pt. at Butler Hole

*Daylight Time starts March 10 at 2 a.m.   **Daylight Saving Time**

DAY OF MONTH	DAY OF WEEK	MARCH CURRENT TURNS TO — NORTHEAST Flood Starts a.m.	**p.m.**	Kts.	SOUTHWEST Ebb Starts a.m.	**p.m.**	Kts.	DAY OF MONTH	DAY OF WEEK	APRIL CURRENT TURNS TO — NORTHEAST Flood Starts a.m.	**p.m.**	Kts.	SOUTHWEST Ebb Starts a.m.	**p.m.**	Kts.
1	F	5 08	**5 29**	2.2	11 42	...	2.1	1	M	7 19	**7 55**	a2.2	1 29	**2 08**	a2.0
2	S	5 52	**6 16**	a2.2	12 05	**12 31**	a2.1	2	T	8 17	**8 58**	a2.0	2 26	**3 11**	a1.8
3	S	6 41	**7 10**	a2.1	12 52	**1 25**	a2.0	3	W	9 23	**10 09**	a1.9	3 30	**4 18**	a1.7
4	M	7 35	**8 10**	a2.0	1 46	**2 26**	a1.9	4	T	10 34	**11 21**	a1.9	4 39	**5 26**	a1.6
5	T	8 38	**9 18**	a1.9	2 47	**3 33**	a1.7	5	F	11 46	...	2.0	5 48	**6 32**	1.5
6	W	9 48	**10 31**	a1.8	3 53	**4 42**	a1.6	6	S	12 30	**12 54**	p2.1	6 54	**7 33**	p1.7
7	T	10 59	**11 42**	a1.9	5 01	**5 49**	a1.6	7	S	1 32	**1 54**	p2.2	7 54	**8 27**	p1.8
8	F	...	**12 07**	2.1	6 07	**6 52**	1.6	8	M	2 26	**2 48**	p2.3	8 49	**9 16**	p1.9
9	S	12 47	**1 09**	p2.2	7 08	**7 48**	1.7	9	T	3 15	**3 37**	p2.3	9 38	**10 01**	1.9
10	S	1 43	***3 04**	p2.3	*9 03	***9 38**	a1.9	10	W	3 58	**4 20**	a2.3	10 24	**10 42**	1.9
11	M	3 34	**3 54**	p2.4	9 54	**10 24**	1.9	11	T	4 38	**5 01**	a2.3	11 08	**11 22**	p1.9
12	T	4 19	**4 39**	p2.3	10 41	**11 08**	a2.0	12	F	5 17	**5 41**	a2.2	11 50	...	1.8
13	W	5 02	**5 23**	2.2	11 27	**11 50**	a2.0	13	S	5 55	**6 21**	a2.1	12 02	**12 32**	a1.8
14	T	5 43	**6 05**	a2.2	...	**12 11**	1.9	14	S	6 35	**7 03**	a2.1	12 43	**1 16**	a1.8
15	F	6 24	**6 47**	a2.1	12 31	**12 56**	a1.9	15	M	7 17	**7 48**	a2.0	1 27	**2 02**	a1.7
16	S	7 06	**7 31**	a2.0	1 14	**1 43**	a1.8	16	T	8 03	**8 38**	a1.9	2 14	**2 51**	a1.6
17	S	7 51	**8 19**	a1.9	2 00	**2 32**	a1.7	17	W	8 53	**9 31**	a1.9	3 05	**3 43**	a1.6
18	M	8 40	**9 12**	a1.9	2 48	**3 25**	a1.6	18	T	9 47	**10 27**	a1.8	3 59	**4 36**	1.5
19	T	9 34	**10 09**	a1.8	3 41	**4 21**	a1.5	19	F	10 42	**11 21**	a1.9	4 54	**5 29**	1.5
20	W	10 30	**11 07**	a1.8	4 37	**5 17**	a1.5	20	S	11 36	...	1.9	5 49	**6 20**	p1.6
21	T	11 27	...	1.9	5 34	**6 12**	a1.5	21	S	12 13	**12 29**	p2.0	6 41	**7 09**	p1.7
22	F	12 04	**12 21**	p1.9	6 28	**7 03**	1.5	22	M	1 01	**1 18**	p2.0	7 30	**7 54**	p1.8
23	S	12 56	**1 12**	p2.0	7 19	**7 51**	1.6	23	T	1 46	**2 04**	p2.1	8 16	**8 37**	p1.9
24	S	1 43	**1 58**	p2.1	8 06	**8 34**	p1.8	24	W	2 28	**2 48**	2.1	9 00	**9 18**	p2.0
25	M	2 26	**2 41**	p2.2	8 50	**9 15**	p1.9	25	T	3 09	**3 32**	2.2	9 44	**10 00**	p2.1
26	T	3 05	**3 21**	p2.2	9 31	**9 54**	2.0	26	F	3 50	**4 16**	a2.3	10 29	**10 43**	p2.2
27	W	3 42	**4 00**	p2.3	10 11	**10 32**	2.1	27	S	4 33	**5 02**	a2.4	11 15	**11 28**	p2.2
28	T	4 20	**4 41**	2.3	10 52	**11 11**	p2.2	28	S	5 19	**5 52**	a2.4	...	**12 04**	2.1
29	F	4 59	**5 23**	a2.3	11 35	**11 53**	p2.2	29	M	6 09	**6 45**	a2.3	12 17	**12 58**	a2.1
30	S	5 41	**6 08**	a2.4	...	**12 21**	2.1	30	T	7 03	**7 44**	a2.2	1 11	**1 55**	a2.0
31	S	6 27	**6 59**	a2.3	12 38	**1 12**	a2.1								

The Kts. (knots) columns show the **maximum** predicted velocities of the stronger one of the Flood Currents and the stronger one of the Ebb Currents for each day.

The letter "a" means the velocity shown should occur **after** the **a.m.** Current Change. The letter "p" means the velocity shown should occur **after** the **p.m.** Current Change (even if next morning). No "a" or "p" means a.m. and p.m. velocities are the same for that day.

Avg. Max. Velocity: Flood 2.0 Kts., Ebb 1.8 Kts.

Max. Flood 3 hrs. 20 min. after Flood Starts, ±15 min.

Max. Ebb 2 hrs. 45 min. after Ebb Starts, ±15 min.

Gay Head (1 1/2 mi. NW of): avg. max velocity, Flood 2.0 kts., Ebb 2.0 kts. Time of Flood and Ebb 1 hr. 35 min. after Pollock Rip. Cross Rip: avg. max. velocity, Flood 1.3 kts., Ebb 0.9 kts. Time of Flood and Ebb 1 hr. 50 min. after Pollock Rip. Use POLLOCK RIP tables with current charts on pp. 66-77. See pp. 22-29 for Current Change at other points.

2013 CURRENT TABLE
POLLOCK RIP CHANNEL, MA

41°33'N, 69°59'W SE of Monomoy Pt. at Butler Hole

Daylight Saving Time   Daylight Saving Time

		MAY						JUNE			
		CURRENT TURNS TO						CURRENT TURNS TO			
DAY OF MONTH	DAY OF WEEK	NORTHEAST Flood Starts			SOUTHWEST Ebb Starts			DAY OF MONTH	DAY OF WEEK	NORTHEAST Flood Starts		
		a.m.	p.m.	Kts.	a.m.	p.m.	Kts.			a.m.	p.m.	Kts.	a.m.	p.m.	Kts.

2013 CURRENT TABLE
POLLOCK RIP CHANNEL, MA

41°33'N, 69°59'W SE of Monomoy Pt. at Butler Hole

Daylight Saving Time   Daylight Saving Time

MAY

Day of Month	Day of Week	Flood Starts a.m.	Flood Starts p.m.	Kts.	Ebb Starts a.m.	Ebb Starts p.m.	Kts.
1	W	8 03	8 48	a2.1	2 10	2 57	a1.8
2	T	9 09	9 57	a2.0	3 15	4 02	a1.7
3	F	10 20	11 07	a2.0	4 23	5 07	1.6
4	S	11 28	...	2.0	5 31	6 10	1.6
5	S	12 11	12 34	p2.1	6 36	7 08	p1.7
6	M	1 11	1 34	p2.2	7 36	8 02	p1.8
7	T	2 04	2 27	2.2	8 30	8 50	1.8
8	W	2 52	3 15	a2.3	9 20	9 35	1.8
9	T	3 34	3 59	a2.3	10 05	10 16	1.8
10	F	4 14	4 39	a2.2	10 48	10 56	p1.8
11	S	4 51	5 18	a2.2	11 28	11 35	p1.8
12	S	5 28	5 56	a2.1	...	12 09	1.7
13	M	6 06	6 37	a2.1	12 15	12 50	a1.8
14	T	6 46	7 19	a2.0	12 57	1 33	a1.7
15	W	7 29	8 06	a2.0	1 42	2 19	a1.7
16	T	8 16	8 55	a2.0	2 30	3 06	a1.7
17	F	9 06	9 46	a1.9	3 21	3 56	1.6
18	S	9 58	10 38	a1.9	4 14	4 46	1.6
19	S	10 51	11 29	a1.9	5 08	5 37	p1.7
20	M	11 44	...	1.9	6 01	6 26	p1.7
21	T	12 18	12 37	1.9	6 52	7 13	p1.8
22	W	1 06	1 27	2.0	7 43	8 00	p1.9
23	T	1 53	2 17	a2.1	8 32	8 45	p2.0
24	F	2 39	3 06	a2.2	9 20	9 31	p2.1
25	S	3 25	3 55	a2.3	10 09	10 19	p2.1
26	S	4 13	4 46	a2.4	10 59	11 08	p2.1
27	M	5 03	5 38	a2.4	11 50	...	2.0
28	T	5 55	6 34	a2.4	12 01	12 44	a2.1
29	W	6 51	7 33	a2.3	12 56	1 41	a2.0
30	T	7 51	8 34	a2.2	1 56	2 40	a1.9
31	F	8 54	9 39	a2.1	2 59	3 41	a1.8

JUNE

Day of Month	Day of Week	Flood Starts a.m.	Flood Starts p.m.	Kts.	Ebb Starts a.m.	Ebb Starts p.m.	Kts.
1	S	9 59	10 43	a2.1	4 04	4 42	1.7
2	S	11 05	11 46	2.0	5 10	5 42	p1.7
3	M	...	12 10	2.0	6 13	6 39	p1.7
4	T	12 44	1 08	2.1	7 13	7 33	p1.8
5	W	1 37	2 02	a2.2	8 08	8 22	p1.8
6	T	2 25	2 51	a2.2	8 58	9 07	p1.8
7	F	3 09	3 36	a2.2	9 44	9 50	p1.8
8	S	3 49	4 16	a2.2	10 26	10 30	p1.8
9	S	4 27	4 54	a2.2	11 06	11 09	p1.8
10	M	5 03	5 32	a2.2	11 45	11 48	p1.8
11	T	5 40	6 10	a2.1	...	12 24	1.7
12	W	6 18	6 50	a2.1	12 29	1 04	a1.8
13	T	6 58	7 32	a2.1	1 11	1 46	a1.8
14	F	7 41	8 17	a2.1	1 56	2 30	1.8
15	S	8 27	9 04	a2.0	2 44	3 16	1.7
16	S	9 17	9 54	a2.0	3 34	4 04	1.7
17	M	10 09	10 45	a1.9	4 28	4 54	1.7
18	T	11 03	11 37	1.9	5 22	5 45	p1.8
19	W	11 59	...	1.8	6 18	6 36	p1.8
20	T	12 30	12 55	a2.0	7 13	7 27	p1.9
21	F	1 22	1 51	a2.1	8 07	8 18	p1.9
22	S	2 14	2 45	a2.2	9 00	9 09	p2.0
23	S	3 06	3 39	a2.3	9 52	10 01	p2.1
24	M	3 58	4 32	a2.4	10 45	10 53	p2.1
25	T	4 50	5 26	a2.4	11 37	11 46	p2.1
26	W	5 43	6 20	a2.4	...	12 29	1.9
27	T	6 38	7 16	a2.3	12 41	1 23	a2.0
28	F	7 35	8 14	a2.2	1 39	2 19	a1.9
29	S	8 33	9 13	a2.1	2 39	3 15	1.8
30	S	9 34	10 14	a2.0	3 40	4 13	1.7

The Kts. (knots) columns show the **maximum** predicted velocities of the stronger one of the Flood Currents and the stronger one of the Ebb Currents for each day.

The letter "a" means the velocity shown should occur **after** the **a.m.** Current Change. The letter "p" means the velocity shown should occur **after** the **p.m.** Current Change (even if next morning). No "a" or "p" means a.m. and p.m. velocities are the same for that day.

Avg. Max. Velocity: Flood 2.0 Kts., Ebb 1.8 Kts.

Max. Flood 3 hrs. 20 min. after Flood Starts, ±15 min.

Max. Ebb 2 hrs. 45 min. after Ebb Starts, ±15 min.

Gay Head (1 1/2 mi. NW of): avg. max velocity, Flood 2.0 kts., Ebb 2.0 kts. Time of Flood and Ebb 1 hr. 35 min. after Pollock Rip. Cross Rip: avg. max. velocity, Flood 1.3 kts., Ebb 0.9 kts. Time of Flood and Ebb 1 hr. 50 min. after Pollock Rip. Use POLLOCK RIP tables with current charts on pp. 66-77. See pp. 22-29 for Current Change at other points.

2013 CURRENT TABLE
POLLOCK RIP CHANNEL, MA

41°33'N, 69°59'W SE of Monomoy Pt. at Butler Hole

Daylight Saving Time **Daylight Saving Time**

Day of Month	Day of Week	JULY — NORTHEAST Flood Starts a.m.	p.m.	Kts.	JULY — SOUTHWEST Ebb Starts a.m.	p.m.	Kts.	Day of Month	Day of Week	AUGUST — NORTHEAST Flood Starts a.m.	p.m.	Kts.	AUGUST — SOUTHWEST Ebb Starts a.m.	p.m.	Kts.
1	M	10 37	11 14	2.0	4 43	5 11	p1.7	1	T	...	12 07	1.8	6 14	6 29	p1.6
2	T	11 39	...	1.9	5 46	6 07	p1.7	2	F	12 33	1 03	a2.0	7 11	7 22	p1.6
3	W	12 13	12 40	a2.0	6 46	7 02	p1.7	3	S	1 26	1 56	a2.1	8 02	8 11	p1.7
4	T	1 07	1 34	a2.1	7 41	7 53	p1.7	4	S	2 12	2 41	a2.2	8 49	8 56	p1.8
5	F	1 57	2 25	a2.2	8 32	8 40	p1.7	5	M	2 55	3 22	a2.2	9 31	9 37	p1.8
6	S	2 42	3 10	a2.2	9 19	9 23	p1.8	6	T	3 34	4 00	a2.2	10 10	10 16	p1.9
7	S	3 23	3 51	a2.2	10 01	10 04	p1.8	7	W	4 10	4 35	a2.2	10 47	10 54	p1.9
8	M	4 02	4 29	a2.2	10 40	10 43	p1.8	8	T	4 46	5 10	a2.2	11 23	11 32	p2.0
9	T	4 38	5 05	a2.2	11 18	11 22	p1.8	9	F	5 21	5 45	a2.2	...	12 01	1.9
10	W	5 14	5 42	a2.2	11 55	...	1.8	10	S	5 58	6 22	a2.2	12 11	12 37	2.0
11	T	5 50	6 19	a2.2	12 01	12 33	a1.9	11	S	6 37	7 02	a2.2	12 52	1 17	2.0
12	F	6 28	6 58	a2.2	12 41	1 12	1.9	12	M	7 20	7 46	a2.1	1 36	2 01	1.9
13	S	7 09	7 39	a2.1	1 23	1 53	1.9	13	T	8 08	8 36	2.0	2 25	2 49	1.9
14	S	7 52	8 24	a2.1	2 08	2 37	1.9	14	W	9 01	9 31	p1.9	3 20	3 42	p1.8
15	M	8 40	9 12	a2.0	2 58	3 25	1.8	15	T	10 01	10 32	p1.8	4 21	4 40	p1.7
16	T	9 32	10 05	1.9	3 51	4 15	p1.8	16	F	11 07	11 37	p1.9	5 25	5 42	p1.7
17	W	10 28	11 01	p1.9	4 48	5 09	p1.7	17	S	...	12 15	1.7	6 29	6 45	p1.7
18	T	11 28	...	1.7	5 48	6 05	p1.7	18	S	12 42	1 20	a2.0	7 31	7 45	p1.8
19	F	12 01	12 30	a1.9	6 48	7 02	p1.8	19	M	1 44	2 20	a2.1	8 30	8 42	p1.9
20	S	12 59	1 32	a2.0	7 47	7 59	p1.9	20	T	2 42	3 15	a2.3	9 23	9 36	p2.0
21	S	1 57	2 31	a2.1	8 44	8 54	p1.9	21	W	3 36	4 06	a2.4	10 14	10 27	p2.1
22	M	2 53	3 27	a2.3	9 38	9 47	p2.0	22	T	4 26	4 54	a2.4	11 02	11 17	p2.1
23	T	3 46	4 20	a2.4	10 30	10 40	p2.1	23	F	5 15	5 42	a2.4	11 49	...	2.0
24	W	4 39	5 12	a2.4	11 21	11 32	p2.1	24	S	6 03	6 29	a2.3	12 07	12 36	a2.0
25	T	5 31	6 03	a2.4	...	12 11	2.0	25	S	6 52	7 17	2.1	12 57	1 23	a1.9
26	F	6 22	6 54	a2.3	12 25	1 01	a2.0	26	M	7 42	8 08	2.0	1 50	2 13	a1.8
27	S	7 15	7 47	a2.2	1 19	1 52	1.9	27	T	8 35	9 02	p1.9	2 44	3 06	1.6
28	S	8 09	8 42	a2.1	2 15	2 45	1.9	28	W	9 32	9 59	p1.9	3 42	4 01	1.5
29	M	9 06	9 39	a2.0	3 13	3 40	1.7	29	T	10 32	10 57	p1.9	4 41	4 58	p1.5
30	T	10 05	10 38	p1.9	4 13	4 37	p1.6	30	F	11 32	11 55	p1.9	5 40	5 55	p1.5
31	W	11 06	11 37	p2.0	5 15	5 34	p1.6	31	S	...	12 29	1.8	6 36	6 49	p1.6

The Kts. (knots) columns show the **maximum** predicted velocities of the stronger one of the Flood Currents and the stronger one of the Ebb Currents for each day.

The letter "a" means the velocity shown should occur **after** the **a.m.** Current Change. The letter "p" means the velocity shown should occur **after** the **p.m.** Current Change (even if next morning). No "a" or "p" means a.m. and p.m. velocities are the same for that day.

Avg. Max. Velocity: Flood 2.0 Kts., Ebb 1.8 Kts.

Max. Flood 3 hrs. 20 min. after Flood Starts, ±15 min.

Max. Ebb 2 hrs. 45 min. after Ebb Starts, ±15 min.

Gay Head (1 1/2 mi. NW of): avg. max velocity, Flood 2.0 kts., Ebb 2.0 kts. Time of Flood and Ebb 1 hr. 35 min. after Pollock Rip. Cross Rip: avg. max. velocity, Flood 1.3 kts., Ebb 0.9 kts. Time of Flood and Ebb 1 hr. 50 min. after Pollock Rip. Use POLLOCK RIP tables with current charts on pp. 66-77. See pp. 22-29 for Current Change at other points.

2013 CURRENT TABLE
POLLOCK RIP CHANNEL, MA

41°33'N, 69°59'W SE of Monomoy Pt. at Butler Hole

Daylight Saving Time   Daylight Saving Time

		SEPTEMBER							OCTOBER				
		CURRENT TURNS TO							CURRENT TURNS TO				
DAY OF MONTH	DAY OF WEEK	NORTHEAST Flood Starts			SOUTHWEST Ebb Starts			DAY OF MONTH	DAY OF WEEK	NORTHEAST Flood Starts			SOUTHWEST Ebb Starts
		a.m.	p.m.	Kts.	a.m.	p.m.	Kts.			a.m.	p.m.	Kts.	a.m.	p.m.	Kts.
1	S	12 49	1 21	a2.0	7 27	7 40	p1.7	1	T	12 58	1 30	a2.1	7 35	7 52	1.7
2	M	1 38	2 08	a2.1	8 14	8 25	p1.7	2	W	1 44	2 12	a2.1	8 18	8 35	1.8
3	T	2 23	2 50	a2.2	8 57	9 08	p1.8	3	T	2 28	2 52	a2.2	8 59	9 16	1.9
4	W	3 02	3 27	a2.2	9 36	9 47	p1.9	4	F	3 06	3 27	2.2	9 37	9 56	2.0
5	T	3 40	4 02	a2.2	10 13	10 25	p2.0	5	S	3 44	4 03	2.2	10 14	10 35	2.1
6	F	4 16	4 36	a2.2	10 49	11 03	2.0	6	S	4 22	4 40	p2.3	10 52	11 16	2.1
7	S	4 52	5 11	2.2	11 25	11 42	p2.1	7	M	5 02	5 19	p2.3	11 31	11 59	2.1
8	S	5 29	5 48	2.2	...	12 03	2.1	8	T	5 45	6 02	p2.3	...	12 14	2.1
9	M	6 09	6 29	2.2	12 23	12 43	a2.1	9	W	6 32	6 50	p2.2	12 47	1 01	2.0
10	T	6 53	7 15	2.1	1 09	1 28	2.0	10	T	7 24	7 44	p2.1	1 40	1 55	1.9
11	W	7 43	8 06	p2.0	2 00	2 18	1.9	11	F	8 24	8 46	p2.0	2 39	2 56	1.7
12	T	8 39	9 05	p1.9	2 57	3 15	1.7	12	S	9 31	9 55	p1.9	3 43	4 02	1.6
13	F	9 43	10 11	p1.8	4 00	4 19	1.6	13	S	10 42	11 06	p1.9	4 50	5 12	p1.6
14	S	10 53	11 21	p1.9	5 07	5 26	p1.6	14	M	11 52	...	1.8	5 56	6 19	1.6
15	S	...	12 04	1.7	6 13	6 32	p1.6	15	T	12 16	12 56	a2.0	6 58	7 21	1.7
16	M	12 29	1 10	a2.0	7 16	7 34	p1.7	16	W	1 20	1 54	a2.2	7 54	8 19	1.8
17	T	1 33	2 09	a2.2	8 14	8 31	p1.9	17	T	2 17	2 45	2.2	8 46	9 11	1.9
18	W	2 31	3 01	a2.3	9 06	9 24	p2.0	18	F	3 09	3 32	p2.3	9 33	10 00	1.9
19	T	3 23	3 50	a2.3	9 55	10 14	p2.0	19	S	3 56	4 15	p2.3	10 18	10 46	1.9
20	F	4 12	4 35	2.3	10 40	11 02	2.0	20	S	4 40	4 56	p2.2	11 00	11 30	a1.9
21	S	4 58	5 19	2.2	11 25	11 48	1.9	21	M	5 22	5 36	p2.2	11 42	...	1.8
22	S	5 43	6 02	p2.2	...	12 09	1.9	22	T	6 04	6 18	p2.1	12 14	12 25	p1.8
23	M	6 28	6 46	p2.1	12 36	12 53	1.8	23	W	6 48	7 01	p2.0	12 59	1 09	p1.7
24	T	7 14	7 33	p2.0	1 24	1 40	1.7	24	T	7 34	7 47	p1.9	1 46	1 57	1.6
25	W	8 04	8 23	p1.9	2 15	2 31	1.6	25	F	8 24	8 38	p1.9	2 36	2 48	1.5
26	T	8 58	9 18	p1.8	3 09	3 25	1.5	26	S	9 18	9 32	p1.8	3 27	3 43	1.5
27	F	9 55	10 15	p1.8	4 05	4 21	1.4	27	S	10 13	10 27	p1.9	4 21	4 39	1.5
28	S	10 54	11 12	p1.9	5 01	5 18	p1.5	28	M	11 08	11 22	p1.9	5 13	5 34	1.5
29	S	11 51	...	1.7	5 56	6 13	1.5	29	T	...	12 01	1.8	6 04	6 26	1.6
30	M	12 07	12 43	a2.0	6 48	7 05	1.6	30	W	12 14	12 48	a2.0	6 52	7 15	1.7
								31	T	1 03	1 32	2.0	7 38	8 01	1.8

The Kts. (knots) columns show the **maximum** predicted velocities of the stronger one of the Flood Currents and the stronger one of the Ebb Currents for each day.

The letter "a" means the velocity shown should occur **after** the **a.m.** Current Change. The letter "p" means the velocity shown should occur **after** the **p.m.** Current Change (even if next morning). No "a" or "p" means a.m. and p.m. velocities are the same for that day.

Avg. Max. Velocity: Flood 2.0 Kts., Ebb 1.8 Kts.

Max. Flood 3 hrs. 20 min. after Flood Starts, ±15 min.

Max. Ebb 2 hrs. 45 min. after Ebb Starts, ±15 min.

Gay Head (1 1/2 mi. NW of): avg. max velocity, Flood 2.0 kts., Ebb 2.0 kts. Time of Flood and Ebb 1 hr. 35 min. after Pollock Rip. Cross Rip: avg. max. velocity, Flood 1.3 kts., Ebb 0.9 kts. Time of Flood and Ebb 1 hr. 50 min. after Pollock Rip. Use POLLOCK RIP tables with current charts on pp. 66-77. See pp. 22-29 for Current Change at other points.

2013 CURRENT TABLE
POLLOCK RIP CHANNEL, MA
41°33'N, 69°59'W SE of Monomoy Pt. at Butler Hole

*Standard Time starts Nov. 3 at 2 a.m.　　　　　　Standard Time

		NOVEMBER						DECEMBER			
		CURRENT TURNS TO						CURRENT TURNS TO			
DAY OF MONTH	DAY OF WEEK	NORTHEAST Flood Starts			SOUTHWEST Ebb Starts		DAY OF MONTH	DAY OF WEEK	NORTHEAST Flood Starts		SOUTHWEST Ebb Starts
		a.m. **p.m.** Kts.			a.m. **p.m.** Kts.				a.m. **p.m.** Kts.		a.m. **p.m.** Kts.
1	F	1 49	**2 13**	2.1	8 20 **8 45** 1.9		1	S	12 58 **1 20** p2.2		7 26 **8 01** a2.0
2	S	2 32	**2 52**	p2.2	9 01 **9 27** a2.0		2	M	1 45 **2 04** p2.3		8 11 **8 48** a2.0
3	S	*2 15	***2 33**	p2.3	*8 41 ***9 10** a2.1		3	T	2 34 **2 51** p2.4		8 56 **9 35** a2.1
4	M	2 56	**3 12**	p2.4	9 21 **9 54** a2.1		4	W	3 20 **3 37** p2.4		9 42 **10 24** a2.2
5	T	3 39	**3 55**	p2.4	10 04 **10 40** a2.2		5	T	4 10 **4 26** p2.4		10 32 **11 15** a2.1
6	W	4 25	**4 41**	p2.4	10 50 **11 30** a2.1		6	F	5 02 **5 19** p2.4		11 25 **...** 2.1
7	T	5 16	**5 32**	p2.3	11 41 **...** 2.0		7	S	5 58 **6 16** p2.3		12 09 **12 21** p2.0
8	F	6 11	**6 29**	p2.2	12 24 **12 37** 1.9		8	S	6 57 **7 16** p2.1		1 06 **1 23** 1.8
9	S	7 12	**7 31**	p2.0	1 23 **1 39** 1.8		9	M	8 00 **8 21** p2.0		2 05 **2 27** 1.7
10	S	8 18	**8 39**	p2.0	2 26 **2 46** a1.7		10	T	9 05 **9 28** p2.0		3 07 **3 34** a1.7
11	M	9 27	**9 50**	p2.0	3 31 **3 55** 1.6		11	W	10 11 **10 36** p2.0		4 09 **4 41** a1.7
12	T	10 35	**10 58**	p2.0	4 35 **5 02** 1.6		12	T	11 14 **11 40** 2.0		5 09 **5 45** a1.7
13	W	11 38	**...**	2.0	5 36 **6 05** 1.7		13	F	... **12 12** 2.1		6 07 **6 44** a1.7
14	T	12 02	**12 35**	p2.2	6 32 **7 03** a1.8		14	S	12 39 **1 04** p2.2		7 00 **7 38** a1.8
15	F	1 00	**1 26**	p2.3	7 24 **7 56** 1.8		15	S	1 32 **1 52** p2.3		7 48 **8 27** a1.8
16	S	1 52	**2 12**	p2.3	8 11 **8 44** a1.9		16	M	2 20 **2 35** p2.3		8 33 **9 11** a1.8
17	S	2 39	**2 55**	p2.3	8 55 **9 29** a1.9		17	T	3 03 **3 14** p2.3		9 15 **9 52** a1.8
18	M	3 22	**3 35**	p2.2	9 37 **10 12** a1.8		18	W	3 43 **3 52** p2.2		9 55 **10 31** a1.8
19	T	4 03	**4 13**	p2.2	10 18 **10 54** a1.8		19	T	4 20 **4 28** p2.2		10 34 **11 10** a1.8
20	W	4 42	**4 52**	p2.1	10 59 **11 35** a1.8		20	F	4 57 **5 05** p2.1		11 14 **11 49** a1.8
21	T	5 23	**5 32**	p2.1	11 41 **...** 1.7		21	S	5 36 **5 44** p2.1		11 55 **...** 1.8
22	F	6 05	**6 15**	p2.0	12 18 **12 25** p1.7		22	S	6 17 **6 25** p2.1		12 29 **12 39** p1.8
23	S	6 50	**7 00**	p2.0	1 03 **1 13** 1.6		23	M	7 00 **7 10** p2.0		1 12 **1 26** a1.8
24	S	7 39	**7 49**	p1.9	1 50 **2 04** 1.6		24	T	7 46 **7 58** p1.9		1 57 **2 15** 1.7
25	M	8 30	**8 41**	p1.9	2 39 **2 57** 1.6		25	W	8 34 **8 48** p1.9		2 44 **3 08** a1.7
26	T	9 21	**9 34**	p1.9	3 29 **3 51** 1.6		26	T	9 24 **9 42** 1.8		3 34 **4 02** a1.7
27	W	10 13	**10 28**	p1.9	4 19 **4 44** 1.6		27	F	10 16 **10 37** 1.8		4 24 **4 57** a1.7
28	T	11 02	**11 20**	p1.9	5 08 **5 36** a1.7		28	S	11 09 **11 33** a1.9		5 15 **5 52** a1.7
29	F	11 50	**...**	2.0	5 56 **6 26** a1.8		29	S	... **12 01** 2.0		6 06 **6 46** a1.8
30	S	12 10	**12 36**	p2.1	6 42 **7 14** a1.9		30	M	12 28 **12 52** p2.1		6 57 **7 38** a1.9
							31	T	1 22 **1 43** p2.3		7 46 **8 29** a2.0

The Kts. (knots) columns show the **maximum** predicted velocities of the stronger one of the Flood Currents and the stronger one of the Ebb Currents for each day.

The letter "a" means the velocity shown should occur **after** the **a.m.** Current Change. The letter "p" means the velocity shown should occur **after** the **p.m.** Current Change (even if next morning). No "a" or "p" means a.m. and p.m. velocities are the same for that day.

Avg. Max. Velocity: Flood 2.0 Kts., Ebb 1.8 Kts.

Max. Flood 3 hrs. 20 min. after Flood Starts, ±15 min.

Max. Ebb 2 hrs. 45 min. after Ebb Starts, ±15 min.

Gay Head (1 1/2 mi. NW of): avg. max velocity, Flood 2.0 kts., Ebb 2.0 kts. Time of Flood and Ebb 1 hr. 35 min. after Pollock Rip. Cross Rip: avg. max. velocity, Flood 1.3 kts., Ebb 0.9 kts. Time of Flood and Ebb 1 hr. 50 min. after Pollock Rip. Use POLLOCK RIP tables with current charts on pp. 66-77. See pp. 22-29 for Current Change at other points.

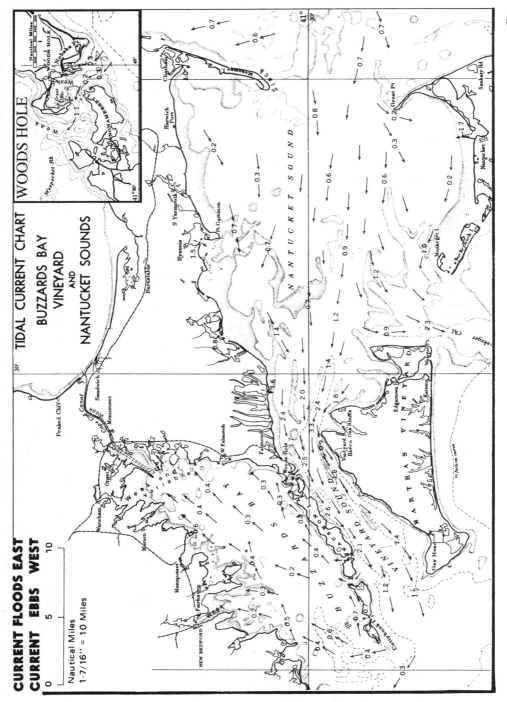

TIDAL CURRENT CHART

BUZZARDS BAY
VINEYARD
AND
NANTUCKET SOUNDS

CURRENT FLOODS EAST
CURRENT EBBS WEST

Nautical Miles
1-7/16" = 10 Miles

0   5   10

FLOOD STARTS AT POLLOCK RIP CHANNEL
OR: 4 HOURS **AFTER** HIGH WATER AT BOSTON

Velocities shown are at Spring Tides. **See Note at bottom of Boston Tables:**
Rule-of-Thumb for Current Velocities. *(Pollock Rip Ch. is SE of Monomoy Pt.)*

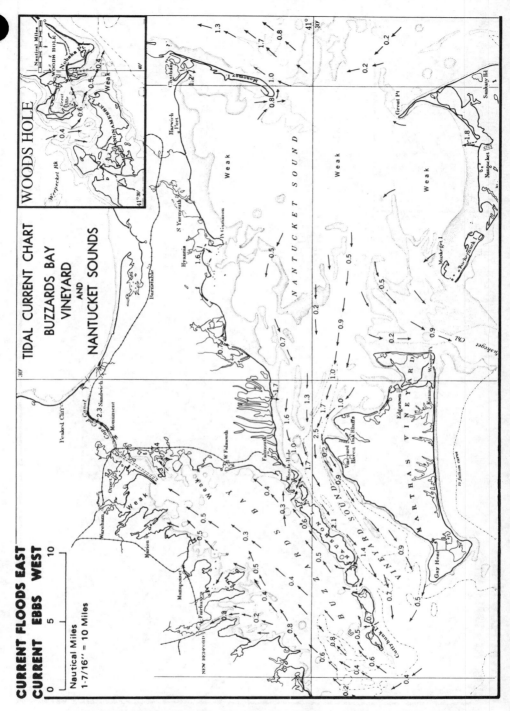

TIDAL CURRENT CHART
BUZZARDS BAY
VINEYARD
AND
NANTUCKET SOUNDS

WOODS HOLE

CURRENT FLOODS EAST
CURRENT EBBS WEST

Nautical Miles
1-7/16'' = 10 Miles

1 HOUR **AFTER** FLOOD STARTS AT POLLOCK RIP CHANNEL
OR: 5 HOURS **AFTER** HIGH WATER AT BOSTON

Velocities shown are at Spring Tides. **See Note at bottom of Boston Tables:**
Rule-of-Thumb for Current Velocities. *(Pollock Rip Ch. is SE of Monomoy Pt.)*

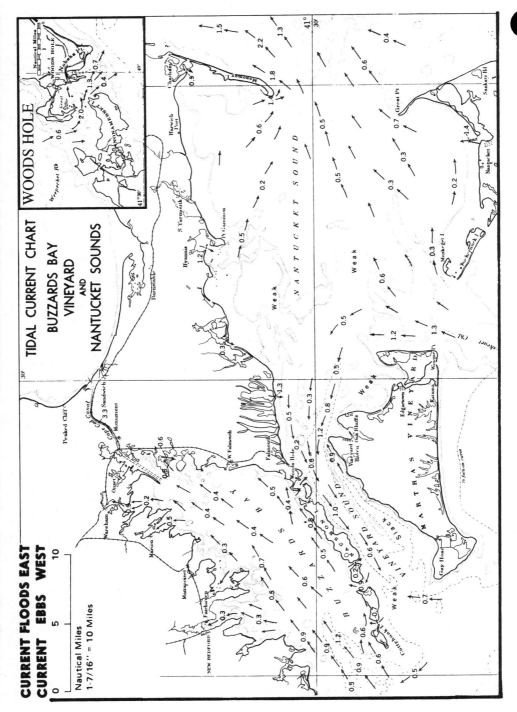

2 HOURS **AFTER** FLOOD STARTS AT POLLOCK RIP CHANNEL
OR: LOW WATER AT BOSTON

Velocities shown are at Spring Tides. **See Note at bottom of Boston Tables:**
Rule-of-Thumb for Current Velocities.   *(Pollock Rip Ch. is SE of Monomoy Pt.)*

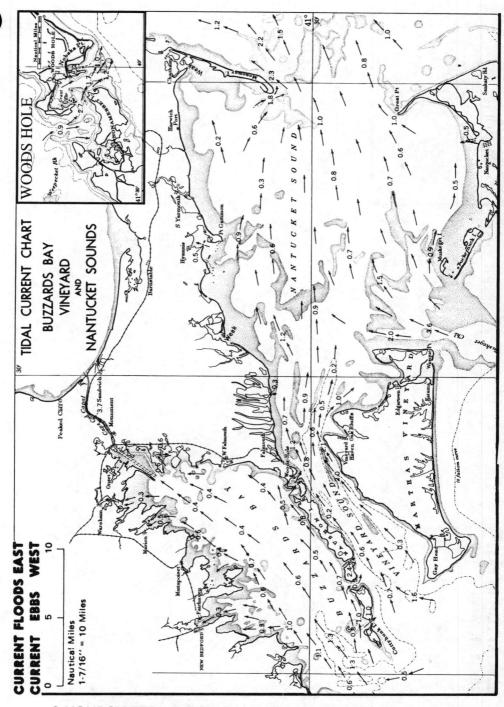

TIDAL CURRENT CHART
BUZZARDS BAY
VINEYARD
AND
NANTUCKET SOUNDS

WOODS HOLE

CURRENT FLOODS EAST
CURRENT EBBS WEST

Nautical Miles
1-7/16'' = 10 Miles

3 HOURS **AFTER** FLOOD STARTS AT POLLOCK RIP CHANNEL
OR: 1 HOUR **AFTER** LOW WATER AT BOSTON

Velocities shown are at Spring Tides. **See Note at bottom of Boston Tables:**
Rule-of-Thumb for Current Velocities.   *(Pollock Rip Ch. is SE of Monomoy Pt.)*

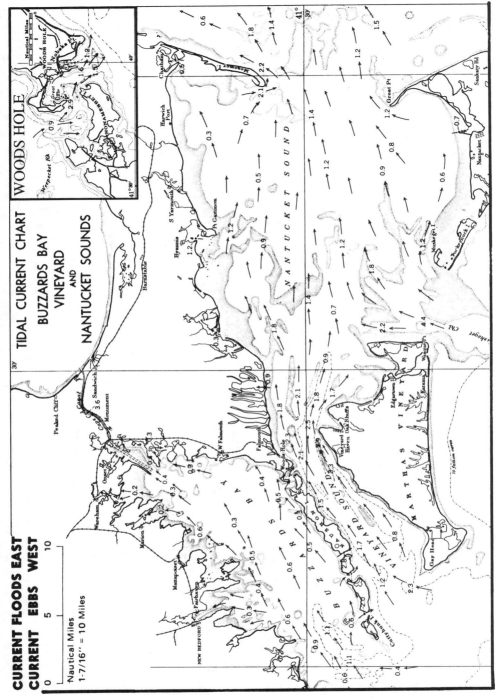

CURRENT FLOODS EAST
CURRENT EBBS WEST

Nautical Miles
1-7/16" = 10 Miles

TIDAL CURRENT CHART
BUZZARDS BAY
VINEYARD
AND
NANTUCKET SOUNDS

WOODS HOLE

4 HOURS **AFTER** FLOOD STARTS AT POLLOCK RIP CHANNEL
OR: 2 HOURS **AFTER** LOW WATER AT BOSTON

Velocities shown are at Spring Tides. **See Note at bottom of Boston Tables:
Rule-of-Thumb for Current Velocities.** *(Pollock Rip Ch. is SE of Monomoy Pt.)*

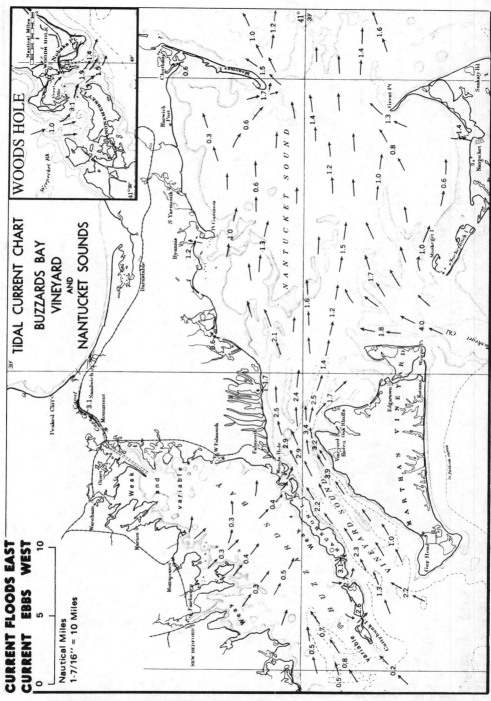

5 HOURS **AFTER** FLOOD STARTS AT POLLOCK RIP CHANNEL
OR: 3 HOURS **AFTER** LOW WATER AT BOSTON

Velocities shown are at Spring Tides. **See Note at bottom of Boston Tables:
Rule-of-Thumb for Current Velocities.** *(Pollock Rip Ch. is SE of Monomoy Pt.)*

71

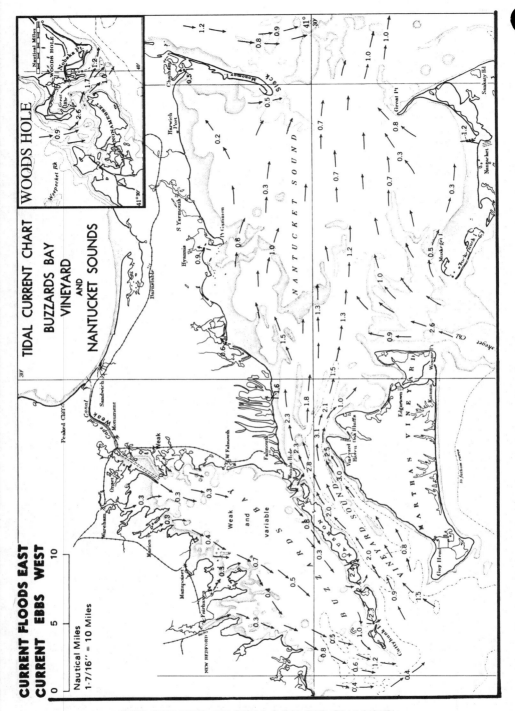

EBB STARTS AT POLLOCK RIP CHANNEL
OR: 4 HOURS **AFTER** LOW WATER AT BOSTON

Velocities shown are at Spring Tides. **See Note at bottom of Boston Tables:**
Rule-of-Thumb for Current Velocities. *(Pollock Rip Ch. is SE of Monomoy Pt.)*

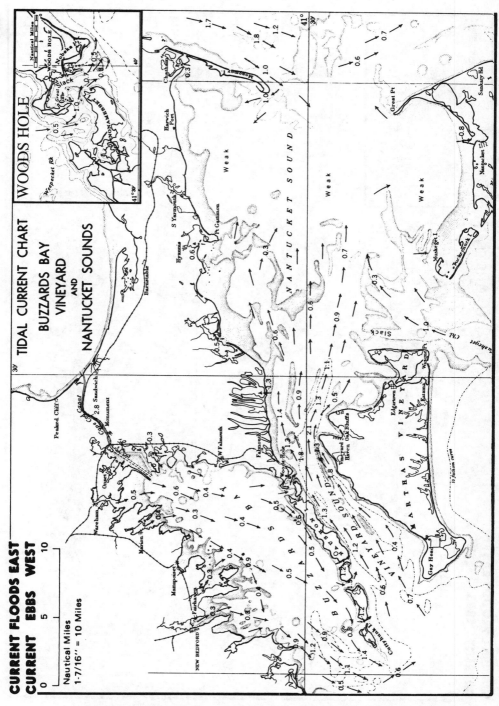

1 HOUR **AFTER** EBB STARTS AT POLLOCK RIP CHANNEL
OR: 5 HOURS **AFTER** LOW WATER AT BOSTON

Velocities shown are at Spring Tides. **See Note at bottom of Boston Tables:
Rule-of-Thumb for Current Velocities.** *(Pollock Rip Ch. is SE of Monomoy Pt.)*

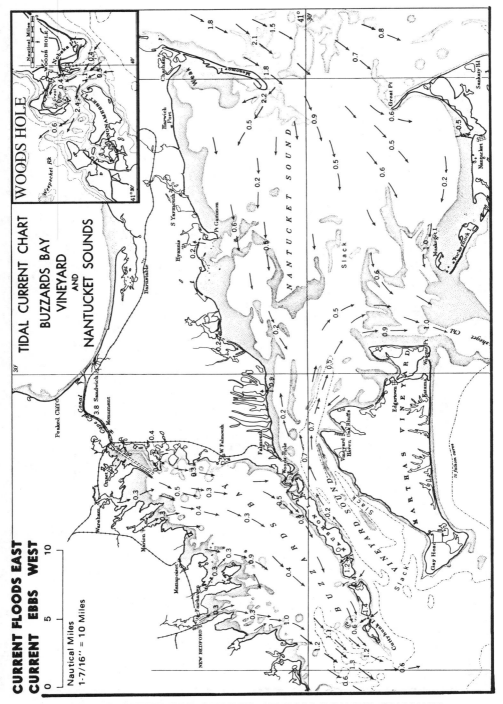

2 HOURS **AFTER** EBB STARTS AT POLLOCK RIP CHANNEL
OR: HIGH WATER AT BOSTON

Velocities shown are at Spring Tides. **See Note at bottom of Boston Tables:**
Rule-of-Thumb for Current Velocities. *(Pollock Rip Ch. is SE of Monomoy Pt.)*

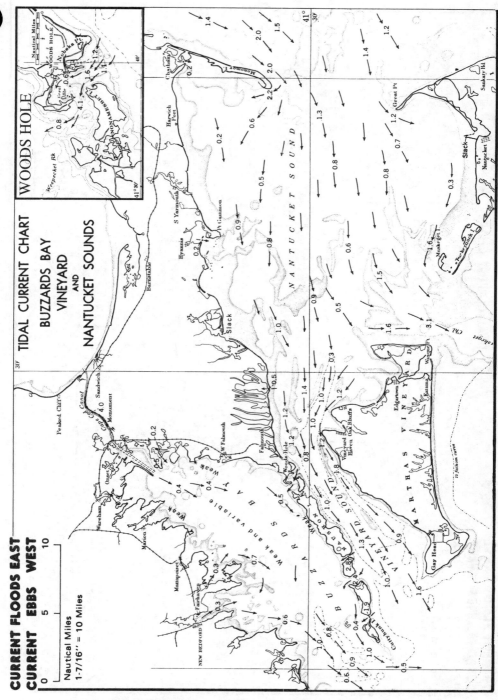

TIDAL CURRENT CHART
BUZZARDS BAY
VINEYARD
AND
NANTUCKET SOUNDS

WOODS HOLE

CURRENT FLOODS EAST
CURRENT EBBS WEST

Nautical Miles
1-7/16″ = 10 Miles

3 HOURS **AFTER** EBB STARTS AT POLLOCK RIP CHANNEL
OR: 1 HOUR **AFTER** HIGH WATER AT BOSTON

Velocities shown are at Spring Tides. **See Note at bottom of Boston Tables:**
Rule-of-Thumb for Current Velocities. *(Pollock Rip Ch. is SE of Monomoy Pt.)*

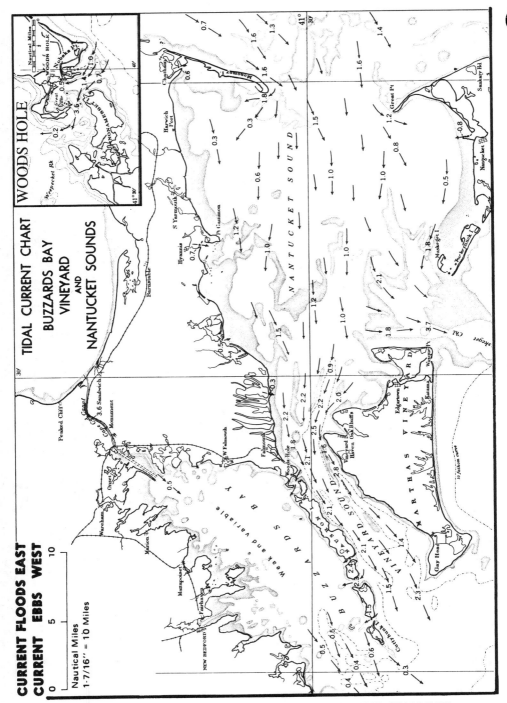

TIDAL CURRENT CHART
BUZZARDS BAY
VINEYARD
AND
NANTUCKET SOUNDS

WOODS HOLE

CURRENT FLOODS EAST
CURRENT EBBS WEST

Nautical Miles
1-7/16" = 10 Miles

0   5   10

4 HOURS **AFTER** EBB STARTS AT POLLOCK RIP CHANNEL
OR: 2 HOURS **AFTER** HIGH WATER AT BOSTON

Velocities shown are at Spring Tides. **See Note at bottom of Boston Tables:**
Rule-of-Thumb for Current Velocities. *(Pollock Rip Ch. is SE of Monomoy Pt.)*

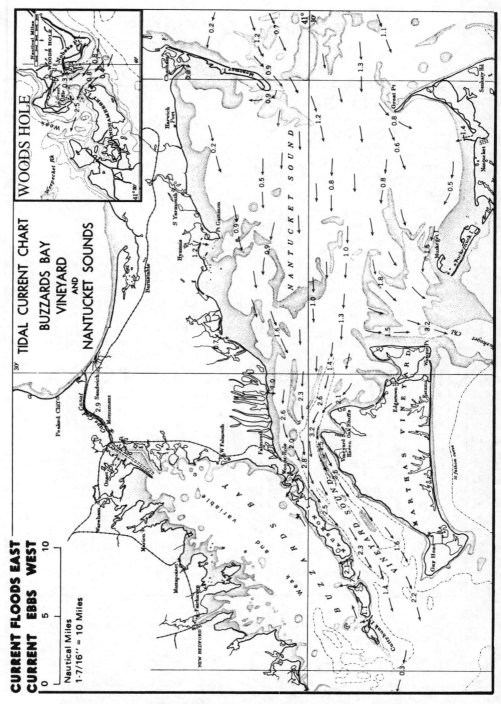

TIDAL CURRENT CHART
BUZZARDS BAY
VINEYARD
AND
NANTUCKET SOUNDS

CURRENT FLOODS EAST
CURRENT EBBS WEST

Nautical Miles
1-7/16'' = 10 Miles

Nautical Miles
0   5   10

5 HOURS **AFTER** EBB STARTS AT POLLOCK RIP CHANNEL
OR: 3 HOURS **AFTER** HIGH WATER AT BOSTON

Velocities shown are at Spring Tides. **See Note at bottom of Boston Tables:
Rule-of-Thumb for Current Velocities.** (Pollock Rip Ch. is SE of Monomoy Pt.)

2013 HIGH & LOW WATER
NEWPORT, RI
41°30.3'N, 71°19.6'W

Standard Time   Standard Time

D A Y O F M O N T H	D A Y O F W E E K	JANUARY						D A Y O F M O N T H	D A Y O F W E E K	FEBRUARY					
		HIGH				LOW				HIGH				LOW	
		a.m.	Ht.	p.m.	Ht.	a.m.	p.m.			a.m.	Ht.	p.m.	Ht.	a.m.	p.m.
1	T	9 57	3.4	10 31	3.2	3 09	3 41	1	F	11 11	3.3	11 42	3.6	4 17	4 29
2	W	10 43	3.3	11 18	3.2	3 50	4 16	2	S	...	...	12 03	3.1	5 08	5 18
3	T	11 33	3.2	...	...	4 36	4 59	3	S	12 38	3.6	1 01	3.0	6 12	6 18
4	F	12 07	3.3	12 24	3.1	5 29	5 49	4	M	1 37	3.6	2 02	3.0	7 36	7 30
5	S	1 01	3.4	1 20	3.0	6 38	6 51	5	T	2 42	3.6	3 09	3.1	9 07	8 47
6	S	1 59	3.5	2 22	3.0	8 00	7 59	6	W	3 50	3.8	4 16	3.3	10 15	9 56
7	M	3 02	3.7	3 28	3.1	9 17	9 05	7	T	4 55	4.0	5 18	3.6	11 10	10 58
8	T	4 07	4.0	4 32	3.3	10 20	10 06	8	F	5 52	4.2	6 13	3.9	11 59	11 55
9	W	5 09	4.3	5 33	3.6	11 17	11 03	9	S	6 44	4.4	7 04	4.1		12 45
10	T	6 06	4.5	6 28	3.9	...	12 11	10	S	7 33	4.4	7 53	4.2	12 48	1 26
11	F	6 59	4.7	7 20	4.1	12 01	1 03	11	M	8 20	4.3	8 40	4.2	1 37	2 03
12	S	7 49	4.7	8 12	4.2	12 54	1 51	12	T	9 07	4.1	9 27	4.1	2 22	2 39
13	S	8 40	4.5	9 02	4.1	1 48	2 34	13	W	9 53	3.8	10 13	3.9	3 04	3 14
14	M	9 30	4.3	9 53	4.0	2 38	3 14	14	T	10 39	3.4	11 00	3.6	3 44	3 50
15	T	10 20	3.9	10 45	3.8	3 26	3 52	15	F	11 26	3.1	11 47	3.3	4 24	4 28
16	W	11 10	3.6	11 36	3.6	4 12	4 30	16	S	...	...	12 13	2.8	5 08	5 11
17	T	...	...	12 01	3.2	5 01	5 11	17	S	12 35	3.0	1 02	2.6	6 03	6 02
18	F	12 27	3.3	12 51	2.9	5 58	5 58	18	M	1 26	2.8	1 55	2.4	7 23	7 05
19	S	1 19	3.1	1 44	2.6	7 24	6 54	19	T	2 24	2.7	2 54	2.4	8 58	8 18
20	S	2 15	2.9	2 40	2.5	8 55	7 57	20	W	3 29	2.7	3 56	2.5	9 55	9 23
21	M	3 16	2.9	3 39	2.5	9 48	8 57	21	T	4 29	2.8	4 50	2.7	10 40	10 18
22	T	4 16	2.9	4 35	2.6	10 31	9 50	22	F	5 17	3.0	5 36	3.0	11 20	11 07
23	W	5 08	3.0	5 24	2.7	11 11	10 39	23	S	5 57	3.2	6 17	3.3	11 58	11 53
24	T	5 51	3.2	6 07	2.9	11 50	11 26	24	S	6 35	3.4	6 55	3.5	...	12 34
25	F	6 28	3.3	6 47	3.1	...	12 29	25	M	7 12	3.6	7 34	3.7	12 36	1 08
26	S	7 04	3.4	7 24	3.3	12 11	1 06	26	T	7 51	3.7	8 14	3.9	1 18	1 41
27	S	7 38	3.5	8 02	3.4	12 54	1 41	27	W	8 32	3.7	8 56	4.0	1 58	2 14
28	M	8 15	3.6	8 40	3.5	1 35	2 13	28	T	9 16	3.7	9 41	4.0	2 38	2 48
29	T	8 54	3.6	9 21	3.5	2 14	2 43								
30	W	9 36	3.5	10 05	3.5	2 53	3 14								
31	T	10 22	3.4	10 52	3.5	3 33	3 49								

Dates when Ht. of **Low** Water is below Mean Lower Low with Ht. of lowest given for each period and Date of lowest in ( ):

6th - 16th: -0.9' (10th, 12th - 13th)   1st - 2nd: -0.3' (1st)
26th - 31st: -0.4' (28th - 30th)   5th - 14th: -0.8' (10th - 11th)
                                          23rd - 28th: -0.5' (26th - 28th)

Average Rise and Fall 3.5 ft.

When a high tide exceeds avg. ht., the *following* **low tide will be lower than avg.**

2013 HIGH & LOW WATER
NEWPORT, RI
41°30.3'N, 71°19.6'W

*Daylight Time starts March 10 at 2 a.m.　　　　　**Daylight Saving Time**

D A Y O F M O N T H	D A Y O F W E E K	MARCH HIGH a.m.	Ht.	p.m.	Ht.	LOW a.m.	p.m.	D A Y O F M O N T H	D A Y O F W E E K	APRIL HIGH a.m.	Ht.	p.m.	Ht.	LOW a.m.	p.m.
1	F	10 03	3.6	10 29	4.0	3 19	3 25	1	M	12 06	4.2	12 35	3.5	5 46	5 42
2	S	10 53	3.4	11 22	3.9	4 03	4 07	2	T	1 04	4.0	1 34	3.4	6 50	6 44
3	S	11 48	3.3	...	...	4 54	4 57	3	W	2 07	3.8	2 37	3.4	8 29	8 13
4	M	12 19	3.8	12 45	3.1	5 56	5 56	4	T	3 10	3.6	3 41	3.5	9 57	10 07
5	T	1 20	3.7	1 48	3.1	7 26	7 13	5	F	4 17	3.6	4 46	3.6	10 53	11 16
6	W	2 26	3.6	2 55	3.2	9 07	8 44	6	S	5 20	3.7	5 46	3.9	11 35	...
7	T	3 35	3.7	4 02	3.4	10 09	10 02	7	S	6 17	3.7	6 39	4.1	12 08	12 10
8	F	4 39	3.8	5 03	3.7	10 58	11 03	8	M	7 07	3.8	7 26	4.3	12 52	12 42
9	S	5 36	4.0	5 57	4.0	11 40	11 55	9	T	7 52	3.9	8 09	4.3	1 30	1 15
10	S	*7 27	4.1	*7 46	4.2	...	*1 17	10	W	8 35	3.8	8 51	4.3	2 05	1 49
11	M	8 14	4.1	8 32	4.3	1 41	1 53	11	T	9 16	3.7	9 31	4.1	2 39	2 26
12	T	8 58	4.0	9 16	4.3	2 23	2 27	12	F	9 57	3.5	10 10	3.9	3 14	3 04
13	W	9 42	3.9	9 59	4.1	3 02	3 02	13	S	10 38	3.3	10 49	3.7	3 50	3 42
14	T	10 25	3.6	10 41	3.9	3 39	3 37	14	S	11 20	3.2	11 29	3.4	4 26	4 22
15	F	11 08	3.4	11 24	3.6	4 15	4 14	15	M	...	...	12 04	3.0	5 05	5 04
16	S	11 52	3.1	...	...	4 52	4 52	16	T	12 09	3.1	12 49	2.9	5 47	5 50
17	S	12 06	3.3	12 36	2.9	5 32	5 34	17	W	12 53	3.0	1 36	2.8	6 38	6 45
18	M	12 50	3.0	1 22	2.7	6 19	6 22	18	T	1 40	2.8	2 27	2.8	7 46	7 55
19	T	1 36	2.8	2 13	2.6	7 19	7 21	19	F	2 34	2.8	3 22	2.9	9 05	9 14
20	W	2 28	2.7	3 09	2.6	8 51	8 37	20	S	3 33	2.8	4 19	3.1	10 03	10 19
21	T	3 28	2.6	4 09	2.7	10 09	9 53	21	S	4 35	3.0	5 13	3.5	10 48	11 13
22	F	4 32	2.7	5 07	2.9	10 58	10 53	22	M	5 33	3.2	6 03	3.8	11 28	...
23	S	5 29	2.9	5 57	3.2	11 39	11 43	23	T	6 25	3.5	6 51	4.2	12 01	12 08
24	S	6 17	3.2	6 42	3.5	...	12 17	24	W	7 13	3.7	7 37	4.5	12 48	12 49
25	M	7 01	3.5	7 24	3.9	12 29	12 53	25	T	8 00	3.9	8 24	4.8	1 35	1 32
26	T	7 43	3.7	8 05	4.2	1 13	1 29	26	F	8 48	4.0	9 12	4.8	2 23	2 16
27	W	8 26	3.9	8 47	4.4	1 57	2 06	27	S	9 38	4.0	10 02	4.8	3 11	3 02
28	T	9 10	3.9	9 32	4.5	2 41	2 44	28	S	10 30	4.0	10 56	4.7	3 59	3 50
29	F	9 56	3.9	10 20	4.5	3 24	3 23	29	M	11 25	3.9	11 52	4.4	4 48	4 40
30	S	10 46	3.8	11 11	4.3	4 08	4 05	30	T	...	...	12 22	3.8	5 42	5 35
31	S	11 39	3.6	...	...	4 54	4 51								

Dates when Ht. of **Low** Water is below Mean Lower Low with Ht. of lowest given for each period and Date of lowest in ( ):

1st - 3rd: -0.5' (1st)　　　　　8th - 12th: -0.3' (10th)
8th - 15th: -0.6' (12th)　　　　24th - 29th: -0.6' (26th - 27th)
26th - 31st: -0.6' (28th - 29th)

Average Rise and Fall 3.5 ft.

When a high tide exceeds avg. ht., the *following* low tide will be lower than avg.

2013 HIGH & LOW WATER
NEWPORT, RI
41°30.3'N, 71°19.6'W

Daylight Saving Time   Daylight Saving Time

DAY OF MONTH	DAY OF WEEK	MAY						DAY OF MONTH	DAY OF WEEK	JUNE					
		HIGH				LOW				HIGH				LOW	
		a.m.	Ht.	p.m.	Ht.	a.m.	p.m.			a.m.	Ht.	p.m.	Ht.	a.m.	p.m.
1	W	12 50	4.2	1 21	3.7	6 46	6 42	1	S	2 28	3.6	3 00	3.9	8 41	10 00
2	T	1 50	3.9	2 22	3.7	8 13	8 34	2	S	3 27	3.4	4 00	3.9	9 35	10 57
3	F	2 52	3.7	3 25	3.7	9 31	10 16	3	M	4 28	3.3	4 59	3.9	10 16	11 44
4	S	3 54	3.5	4 25	3.8	10 22	11 14	4	T	5 25	3.2	5 52	3.9	10 49	...
5	S	4 56	3.5	5 24	4.0	11 00	11 59	5	W	6 17	3.2	6 40	4.0	12 21	-A-
6	M	5 53	3.5	6 17	4.1	11 31	...	6	T	7 03	3.3	7 24	4.0	12 52	12 04
7	T	6 43	3.5	7 04	4.2	12 40	12 03	7	F	7 46	3.3	8 04	4.0	1 23	12 45
8	W	7 29	3.6	7 46	4.2	1 13	12 37	8	S	8 26	3.4	8 41	3.9	1 57	1 28
9	T	8 11	3.6	8 26	4.2	1 44	1 14	9	S	9 06	3.4	9 17	3.8	2 34	2 11
10	F	8 51	3.5	9 05	4.1	2 17	1 54	10	M	9 45	3.4	9 52	3.7	3 11	2 55
11	S	9 31	3.4	9 42	3.9	2 52	2 35	11	T	10 25	3.3	10 29	3.6	3 48	3 37
12	S	10 11	3.3	10 19	3.7	3 29	3 16	12	W	11 06	3.3	11 07	3.5	4 23	4 18
13	M	10 52	3.2	10 56	3.5	4 06	3 57	13	T	11 48	3.3	11 49	3.3	4 58	5 00
14	T	11 35	3.1	11 36	3.3	4 43	4 39	14	F	...	...	12 31	3.3	5 34	5 45
15	W	...	...	12 18	3.1	5 22	5 23	15	S	12 33	3.3	1 16	3.3	6 14	6 38
16	T	12 18	3.2	1 03	3.0	6 05	6 13	16	S	1 22	3.2	2 04	3.5	7 02	7 43
17	F	1 04	3.1	1 50	3.1	6 55	7 14	17	M	2 15	3.2	2 57	3.6	7 58	8 57
18	S	1 53	3.0	2 40	3.2	7 55	8 27	18	T	3 13	3.2	3 54	3.9	8 59	10 06
19	S	2 49	3.0	3 34	3.4	8 57	9 39	19	W	4 16	3.3	4 55	4.2	9 57	11 05
20	M	3 48	3.1	4 30	3.7	9 51	10 39	20	T	5 19	3.4	5 55	4.5	10 52	11 59
21	T	4 50	3.3	5 26	4.0	10 39	11 31	21	F	6 20	3.7	6 51	4.8	11 46	...
22	W	5 50	3.5	6 20	4.4	11 26	...	22	S	7 16	3.9	7 45	5.0	12 56	12 41
23	T	6 45	3.7	7 12	4.7	12 23	12 14	23	S	8 10	4.2	8 38	5.1	1 51	1 37
24	F	7 37	3.9	8 03	5.0	1 14	1 03	24	M	9 04	4.3	9 31	5.0	2 45	2 33
25	S	8 29	4.1	8 54	5.1	2 07	1 54	25	T	9 58	4.4	10 24	4.9	3 35	3 29
26	S	9 21	4.2	9 47	5.0	2 59	2 46	26	W	10 52	4.4	11 18	4.6	4 23	4 24
27	M	10 15	4.2	10 41	4.8	3 50	3 38	27	T	11 47	4.3	...	...	5 09	5 20
28	T	11 10	4.1	11 37	4.6	4 41	4 32	28	F	12 12	4.2	12 42	4.2	5 55	6 23
29	W	...	...	12 07	4.1	5 32	5 30	29	S	1 06	3.9	1 37	4.0	6 42	7 54
30	T	12 33	4.3	1 04	4.0	6 28	6 39	30	S	2 00	3.6	2 32	3.9	7 34	9 29
31	F	1 30	3.9	2 02	3.9	7 32	8 34								

A also at 11:25 a.m.

Dates when Ht. of **Low** Water is below Mean Lower Low with Ht. of lowest given for each period and Date of lowest in ( ):

    23rd - 29th: -0.6' (25th - 26th)   20th - 27th: -0.6' (23rd)

Average Rise and Fall 3.5 ft.

When a high tide exceeds avg. ht., the *following* **low tide will be lower than avg.**

2013 HIGH & LOW WATER
NEWPORT, RI
41°30.3'N, 71°19.6'W

Daylight Saving Time   Daylight Saving Time

DAY OF MONTH	DAY OF WEEK	JULY HIGH a.m.	Ht.	p.m.	Ht.	LOW a.m.	p.m.	DAY OF MONTH	DAY OF WEEK	AUGUST HIGH a.m.	Ht.	p.m.	Ht.	LOW a.m.	p.m.
1	M	2 56	3.3	3 29	3.7	8 30	10 30	1	T	4 17	2.9	4 54	3.4	9 31	11 25
2	T	3 54	3.1	4 28	3.7	9 22	11 17	2	F	5 16	2.9	5 49	3.4	10 26	11 59
3	W	4 53	3.0	5 26	3.7	10 10	11 56	3	S	6 09	3.1	6 37	3.6	11 17	...
4	T	5 47	3.0	6 16	3.7	10 53	...	4	S	6 54	3.3	7 15	3.7	12 36	12 04
5	F	6 37	3.1	7 01	3.8	12 28	-A-	5	M	7 34	3.4	7 51	3.8	1 12	12 50
6	S	7 21	3.2	7 41	3.8	1 01	12 22	6	T	8 12	3.6	8 25	3.8	1 49	1 35
7	S	8 01	3.4	8 17	3.8	1 37	1 07	7	W	8 49	3.7	8 59	3.9	2 24	2 18
8	M	8 40	3.4	8 52	3.8	2 15	1 53	8	T	9 26	3.8	9 36	3.8	2 57	2 59
9	T	9 19	3.5	9 27	3.8	2 52	2 36	9	F	10 05	3.8	10 15	3.8	3 28	3 38
10	W	9 57	3.5	10 02	3.7	3 26	3 18	10	S	10 46	3.9	10 58	3.7	3 58	4 16
11	T	10 36	3.5	10 41	3.6	3 59	3 58	11	S	11 30	3.9	11 45	3.6	4 30	4 57
12	F	11 17	3.5	11 22	3.5	4 30	4 38	12	M	...	...	12 17	3.9	5 07	5 44
13	S	11 59	3.6	...	...	5 02	5 20	13	T	12 35	3.4	1 09	3.9	5 50	6 40
14	S	12 07	3.4	12 45	3.6	5 38	6 08	14	W	1 29	3.3	2 05	4.0	6 43	7 54
15	M	12 56	3.3	1 34	3.7	6 21	7 07	15	T	2 28	3.3	3 06	4.0	7 48	9 25
16	T	1 49	3.3	2 27	3.8	7 14	8 20	16	F	3 32	3.4	4 12	4.2	9 03	10 39
17	W	2 46	3.2	3 26	4.0	8 18	9 39	17	S	4 40	3.5	5 18	4.4	10 16	11 36
18	T	3 50	3.3	4 30	4.2	9 25	10 47	18	S	5 44	3.8	6 19	4.6	11 21	...
19	F	4 56	3.4	5 34	4.5	10 28	11 46	19	M	6 43	4.2	7 13	4.8	12 27	12 20
20	S	6 00	3.7	6 34	4.7	11 28	...	20	T	7 36	4.5	8 04	4.9	1 14	1 17
21	S	6 59	4.0	7 29	4.9	12 41	12 27	21	W	8 27	4.7	8 53	4.8	1 58	2 11
22	M	7 53	4.3	8 22	5.0	1 35	1 25	22	T	9 16	4.8	9 41	4.6	2 40	3 01
23	T	8 46	4.5	9 13	5.0	2 25	2 22	23	F	10 05	4.7	10 30	4.3	3 19	3 48
24	W	9 38	4.6	10 04	4.8	3 12	3 17	24	S	10 54	4.5	11 18	4.0	3 57	4 32
25	T	10 30	4.6	10 55	4.5	3 55	4 09	25	S	11 43	4.2	...	...	4 34	5 15
26	F	11 22	4.5	11 47	4.2	4 35	5 00	26	M	12 08	3.7	12 33	3.9	5 13	6 01
27	S	...	...	12 15	4.3	5 15	5 51	27	T	12 57	3.4	1 24	3.6	5 55	6 58
28	S	12 38	3.8	1 07	4.0	5 55	6 51	28	W	1 48	3.1	2 17	3.4	6 44	8 40
29	M	1 30	3.5	2 00	3.8	6 39	8 28	29	T	2 42	2.9	3 14	3.2	7 45	10 03
30	T	2 23	3.2	2 55	3.6	7 31	9 52	30	F	3 40	2.9	4 15	3.2	8 56	10 50
31	W	3 18	3.0	3 53	3.4	8 31	10 45	31	S	4 40	2.9	5 13	3.2	10 03	11 28

A also at 11:37 a.m.

Dates when Ht. of **Low** Water is below Mean Lower Low with Ht. of lowest given for each period and Date of lowest in ( ):

20th - 26th: -0.5' (22nd - 25th)   19th - 24th: -0.4' (20th - 23rd)

Average Rise and Fall 3.5 ft.

When a high tide exceeds avg. ht., the *following* **low tide will be lower than avg.**

2013 HIGH & LOW WATER
NEWPORT, RI
41°30.3'N, 71°19.6'W

Daylight Saving Time · Daylight Saving Time

Day of Month	Day of Week	SEPTEMBER HIGH a.m.	Ht.	p.m.	Ht.	LOW a.m.	p.m.	Day of Month	Day of Week	OCTOBER HIGH a.m.	Ht.	p.m.	Ht.	LOW a.m.	p.m.
1	S	5 35	3.1	6 02	3.4	10 58	11 59	1	T	5 43	3.4	6 01	3.4	11 26	11 59
2	M	6 22	3.3	6 42	3.6	11 47	...	2	W	6 26	3.7	6 42	3.6	...	12 10
3	T	7 04	3.6	7 20	3.7	12 40	12 33	3	T	7 07	4.0	7 23	3.8	12 35	12 53
4	W	7 41	3.8	7 54	3.9	1 14	1 16	4	F	7 46	4.2	8 02	4.0	1 08	1 34
5	T	8 18	4.0	8 31	4.0	1 48	1 58	5	S	8 26	4.4	8 44	4.0	1 43	2 16
6	F	8 55	4.1	9 10	4.0	2 21	2 38	6	S	9 08	4.5	9 29	4.0	2 19	2 59
7	S	9 35	4.2	9 51	3.9	2 53	3 17	7	M	9 54	4.5	10 17	3.9	2 58	3 42
8	S	10 18	4.2	10 36	3.8	3 26	3 57	8	T	10 43	4.5	11 08	3.8	3 38	4 27
9	M	11 04	4.2	11 25	3.7	4 02	4 39	9	W	11 37	4.4	...	...	4 22	5 16
10	T	11 55	4.2	...	...	4 41	5 27	10	T	12 04	3.6	12 35	4.2	5 11	6 15
11	W	12 18	3.5	12 50	4.1	5 27	6 23	11	F	1 03	3.6	1 35	4.1	6 09	7 38
12	T	1 15	3.4	1 49	4.0	6 21	7 41	12	S	2 04	3.6	2 37	4.0	7 24	9 22
13	F	2 15	3.4	2 52	4.0	7 30	9 26	13	S	3 07	3.7	3 42	3.9	9 12	10 22
14	S	3 20	3.5	3 58	4.1	8 57	10 35	14	M	4 12	3.8	4 45	4.0	10 37	11 07
15	S	4 26	3.7	5 03	4.2	10 20	11 25	15	T	5 14	4.1	5 44	4.1	11 34	11 44
16	M	5 30	4.0	6 03	4.4	11 25	...	16	W	6 09	4.4	6 37	4.1	...	12 21
17	T	6 27	4.3	6 56	4.5	12 08	12 20	17	T	7 00	4.5	7 25	4.2	12 18	1 03
18	W	7 18	4.6	7 45	4.6	12 48	1 11	18	F	7 46	4.6	8 10	4.1	12 53	1 42
19	T	8 07	4.8	8 32	4.5	1 26	1 58	19	S	8 30	4.6	8 53	4.0	1 29	2 20
20	F	8 53	4.8	9 17	4.4	2 04	2 41	20	S	9 12	4.5	9 36	3.8	2 06	2 56
21	S	9 38	4.7	10 03	4.1	2 41	3 22	21	M	9 55	4.2	10 20	3.6	2 44	3 33
22	S	10 24	4.4	10 49	3.8	3 19	4 01	22	T	10 37	3.9	11 04	3.4	3 24	4 11
23	M	11 10	4.1	11 36	3.5	3 56	4 40	23	W	11 21	3.6	11 50	3.2	4 05	4 51
24	T	11 57	3.8	...	...	4 36	5 22	24	T	...	...	12 05	3.4	4 47	5 35
25	W	12 24	3.3	12 45	3.5	5 18	6 10	25	F	12 38	3.0	12 51	3.1	5 34	6 27
26	T	1 13	3.1	1 35	3.2	6 06	7 15	26	S	1 27	2.9	1 38	3.0	6 28	7 37
27	F	2 05	2.9	2 27	3.1	7 04	8 58	27	S	2 18	2.9	2 29	2.9	7 37	9 00
28	S	3 00	2.9	3 24	3.0	8 19	10 05	28	M	3 12	3.0	3 23	2.9	8 58	9 56
29	S	3 58	3.0	4 23	3.1	9 36	10 48	29	T	4 06	3.2	4 19	3.1	10 05	10 37
30	M	4 54	3.2	5 16	3.2	10 37	11 25	30	W	4 58	3.4	5 13	3.2	10 57	11 14
								31	T	5 46	3.7	6 03	3.5	11 42	11 51

Dates when Ht. of **Low** Water is below Mean Lower Low with Ht. of lowest given for each period and Date of lowest in ( ):

18th - 22nd: -0.3' (19th - 21st)

6th - 8th: -0.2'
18th - 20th: -0.2'

Average Rise and Fall 3.5 ft.

When a high tide exceeds avg. ht., the *following* **low tide will be lower than avg.**

2013 HIGH & LOW WATER
NEWPORT, RI
41°30.3'N, 71°19.6'W

*Standard Time starts Nov. 3 at 2 a.m.   **Standard Time**

D A Y O F M O N T H	D A Y O F W E E K	NOVEMBER						D A Y O F M O N T H	D A Y O F W E E K	DECEMBER					
		HIGH				LOW				HIGH				LOW	
		a.m.	Ht.	p.m.	Ht.	a.m.	p.m.			a.m.	Ht.	p.m.	Ht.	a.m.	p.m.
1	F	6 31	4.1	6 49	3.7	...	12 26	1	S	5 49	4.3	6 10	3.7	11 49	11 40
2	S	7 15	4.4	7 35	3.9	12 29	1 11	2	M	6 38	4.6	7 01	3.9	...	12 39
3	S	*7 01	4.6	*7 22	4.0	1 10	*12 57	3	T	7 29	4.8	7 52	4.0	12 29	1 30
4	M	7 46	4.7	8 09	4.0	12 51	1 43	4	W	8 19	4.8	8 44	4.0	1 18	2 19
5	T	8 35	4.7	8 59	3.9	1 35	2 30	5	T	9 12	4.7	9 38	4.0	2 10	3 08
6	W	9 27	4.6	9 53	3.9	2 21	3 18	6	F	10 07	4.5	10 34	3.9	3 02	3 58
7	T	10 22	4.5	10 50	3.8	3 10	4 09	7	S	11 03	4.2	11 32	3.9	3 57	4 51
8	F	11 20	4.3	11 49	3.7	4 02	5 08	8	S	...	...	12 01	3.9	4 58	5 51
9	S	...	...	12 19	4.0	5 03	6 25	9	M	12 30	3.8	12 58	3.6	6 23	7 03
10	S	12 50	3.7	1 20	3.8	6 26	7 55	10	T	1 29	3.7	1 57	3.4	8 23	8 12
11	M	1 51	3.7	2 22	3.7	8 33	8 56	11	W	2 30	3.7	2 58	3.2	9 31	9 03
12	T	2 53	3.8	3 24	3.6	9 43	9 40	12	T	3 31	3.7	3 57	3.2	10 24	9 41
13	W	3 54	4.0	4 22	3.6	10 34	10 15	13	F	4 29	3.7	4 53	3.2	11 07	10 16
14	T	4 50	4.1	5 16	3.7	11 17	10 47	14	S	5 21	3.8	5 42	3.2	11 43	10 53
15	F	5 40	4.3	6 04	3.7	11 54	11 21	15	S	6 07	3.8	6 27	3.3	-A-	12 14
16	S	6 26	4.3	6 48	3.7	...	12 27	16	M	6 50	3.8	7 09	3.3	...	12 44
17	S	7 09	4.3	7 30	3.6	12 01	1 00	17	T	7 29	3.8	7 49	3.3	12 13	1 17
18	M	7 49	4.1	8 12	3.5	12 36	1 35	18	W	8 06	3.7	8 28	3.3	12 56	1 53
19	T	8 29	4.0	8 53	3.4	1 17	2 11	19	T	8 43	3.5	9 08	3.2	1 38	2 29
20	W	9 08	3.7	9 35	3.2	1 58	2 48	20	F	9 18	3.4	9 48	3.1	2 21	3 04
21	T	9 48	3.5	10 19	3.1	2 40	3 27	21	S	9 55	3.2	10 29	3.0	3 02	3 40
22	F	10 28	3.3	11 03	3.0	3 23	4 06	22	S	10 34	3.1	11 11	3.0	3 43	4 15
23	S	11 09	3.1	11 49	2.9	4 07	4 49	23	M	11 16	3.0	11 54	3.0	4 26	4 54
24	S	11 53	2.9	...	...	4 56	5 39	24	T	...	...	12 02	2.9	5 14	5 38
25	M	12 36	2.9	12 40	2.9	5 54	6 39	25	W	12 41	3.0	12 52	2.8	6 13	6 33
26	T	1 24	3.0	1 32	2.9	7 06	7 44	26	T	1 31	3.1	1 47	2.8	7 25	7 35
27	W	2 16	3.1	2 28	2.9	8 20	8 39	27	F	2 27	3.3	2 48	2.9	8 39	8 36
28	T	3 10	3.3	3 27	3.0	9 21	9 25	28	S	3 28	3.5	3 51	3.0	9 42	9 32
29	F	4 05	3.7	4 25	3.2	10 12	10 09	29	S	4 29	3.9	4 52	3.3	10 37	10 25
30	S	4 58	4.0	5 19	3.5	11 01	10 54	30	M	5 26	4.2	5 49	3.6	11 31	11 19
								31	T	6 20	4.5	6 43	3.8	...	12 23

A also at 11:32 p.m.

Dates when Ht. of **Low** Water is below Mean Lower Low with Ht. of lowest given for each period and Date of lowest in ( ):

2nd - 7th: -0.5' (5th)	1st - 7th: -0.7' (3rd - 5th)
18th: -0.2'	17th - 19th: -0.2'
30th: -0.4'	28th - 31st: -0.7' (30th)

Average Rise and Fall 3.5 ft.

When a high tide exceeds avg. ht., the *following* **low tide will be lower than avg.**

Narragansett Bay Currents

This Current Diagram shows average maximum currents with a normal range (3.5 ft.) of tides at Newport. See pp. 78-83.

Maximum Ebb Currents, 3 hours *after* High Water at Newport, are shown by double-headed arrows and velocities are <u>underlined.</u>

Maximum Flood Currents, 2 1/2 hours *before* High Water at Newport, are shown by single-headed arrows and velocities are <u>not</u> underlined.

When height of High Water at Newport is 3.0 ft., subtract 30% from all velocities shown. When height is 4.0 ft., add 20%; when 4.5 ft., add 40%; when 5.0 ft., add 60%.

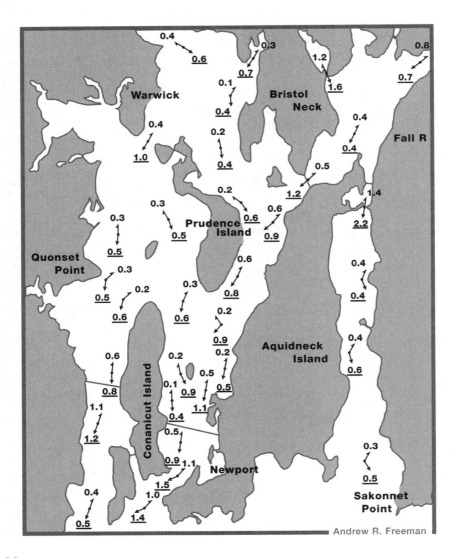

Andrew R. Freeman

Holding a Fair Current between Eastern Long Island and Nantucket

There is a curious phenomenon which can be used to advantage by every vessel, and particularly the slower cruiser or auxiliary, in making the passage *either* way between eastern Long Island Sound, on the west, and Buzzards Bay, Vineyard and Nantucket Sounds on the east.

Note in the very simplified diagram below, that in Long Island Sound, the Ebb Current flows to the *east*, and in Buzzards Bay, Vineyard and Nantucket Sounds the Ebb Current flows to the *west*. (Off Newport, these opposed Ebb Currents merge and flow *south*.) The reverse is also true: the Flood Current flows *west* through Long Island Sound and *east* through Buzzards Bay, Vineyard and Nantucket Sounds. (Half arrow indicates Ebb Current, whole arrow indicates Flood Current.)

In making a *complete* passage through the area of the diagram, simply ride the favoring Ebb Current toward Newport from either direction and, pick up the favoring Flood Current in leaving the Newport area.

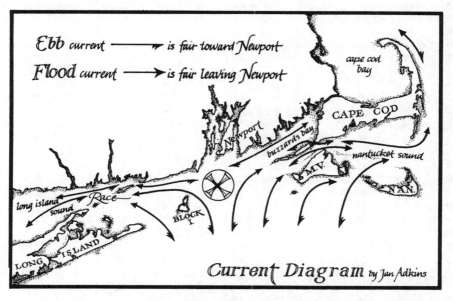

Arrive at "X" at the times shown for "Current Turns to Northwest at The Race," tables pp. 86-91.

The E-W currents between Pt. Judith and Cuttyhunk are only 1/2 to 1 kt., while those to the West of Pt. Judith and to the East of Cuttyhunk are much greater. Bearing this in mind, those making *only a partial trip* through the area may find it better even to buck a slight head current in the Pt. Judith-Cuttyhunk area so as to pick up the maximum hours of strong favoring currents beyond those points.

For example, if headed for the Cape Cod Canal, refer to the Vineyard & Nantucket Sound Current Charts, pp. 66-77 and arrive just N. of Cuttyhunk as Flood Starts at Pollock Rip, pp. 60-65 to ensure the most favorable currents. If headed for Nantucket, refer to the same Charts and arrive just S. of Cuttyhunk at 3 hours after Flood Starts at Pollock Rip, pp. 60-65. If headed into Long Island Sound, refer to the Long Island Sound Current Charts, pp. 92-97 and arrive at Pt. Judith when Flood Current turns West at The Race, p. 95.

2013 CURRENT TABLE
THE RACE, LONG ISLAND SOUND
41°13.69'N, 72°03.75'W 0.2 nm E.N.E. of Valiant Rock

Standard Time   **Standard Time**

DAY OF MONTH	DAY OF WEEK	NORTHWEST Flood Starts a.m.	**p.m.**	Kts.	SOUTHEAST Ebb Starts a.m.	**p.m.**	Kts.	DAY OF MONTH	DAY OF WEEK	NORTHWEST Flood Starts a.m.	**p.m.**	Kts.	SOUTHEAST Ebb Starts a.m.	**p.m.**	Kts.
		JANUARY								**FEBRUARY**					
1	T	8 09	8 26	p3.6	1 41	1 51	p4.4	1	F	9 19	9 29	p3.7	2 42	3 04	a4.7
2	W	8 54	9 08	p3.6	2 23	2 36	a4.4	2	S	10 14	10 24	p3.5	3 32	3 58	a4.6
3	T	9 45	9 56	p3.5	3 08	3 25	a4.4	3	S	11 16	11 26	p3.4	4 28	4 59	a4.4
4	F	10 38	10 47	p3.5	3 57	4 18	a4.4	4	M	...	12 20	2.9	5 28	6 04	a4.3
5	S	11 37	11 44	p3.5	4 50	5 17	a4.4	5	T	12 29	1 24	a3.4	6 32	7 12	a4.4
6	S	...	12 38	2.9	5 48	6 21	a4.4	6	W	1 34	2 25	a3.4	7 37	8 17	a4.5
7	M	12 45	1 39	a3.5	6 49	7 26	a4.6	7	T	2 37	3 23	a3.6	8 39	9 17	a4.8
8	T	1 46	2 39	a3.6	7 51	8 30	a4.8	8	F	3 37	4 17	3.9	9 37	10 13	a5.0
9	W	2 47	3 36	a3.8	8 51	9 30	a5.1	9	S	4 33	5 08	p4.2	10 32	11 04	a5.2
10	T	3 46	4 31	a4.0	9 48	10 27	a5.3	10	S	5 27	5 56	p4.3	11 23	11 54	a5.2
11	F	4 43	5 24	4.2	10 43	11 21	a5.4	11	M	6 19	6 43	p4.3	...	12 12	5.1
12	S	5 39	6 15	4.3	11 37	...	5.4	12	T	7 10	7 29	p4.1	12 41	1 01	a5.1
13	S	6 34	7 05	p4.3	12 13	12 29	p5.3	13	W	8 00	8 16	p3.8	1 28	1 49	a4.9
14	M	7 28	7 54	p4.1	1 04	1 21	5.0	14	T	8 50	9 04	p3.4	2 14	2 37	a4.6
15	T	8 23	8 45	p3.9	1 55	2 13	a4.9	15	F	9 43	9 54	p3.0	3 00	3 26	a4.3
16	W	9 19	9 36	p3.5	2 46	3 06	a4.6	16	S	10 36	10 47	p2.7	3 48	4 16	a3.9
17	T	10 17	10 30	p3.2	3 37	4 00	a4.3	17	S	11 32	11 42	p2.5	4 37	5 09	a3.6
18	F	11 16	11 26	p2.9	4 29	4 56	a4.0	18	M	...	12 27	2.2	5 28	6 04	a3.3
19	S	...	12 15	2.4	5 22	5 54	a3.8	19	T	12 36	1 20	a2.4	6 21	6 58	a3.3
20	S	12 22	1 11	a2.7	6 15	6 51	a3.6	20	W	1 29	2 09	2.4	7 13	7 49	a3.4
21	M	1 16	2 04	a2.6	7 08	7 46	a3.6	21	T	2 18	2 54	p2.6	8 03	8 36	a3.5
22	T	2 08	2 52	a2.6	7 58	8 35	a3.7	22	F	3 04	3 35	p2.9	8 50	9 20	3.8
23	W	2 56	3 35	2.7	8 44	9 19	a3.8	23	S	3 48	4 14	p3.2	9 34	10 01	4.1
24	T	3 40	4 15	2.9	9 27	10 00	a4.0	24	S	4 29	4 52	p3.5	10 17	10 41	p4.5
25	F	4 22	4 53	p3.2	10 08	10 38	a4.1	25	M	5 10	5 30	p3.8	10 58	11 21	p4.8
26	S	5 02	5 29	p3.4	10 47	11 16	a4.3	26	T	5 52	6 09	p4.0	11 40	...	4.7
27	S	5 41	6 05	p3.6	11 26	11 54	a4.5	27	W	6 34	6 49	p4.1	12 02	12 23	a5.0
28	M	6 20	6 40	p3.8	...	12 05	4.6	28	T	7 19	7 31	p4.1	12 45	1 08	a5.1
29	T	7 00	7 18	p3.8	12 32	12 46	4.6								
30	W	7 43	7 57	p3.9	1 13	1 29	a4.7								
31	T	8 29	8 41	p3.8	1 56	2 14	a4.8								

The Kts. (knots) columns show the **maximum** predicted velocities of the stronger one of the Flood Currents and the stronger one of the Ebb Currents for each day.

The letter "a" means the velocity shown should occur **after** the a.m. Current Change. The letter "p" means the velocity shown should occur **after** the p.m. Current Change (even if next morning). No "a" or "p" means a.m. and p.m. velocities are the same for that day.

Avg. Max. Velocity: Flood 3.3 Kts., Ebb 4.2 Kts.

Max. Flood 2 hrs. 45 min. after Flood Starts, ±15 min.

Max. Ebb 3 hrs. 25 min. after Ebb Starts, ±15 min.

Use THE RACE tables with current charts pp. 92-97

See pp. 22-29 for Current Change at other points.

2013 CURRENT TABLE
THE RACE, LONG ISLAND SOUND
41°13.69'N, 72°03.75'W 0.2 nm E.N.E. of Valiant Rock

Daylight Time starts March 10 at 2 a.m. **Daylight Saving Time**

		MARCH								APRIL					
		CURRENT TURNS TO								CURRENT TURNS TO					
		NORTHWEST Flood Starts			SOUTHEAST Ebb Starts					NORTHWEST Flood Starts			SOUTHEAST Ebb Starts		
DAY OF MONTH	DAY OF WEEK	a.m.	p.m.	Kts.	a.m.	p.m.	Kts.	DAY OF MONTH	DAY OF WEEK	a.m.	p.m.	Kts.	a.m.	p.m.	Kts.
1	F	8 06	8 18	p3.9	1 30	1 56	a5.1	1	M	10 39	10 56	p3.4	3 54	4 33	a4.8
2	S	8 58	9 10	p3.7	2 19	2 47	a4.9	2	T	11 43	...	3.1	4 55	5 36	a4.4
3	S	9 56	10 09	p3.5	3 12	3 44	a4.7	3	W	12 04	12 50	a3.2	6 00	6 42	a4.2
4	M	10 58	11 13	p3.3	4 10	4 46	a4.4	4	T	1 12	1 53	3.1	7 08	7 48	4.1
5	T	...	12 05	2.9	5 13	5 53	a4.2	5	F	2 19	2 54	p3.4	8 15	8 50	p4.3
6	W	12 20	1 10	a3.2	6 20	7 01	a4.2	6	S	3 22	3 49	p3.6	9 17	9 46	p4.7
7	T	1 27	2 11	a3.3	7 26	8 05	a4.3	7	S	4 19	4 40	p3.8	10 14	10 38	p4.9
8	F	2 30	3 08	p3.6	8 29	9 03	p4.6	8	M	5 11	5 28	p3.9	11 06	11 25	p5.0
9	S	3 29	4 00	p3.9	9 27	9 57	p4.9	9	T	6 00	6 13	p4.0	11 53	...	4.5
10	S	*5 23	*5 49	p4.1	*11 20	*11 46	p5.1	10	W	6 46	6 56	p3.9	12 08	12 37	a5.0
11	M	6 14	6 35	p4.2	...	12 09	4.8	11	T	7 29	7 38	p3.7	12 50	1 19	a4.9
12	T	7 03	7 20	p4.1	12 32	12 55	a5.1	12	F	8 11	8 20	3.4	1 30	1 59	a4.7
13	W	7 50	8 04	p3.9	1 16	1 40	a5.1	13	S	8 52	9 02	a3.2	2 09	2 39	a4.4
14	T	8 35	8 47	p3.6	1 59	2 24	a4.9	14	S	9 34	9 45	2.9	2 48	3 19	a4.1
15	F	9 21	9 32	p3.3	2 41	3 07	a4.5	15	M	10 16	10 31	a2.7	3 28	4 01	a3.8
16	S	10 08	10 19	2.9	3 23	3 51	a4.2	16	T	11 01	11 20	a2.6	4 10	4 45	a3.6
17	S	10 56	11 08	2.6	4 07	4 37	a3.8	17	W	11 49	...	2.5	4 55	5 32	a3.4
18	M	11 46	...	2.4	4 52	5 25	a3.5	18	T	12 12	12 38	p2.5	5 45	6 22	3.3
19	T	12 01	12 38	a2.4	5 40	6 16	a3.3	19	F	1 05	1 27	p2.6	6 38	7 13	p3.5
20	W	12 54	1 30	2.3	6 32	7 08	a3.2	20	S	1 57	2 15	p2.8	7 33	8 04	p3.8
21	T	1 47	2 19	p2.4	7 25	8 00	3.2	21	S	2 47	3 03	p3.1	8 28	8 55	p4.2
22	F	2 38	3 06	p2.6	8 18	8 50	p3.6	22	M	3 36	3 49	p3.4	9 21	9 44	p4.6
23	S	3 26	3 50	p3.0	9 10	9 37	p4.0	23	T	4 24	4 35	p3.8	10 13	10 32	p5.0
24	S	4 12	4 32	p3.3	9 58	10 22	p4.4	24	W	5 11	5 22	p4.1	11 03	11 20	p5.3
25	M	4 56	5 13	p3.7	10 45	11 06	p4.8	25	T	5 59	6 09	p4.3	11 52	...	4.8
26	T	5 40	5 55	p4.0	11 30	11 49	p5.1	26	F	6 47	6 58	p4.3	12 08	12 41	a5.5
27	W	6 24	6 38	p4.2	...	12 15	4.8	27	S	7 37	7 49	p4.3	12 57	1 32	a5.6
28	T	7 09	7 22	p4.2	12 34	1 02	a5.3	28	S	8 29	8 43	p4.1	1 48	2 25	a5.4
29	F	7 56	8 09	p4.2	1 19	1 49	a5.4	29	M	9 24	9 42	3.8	2 42	3 21	a5.2
30	S	8 46	8 59	p4.0	2 07	2 40	a5.3	30	T	10 23	10 45	a3.6	3 39	4 21	a4.9
31	S	9 40	9 55	p3.7	2 59	3 34	a5.1								

The Kts. (knots) columns show the **maximum** predicted velocities of the stronger one of the Flood Currents and the stronger one of the Ebb Currents for each day.
The letter "a" means the velocity shown should occur **after** the **a.m.** Current Change. The letter "p" means the velocity shown should occur **after** the **p.m.** Current Change (even if next morning). No "a" or "p" means a.m. and p.m. velocities are the same for that day.
Avg. Max. Velocity: Flood 3.3 Kts., Ebb 4.2 Kts.
Max. Flood 2 hrs. 45 min. after Flood Starts, ±15 min.
Max. Ebb 3 hrs. 25 min. after Ebb Starts, ±15 min.
Use THE RACE tables with current charts pp. 92-97

See pp. 22-29 for Current Change at other points.

Daylight Saving Time   Daylight Saving Time

DAY OF MONTH	DAY OF WEEK	NORTHWEST Flood Starts a.m.	**p.m.**	Kts.	SOUTHEAST Ebb Starts a.m.	**p.m.**	Kts.	DAY OF MONTH	DAY OF WEEK	NORTHWEST Flood Starts a.m.	**p.m.**	Kts.	SOUTHEAST Ebb Starts a.m.	**p.m.**	Kts.
		MAY								**JUNE**					
1	W	11 25	**11 52**	a3.4	4 40	**5 23**	a4.5	1	S	12 43	**1 05**	p3.4	6 31	**7 05**	p4.3
2	T	...	**12 29**	3.3	5 45	**6 27**	a4.2	2	S	1 49	**2 04**	p3.4	7 36	**8 04**	p4.3
3	F	1 02	**1 33**	p3.3	6 52	**7 30**	p4.2	3	M	2 51	**3 01**	p3.4	8 39	**8 59**	p4.5
4	S	2 07	**2 31**	p3.4	7 59	**8 30**	p4.4	4	T	3 46	**3 53**	p3.4	9 36	**9 50**	p4.5
5	S	3 09	**3 26**	p3.6	9 01	**9 25**	p4.6	5	W	4 36	**4 41**	p3.4	10 27	**10 36**	p4.6
6	M	4 05	**4 18**	p3.7	9 58	**10 15**	p4.8	6	T	5 22	**5 26**	p3.4	11 12	**11 18**	p4.5
7	T	4 56	**5 05**	p3.7	10 49	**11 01**	p4.9	7	F	6 05	**6 09**	3.3	11 53	**11 58**	p4.5
8	W	5 43	**5 50**	p3.7	11 35	**11 44**	p4.8	8	S	6 44	**6 49**	3.3	...	**12 31**	3.8
9	T	6 26	**6 33**	p3.6	...	**12 17**	4.0	9	S	7 20	**7 28**	a3.3	12 35	**1 08**	a4.4
10	F	7 07	**7 14**	a3.5	12 24	**12 56**	a4.7	10	M	7 56	**8 06**	a3.3	1 11	**1 43**	a4.3
11	S	7 46	**7 54**	3.3	1 02	**1 34**	a4.5	11	T	8 31	**8 45**	a3.2	1 46	**2 19**	a4.2
12	S	8 24	**8 34**	a3.2	1 39	**2 11**	a4.3	12	W	9 06	**9 25**	a3.2	2 23	**2 56**	a4.1
13	M	9 02	**9 14**	a3.1	2 15	**2 49**	a4.1	13	T	9 43	**10 08**	a3.2	3 02	**3 36**	a4.0
14	T	9 40	**9 57**	a3.0	2 53	**3 28**	a3.9	14	F	10 23	**10 54**	a3.2	3 44	**4 18**	p4.0
15	W	10 20	**10 42**	a2.9	3 33	**4 09**	a3.8	15	S	11 06	**11 45**	a3.2	4 30	**5 04**	p4.0
16	T	11 03	**11 31**	a2.8	4 17	**4 53**	a3.6	16	S	11 54	...	3.2	5 20	**5 53**	p4.1
17	F	11 49	...	2.9	5 04	**5 40**	p3.6	17	M	12 39	**12 46**	p3.3	6 15	**6 46**	p4.2
18	S	12 23	**12 37**	p2.9	5 56	**6 30**	p3.8	18	T	1 35	**1 41**	p3.4	7 14	**7 42**	p4.5
19	S	1 16	**1 27**	p3.1	6 51	**7 22**	p4.0	19	W	2 31	**2 37**	p3.6	8 15	**8 40**	p4.7
20	M	2 09	**2 18**	p3.3	7 49	**8 16**	p4.4	20	T	3 28	**3 34**	p3.8	9 16	**9 37**	p5.1
21	T	3 02	**3 10**	p3.6	8 46	**9 09**	p4.8	21	F	4 23	**4 30**	p4.0	10 15	**10 33**	p5.3
22	W	3 53	**4 01**	p3.8	9 43	**10 02**	p5.1	22	S	5 17	**5 26**	p4.2	11 12	**11 28**	p5.5
23	T	4 45	**4 53**	p4.1	10 37	**10 54**	p5.4	23	S	6 10	**6 22**	p4.3	...	**12 06**	4.9
24	F	5 36	**5 45**	p4.3	11 30	**11 45**	p5.6	24	M	7 03	**7 18**	4.3	12 22	**1 01**	a5.6
25	S	6 27	**6 38**	p4.4	...	**12 23**	4.9	25	T	7 55	**8 15**	a4.3	1 16	**1 55**	a5.5
26	S	7 20	**7 33**	p4.3	12 38	**1 16**	a5.6	26	W	8 48	**9 13**	a4.2	2 10	**2 49**	a5.3
27	M	8 13	**8 29**	a4.2	1 31	**2 11**	a5.5	27	T	9 42	**10 13**	a4.0	3 06	**3 44**	a5.0
28	T	9 07	**9 28**	a4.0	2 26	**3 07**	a5.3	28	F	10 38	**11 15**	a3.8	4 03	**4 40**	4.6
29	W	10 04	**10 31**	a3.8	3 23	**4 05**	a5.0	29	S	11 35	...	3.5	5 03	**5 37**	p4.3
30	T	11 03	**11 37**	a3.6	4 23	**5 04**	a4.6	30	S	12 19	**12 34**	p3.3	6 05	**6 35**	p4.2
31	F	...	**12 04**	3.5	5 26	**6 05**	p4.3								

The Kts. (knots) columns show the **maximum** predicted velocities of the stronger one of the Flood Currents and the stronger one of the Ebb Currents for each day.

The letter "a" means the velocity shown should occur **after** the a.m. Current Change. The letter "p" means the velocity shown should occur **after** the p.m. Current Change (even if next morning). No "a" or "p" means a.m. and p.m. velocities are the same for that day.

Avg. Max. Velocity: Flood 3.3 Kts., Ebb 4.2 Kts.

Max. Flood 2 hrs. 45 min. after Flood Starts, ±15 min.

Max. Ebb 3 hrs. 25 min. after Ebb Starts, ±15 min.

Use THE RACE tables with current charts pp. 92-97

See pp. 22-29 for Current Change at other points.

2013 CURRENT TABLE
THE RACE, LONG ISLAND SOUND
41°13.69'N, 72°03.75'W 0.2 nm E.N.E. of Valiant Rock

Daylight Saving Time   Daylight Saving Time

		JULY								AUGUST					
		CURRENT TURNS TO								CURRENT TURNS TO					
		NORTHWEST Flood Starts			SOUTHEAST Ebb Starts					NORTHWEST Flood Starts			SOUTHEAST Ebb Starts		
DAY OF MONTH	DAY OF WEEK	a.m.	p.m.	Kts.	a.m.	p.m.	Kts.	DAY OF MONTH	DAY OF WEEK	a.m.	p.m.	Kts.	a.m.	p.m.	Kts.
1	M	1 23	1 34	p3.1	7 08	7 33	p4.1	1	T	2 47	2 53	p2.7	8 31	8 45	p3.7
2	T	2 24	2 31	p3.0	8 10	8 28	p4.1	2	F	3 38	3 44	p2.7	9 23	9 34	p3.8
3	W	3 21	3 26	p3.0	9 07	9 20	p4.1	3	S	4 25	4 31	p2.9	10 09	10 19	p3.9
4	T	4 11	4 14	p3.0	9 59	10 08	p4.2	4	S	5 05	5 13	p3.0	10 50	10 59	p4.0
5	F	4 57	5 00	p3.1	10 44	10 51	p4.2	5	M	5 43	5 53	p3.2	11 28	11 38	p4.2
6	S	5 38	5 43	3.1	11 25	11 30	p4.2	6	T	6 18	6 31	3.3	...	12 04	4.1
7	S	6 16	6 22	3.2	...	12 02	3.8	7	W	6 53	7 08	3.5	12 15	12 40	4.3
8	M	6 52	7 00	3.3	12 07	12 38	a4.3	8	T	7 27	7 47	a3.7	12 52	1 17	p4.5
9	T	7 26	7 38	a3.4	12 43	1 13	a4.3	9	F	8 02	8 26	a3.8	1 30	1 54	p4.6
10	W	8 00	8 16	a3.5	1 19	1 49	a4.3	10	S	8 38	9 08	a3.8	2 10	2 34	p4.7
11	T	8 34	8 55	a3.5	1 56	2 25	4.3	11	S	9 18	9 54	a3.7	2 52	3 17	p4.7
12	F	9 09	9 36	a3.5	2 35	3 04	4.3	12	M	10 03	10 45	a3.6	3 38	4 04	p4.6
13	S	9 48	10 22	a3.5	3 16	3 46	a4.3	13	T	10 54	11 42	a3.5	4 29	4 56	p4.4
14	S	10 31	11 12	a3.5	4 01	4 32	p4.3	14	W	11 51	...	3.4	5 25	5 53	p4.3
15	M	11 20	...	3.4	4 51	5 22	p4.3	15	T	12 43	12 54	p3.3	6 27	6 55	p4.3
16	T	12 07	12 14	p3.4	5 46	6 16	p4.3	16	F	1 47	1 59	p3.4	7 34	8 00	p4.4
17	W	1 06	1 13	p3.4	6 47	7 15	p4.4	17	S	2 50	3 03	p3.5	8 40	9 04	p4.6
18	T	2 07	2 14	p3.5	7 51	8 17	p4.6	18	S	3 49	4 04	p3.7	9 43	10 05	p4.9
19	F	3 07	3 15	p3.7	8 55	9 18	p4.9	19	M	4 44	5 02	p4.0	10 40	11 01	p5.1
20	S	4 05	4 14	p3.9	9 57	10 17	p5.1	20	T	5 37	5 58	p4.2	11 34	11 55	p5.2
21	S	5 00	5 13	p4.1	10 55	11 14	p5.4	21	W	6 27	6 51	a4.3	...	12 25	5.3
22	M	5 54	6 09	p4.3	11 51	...	5.0	22	T	7 15	7 43	a4.4	12 46	1 14	p5.3
23	T	6 46	7 05	4.3	12 08	12 44	a5.5	23	F	8 03	8 35	a4.3	1 36	2 03	p5.2
24	W	7 36	7 59	a4.4	1 01	1 36	a5.4	24	S	8 52	9 27	a4.0	2 26	2 51	p4.9
25	T	8 26	8 54	a4.3	1 53	2 27	a5.2	25	S	9 41	10 20	a3.7	3 16	3 39	p4.6
26	F	9 17	9 51	a4.1	2 46	3 19	4.9	26	M	10 33	11 15	a3.3	4 07	4 29	p4.1
27	S	10 10	10 49	a3.8	3 40	4 11	p4.6	27	T	11 28	...	2.9	5 00	5 21	p3.8
28	S	11 04	11 49	a3.4	4 36	5 05	p4.3	28	W	12 13	12 25	p2.6	5 55	6 14	p3.5
29	M	...	12 02	3.1	5 34	6 00	p4.0	29	T	1 10	1 22	p2.4	6 51	7 09	p3.3
30	T	12 51	1 00	p2.8	6 33	6 56	p3.8	30	F	2 05	2 18	p2.4	7 46	8 03	p3.3
31	W	1 51	1 58	p2.7	7 33	7 52	p3.7	31	S	2 56	3 09	p2.5	8 38	8 54	p3.5

The Kts. (knots) columns show the **maximum** predicted velocities of the stronger one of the Flood Currents and the stronger one of the Ebb Currents for each day.

The letter "a" means the velocity shown should occur **after** the **a.m.** Current Change. The letter "p" means the velocity shown should occur **after** the **p.m.** Current Change (even if next morning). No "a" or "p" means a.m. and p.m. velocities are the same for that day.

Avg. Max. Velocity: Flood 3.3 Kts., Ebb 4.2 Kts.

Max. Flood 2 hrs. 45 min. after Flood Starts, ±15 min.

Max. Ebb 3 hrs. 25 min. after Ebb Starts, ±15 min.

Use THE RACE tables with current charts pp. 92-97

See pp. 22-29 for Current Change at other points.

THE RACE, LONG ISLAND SOUND
41°13.69'N, 72°03.75'W 0.2 nm E.N.E. of Valiant Rock

Daylight Saving Time · Daylight Saving Time

DAY OF MONTH	DAY OF WEEK	CURRENT TURNS TO						DAY OF MONTH	DAY OF WEEK	CURRENT TURNS TO					
		NORTHWEST Flood Starts			SOUTHEAST Ebb Starts					NORTHWEST Flood Starts			SOUTHEAST Ebb Starts		
		a.m.	**p.m.**	Kts.	a.m.	**p.m.**	Kts.			a.m.	**p.m.**	Kts.	a.m.	**p.m.**	Kts.
1	S	3 42	**3 55**	p2.7	9 26	**9 41**	p3.6	1	T	3 37	**4 01**	p2.9	9 23	**9 45**	a3.8
2	M	4 24	**4 39**	p2.9	10 09	**10 24**	p3.9	2	W	4 18	**4 44**	p3.2	10 07	**10 30**	a4.2
3	T	5 04	**5 21**	p3.2	10 49	**11 05**	p4.1	3	T	4 59	**5 27**	p3.5	10 49	**11 14**	a4.6
4	W	5 40	**5 59**	3.4	11 27	**11 45**	4.3	4	F	5 38	**6 08**	3.7	11 30	**11 57**	a4.9
5	T	6 16	**6 38**	3.6	...	**12 05**	4.6	5	S	6 19	**6 50**	a4.0	...	**12 13**	5.1
6	F	6 53	**7 18**	a3.8	12 25	**12 44**	p4.9	6	S	7 01	**7 35**	a4.1	12 41	**12 56**	p5.3
7	S	7 30	**7 59**	a3.9	1 05	**1 24**	p5.0	7	M	7 45	**8 21**	a4.1	1 26	**1 42**	p5.3
8	S	8 10	**8 43**	a4.0	1 47	**2 06**	p5.0	8	T	8 33	**9 11**	a4.0	2 14	**2 30**	p5.1
9	M	8 54	**9 31**	a3.9	2 32	**2 52**	p4.9	9	W	9 25	**10 06**	a3.8	3 05	**3 23**	p4.9
10	T	9 42	**10 23**	a3.7	3 20	**3 41**	p4.7	10	T	10 22	**11 06**	a3.5	4 00	**4 20**	p4.6
11	W	10 36	**11 22**	a3.5	4 12	**4 36**	p4.5	11	F	11 26	**...**	3.3	5 00	**5 22**	p4.3
12	T	11 37	**...**	3.3	5 11	**5 36**	p4.3	12	S	12 09	**12 34**	3.1	6 03	**6 28**	p4.1
13	F	12 26	**12 43**	p3.2	6 14	**6 41**	p4.2	13	S	1 14	**1 42**	3.1	7 09	**7 36**	4.1
14	S	1 31	**1 50**	p3.2	7 21	**7 48**	p4.2	14	M	2 16	**2 47**	3.3	8 13	**8 41**	a4.3
15	S	2 34	**2 55**	p3.4	8 27	**8 53**	p4.4	15	T	3 14	**3 47**	3.5	9 12	**9 42**	a4.6
16	M	3 33	**3 56**	p3.6	9 28	**9 54**	p4.6	16	W	4 08	**4 42**	a3.8	10 07	**10 37**	a4.9
17	T	4 27	**4 53**	p3.9	10 25	**10 50**	a4.9	17	T	4 59	**5 34**	a4.0	10 58	**11 28**	a5.1
18	W	5 18	**5 46**	a4.1	11 17	**11 42**	a5.2	18	F	5 47	**6 22**	a4.0	11 45	**...**	5.2
19	T	6 07	**6 37**	a4.2	...	**12 05**	5.3	19	S	6 33	**7 08**	a4.0	12 16	**12 29**	p5.1
20	F	6 54	**7 26**	a4.2	12 31	**12 52**	p5.3	20	S	7 18	**7 53**	a3.8	1 00	**1 12**	p4.9
21	S	7 41	**8 14**	a4.1	1 19	**1 37**	p5.1	21	M	8 03	**8 36**	a3.6	1 44	**1 54**	p4.6
22	S	8 27	**9 01**	a3.8	2 05	**2 22**	p4.8	22	T	8 47	**9 20**	a3.3	2 26	**2 35**	p4.3
23	M	9 14	**9 50**	a3.5	2 51	**3 07**	p4.4	23	W	9 32	**10 04**	a3.0	3 08	**3 17**	p4.0
24	T	10 02	**10 39**	a3.1	3 38	**3 52**	p4.0	24	T	10 20	**10 49**	2.7	3 51	**3 59**	p3.7
25	W	10 53	**11 31**	a2.7	4 25	**4 39**	p3.6	25	F	11 09	**11 36**	2.5	4 35	**4 44**	p3.4
26	T	11 47	**...**	2.4	5 14	**5 29**	p3.3	26	S	...	**12 01**	2.3	5 21	**5 32**	3.2
27	F	12 24	**12 43**	2.3	6 05	**6 21**	p3.2	27	S	12 24	**12 53**	a2.5	6 09	**6 24**	3.2
28	S	1 16	**1 37**	2.3	6 57	**7 14**	p3.1	28	M	1 13	**1 45**	a2.6	6 58	**7 17**	a3.3
29	S	2 07	**2 28**	2.4	7 49	**8 07**	3.2	29	T	2 00	**2 34**	a2.7	7 48	**8 11**	a3.6
30	M	2 53	**3 16**	2.6	8 37	**8 57**	p3.5	30	W	2 47	**3 22**	a2.9	8 37	**9 03**	a4.0
								31	T	3 32	**4 08**	a3.2	9 24	**9 54**	a4.4

The Kts. (knots) columns show the **maximum** predicted velocities of the stronger one of the Flood Currents and the stronger one of the Ebb Currents for each day.

The letter "a" means the velocity shown should occur **after** the **a.m.** Current Change. The letter "p" means the velocity shown should occur **after** the **p.m.** Current Change (even if next morning). No "a" or "p" means a.m. and p.m. velocities are the same for that day.

Avg. Max. Velocity: Flood 3.3 Kts., Ebb 4.2 Kts.

Max. Flood 2 hrs. 45 min. after Flood Starts, ±15 min.

Max. Ebb 3 hrs. 25 min. after Ebb Starts, ±15 min.

Use THE RACE tables with current charts pp. 92-97

See pp. 22-29 for Current Change at other points.

2013 CURRENT TABLE
THE RACE, LONG ISLAND SOUND
41°13.69'N, 72°03.75'W 0.2 nm E.N.E. of Valiant Rock

Standard Time starts Nov. 3 at 2 a.m.   Standard Time

		NOVEMBER						DECEMBER				
		CURRENT TURNS TO						CURRENT TURNS TO				
DAY OF MONTH	DAY OF WEEK	NORTHWEST Flood Starts			SOUTHEAST Ebb Starts		DAY OF MONTH	DAY OF WEEK	NORTHWEST Flood Starts			SOUTHEAST Ebb Starts
		a.m.	p.m.	Kts.	a.m.	p.m.	Kts.			a.m.	p.m.	Kts.	a.m.	p.m.	Kts.
1	F	4 17	4 53	3.5	10 11	10 42	a4.8	1	S	3 29	4 13	a3.9	9 29	10 05	a5.2
2	S	5 02	5 39	a3.8	10 58	11 30	a5.1	2	M	4 20	5 03	a4.1	10 20	10 57	a5.4
3	S	*4 48	*5 26	a4.1	*10 44	*11 18	a5.3	3	T	5 13	5 54	a4.3	11 11	11 49	a5.5
4	M	5 34	6 13	a4.2	11 32	...	5.4	4	W	6 05	6 45	a4.3	...	12 03	5.5
5	T	6 23	7 02	a4.2	12 07	12 21	p5.4	5	T	7 00	7 37	a4.2	12 42	12 56	p5.4
6	W	7 15	7 54	a4.1	12 58	1 12	p5.3	6	F	7 57	8 32	4.0	1 36	1 52	p5.1
7	T	8 11	8 50	a3.9	1 51	2 07	p5.0	7	S	8 57	9 28	p3.8	2 33	2 50	p4.8
8	F	9 11	9 48	a3.6	2 48	3 05	p4.7	8	S	10 01	10 28	p3.6	3 31	3 51	a4.6
9	S	10 15	10 50	p3.4	3 47	4 08	4.3	9	M	11 07	11 29	p3.5	4 30	4 55	a4.4
10	S	11 23	11 53	p3.4	4 49	5 13	a4.2	10	T	...	12 14	3.0	5 31	6 01	a4.4
11	M	...	12 31	3.1	5 53	6 21	a4.2	11	W	12 30	1 18	a3.4	6 32	7 07	a4.4
12	T	12 55	1 35	a3.4	6 54	7 26	a4.4	12	T	1 30	2 18	a3.4	7 30	8 08	a4.5
13	W	1 53	2 35	a3.5	7 53	8 27	a4.6	13	F	2 26	3 13	a3.4	8 25	9 04	a4.6
14	T	2 48	3 30	a3.6	8 47	9 22	a4.8	14	S	3 18	4 03	a3.4	9 16	9 53	a4.6
15	F	3 39	4 20	a3.7	9 37	10 13	a4.9	15	S	4 07	4 48	a3.5	10 02	10 38	a4.6
16	S	4 27	5 07	a3.7	10 24	10 58	a4.9	16	M	4 53	5 29	3.4	10 44	11 19	a4.6
17	S	5 13	5 50	a3.7	11 07	11 41	a4.9	17	T	5 35	6 08	3.4	11 24	11 57	a4.5
18	M	5 57	6 31	a3.6	11 48	...	4.7	18	W	6 16	6 45	3.3	...	12 01	4.4
19	T	6 40	7 11	a3.4	12 22	12 27	p4.5	19	T	6 55	7 20	p3.3	12 33	12 37	p4.2
20	W	7 21	7 50	3.2	1 01	1 05	p4.2	20	F	7 34	7 55	p3.3	1 09	1 13	p4.1
21	T	8 03	8 29	3.0	1 39	1 43	p4.0	21	S	8 14	8 31	p3.2	1 45	1 50	p4.0
22	F	8 46	9 09	p2.9	2 18	2 23	p3.8	22	S	8 55	9 09	p3.2	2 23	2 30	3.9
23	S	9 31	9 50	p2.8	2 58	3 04	3.6	23	M	9 39	9 49	p3.1	3 02	3 12	a3.9
24	S	10 19	10 34	p2.8	3 40	3 49	3.5	24	T	10 27	10 34	p3.1	3 45	3 59	a3.9
25	M	11 09	11 20	p2.8	4 25	4 38	a3.5	25	W	11 18	11 23	p3.2	4 31	4 51	a4.0
26	T	...	12 01	2.5	5 12	5 31	a3.6	26	T	...	12 12	2.7	5 21	5 47	a4.1
27	W	12 08	12 52	a2.9	6 02	6 26	a3.8	27	F	12 16	1 07	a3.2	6 15	6 47	a4.2
28	T	12 58	1 43	a3.1	6 53	7 23	a4.1	28	S	1 11	2 02	a3.4	7 11	7 47	a4.5
29	F	1 48	2 33	a3.3	7 45	8 19	a4.5	29	S	2 07	2 56	a3.6	8 09	8 46	a4.8
30	S	2 38	3 23	a3.6	8 37	9 13	a4.8	30	M	3 03	3 50	a3.8	9 05	9 43	a5.1
								31	T	3 59	4 43	a4.1	10 00	10 38	a5.4

The Kts. (knots) columns show the **maximum** predicted velocities of the stronger one of the Flood Currents and the stronger one of the Ebb Currents for each day.

The letter "a" means the velocity shown should occur **after** the **a.m.** Current Change. The letter "p" means the velocity shown should occur **after** the **p.m.** Current Change (even if next morning). No "a" or "p" means a.m. and p.m. velocities are the same for that day.

Avg. Max. Velocity: Flood 3.3 Kts., Ebb 4.2 Kts.

Max. Flood 2 hrs. 45 min. after Flood Starts, ±15 min.

Max. Ebb 3 hrs. 25 min. after Ebb Starts, ±15 min.

Use THE RACE tables with current charts pp. 92-97

See pp. 22-29 for Current Change at other points.

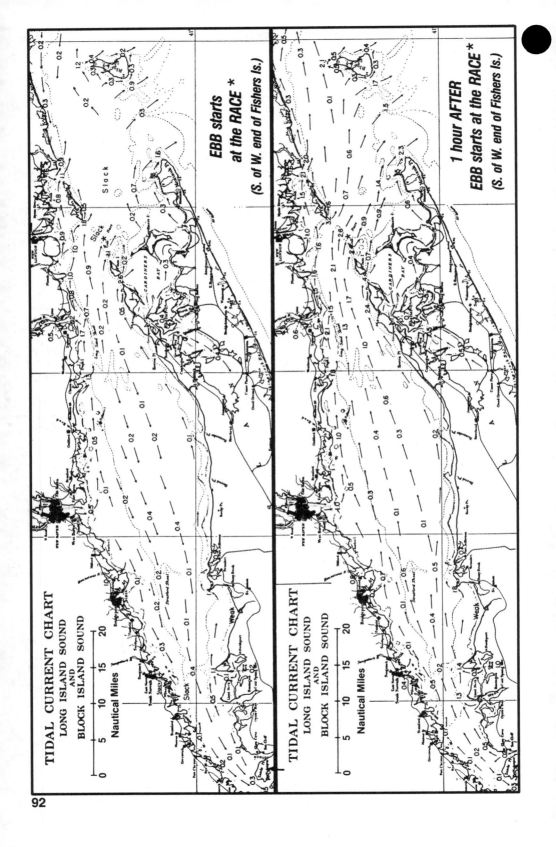

TIDAL CURRENT CHART
LONG ISLAND SOUND
AND
BLOCK ISLAND SOUND

Nautical Miles
0 5 10 15 20

*EBB starts
at the RACE* *
(S. of W. end of Fishers Is.)

*1 hour AFTER
EBB starts at the RACE* *
(S. of W. end of Fishers Is.)

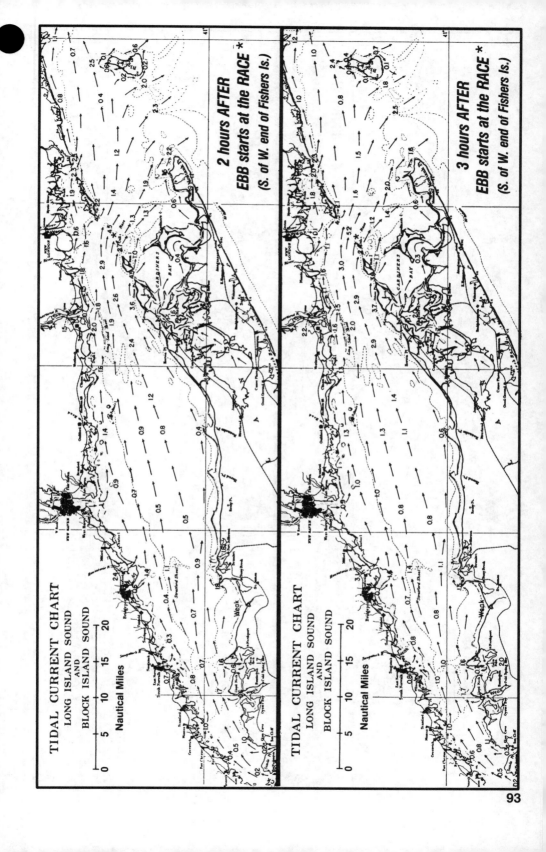

TIDAL CURRENT CHART
LONG ISLAND SOUND
AND
BLOCK ISLAND SOUND

Nautical Miles

2 hours AFTER
EBB starts at the RACE *
(S. of W. end of Fishers Is.)

TIDAL CURRENT CHART
LONG ISLAND SOUND
AND
BLOCK ISLAND SOUND

Nautical Miles

3 hours AFTER
EBB starts at the RACE *
(S. of W. end of Fishers Is.)

93

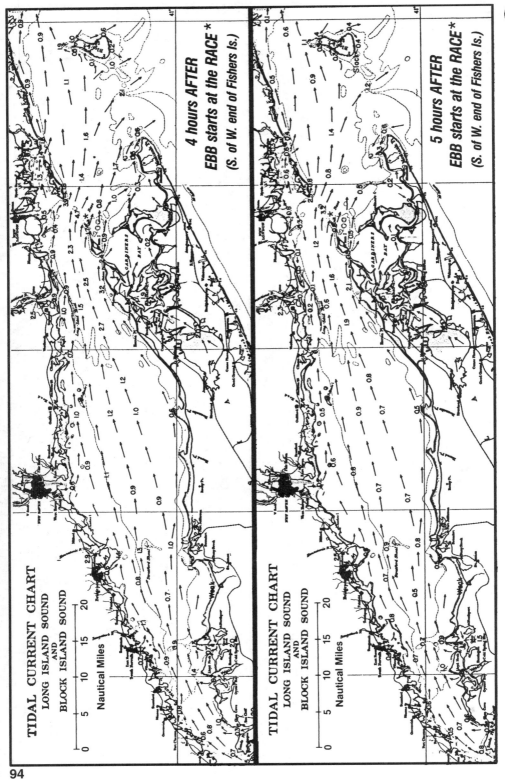

TIDAL CURRENT CHART
LONG ISLAND SOUND
AND
BLOCK ISLAND SOUND

Nautical Miles

4 hours AFTER
EBB starts at the RACE *
(S. of W. end of Fishers Is.)

5 hours AFTER
EBB starts at the RACE *
(S. of W. end of Fishers Is.)

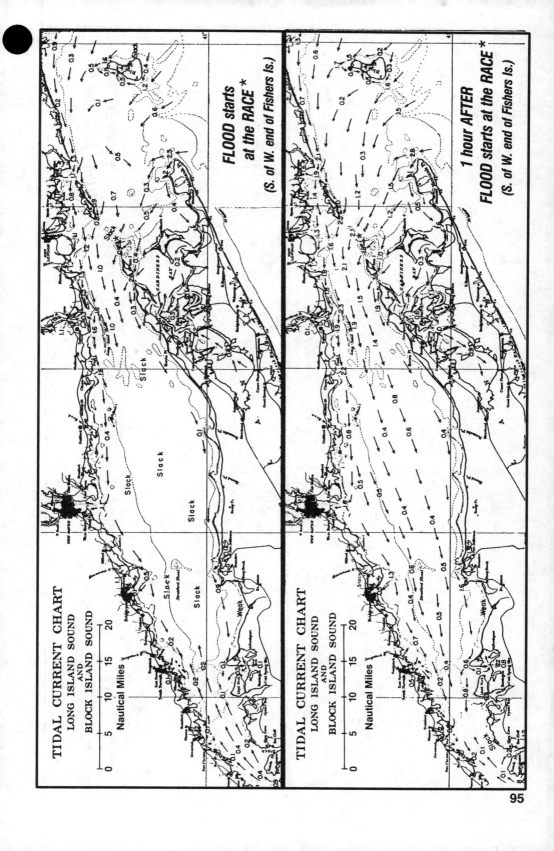

TIDAL CURRENT CHART
LONG ISLAND SOUND
AND
BLOCK ISLAND SOUND
Nautical Miles

*FLOOD starts
at the RACE* *
(S. of W. end of Fishers Is.)

*1 hour AFTER
FLOOD starts at the RACE* *
(S. of W. end of Fishers Is.)

95

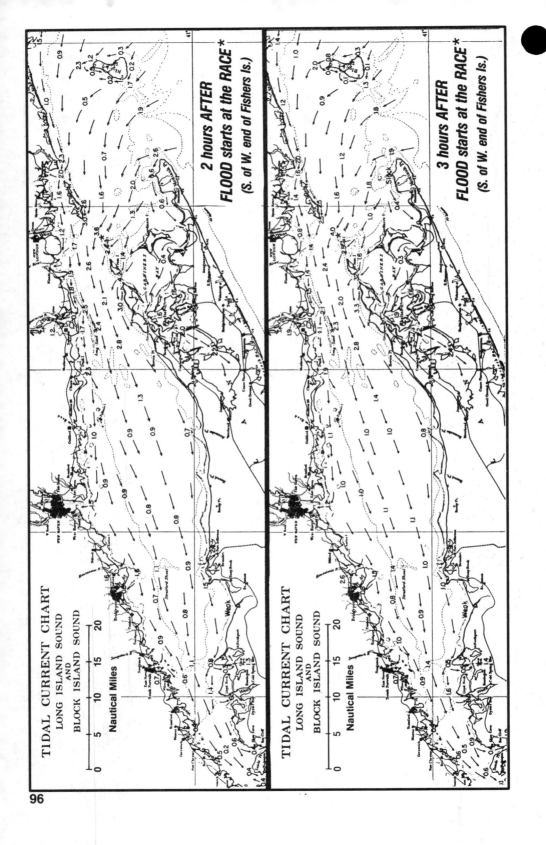

TIDAL CURRENT CHART
LONG ISLAND SOUND
AND
BLOCK ISLAND SOUND

Nautical Miles

2 hours AFTER
FLOOD starts at the RACE*
(S. of W. end of Fishers Is.)

TIDAL CURRENT CHART
LONG ISLAND SOUND
AND
BLOCK ISLAND SOUND

Nautical Miles

3 hours AFTER
FLOOD starts at the RACE*
(S. of W. end of Fishers Is.)

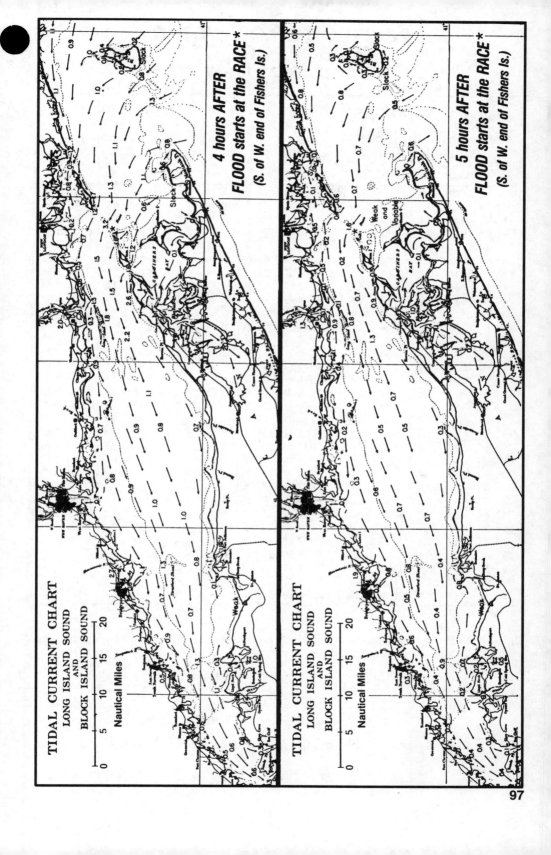

TIDAL CURRENT CHART
LONG ISLAND SOUND
AND
BLOCK ISLAND SOUND

Nautical Miles
0   5   10   15   20

4 hours AFTER
FLOOD starts at the RACE*
(S. of W. end of Fishers Is.)

TIDAL CURRENT CHART
LONG ISLAND SOUND
AND
BLOCK ISLAND SOUND

Nautical Miles
0   5   10   15   20

5 hours AFTER
FLOOD starts at the RACE*
(S. of W. end of Fishers Is.)

2013 HIGH & LOW WATER
BRIDGEPORT, CT
41°10.4'N, 73°10.9'W

Standard Time | Standard Time

D A Y O F M O N T H	D A Y O F W E E K	JANUARY HIGH a.m.	Ht.	HIGH p.m.	Ht.	LOW a.m.	LOW p.m.	D A Y O F M O N T H	D A Y O F W E E K	FEBRUARY HIGH a.m.	Ht.	HIGH p.m.	Ht.	LOW a.m.	LOW p.m.
1	T	1 22	6.6	1 32	6.8	7 29	7 54	1	F	2 19	7.1	2 43	6.6	8 41	8 58
2	W	2 03	6.7	2 17	6.6	8 14	8 38	2	S	3 08	7.1	3 38	6.3	9 36	9 52
3	T	2 49	6.7	3 07	6.4	9 06	9 27	3	S	4 05	7.0	4 40	6.1	10 38	10 53
4	F	3 37	6.8	4 02	6.3	10 00	10 19	4	M	5 05	7.0	5 45	6.1	11 42	11 57
5	S	4 31	6.9	5 02	6.2	11 01	11 17	5	T	6 11	7.1	6 51	6.2	...	12 48
6	S	5 30	7.0	6 05	6.2	...	12 04	6	W	7 16	7.2	7 54	6.4	1 03	1 51
7	M	6 31	7.2	7 09	6.3	12 18	1 07	7	T	8 18	7.5	8 53	6.8	2 06	2 50
8	T	7 32	7.5	8 10	6.5	1 19	2 07	8	F	9 16	7.7	9 47	7.2	3 05	3 44
9	W	8 31	7.8	9 07	6.8	2 19	3 05	9	S	10 10	7.8	10 38	7.4	4 01	4 33
10	T	9 28	8.0	10 02	7.1	3 17	3 59	10	S	11 00	7.8	11 25	7.6	4 52	5 21
11	F	10 23	8.1	10 54	7.3	4 12	4 51	11	M	11 48	7.7	...	...	5 42	6 06
12	S	11 15	8.1	11 45	7.5	5 06	5 41	12	T	12 11	7.7	12 34	7.5	6 29	6 49
13	S	...	...	12 06	8.0	5 58	6 29	13	W	12 56	7.6	1 20	7.1	7 16	7 33
14	M	12 35	7.5	12 56	7.7	6 50	7 17	14	T	1 41	7.3	2 07	6.8	8 03	8 17
15	T	1 24	7.4	1 46	7.3	7 42	8 05	15	F	2 27	7.1	2 55	6.4	8 52	9 03
16	W	2 14	7.3	2 38	6.8	8 34	8 54	16	S	3 15	6.7	3 47	6.0	9 43	9 53
17	T	3 05	7.0	3 31	6.4	9 29	9 44	17	S	4 06	6.4	4 42	5.7	10 37	10 47
18	F	3 57	6.8	4 26	6.0	10 25	10 37	18	M	5 02	6.2	5 40	5.6	11 34	11 45
19	S	4 52	6.5	5 24	5.8	11 23	11 32	19	T	6 01	6.1	6 38	5.6	...	12 31
20	S	5 48	6.4	6 22	5.7	...	12 20	20	W	6 58	6.1	7 33	5.8	12 43	1 26
21	M	6 44	6.3	7 18	5.7	12 28	1 16	21	T	7 53	6.2	8 24	6.1	1 39	2 17
22	T	7 37	6.4	8 10	5.9	1 22	2 07	22	F	8 42	6.5	9 10	6.4	2 29	3 02
23	W	8 27	6.5	8 58	6.1	2 13	2 54	23	S	9 26	6.7	9 52	6.7	3 16	3 45
24	T	9 13	6.6	9 42	6.3	3 00	3 37	24	S	10 08	6.9	10 32	6.9	3 59	4 24
25	F	9 55	6.8	10 23	6.5	3 44	4 17	25	M	10 48	7.1	11 10	7.2	4 41	5 03
26	S	10 35	6.9	11 02	6.7	4 26	4 55	26	T	11 27	7.2	11 48	7.4	5 22	5 42
27	S	11 13	7.0	11 39	6.8	5 06	5 32	27	W	...	...	12 08	7.2	6 03	6 21
28	M	11 51	7.0	...	...	5 45	6 10	28	T	12 27	7.5	12 50	7.2	6 46	7 02
29	T	12 17	6.9	12 30	7.0	6 25	6 48								
30	W	12 55	7.0	1 10	6.9	7 07	7 27								
31	T	1 35	7.1	1 54	6.8	7 52	8 10								

Dates when Ht. of **Low** Water is below Mean Lower Low with Ht. of lowest given for each period and Date of lowest in ( ):

7th - 16th: -1.3' (12th)   6th - 14th: -1.1' (10th)
26th - 31st: -0.5' (28th - 29th)   24th - 28th: -0.6' (28th)

Average Rise and Fall 6.8 ft.

When a high tide exceeds avg. ht., the *following* low tide will be lower than avg.

2013 HIGH & LOW WATER
BRIDGEPORT, CT
41°10.4'N, 73°10.9'W

*Daylight Time starts March 10 at 2 a.m.   **Daylight Saving Time**

DAY OF MONTH	DAY OF WEEK	MARCH						DAY OF MONTH	DAY OF WEEK	APRIL					
		HIGH				LOW				HIGH				LOW	
		a.m.	Ht.	p.m.	Ht.	a.m.	p.m.			a.m.	Ht.	p.m.	Ht.	a.m.	p.m.
1	F	1 09	7.6	1 36	7.0	7 32	7 47	1	M	3 30	7.7	4 08	6.8	10 03	10 20
2	S	1 55	7.5	2 26	6.8	8 22	8 37	2	T	4 30	7.4	5 10	6.6	11 04	11 25
3	S	2 47	7.4	3 22	6.5	9 19	9 34	3	W	5 36	7.1	6 17	6.6	...	12 10
4	M	3 44	7.2	4 23	6.3	10 19	10 36	4	T	6 43	7.0	7 21	6.7	12 34	1 14
5	T	4 48	7.0	5 29	6.2	11 25	11 44	5	F	7 49	7.0	8 23	7.0	1 41	2 15
6	W	5 56	7.0	6 36	6.4	...	12 32	6	S	8 51	7.0	9 19	7.3	2 44	3 11
7	T	7 03	7.1	7 40	6.6	12 52	1 35	7	S	9 47	7.2	10 10	7.6	3 41	4 02
8	F	8 06	7.2	8 38	7.0	1 56	2 33	8	M	10 37	7.2	10 56	7.7	4 33	4 49
9	S	9 03	7.4	9 30	7.4	2 55	3 25	9	T	11 23	7.3	11 39	7.8	5 20	5 32
10	S	*10 55	7.5	*11 18	7.6	*4 48	*5 13	10	W	...	...	12 07	7.2	6 04	6 13
11	M	11 43	7.6	...	...	5 37	5 57	11	T	12 19	7.8	12 48	7.1	6 45	6 52
12	T	12 03	7.8	12 28	7.5	6 24	6 40	12	F	12 59	7.6	1 29	7.0	7 24	7 31
13	W	12 46	7.8	1 11	7.3	7 07	7 20	13	S	1 38	7.4	2 10	6.8	8 04	8 11
14	T	1 27	7.7	1 54	7.1	7 50	8 01	14	S	2 18	7.2	2 52	6.6	8 44	8 52
15	F	2 08	7.4	2 37	6.8	8 33	8 42	15	M	3 01	6.9	3 37	6.4	9 27	9 38
16	S	2 51	7.1	3 22	6.4	9 16	9 25	16	T	3 46	6.6	4 25	6.2	10 13	10 28
17	S	3 35	6.8	4 10	6.1	10 02	10 12	17	W	4 36	6.4	5 16	6.1	11 03	11 23
18	M	4 24	6.5	5 01	5.9	10 52	11 05	18	T	5 31	6.2	6 11	6.2	11 57	...
19	T	5 17	6.2	5 57	5.8	11 47	...	19	F	6 28	6.1	7 06	6.3	12 21	12 52
20	W	6 15	6.0	6 54	5.8	12 03	12 44	20	S	7 26	6.2	7 59	6.6	1 19	1 45
21	T	7 15	6.0	7 51	6.0	1 02	1 40	21	S	8 21	6.4	8 48	6.9	2 15	2 36
22	F	8 11	6.1	8 43	6.3	2 00	2 33	22	M	9 13	6.6	9 36	7.3	3 07	3 25
23	S	9 04	6.4	9 31	6.6	2 54	3 22	23	T	10 02	6.9	10 21	7.7	3 57	4 12
24	S	9 52	6.7	10 16	7.0	3 43	4 07	24	W	10 50	7.1	11 06	8.0	4 45	4 58
25	M	10 36	6.9	10 57	7.3	4 29	4 49	25	T	11 37	7.3	11 52	8.3	5 32	5 44
26	T	11 20	7.2	11 38	7.7	5 14	5 31	26	F	...	...	12 25	7.5	6 20	6 31
27	W	...	...	12 03	7.3	5 57	6 12	27	S	12 39	8.4	1 14	7.5	7 09	7 21
28	T	12 19	7.9	12 46	7.4	6 41	6 55	28	S	1 28	8.4	2 05	7.4	8 00	8 13
29	F	1 02	8.0	1 31	7.3	7 27	7 40	29	M	2 21	8.2	2 59	7.3	8 53	9 09
30	S	1 47	8.0	2 20	7.2	8 15	8 28	30	T	3 17	7.9	3 56	7.1	9 49	10 09
31	S	2 36	7.9	3 12	7.0	9 07	9 21								

Dates when Ht. of **Low** Water is below Mean Lower Low with Ht. of lowest given for each period and Date of lowest in ( ):

1st - 3rd: -0.6' (1st)   1st: -0.3'
8th - 15th: -0.8' (12th)   7th - 12th: -0.5' (9th - 11th)
26th - 31st: -0.8' (28th - 30th)   24th - 30th: -0.9' (26th - 28th)

Average Rise and Fall 6.8 ft.

When a high tide exceeds avg. ht., the *following* low tide will be lower than avg.

2013 HIGH & LOW WATER
BRIDGEPORT, CT
41°10.4'N, 73°10.9'W

Daylight Saving Time						Daylight Saving Time					

D A Y O F M O N T H	D A Y O F W E E K	MAY				D A Y O F M O N T H	D A Y O F W E E K	JUNE			
		HIGH		LOW				HIGH		LOW	
		a.m.	Ht.	p.m.	Ht.	a.m.	p.m.	a.m.	Ht.	p.m.	Ht.	a.m.	p.m.

D.o.M	D.o.W	a.m.	Ht.	p.m.	Ht.	a.m.	p.m.	D.o.M	D.o.W	a.m.	Ht.	p.m.	Ht.	a.m.	p.m.
1	W	4 17	7.5	4 57	7.1	10 48	11 14	1	S	6 03	6.9	6 37	7.4	12 01	12 23
2	T	5 20	7.2	5 59	7.0	11 50	...	2	S	7 05	6.7	7 34	7.4	1 04	1 20
3	F	6 27	7.0	7 03	7.1	12 21	12 52	3	M	8 05	6.6	8 29	7.4	2 05	2 16
4	S	7 30	6.9	8 01	7.3	1 26	1 50	4	T	9 00	6.6	9 18	7.5	2 59	3 06
5	S	8 30	6.8	8 56	7.5	2 27	2 45	5	W	9 51	6.6	10 05	7.5	3 50	3 54
6	M	9 25	6.9	9 46	7.6	3 23	3 36	6	T	10 38	6.6	10 48	7.5	4 36	4 39
7	T	10 16	6.9	10 31	7.7	4 14	4 22	7	F	11 21	6.7	11 30	7.4	5 18	5 21
8	W	11 02	6.9	11 14	7.7	5 00	5 06	8	S	...	...	12 02	6.7	5 58	6 01
9	T	11 45	6.9	11 54	7.6	5 42	5 46	9	S	12 09	7.4	12 42	6.8	6 36	6 41
10	F	...	...	12 26	6.9	6 22	6 26	10	M	12 48	7.3	1 21	6.8	7 13	7 20
11	S	12 33	7.5	1 06	6.8	7 00	7 04	11	T	1 27	7.2	2 00	6.8	7 51	8 00
12	S	1 12	7.4	1 45	6.8	7 38	7 44	12	W	2 06	7.1	2 40	6.8	8 29	8 42
13	M	1 51	7.2	2 26	6.7	8 17	8 25	13	T	2 46	6.9	3 21	6.8	9 09	9 27
14	T	2 31	7.0	3 08	6.6	8 57	9 09	14	F	3 29	6.8	4 04	6.8	9 51	10 14
15	W	3 14	6.8	3 52	6.5	9 39	9 56	15	S	4 15	6.6	4 50	6.9	10 36	11 06
16	T	4 00	6.6	4 39	6.5	10 25	10 47	16	S	5 06	6.5	5 40	7.0	11 25	...
17	F	4 50	6.4	5 29	6.5	11 14	11 42	17	M	6 02	6.4	6 32	7.2	12 02	12 17
18	S	5 44	6.3	6 21	6.7	...	12 06	18	T	7 00	6.4	7 27	7.4	1 00	1 12
19	S	6 41	6.3	7 13	6.9	12 39	12 59	19	W	8 00	6.5	8 23	7.7	1 59	2 09
20	M	7 38	6.4	8 05	7.2	1 36	1 52	20	T	8 59	6.7	9 19	8.0	2 57	3 06
21	T	8 34	6.6	8 56	7.6	2 31	2 44	21	F	9 56	7.0	10 14	8.3	3 53	4 02
22	W	9 29	6.8	9 47	8.0	3 25	3 36	22	S	10 51	7.2	11 09	8.5	4 48	4 58
23	T	10 21	7.1	10 38	8.3	4 18	4 27	23	S	11 45	7.5	...	...	5 42	5 53
24	F	11 13	7.3	11 28	8.5	5 09	5 19	24	M	12 03	8.6	12 39	7.7	6 34	6 48
25	S	...	...	12 05	7.5	6 00	6 11	25	T	12 57	8.5	1 32	7.8	7 26	7 43
26	S	12 20	8.6	12 56	7.6	6 52	7 04	26	W	1 51	8.3	2 25	7.8	8 18	8 40
27	M	1 12	8.5	1 49	7.6	7 44	7 59	27	T	2 45	8.0	3 19	7.8	9 10	9 37
28	T	2 07	8.3	2 44	7.6	8 37	8 56	28	F	3 40	7.6	4 14	7.7	10 02	10 36
29	W	3 03	8.0	3 40	7.5	9 32	9 56	29	S	4 37	7.2	5 09	7.5	10 56	11 36
30	T	4 01	7.6	4 38	7.4	10 28	10 58	30	S	5 36	6.8	6 06	7.4	11 51	...
31	F	5 01	7.2	5 38	7.4	11 25	...								

Dates when Ht. of **Low** Water is below Mean Lower Low with Ht. of lowest given for each period and Date of lowest in ( ):

8th - 10th: -0.2'
23rd - 30th: -1.0' (26th)

21st - 28th: -0.9' (24th - 25th)

Average Rise and Fall 6.8 ft.

When a high tide exceeds avg. ht., the *following* low tide will be lower than avg.

2013 HIGH & LOW WATER
BRIDGEPORT, CT
41°10.4'N, 73°10.9'W

Daylight Saving Time   **Daylight Saving Time**

DAY OF MONTH	DAY OF WEEK	JULY						DAY OF MONTH	DAY OF WEEK	AUGUST					
		HIGH				LOW				HIGH				LOW	
		a.m.	Ht.	p.m.	Ht.	a.m.	p.m.			a.m.	Ht.	p.m.	Ht.	a.m.	p.m.
1	M	6 35	6.5	7 02	7.3	12 36	12 47	1	T	7 57	6.2	8 17	6.9	1 56	2 01
2	T	7 33	6.4	7 56	7.2	1 34	1 41	2	F	8 50	6.2	9 08	6.9	2 48	2 54
3	W	8 31	6.3	8 50	7.2	2 31	2 35	3	S	9 41	6.4	9 57	7.0	3 38	3 44
4	T	9 22	6.3	9 37	7.2	3 22	3 25	4	S	10 26	6.6	10 40	7.1	4 21	4 28
5	F	10 11	6.4	10 23	7.2	4 09	4 11	5	M	11 08	6.8	11 21	7.2	5 02	5 11
6	S	10 55	6.6	11 06	7.2	4 52	4 55	6	T	11 48	7.0	11 59	7.3	5 41	5 52
7	S	11 37	6.7	11 46	7.3	5 32	5 37	7	W	...	...	12 26	7.1	6 18	6 31
8	M	...	...	12 17	6.8	6 10	6 17	8	T	12 37	7.3	1 03	7.2	6 55	7 11
9	T	12 25	7.3	12 55	6.9	6 47	6 56	9	F	1 15	7.3	1 40	7.3	7 31	7 51
10	W	1 03	7.2	1 33	6.9	7 24	7 36	10	S	1 54	7.2	2 18	7.4	8 09	8 33
11	T	1 41	7.2	2 11	7.0	8 01	8 17	11	S	2 35	7.1	2 59	7.4	8 50	9 19
12	F	2 19	7.1	2 50	7.1	8 39	8 59	12	M	3 21	6.9	3 44	7.5	9 34	10 10
13	S	3 01	6.9	3 31	7.1	9 19	9 45	13	T	4 11	6.7	4 35	7.5	10 23	11 07
14	S	3 46	6.8	4 15	7.2	10 03	10 36	14	W	5 08	6.6	5 33	7.5	11 19	...
15	M	4 36	6.6	5 04	7.3	10 51	11 31	15	T	6 10	6.5	6 35	7.5	12 09	12 21
16	T	5 31	6.5	5 58	7.4	11 44	...	16	F	7 14	6.5	7 40	7.6	1 13	1 26
17	W	6 31	6.4	6 56	7.5	12 31	12 42	17	S	8 18	6.7	8 43	7.8	2 16	2 30
18	T	7 33	6.5	7 57	7.7	1 32	1 42	18	S	9 18	7.1	9 42	8.0	3 16	3 31
19	F	8 35	6.7	8 57	8.0	2 34	2 44	19	M	10 15	7.5	10 38	8.2	4 11	4 29
20	S	9 35	6.9	9 56	8.2	3 33	3 44	20	T	11 08	7.8	11 31	8.3	5 04	5 23
21	S	10 32	7.3	10 53	8.4	4 29	4 42	21	W	11 59	8.1	...	...	5 53	6 16
22	M	11 27	7.6	11 47	8.5	5 23	5 38	22	T	12 22	8.2	12 47	8.2	6 41	7 06
23	T	...	...	12 19	7.8	6 15	6 32	23	F	1 11	8.0	1 35	8.1	7 27	7 56
24	W	12 40	8.4	1 11	8.0	7 05	7 26	24	S	1 59	7.7	2 22	8.0	8 13	8 46
25	T	1 32	8.2	2 02	8.0	7 54	8 19	25	S	2 48	7.3	3 10	7.7	8 59	9 36
26	F	2 23	7.9	2 52	7.9	8 43	9 13	26	M	3 38	6.9	3 59	7.4	9 48	10 28
27	S	3 16	7.5	3 44	7.8	9 32	10 08	27	T	4 31	6.6	4 52	7.1	10 39	11 23
28	S	4 09	7.1	4 36	7.5	10 23	11 04	28	W	5 26	6.3	5 47	6.8	11 33	...
29	M	5 04	6.7	5 30	7.3	11 16	...	29	T	6 23	6.1	6 45	6.7	12 20	12 30
30	T	6 01	6.4	6 26	7.1	12 02	12 11	30	F	7 20	6.1	7 42	6.6	1 16	1 27
31	W	7 00	6.2	7 22	6.9	12 59	1 06	31	S	8 15	6.3	8 35	6.7	2 10	2 21

Dates when Ht. of **Low** Water is below Mean Lower Low with Ht. of lowest given for each period and Date of lowest in ( ):

20th - 27th: -0.9' (23rd - 24th)   19th - 24th: -0.7' (21st - 22nd)

Average Rise and Fall 6.8 ft.

When a high tide exceeds avg. ht., the *following* low tide will be lower than avg.

2013 HIGH & LOW WATER
BRIDGEPORT, CT
41°10.4'N, 73°10.9'W

Daylight Saving Time   Daylight Saving Time

DAY OF MONTH	DAY OF WEEK	SEPTEMBER HIGH a.m.	Ht.	HIGH p.m.	Ht.	LOW a.m.	LOW p.m.	DAY OF MONTH	DAY OF WEEK	OCTOBER HIGH a.m.	Ht.	HIGH p.m.	Ht.	LOW a.m.	LOW p.m.
1	S	9 06	6.5	9 24	6.9	3 00	3 12	1	T	9 14	6.9	9 34	6.9	3 04	3 26
2	M	9 52	6.7	10 09	7.0	3 45	3 59	2	W	9 58	7.2	10 18	7.1	3 48	4 11
3	T	10 36	7.0	10 52	7.2	4 28	4 43	3	T	10 40	7.5	11 01	7.2	4 31	4 55
4	W	11 15	7.2	11 31	7.3	5 07	5 24	4	F	11 18	7.7	11 41	7.3	5 10	5 36
5	T	11 53	7.4	...	...	5 45	6 04	5	S	11 58	7.9	...	...	5 50	6 19
6	F	12 09	7.4	12 30	7.6	6 22	6 44	6	S	12 23	7.4	12 38	8.0	6 31	7 02
7	S	12 49	7.4	1 08	7.7	7 01	7 26	7	M	1 07	7.3	1 21	8.0	7 14	7 49
8	S	1 29	7.3	1 48	7.7	7 40	8 10	8	T	1 53	7.2	2 09	8.0	8 01	8 39
9	M	2 13	7.2	2 31	7.7	8 23	8 57	9	W	2 43	7.1	3 01	7.8	8 52	9 34
10	T	3 00	7.0	3 19	7.7	9 10	9 50	10	T	3 38	6.9	3 59	7.6	9 49	10 34
11	W	3 53	6.8	4 14	7.5	10 03	10 49	11	F	4 39	6.8	5 02	7.4	10 52	11 37
12	T	4 52	6.6	5 15	7.4	11 03	11 52	12	S	5 43	6.8	6 09	7.2	11 59	...
13	F	5 55	6.6	6 21	7.4	...	12 09	13	S	6 47	6.9	7 15	7.2	12 41	1 06
14	S	7 01	6.7	7 27	7.5	12 57	1 15	14	M	7 50	7.2	8 17	7.3	1 42	2 10
15	S	8 04	7.0	8 30	7.6	2 00	2 20	15	T	8 47	7.5	9 14	7.4	2 39	3 09
16	M	9 03	7.3	9 29	7.8	2 58	3 20	16	W	9 40	7.8	10 07	7.5	3 32	4 03
17	T	9 58	7.7	10 23	7.9	3 52	4 16	17	T	10 28	8.0	10 56	7.5	4 20	4 53
18	W	10 49	8.0	11 14	8.0	4 43	5 08	18	F	11 14	8.1	11 42	7.5	5 06	5 39
19	T	11 36	8.2	...	...	5 30	5 58	19	S	11 57	8.0	...	...	5 49	6 23
20	F	12 02	7.9	12 22	8.2	6 15	6 45	20	S	12 26	7.3	12 39	7.9	6 31	7 06
21	S	12 48	7.7	1 06	8.1	6 59	7 31	21	M	1 09	7.1	1 21	7.6	7 13	7 48
22	S	1 34	7.4	1 50	7.9	7 42	8 16	22	T	1 52	6.9	2 03	7.4	7 55	8 30
23	M	2 20	7.1	2 35	7.6	8 26	9 03	23	W	2 36	6.7	2 47	7.0	8 38	9 15
24	T	3 07	6.8	3 22	7.2	9 12	9 51	24	T	3 23	6.4	3 35	6.7	9 25	10 02
25	W	3 56	6.5	4 12	6.9	10 01	10 42	25	F	4 12	6.3	4 26	6.5	10 16	10 53
26	T	4 49	6.3	5 07	6.6	10 54	11 37	26	S	5 04	6.2	5 21	6.3	11 11	11 46
27	F	5 44	6.2	6 04	6.4	11 51	...	27	S	5 59	6.2	6 18	6.2	...	12 09
28	S	6 41	6.2	7 02	6.4	12 32	12 49	28	M	6 53	6.4	7 13	6.3	12 39	1 05
29	S	7 36	6.3	7 57	6.5	1 27	1 45	29	T	7 44	6.6	8 06	6.4	1 31	1 59
30	M	8 27	6.6	8 48	6.7	2 18	2 38	30	W	8 33	6.9	8 56	6.6	2 20	2 50
								31	T	9 18	7.2	9 43	6.8	3 07	3 38

Dates when Ht. of **Low** Water is below Mean Lower Low with Ht. of lowest given for each period and Date of lowest in ( ):

17th - 21st: -0.5' (18th - 20th)   5th - 8th: -0.3' (5th - 7th)
     16th - 20th: -0.5' (18th)

Average Rise and Fall 6.8 ft.

When a high tide exceeds avg. ht., the *following* low tide will be lower than avg.

2013 HIGH & LOW WATER
BRIDGEPORT, CT
41°10.4'N, 73°10.9'W

*Standard Time starts Nov. 3 at 2 a.m.   **Standard Time**

D A Y O F M O N T H	D A Y O F W E E K	NOVEMBER						D A Y O F M O N T H	D A Y O F W E E K	DECEMBER					
		HIGH				LOW				HIGH				LOW	
		a.m.	Ht.	p.m.	Ht.	a.m.	p.m.			a.m.	Ht.	p.m.	Ht.	a.m.	p.m.
1	F	10 02	7.6	10 28	7.0	3 52	4 24	1	S	9 15	7.9	9 48	7.0	3 04	3 44
2	S	10 45	7.9	11 14	7.2	4 36	5 09	2	M	10 03	8.1	10 37	7.2	3 54	4 34
3	S	*10 29	8.1	*11 00	7.3	*4 21	*4 56	3	T	10 54	8.3	11 28	7.3	4 44	5 24
4	M	11 13	8.2	11 46	7.3	5 05	5 42	4	W	11 44	8.3	...	...	5 35	6 14
5	T	...	...	12 01	8.2	5 52	6 31	5	T	12 18	7.3	12 36	8.1	6 28	7 06
6	W	12 35	7.3	12 51	8.1	6 43	7 23	6	F	1 12	7.3	1 31	7.9	7 24	8 00
7	T	1 28	7.2	1 46	7.9	7 37	8 18	7	S	2 07	7.3	2 29	7.5	8 22	8 56
8	F	2 24	7.0	2 45	7.6	8 37	9 17	8	S	3 05	7.2	3 29	7.1	9 24	9 54
9	S	3 24	7.0	3 48	7.3	9 40	10 18	9	M	4 05	7.1	4 32	6.8	10 29	10 54
10	S	4 27	7.0	4 53	7.0	10 47	11 20	10	T	5 06	7.1	5 35	6.6	11 33	11 53
11	M	5 30	7.1	5 58	6.9	11 53	...	11	W	6 06	7.2	6 37	6.5	...	12 36
12	T	6 31	7.3	7 00	6.9	12 20	12 56	12	T	7 03	7.2	7 35	6.4	12 50	1 35
13	W	7 27	7.5	7 57	6.9	1 16	1 54	13	F	7 57	7.3	8 29	6.5	1 44	2 28
14	T	8 19	7.7	8 49	7.0	2 09	2 47	14	S	8 46	7.3	9 17	6.5	2 35	3 16
15	F	9 07	7.8	9 37	7.0	2 58	3 36	15	S	9 31	7.3	10 02	6.6	3 21	4 01
16	S	9 52	7.8	10 22	7.0	3 43	4 20	16	M	10 14	7.3	10 44	6.6	4 05	4 42
17	S	10 34	7.7	11 05	6.9	4 26	5 02	17	T	10 54	7.2	11 24	6.6	4 46	5 20
18	M	11 15	7.6	11 46	6.8	5 07	5 42	18	W	11 33	7.1	...	...	5 25	5 58
19	T	11 55	7.4	...	...	5 47	6 22	19	T	12 03	6.6	12 12	7.0	6 04	6 35
20	W	12 27	6.7	12 36	7.1	6 28	7 01	20	F	12 42	6.5	12 51	6.8	6 44	7 12
21	T	1 08	6.6	1 17	6.9	7 09	7 42	21	S	1 21	6.5	1 31	6.6	7 25	7 51
22	F	1 51	6.4	2 01	6.6	7 53	8 25	22	S	2 02	6.5	2 13	6.4	8 08	8 32
23	S	2 36	6.3	2 48	6.4	8 41	9 11	23	M	2 44	6.4	2 58	6.2	8 54	9 16
24	S	3 24	6.3	3 38	6.2	9 32	10 00	24	T	3 30	6.4	3 47	6.1	9 45	10 04
25	M	4 14	6.3	4 31	6.1	10 26	10 51	25	W	4 18	6.5	4 41	6.0	10 39	10 56
26	T	5 06	6.4	5 26	6.1	11 22	11 43	26	T	5 10	6.6	5 39	5.9	11 37	11 51
27	W	5 57	6.6	6 22	6.1	...	12 18	27	F	6 05	6.8	6 38	6.0	...	12 35
28	T	6 48	6.9	7 16	6.3	12 34	1 12	28	S	7 00	7.1	7 36	6.2	12 47	1 33
29	F	7 38	7.2	8 08	6.5	1 25	2 04	29	S	7 56	7.4	8 32	6.5	1 43	2 29
30	S	8 26	7.5	8 59	6.8	2 15	2 55	30	M	8 50	7.7	9 25	6.8	2 38	3 22
								31	T	9 44	8.0	10 18	7.1	3 33	4 15

Dates when Ht. of **Low** Water is below Mean Lower Low with Ht. of lowest given for each period and Date of lowest in ( ):

2nd - 7th: -0.7' (4th - 5th)   1st - 8th: -1.0' (3rd - 4th)
14th - 18th: -0.4' (15th - 16th)   13th - 18th: -0.3' (15th - 16th)
30th: -0.3'   29th - 31st: -1.0' (31st)

Average Rise and Fall 6.8 ft.

When a high tide exceeds avg. ht., the *following* low tide will be lower than avg.

2013 HIGH & LOW WATER
KINGS POINT, NY
40°48.6'N, 73°45.9'W

DAY OF MONTH	DAY OF WEEK	JANUARY HIGH a.m.	Ht.	HIGH p.m.	Ht.	LOW a.m.	LOW p.m.	DAY OF MONTH	DAY OF WEEK	FEBRUARY HIGH a.m.	Ht.	HIGH p.m.	Ht.	LOW a.m.	LOW p.m.
1	T	12 59	7.2	1 09	7.6	7 12	7 39	1	F	1 58	7.9	2 21	7.4	8 24	8 43
2	W	1 39	7.4	1 54	7.5	7 57	8 22	2	S	2 47	7.9	3 14	7.2	9 17	9 35
3	T	2 25	7.5	2 44	7.3	8 47	9 10	3	S	3 41	7.8	4 13	6.9	10 19	10 35
4	F	3 13	7.6	3 36	7.1	9 40	10 01	4	M	4 40	7.6	5 20	6.6	11 37	11 44
5	S	4 06	7.6	4 34	6.9	10 40	10 58	5	T	5 51	7.6	6 47	6.6	...	1 26
6	S	5 05	7.7	5 39	6.8	11 50	...	6	W	7 17	7.7	8 14	7.0	1 24	2 36
7	M	6 09	7.8	6 53	6.8	12 01	1 21	7	T	8 36	8.0	9 17	7.4	2 47	3 34
8	T	7 20	8.0	8 11	7.1	1 12	2 42	8	F	9 37	8.3	10 11	7.8	3 49	4 27
9	W	8 31	8.3	9 18	7.4	2 35	3 44	9	S	10 30	8.5	11 01	8.1	4 44	5 16
10	T	9 33	8.6	10 15	7.7	3 47	4 39	10	S	11 20	8.5	11 48	8.3	5 35	6 02
11	F	10 30	8.8	11 09	8.0	4 47	5 31	11	M	...	...	12 07	8.4	6 23	6 46
12	S	11 24	8.8	...	...	5 42	6 20	12	T	12 33	8.3	12 53	8.1	7 10	7 28
13	S	12 02	8.1	12 17	8.6	6 35	7 08	13	W	1 17	8.1	1 39	7.7	7 57	8 09
14	M	12 54	8.1	1 10	8.3	7 27	7 56	14	T	2 01	7.9	2 26	7.3	8 46	8 46
15	T	1 46	8.0	2 04	7.9	8 22	8 46	15	F	2 44	7.5	3 16	6.9	9 38	9 18
16	W	2 38	7.8	3 00	7.4	9 19	9 37	16	S	3 30	7.1	4 11	6.5	10 34	9 53
17	T	3 33	7.5	3 58	6.9	10 19	10 33	17	S	4 26	6.8	5 15	6.2	11 33	11 28
18	F	4 30	7.3	5 00	6.6	11 18	11 30	18	M	5 36	6.5	6 21	6.1	...	12 32
19	S	5 30	7.0	6 03	6.3	...	12 17	19	T	6 46	6.5	7 21	6.2	12 38	1 28
20	S	6 31	6.9	7 04	6.3	12 28	1 13	20	W	7 46	6.6	8 15	6.4	1 37	2 20
21	M	7 29	6.9	7 59	6.4	1 23	2 06	21	T	8 37	6.8	9 03	6.6	2 30	3 08
22	T	8 22	7.0	8 50	6.6	2 16	2 56	22	F	9 21	7.0	9 44	6.9	3 16	3 51
23	W	9 09	7.1	9 35	6.7	3 05	3 43	23	S	9 57	7.2	10 17	7.2	3 57	4 28
24	T	9 51	7.3	10 16	6.9	3 49	4 25	24	S	10 24	7.4	10 40	7.4	4 30	4 58
25	F	10 27	7.4	10 51	7.0	4 28	5 03	25	M	10 43	7.6	10 59	7.7	4 56	5 18
26	S	10 54	7.4	11 18	7.1	4 59	5 34	26	T	11 11	7.8	11 29	8.0	5 23	5 40
27	S	11 08	7.5	11 34	7.3	5 17	5 52	27	W	11 47	7.9	...	...	5 57	6 13
28	M	11 32	7.6	11 58	7.5	5 40	6 08	28	T	12 06	8.3	12 29	7.9	6 36	6 51
29	T	...	...	12 07	7.7	6 14	6 37								
30	W	12 32	7.7	12 48	7.7	6 53	7 14								
31	T	1 13	7.8	1 33	7.6	7 37	7 56								

Dates when Ht. of **Low** Water is below Mean Lower Low with Ht. of lowest given for each period and Date of lowest in ( ):

1st - 2nd: -0.3' (1st)
8th - 16th: -1.5' (11th - 12th)
24th - 31st: -0.6' (30th)

1st: -0.3'
6th - 14th: -1.4' (9th - 10th)
24th - 28th: -0.8' (28th)

Average Rise and Fall 7.1 ft.

When a high tide exceeds avg. ht., the *following* low tide will be lower than avg.

2013 HIGH & LOW WATER
KINGS POINT, NY
40°48.6'N, 73°45.9'W

*Daylight Time starts March 10 at 2 a.m.   Daylight Saving Time

DAY OF MONTH	DAY OF WEEK	MARCH HIGH a.m.	Ht.	p.m.	Ht.	LOW a.m.	p.m.	DAY OF MONTH	DAY OF WEEK	APRIL HIGH a.m.	Ht.	p.m.	Ht.	LOW a.m.	p.m.
1	F	12 48	8.4	1 14	7.8	7 20	7 35	1	M	3 10	8.4	3 49	7.4	9 58	10 10
2	S	1 35	8.4	2 04	7.6	8 08	8 23	2	T	4 09	8.0	4 58	7.1	11 25	11 40
3	S	2 26	8.2	2 59	7.3	9 03	9 18	3	W	5 23	7.6	6 33	7.1	...	12 55
4	M	3 21	7.9	3 58	6.9	10 08	10 22	4	T	7 04	7.4	7 55	7.3	1 21	2 03
5	T	4 25	7.6	5 16	6.7	11 57	...	5	F	8 24	7.5	9 00	7.7	2 31	3 03
6	W	5 48	7.4	6 59	6.8	12 04	1 19	6	S	9 26	7.7	9 54	8.1	3 31	3 58
7	T	7 29	7.5	8 12	7.2	1 39	2 23	7	S	10 20	8.0	10 43	8.4	4 27	4 49
8	F	8 37	7.8	9 10	7.7	2 44	3 19	8	M	11 08	8.1	11 27	8.6	5 17	5 35
9	S	9 33	8.1	10 00	8.1	3 41	4 10	9	T	11 52	8.1	...	...	6 04	6 19
10	S	*11 22	8.3	*11 46	8.4	*5 33	*5 57	10	W	12 08	8.6	12 34	8.0	6 48	6 58
11	M	...	...	12 08	8.3	6 21	6 41	11	T	12 45	8.4	1 14	7.8	7 30	7 33
12	T	12 29	8.5	12 52	8.2	7 07	7 22	12	F	1 18	8.2	1 51	7.6	8 08	7 53
13	W	1 09	8.4	1 34	8.0	7 50	8 00	13	S	1 45	7.9	2 26	7.3	8 40	8 02
14	T	1 47	8.2	2 14	7.7	8 32	8 30	14	S	2 10	7.6	2 57	7.1	8 53	8 33
15	F	2 21	7.9	2 54	7.3	9 11	8 43	15	M	2 42	7.4	3 29	6.9	9 11	9 14
16	S	2 52	7.6	3 33	6.9	9 48	9 09	16	T	3 21	7.1	4 08	6.7	9 49	10 01
17	S	3 26	7.2	4 15	6.6	10 14	9 48	17	W	4 07	6.8	4 54	6.6	10 37	10 54
18	M	4 05	6.9	5 06	6.3	10 47	10 37	18	T	4 58	6.6	5 49	6.5	11 32	11 53
19	T	4 54	6.5	6 18	6.2	-A-	12 33	19	F	5 55	6.5	6 54	6.6	...	12 32
20	W	5 57	6.3	7 31	6.2	...	1 37	20	S	7 02	6.6	7 58	6.9	12 58	1 37
21	T	7 51	6.3	8 31	6.4	12 48	2 33	21	S	8 14	6.8	8 47	7.3	2 12	2 38
22	F	8 52	6.5	9 20	6.7	2 41	3 23	22	M	9 11	7.1	9 28	7.8	3 19	3 28
23	S	9 39	6.8	10 00	7.1	3 33	4 06	23	T	9 56	7.5	10 08	8.3	4 11	4 13
24	S	10 15	7.1	10 29	7.4	4 17	4 42	24	W	10 39	7.8	10 50	8.7	4 56	4 57
25	M	10 44	7.5	10 53	7.9	4 54	5 10	25	T	11 23	8.0	11 34	9.1	5 41	5 42
26	T	11 12	7.7	11 23	8.3	5 27	5 37	26	F	...	...	12 09	8.2	6 26	6 27
27	W	11 47	8.0	...	...	6 02	6 10	27	S	12 21	9.2	12 57	8.2	7 12	7 16
28	T	12 01	8.6	12 27	8.1	6 40	6 49	28	S	1 10	9.1	1 49	8.1	8 03	8 08
29	F	12 42	8.8	1 12	8.1	7 22	7 31	29	M	2 03	8.9	2 46	7.9	8 59	9 06
30	S	1 27	8.8	2 00	8.0	8 07	8 18	30	T	3 01	8.5	3 51	7.7	10 09	10 24
31	S	2 16	8.7	2 52	7.7	8 58	9 09								

A also at 11:34 p.m.

Dates when Ht. of **Low** Water is below Mean Lower Low with Ht. of lowest given for each period and Date of lowest in ( ):

1st - 3rd: -0.7' (1st)	1st: -0.2'
7th - 15th: -1.2' (11th)	5th - 12th: -1.0' (9th)
26th - 31st: -1.0' (29th)	24th - 30th: -1.0' (26th - 27th)

Average Rise and Fall 7.1 ft.

When a high tide exceeds avg. ht., the *following* low tide will be lower than avg.

2013 HIGH & LOW WATER
KINGS POINT, NY
40°48.6'N, 73°45.9'W

Daylight Saving Time　　　　　**Daylight Saving Time**

D A Y O F M O N T H	D A Y O F W E E K	MAY HIGH a.m.	Ht.	p.m.	Ht.	LOW a.m.	p.m.	D A Y O F M O N T H	D A Y O F W E E K	JUNE HIGH a.m.	Ht.	p.m.	Ht.	LOW a.m.	p.m.
1	W	4 07	8.0	5 09	7.5	11 27	11 57	1	S	6 36	7.5	7 13	8.0	12 50	1 13
2	T	5 31	7.6	6 29	7.6	...	12 37	2	S	7 43	7.3	8 13	8.1	1 52	2 10
3	F	6 58	7.5	7 39	7.7	1 11	1 41	3	M	8 44	7.3	9 08	8.2	2 50	3 06
4	S	8 07	7.5	8 39	8.0	2 14	2 39	4	T	9 37	7.4	9 57	8.3	3 43	3 57
5	S	9 07	7.6	9 33	8.3	3 13	3 33	5	W	10 26	7.5	10 42	8.3	4 34	4 45
6	M	10 01	7.7	10 21	8.5	4 07	4 24	6	T	11 11	7.5	11 24	8.2	5 21	5 30
7	T	10 49	7.8	11 05	8.5	4 57	5 11	7	F	11 54	7.5	...	...	6 05	6 11
8	W	11 33	7.8	11 46	8.4	5 44	5 55	8	S	12 02	8.1	12 33	7.5	6 45	6 46
9	T	...	...	12 15	7.7	6 28	6 34	9	S	12 35	7.9	1 09	7.4	7 22	7 09
10	F	12 22	8.3	12 54	7.6	7 08	7 08	10	M	12 57	7.7	1 40	7.3	7 51	7 15
11	S	12 54	8.0	1 30	7.5	7 45	7 27	11	T	1 14	7.6	2 00	7.3	7 59	7 44
12	S	1 17	7.8	2 02	7.3	8 14	7 35	12	W	1 43	7.6	2 23	7.3	8 16	8 22
13	M	1 38	7.6	2 27	7.2	8 21	8 06	13	T	2 21	7.5	2 57	7.3	8 50	9 06
14	T	2 10	7.5	2 54	7.1	8 40	8 46	14	F	3 03	7.5	3 37	7.4	9 31	9 53
15	W	2 49	7.3	3 30	7.0	9 17	9 32	15	S	3 50	7.3	4 22	7.5	10 16	10 44
16	T	3 33	7.2	4 12	7.0	10 01	10 21	16	S	4 39	7.2	5 11	7.7	11 05	11 39
17	F	4 20	7.0	4 59	7.0	10 50	11 16	17	M	5 34	7.1	6 04	7.8	11 58	...
18	S	5 13	6.9	5 51	7.2	11 42	...	18	T	6 33	7.1	7 01	8.1	12 39	12 54
19	S	6 10	6.9	6 46	7.4	12 14	12 37	19	W	7 36	7.1	8 01	8.3	1 44	1 53
20	M	7 11	6.9	7 42	7.7	1 17	1 34	20	T	8 43	7.3	9 02	8.7	2 57	2 55
21	T	8 15	7.1	8 38	8.2	2 22	2 31	21	F	9 46	7.6	10 01	9.0	4 11	4 00
22	W	9 15	7.4	9 31	8.6	3 28	3 27	22	S	10 46	7.9	10 58	9.2	5 14	5 06
23	T	10 10	7.7	10 22	9.0	4 29	4 23	23	S	11 43	8.2	11 55	9.3	6 10	6 09
24	F	11 02	8.0	11 13	9.2	5 24	5 18	24	M	...	...	12 40	8.3	7 04	7 10
25	S	11 53	8.2	...	...	6 17	6 13	25	T	12 52	9.2	1 38	8.4	7 56	8 10
26	S	12 04	9.3	12 47	8.2	7 09	7 08	26	W	1 52	8.9	2 37	8.4	8 50	9 13
27	M	12 59	9.2	1 44	8.2	8 04	8 08	27	T	2 53	8.6	3 38	8.4	9 45	10 17
28	T	1 56	8.9	2 46	8.1	9 02	9 16	28	F	3 57	8.1	4 38	8.2	10 43	11 22
29	W	2 59	8.5	3 52	8.0	10 05	10 32	29	S	5 03	7.7	5 40	8.1	11 42	...
30	T	4 08	8.1	5 01	8.0	11 09	11 44	30	S	6 09	7.4	6 41	8.0	12 24	12 41
31	F	5 24	7.7	6 09	8.0	...	12 12								

Dates when Ht. of **Low** Water is below Mean Lower Low with Ht. of lowest given for each period and Date of lowest in ( ):

5th - 11th: -0.7' (7th - 9th)　　　　4th - 8th: -0.4' (5th - 7th)
23rd - 30th: -1.1' (26th)　　　　21st - 28th: -1.1' (24th - 25th)

Average Rise and Fall 7.1 ft.

When a high tide exceeds avg. ht., the *following* low tide will be lower than avg.

2013 HIGH & LOW WATER
KINGS POINT, NY
40°48.6'N, 73°45.9'W

Daylight Saving Time **Daylight Saving Time**

DAY OF MONTH	DAY OF WEEK	JULY HIGH a.m.	Ht.	JULY HIGH p.m.	Ht.	LOW a.m.	LOW p.m.	DAY OF MONTH	DAY OF WEEK	AUGUST HIGH a.m.	Ht.	AUGUST HIGH p.m.	Ht.	LOW a.m.	LOW p.m.
1	M	7 13	7.1	7 41	7.9	1 24	1 39	1	T	8 39	6.9	9 01	7.5	2 45	2 57
2	T	8 14	7.0	8 38	7.9	2 22	2 35	2	F	9 31	7.0	9 51	7.6	3 37	3 49
3	W	9 10	7.1	9 31	7.9	3 17	3 29	3	S	10 20	7.2	10 37	7.7	4 26	4 37
4	T	10 00	7.2	10 18	7.9	4 07	4 18	4	S	11 02	7.4	11 16	7.7	5 10	5 19
5	F	10 47	7.3	11 01	7.9	4 55	5 04	5	M	11 41	7.5	11 50	7.8	5 50	5 56
6	S	11 30	7.4	11 41	7.9	5 39	5 46	6	T	...	...	12 15	7.6	6 25	6 25
7	S	...	...	12 10	7.4	6 20	6 23	7	W	12 14	7.8	12 37	7.7	6 51	6 40
8	M	12 15	7.8	12 45	7.4	6 56	6 50	8	T	12 27	7.8	12 51	7.8	7 00	7 04
9	T	12 39	7.7	1 13	7.4	7 24	7 00	9	F	12 54	7.9	1 18	8.0	7 21	7 38
10	W	12 52	7.7	1 28	7.5	7 33	7 24	10	S	1 31	7.9	1 54	8.2	7 55	8 18
11	T	1 19	7.7	1 51	7.6	7 50	8 00	11	S	2 12	7.9	2 35	8.3	8 34	9 02
12	F	1 55	7.7	2 25	7.7	8 23	8 41	12	M	2 58	7.7	3 21	8.3	9 18	9 51
13	S	2 37	7.7	3 05	7.9	9 02	9 26	13	T	3 48	7.6	4 12	8.3	10 07	10 46
14	S	3 22	7.6	3 50	8.0	9 46	10 16	14	W	4 42	7.4	5 07	8.2	11 01	11 50
15	M	4 11	7.4	4 39	8.1	10 33	11 10	15	T	5 42	7.2	6 09	8.1	...	12 03
16	T	5 05	7.3	5 32	8.1	11 26	...	16	F	6 53	7.1	7 21	8.1	1 11	1 14
17	W	6 04	7.1	6 31	8.2	12 10	12 23	17	S	8 18	7.3	8 42	8.3	2 50	2 50
18	T	7 09	7.1	7 35	8.3	1 19	1 26	18	S	9 35	7.7	9 54	8.6	3 57	4 10
19	F	8 22	7.3	8 44	8.5	2 45	2 37	19	M	10 35	8.2	10 53	8.8	4 53	5 11
20	S	9 35	7.6	9 51	8.8	4 05	3 57	20	T	11 28	8.6	11 47	8.9	5 45	6 05
21	S	10 39	7.9	10 53	9.0	5 06	5 10	21	W	...	...	12 17	8.8	6 33	6 57
22	M	11 36	8.3	11 51	9.1	6 00	6 11	22	T	12 37	8.9	1 05	8.9	7 19	7 47
23	T	...	...	12 31	8.5	6 51	7 07	23	F	1 27	8.6	1 53	8.8	8 04	8 37
24	W	12 47	9.0	1 25	8.7	7 40	8 02	24	S	2 18	8.3	2 40	8.6	8 48	9 28
25	T	1 42	8.8	2 18	8.7	8 29	8 57	25	S	3 09	7.9	3 28	8.3	9 34	10 22
26	F	2 38	8.5	3 12	8.5	9 19	9 55	26	M	4 02	7.5	4 19	7.9	10 23	11 19
27	S	3 36	8.0	4 07	8.3	10 11	10 54	27	T	5 00	7.1	5 17	7.5	11 21	...
28	S	4 35	7.6	5 04	8.1	11 07	11 54	28	W	6 02	6.8	6 23	7.2	12 18	12 24
29	M	5 36	7.2	6 04	7.8	...	12 06	29	T	7 04	6.7	7 28	7.1	1 15	1 26
30	T	6 39	6.9	7 05	7.6	12 53	1 05	30	F	8 04	6.7	8 27	7.1	2 10	2 23
31	W	7 41	6.8	8 05	7.5	1 51	2 02	31	S	8 58	6.9	9 20	7.3	3 02	3 15

Dates when Ht. of **Low** Water is below Mean Lower Low with Ht. of lowest given for each period and Date of lowest in ( ):

20th - 27th: -1.1' (23rd - 24th)   19th - 24th: -1.0' (21st)

Average Rise and Fall 7.1 ft.

When a high tide exceeds avg. ht., the *following* low tide will be lower than avg.

2013 HIGH & LOW WATER
KINGS POINT, NY
40°48.6'N, 73°45.9'W

Daylight Saving Time   Daylight Saving Time

D A Y O F M O N T H	D A Y O F W E E K	SEPTEMBER						D A Y O F M O N T H	D A Y O F W E E K	OCTOBER					
		HIGH				LOW				HIGH				LOW	
		a.m.	Ht.	p.m.	Ht.	a.m.	p.m.			a.m.	Ht.	p.m.	Ht.	a.m.	p.m.
1	S	9 47	7.2	10 06	7.4	3 51	4 03	1	T	9 50	7.4	10 07	7.4	3 51	4 08
2	M	10 30	7.4	10 46	7.6	4 35	4 46	2	W	10 24	7.7	10 38	7.6	4 28	4 46
3	T	11 08	7.6	11 19	7.7	5 15	5 25	3	T	10 48	8.0	11 02	7.8	4 57	5 18
4	W	11 36	7.8	11 40	7.8	5 46	5 53	4	F	11 08	8.4	11 28	7.9	5 17	5 45
5	T	11 53	8.0	11 58	7.9	6 07	6 14	5	S	11 39	8.7	...	...	5 46	6 18
6	F	...	...	12 13	8.2	6 23	6 41	6	S	12 04	8.1	12 17	8.9	6 23	6 57
7	S	12 29	8.0	12 46	8.5	6 51	7 16	7	M	12 45	8.1	1 00	9.0	7 03	7 40
8	S	1 07	8.0	1 25	8.6	7 28	7 57	8	T	1 31	8.0	1 47	8.9	7 48	8 27
9	M	1 50	8.0	2 09	8.7	8 09	8 42	9	W	2 21	7.8	2 38	8.7	8 37	9 21
10	T	2 37	7.8	2 57	8.6	8 55	9 32	10	T	3 15	7.6	3 35	8.3	9 33	10 28
11	W	3 29	7.6	3 50	8.4	9 46	10 31	11	F	4 17	7.4	4 38	8.0	10 41	...
12	T	4 25	7.4	4 49	8.1	10 45	11 44	12	S	5 34	7.3	5 59	7.7	12 06	12 30
13	F	5 31	7.2	5 57	7.9	11 56	...	13	S	7 11	7.4	7 38	7.7	1 25	1 53
14	S	6 56	7.2	7 25	7.9	1 31	1 44	14	M	8 23	7.8	8 48	7.9	2 28	2 58
15	S	8 28	7.5	8 52	8.1	2 44	3 05	15	T	9 21	8.2	9 46	8.1	3 25	3 56
16	M	9 32	8.0	9 55	8.4	3 43	4 07	16	W	10 12	8.6	10 37	8.3	4 17	4 49
17	T	10 26	8.5	10 48	8.6	4 37	5 02	17	T	10 59	8.9	11 24	8.3	5 06	5 38
18	W	11 15	8.8	11 37	8.7	5 26	5 54	18	F	11 42	8.9	...	...	5 52	6 25
19	T	...	...	12 01	9.0	6 13	6 42	19	S	12 09	8.2	12 22	8.8	6 34	7 09
20	F	12 24	8.6	12 43	9.0	6 57	7 29	20	S	12 51	8.0	12 59	8.6	7 13	7 52
21	S	1 09	8.4	1 25	8.8	7 38	8 14	21	M	1 33	7.7	1 33	8.2	7 46	8 32
22	S	1 55	8.1	2 05	8.5	8 16	9 00	22	T	2 13	7.5	2 04	7.9	8 02	9 11
23	M	2 40	7.7	2 45	8.1	8 48	9 47	23	W	2 53	7.2	2 37	7.5	8 24	9 43
24	T	3 28	7.3	3 26	7.7	9 11	10 39	24	T	3 35	6.9	3 16	7.2	9 02	9 59
25	W	4 19	7.0	4 12	7.3	9 46	11 35	25	F	4 20	6.7	4 01	6.9	9 49	10 41
26	T	5 17	6.7	5 14	6.9	10 36	...	26	S	5 15	6.6	4 53	6.7	10 43	11 45
27	F	6 21	6.6	6 36	6.8	12 33	12 34	27	S	6 21	6.6	5 57	6.6	11 46	...
28	S	7 23	6.7	7 44	6.8	1 28	1 40	28	M	7 22	6.7	7 27	6.6	1 11	1 16
29	S	8 19	6.9	8 40	6.9	2 21	2 35	29	T	8 13	7.0	8 28	6.8	2 00	2 29
30	M	9 08	7.1	9 27	7.1	3 08	3 25	30	W	8 53	7.3	9 11	7.0	2 40	3 18
								31	T	9 23	7.7	9 46	7.3	3 15	4 00

Dates when Ht. of **Low** Water is below Mean Lower Low with Ht. of lowest given for each period and Date of lowest in ( ):

8th: -0.2'
17th - 21st: -0.9' (19th)

4th - 8th: -0.5' (6th - 7th)
15th - 20th: -0.9' (17th - 18th)

Average Rise and Fall 7.1 ft.

When a high tide exceeds avg. ht., the *following* low tide will be lower than avg.

2013 HIGH & LOW WATER
KINGS POINT, NY
40°48.6'N, 73°45.9'W

*Standard Time starts Nov. 3 at 2 a.m.   **Standard Time**

DAY OF MONTH	DAY OF WEEK	NOVEMBER HIGH a.m.	Ht.	HIGH p.m.	Ht.	LOW a.m.	LOW p.m.	DAY OF MONTH	DAY OF WEEK	DECEMBER HIGH a.m.	Ht.	HIGH p.m.	Ht.	LOW a.m.	LOW p.m.
1	F	9 54	8.2	10 21	7.6	3 52	4 39	1	S	8 59	8.6	9 35	7.6	2 56	3 56
2	S	10 30	8.6	11 00	7.8	4 32	5 18	2	M	9 47	8.9	10 23	7.8	3 48	4 46
3	S	*10 11	8.9	*10 42	8.0	*4 15	*5 00	3	T	10 37	9.1	11 14	8.0	4 41	5 36
4	M	10 53	9.1	11 27	8.0	4 58	5 42	4	W	11 27	9.1	...	...	5 32	6 27
5	T	11 40	9.1	...	...	5 44	6 29	5	T	12 06	8.0	12 21	8.9	6 27	7 21
6	W	12 16	8.0	12 31	8.9	6 33	7 21	6	F	1 03	7.9	1 19	8.5	7 27	8 22
7	T	1 09	7.8	1 26	8.6	7 27	8 21	7	S	2 05	7.8	2 22	8.1	8 40	9 29
8	F	2 09	7.7	2 26	8.2	8 31	9 39	8	S	3 15	7.7	3 36	7.7	10 03	10 37
9	S	3 18	7.5	3 37	7.8	10 03	10 59	9	M	4 29	7.7	4 56	7.3	11 16	11 41
10	S	4 43	7.5	5 08	7.5	11 32	...	10	T	5 39	7.7	6 09	7.1	...	12 22
11	M	6 01	7.7	6 29	7.5	12 06	12 41	11	W	6 43	7.8	7 14	7.1	12 41	1 22
12	T	7 07	8.0	7 34	7.5	1 07	1 43	12	T	7 42	8.0	8 11	7.2	1 39	2 19
13	W	8 04	8.3	8 31	7.7	2 03	2 39	13	F	8 34	8.1	9 03	7.3	2 33	3 11
14	T	8 55	8.5	9 22	7.8	2 56	3 32	14	S	9 23	8.2	9 51	7.4	3 24	4 01
15	F	9 41	8.6	10 09	7.8	3 45	4 21	15	S	10 07	8.1	10 35	7.4	4 11	4 46
16	S	10 24	8.6	10 52	7.8	4 31	5 07	16	M	10 47	8.0	11 16	7.3	4 54	5 29
17	S	11 03	8.4	11 34	7.6	5 14	5 50	17	T	11 24	7.8	11 54	7.2	5 34	6 08
18	M	11 39	8.2	...	...	5 53	6 30	18	W	11 55	7.6	...	...	6 06	6 43
19	T	12 13	7.4	12 10	7.9	6 24	7 07	19	T	12 28	7.1	12 15	7.5	6 20	7 07
20	W	12 50	7.2	12 35	7.6	6 34	7 37	20	F	12 55	7.0	12 36	7.3	6 33	7 09
21	T	1 23	7.0	1 02	7.4	6 54	7 42	21	S	1 15	7.0	1 08	7.2	7 06	7 35
22	F	1 52	6.9	1 38	7.2	7 31	8 08	22	S	1 44	7.0	1 47	7.1	7 47	8 13
23	S	2 25	6.8	2 20	7.0	8 15	8 48	23	M	2 21	7.0	2 31	7.0	8 32	8 56
24	S	3 04	6.7	3 07	6.8	9 04	9 35	24	T	3 03	7.0	3 19	6.8	9 21	9 43
25	M	3 49	6.7	3 57	6.6	9 58	10 26	25	W	3 50	7.1	4 10	6.7	10 15	10 34
26	T	4 39	6.8	4 53	6.6	10 57	11 20	26	T	4 41	7.2	5 07	6.6	11 13	11 29
27	W	5 32	7.0	5 54	6.6	11 59	...	27	F	5 36	7.4	6 09	6.6	...	12 16
28	T	6 27	7.3	6 56	6.7	12 15	1 05	28	S	6 35	7.7	7 14	6.8	12 27	1 25
29	F	7 20	7.7	7 54	7.0	1 09	2 08	29	S	7 36	8.0	8 17	7.1	1 27	2 39
30	S	8 10	8.2	8 46	7.3	2 03	3 04	30	M	8 35	8.4	9 16	7.4	2 30	3 43
								31	T	9 31	8.7	10 10	7.7	3 33	4 39

Dates when Ht. of **Low** Water is below Mean Lower Low with Ht. of lowest given for each period and Date of lowest in ( ):

2nd - 7th: -0.8' (4th)
12th - 18th: -0.9' (15th - 16th)
30th: -0.3'

1st - 9th: -1.1' (3rd - 4th)
11th - 18th: -0.8' (14th - 15th)
29th - 31st: -1.1' (31st)

Average Rise and Fall 7.1 ft.

When a high tide exceeds avg. ht., the *following* low tide will be lower than avg.

2013 CURRENT TABLE
HELL GATE, NY (EAST RIVER)

40°46.7'N, 73°56.3'W Off Mill Rock

Standard Time   Standard Time

JANUARY

DAY OF MONTH	DAY OF WEEK	CURRENT TURNS TO					
		NORTHEAST Flood Starts			SOUTHWEST Ebb Starts		
		a.m.	p.m.	Kts.	a.m.	p.m.	Kts.
1	T	6 15	6 42	a3.4	...	12 15	4.9
2	W	6 57	7 24	a3.4	12 35	12 58	4.8
3	T	7 45	8 11	a3.3	1 19	1 45	a4.8
4	F	8 38	9 03	3.2	2 08	2 38	a4.7
5	S	9 38	10 02	p3.2	3 04	3 36	a4.7
6	S	10 44	11 06	p3.3	4 05	4 39	a4.7
7	M	11 50	...	3.2	5 09	5 44	a4.7
8	T	12 11	12 54	3.4	6 14	6 47	a4.8
9	W	1 13	1 54	a3.6	7 16	7 47	a5.0
10	T	2 12	2 51	3.7	8 15	8 44	a5.1
11	F	3 09	3 45	a3.9	9 11	9 39	a5.2
12	S	4 03	4 37	a4.0	10 05	10 31	a5.3
13	S	4 56	5 28	a4.0	10 57	11 22	a5.2
14	M	5 49	6 19	a3.9	11 48	...	5.1
15	T	6 41	7 09	a3.7	12 12	12 38	a5.0
16	W	7 33	8 00	a3.5	1 02	1 29	a4.8
17	T	8 27	8 52	a3.2	1 53	2 20	a4.6
18	F	9 22	9 46	3.0	2 44	3 12	a4.4
19	S	10 18	10 40	2.9	3 37	4 05	a4.2
20	S	11 13	11 34	2.8	4 31	4 59	a4.1
21	M	...	12 06	2.8	5 24	5 51	4.1
22	T	12 24	12 56	2.9	6 15	6 41	4.2
23	W	1 11	1 41	3.0	7 03	7 27	4.3
24	T	1 55	2 24	3.2	7 49	8 11	4.5
25	F	2 36	3 04	3.3	8 32	8 53	a4.7
26	S	3 15	3 42	a3.5	9 13	9 33	4.8
27	S	3 53	4 20	a3.6	9 53	10 11	4.9
28	M	4 31	4 56	a3.7	10 32	10 50	5.0
29	T	5 09	5 33	a3.7	11 12	11 29	5.0
30	W	5 48	6 11	a3.7	11 53	...	5.0
31	T	6 31	6 53	a3.6	12 10	12 35	a5.0

FEBRUARY

DAY OF MONTH	DAY OF WEEK	CURRENT TURNS TO					
		NORTHEAST Flood Starts			SOUTHWEST Ebb Starts		
		a.m.	p.m.	Kts.	a.m.	p.m.	Kts.
1	F	7 17	7 39	a3.5	12 54	1 22	a4.9
2	S	8 11	8 32	3.3	1 44	2 15	a4.9
3	S	9 12	9 35	3.2	2 40	3 14	a4.7
4	M	10 19	10 43	p3.2	3 43	4 20	a4.6
5	T	11 30	11 53	p3.3	4 52	5 28	a4.6
6	W	...	12 37	3.3	6 00	6 34	4.6
7	T	12 59	1 39	3.5	7 05	7 35	4.8
8	F	2 00	2 36	3.7	8 05	8 32	4.9
9	S	2 56	3 28	a3.9	9 00	9 25	5.1
10	S	3 48	4 17	a4.0	9 52	10 14	5.1
11	M	4 38	5 05	a4.0	10 41	11 02	5.1
12	T	5 26	5 51	a3.9	11 28	11 48	5.0
13	W	6 13	6 36	a3.8	...	12 14	4.9
14	T	7 00	7 22	a3.6	12 34	1 00	a4.8
15	F	7 48	8 09	a3.3	1 20	1 47	a4.6
16	S	8 37	8 59	a3.1	2 08	2 35	a4.4
17	S	9 29	9 51	a2.9	2 58	3 26	a4.2
18	M	10 24	10 46	p2.8	3 50	4 19	a4.0
19	T	11 20	11 40	p2.8	4 45	5 14	a4.0
20	W	...	12 13	2.8	5 39	6 07	4.0
21	T	12 31	1 02	3.0	6 31	6 56	4.2
22	F	1 18	1 47	p3.2	7 20	7 42	p4.4
23	S	2 02	2 29	3.3	8 05	8 25	4.6
24	S	2 43	3 08	3.5	8 48	9 06	p4.8
25	M	3 23	3 46	3.7	9 29	9 46	p5.0
26	T	4 02	4 24	3.8	10 10	10 26	p5.1
27	W	4 42	5 02	a3.9	10 51	11 06	p5.1
28	T	5 23	5 42	a3.9	11 33	11 49	p5.1

The Kts. (knots) columns show the **maximum** predicted velocities of the stronger one of the Flood Currents and the stronger one of the Ebb Currents for each day.

The letter "a" means the velocity shown should occur **after** the a.m. Current Change. The letter "p" means the velocity shown should occur **after** the p.m. Current Change (even if next morning). No "a" or "p" means a.m. and p.m. velocities are the same for that day.

Avg. Max. Velocity: Flood 3.4 Kts., Ebb 4.6 Kts.

Max. Flood 3 hrs. after Flood Starts, ±10 min.

Max. Ebb 3 hrs. after Ebb Starts, ±10 min.

At **City Island** the Current turns 2 hours before Hell Gate. At **Throg's Neck** the Current turns 1 hour before Hell Gate. At **Whitestone Pt.** the Current turns 35 min. before Hell Gate. At **College Pt.** the Current turns 20 min. before Hell Gate.

2013 CURRENT TABLE
HELL GATE, NY (EAST RIVER)
40°46.7'N, 73°56.3'W Off Mill Rock

*Daylight Time starts March 10 at 2 a.m.　　　　　**Daylight Saving Time**

		MARCH									APRIL					
		CURRENT TURNS TO									CURRENT TURNS TO					
D A Y O F M O N T H	D A Y O F W E E K	NORTHEAST Flood Starts			SOUTHWEST Ebb Starts			D A Y O F M O N T H	D A Y O F W E E K	NORTHEAST Flood Starts			SOUTHWEST Ebb Starts		
		a.m.	p.m.	Kts.	a.m.	p.m.	Kts.			a.m.	p.m.	Kts.	a.m.	p.m.	Kts.
1	F	6 07	6 26	a3.8	...	12 17	5.0	1	M	8 37	8 57	3.5	2 15	2 49	a4.9
2	S	6 55	7 14	3.6	12 36	1 06	a5.0	2	T	9 40	10 05	3.3	3 15	3 51	a4.6
3	S	7 51	8 11	a3.5	1 27	2 00	a4.9	3	W	10 50	11 18	3.2	4 21	4 58	a4.4
4	M	8 52	9 14	3.3	2 26	3 01	a4.7	4	T	11 59	...	3.2	5 31	6 05	4.3
5	T	10 01	10 26	p3.2	3 31	4 08	a4.5	5	F	12 28	1 04	3.3	6 39	7 09	p4.4
6	W	11 13	11 39	p3.3	4 41	5 17	a4.4	6	S	1 33	2 03	3.5	7 41	8 07	p4.6
7	T	...	12 21	3.3	5 51	6 23	4.4	7	S	2 30	2 56	p3.7	8 37	8 59	p4.8
8	F	12 46	1 22	3.5	6 55	7 23	4.6	8	M	3 22	3 43	3.8	9 27	9 46	p4.9
9	S	1 46	2 17	3.7	7 54	8 18	4.8	9	T	4 08	4 28	3.8	10 13	10 30	p4.9
10	S	*3 40	*4 07	a3.9	*9 47	*10 08	p5.0	10	W	4 52	5 09	a3.9	10 56	11 13	p4.9
11	M	4 29	4 53	a4.0	10 35	10 55	5.0	11	T	5 34	5 50	3.8	11 38	11 53	p4.9
12	T	5 16	5 37	a4.0	11 21	11 39	5.0	12	F	6 14	6 29	a3.7	...	12 18	4.7
13	W	6 00	6 20	a3.9	...	12 05	4.9	13	S	6 54	7 09	a3.6	12 34	12 59	a4.8
14	T	6 43	7 02	a3.8	12 22	12 48	a4.9	14	S	7 35	7 50	a3.4	1 15	1 40	a4.6
15	F	7 26	7 44	a3.6	1 05	1 30	a4.8	15	M	8 18	8 33	a3.2	1 57	2 24	a4.5
16	S	8 09	8 27	a3.4	1 48	2 14	a4.6	16	T	9 03	9 20	3.0	2 42	3 10	a4.3
17	S	8 54	9 12	a3.2	2 32	2 59	a4.4	17	W	9 52	10 12	2.9	3 30	3 59	a4.2
18	M	9 42	10 02	a3.0	3 19	3 48	a4.2	18	T	10 45	11 07	p2.9	4 22	4 52	a4.1
19	T	10 35	10 56	2.8	4 10	4 40	a4.0	19	F	11 40	...	2.9	5 17	5 45	4.1
20	W	11 30	11 52	2.8	5 05	5 35	a4.0	20	S	12 02	12 33	3.0	6 12	6 38	p4.2
21	T	...	12 26	2.8	6 01	6 29	a4.0	21	S	12 56	1 23	p3.2	7 05	7 28	p4.4
22	F	12 47	1 18	p3.0	6 55	7 20	4.1	22	M	1 47	2 10	p3.4	7 56	8 16	p4.7
23	S	1 37	2 06	p3.2	7 46	8 08	p4.4	23	T	2 36	2 56	p3.6	8 44	9 02	p4.9
24	S	2 24	2 50	3.4	8 33	8 53	p4.6	24	W	3 23	3 41	p3.8	9 31	9 49	p5.1
25	M	3 09	3 32	3.6	9 18	9 36	p4.9	25	T	4 10	4 26	3.9	10 18	10 36	p5.2
26	T	3 52	4 12	3.8	10 02	10 18	p5.0	26	F	4 58	5 13	p4.0	11 06	11 24	p5.3
27	W	4 34	4 53	3.9	10 45	11 01	p5.2	27	S	5 46	6 02	p4.0	11 54	...	5.1
28	T	5 17	5 35	a4.0	11 29	11 45	p5.2	28	S	6 37	6 54	a3.9	12 14	12 45	a5.2
29	F	6 02	6 19	3.9	...	12 14	5.0	29	M	7 31	7 50	3.7	1 07	1 39	a5.1
30	S	6 49	7 06	a3.9	12 31	1 01	a5.2	30	T	8 30	8 52	3.5	2 03	2 37	a4.9
31	S	7 40	7 58	3.7	1 20	1 52	a5.1								

The Kts. (knots) columns show the **maximum** predicted velocities of the stronger one of the Flood Currents and the stronger one of the Ebb Currents for each day.

The letter "a" means the velocity shown should occur **after** the **a.m.** Current Change. The letter "p" means the velocity shown should occur **after** the **p.m.** Current Change (even if next morning). No "a" or "p" means a.m. and p.m. velocities are the same for that day.

Avg. Max. Velocity: Flood 3.4 Kts., Ebb 4.6 Kts.

Max. Flood 3 hrs. after Flood Starts, ±10 min.

Max. Ebb 3 hrs. after Ebb Starts, ±10 min.

See pp. 22-29 for Current Change at other points.

2013 CURRENT TABLE
HELL GATE, NY (EAST RIVER)
40°46.7'N, 73°56.3'W Off Mill Rock

Daylight Saving Time   **Daylight Saving Time**

D A Y O F M O N T H	D A Y O F W E E K	NORTHEAST Flood Starts a.m.	**p.m.**	Kts.	SOUTHWEST Ebb Starts a.m.	**p.m.**	Kts.	D A Y O F M O N T H	D A Y O F W E E K	NORTHEAST Flood Starts a.m.	**p.m.**	Kts.	SOUTHWEST Ebb Starts a.m.	**p.m.**	Kts.
		MAY								**JUNE**					
1	W	9 32	**9 59**	a3.4	3 04	**3 39**	a4.7	1	S	11 24	**11 56**	3.2	4 53	**5 22**	4.4
2	T	10 38	**11 08**	p3.3	4 09	**4 43**	a4.5	2	S	...	**12 23**	3.2	5 53	**6 20**	p4.4
3	F	11 45	...	3.2	5 15	**5 47**	4.3	3	M	12 56	**1 18**	p3.3	6 50	**7 14**	p4.5
4	S	12 15	**12 46**	3.3	6 19	**6 48**	p4.4	4	T	1 49	**2 07**	3.3	7 42	**8 04**	p4.6
5	S	1 17	**1 42**	3.4	7 19	**7 43**	p4.6	5	W	2 38	**2 53**	p3.4	8 30	**8 50**	p4.6
6	M	2 12	**2 33**	3.5	8 12	**8 33**	p4.7	6	T	3 23	**3 36**	p3.5	9 15	**9 33**	p4.7
7	T	3 01	**3 19**	3.6	9 01	**9 19**	p4.8	7	F	4 04	**4 16**	p3.5	9 57	**10 14**	p4.7
8	W	3 47	**4 02**	p3.7	9 45	**10 02**	p4.8	8	S	4 44	**4 56**	p3.5	10 37	**10 54**	p4.8
9	T	4 29	**4 43**	p3.7	10 27	**10 43**	p4.8	9	S	5 23	**5 34**	p3.5	11 17	**11 34**	p4.8
10	F	5 09	**5 22**	3.6	11 08	**11 23**	p4.8	10	M	6 02	**6 13**	p3.5	11 56	...	4.6
11	S	5 48	**6 01**	3.6	11 47	...	4.7	11	T	6 40	**6 51**	3.4	12 13	**12 36**	a4.8
12	S	6 27	**6 40**	3.5	12 03	**12 27**	a4.8	12	W	7 19	**7 31**	3.3	12 53	**1 16**	a4.7
13	M	7 07	**7 19**	a3.4	12 43	**1 07**	a4.7	13	T	7 59	**8 12**	3.2	1 34	**1 56**	a4.7
14	T	7 48	**8 01**	3.2	1 23	**1 49**	a4.6	14	F	8 41	**8 57**	p3.2	2 17	**2 39**	a4.6
15	W	8 31	**8 45**	3.1	2 06	**2 32**	a4.5	15	S	9 25	**9 47**	3.1	3 02	**3 26**	4.5
16	T	9 16	**9 33**	3.0	2 51	**3 18**	a4.4	16	S	10 13	**10 41**	3.1	3 51	**4 16**	4.5
17	F	10 05	**10 25**	p3.0	3 40	**4 07**	a4.3	17	M	11 05	**11 39**	3.1	4 45	**5 11**	p4.6
18	S	10 56	**11 21**	3.0	4 32	**4 59**	4.3	18	T	...	**12 01**	3.2	5 42	**6 08**	p4.7
19	S	11 48	...	3.0	5 26	**5 52**	p4.4	19	W	12 39	**12 58**	p3.4	6 40	**7 06**	p4.8
20	M	12 17	**12 41**	p3.2	6 21	**6 45**	p4.6	20	T	1 38	**1 55**	p3.6	7 38	**8 03**	p5.0
21	T	1 12	**1 33**	p3.4	7 16	**7 38**	p4.8	21	F	2 35	**2 52**	p3.7	8 35	**9 00**	p5.1
22	W	2 06	**2 23**	p3.6	8 09	**8 30**	p5.0	22	S	3 32	**3 48**	p3.9	9 31	**9 56**	p5.2
23	T	2 58	**3 14**	p3.8	9 01	**9 22**	p5.2	23	S	4 27	**4 43**	p4.0	10 26	**10 51**	p5.3
24	F	3 50	**4 05**	p3.9	9 52	**10 13**	p5.3	24	M	5 21	**5 38**	p4.0	11 20	**11 46**	p5.2
25	S	4 42	**4 57**	p4.0	10 44	**11 05**	p5.3	25	T	6 15	**6 34**	3.9	...	**12 14**	5.1
26	S	5 34	**5 50**	p4.0	11 36	**11 59**	p5.2	26	W	7 09	**7 31**	3.8	12 41	**1 09**	a5.1
27	M	6 28	**6 45**	p3.9	...	**12 29**	5.0	27	T	8 04	**8 29**	a3.7	1 36	**2 04**	a5.0
28	T	7 23	**7 43**	3.7	12 54	**1 24**	a5.1	28	F	9 00	**9 28**	a3.5	2 32	**3 00**	a4.8
29	W	8 21	**8 44**	a3.6	1 50	**2 22**	a4.9	29	S	9 58	**10 28**	3.3	3 29	**3 56**	a4.6
30	T	9 21	**9 48**	3.4	2 50	**3 21**	a4.7	30	S	10 55	**11 28**	3.2	4 26	**4 54**	4.4
31	F	10 22	**10 53**	3.3	3 51	**4 22**	4.5								

The Kts. (knots) columns show the **maximum** predicted velocities of the stronger one of the Flood Currents and the stronger one of the Ebb Currents for each day.

The letter "a" means the velocity shown should occur **after** the **a.m.** Current Change. The letter "p" means the velocity shown should occur **after** the **p.m.** Current Change (even if next morning). No "a" or "p" means a.m. and p.m. velocities are the same for that day.

Avg. Max. Velocity: Flood 3.4 Kts., Ebb 4.6 Kts.

Max. Flood 3 hrs. after Flood Starts, ±10 min.

Max. Ebb 3 hrs. after Ebb Starts, ±10 min.

At **City Island** the Current turns 2 hours before Hell Gate. At **Throg's Neck** the Current turns 1 hour before Hell Gate. At **Whitestone Pt.** the Current turns 35 min. before Hell Gate. At **College Pt.** the Current turns 20 min. before Hell Gate.

2013 CURRENT TABLE
HELL GATE, NY (EAST RIVER)

40°46.7'N, 73°56.3'W Off Mill Rock

Daylight Saving Time   Daylight Saving Time

		JULY							AUGUST				
		CURRENT TURNS TO							CURRENT TURNS TO				
DAY OF MONTH	DAY OF WEEK	NORTHEAST Flood Starts			SOUTHWEST Ebb Starts			DAY OF MONTH	DAY OF WEEK	NORTHEAST Flood Starts			SOUTHWEST Ebb Starts		
		a.m.	p.m.	Kts.	a.m.	p.m.	Kts.			a.m.	p.m.	Kts.	a.m.	p.m.	Kts.
1	M	11 52	...	3.2	5 23	5 50	p4.3	1	T	12 41	1 00	p3.1	6 40	7 05	p4.1
2	T	12 25	12 46	3.1	6 19	6 44	p4.3	2	F	1 33	1 49	p3.1	7 31	7 54	p4.2
3	W	1 20	1 38	p3.2	7 11	7 34	p4.3	3	S	2 21	2 35	p3.3	8 18	8 40	p4.3
4	T	2 09	2 24	p3.2	8 00	8 21	p4.4	4	S	3 03	3 16	p3.4	9 02	9 23	p4.5
5	F	2 54	3 07	p3.3	8 45	9 05	p4.5	5	M	3 44	3 56	p3.5	9 44	10 04	p4.6
6	S	3 36	3 48	p3.4	9 28	9 48	p4.6	6	T	4 23	4 34	p3.6	10 24	10 44	p4.7
7	S	4 16	4 27	p3.5	10 10	10 28	p4.7	7	W	5 00	5 12	p3.7	11 02	11 23	p4.8
8	M	4 55	5 06	p3.5	10 50	11 08	p4.8	8	T	5 36	5 49	p3.7	11 40	...	4.8
9	T	5 33	5 44	p3.6	11 29	11 47	p4.8	9	F	6 12	6 26	p3.7	12 02	12 18	p4.9
10	W	6 10	6 21	3.5	...	12 07	4.7	10	S	6 48	7 06	p3.7	12 41	12 57	p4.9
11	T	6 47	6 59	p3.5	12 27	12 46	a4.8	11	S	7 26	7 48	3.6	1 22	1 39	4.8
12	F	7 25	7 39	3.4	1 06	1 25	a4.8	12	M	8 08	8 36	3.5	2 06	2 25	4.7
13	S	8 03	8 21	3.4	1 47	2 07	4.7	13	T	8 56	9 31	a3.4	2 55	3 18	4.6
14	S	8 45	9 09	3.3	2 31	2 52	4.7	14	W	9 52	10 34	a3.4	3 50	4 17	4.5
15	M	9 32	10 03	a3.3	3 19	3 42	4.6	15	T	10 56	11 43	3.3	4 52	5 22	p4.5
16	T	10 25	11 04	a3.3	4 13	4 39	p4.6	16	F	...	12 06	3.4	5 58	6 29	p4.5
17	W	11 25	...	3.3	5 11	5 40	p4.6	17	S	12 52	1 14	p3.5	7 03	7 35	p4.6
18	T	12 08	12 28	p3.4	6 14	6 43	p4.7	18	S	1 57	2 19	p3.7	8 06	8 37	p4.8
19	F	1 13	1 32	p3.6	7 17	7 46	p4.8	19	M	2 56	3 18	p3.9	9 04	9 34	p4.9
20	S	2 15	2 34	p3.7	8 18	8 46	p5.0	20	T	3 51	4 13	p4.1	9 59	10 28	5.0
21	S	3 14	3 32	p3.9	9 16	9 44	p5.1	21	W	4 43	5 05	p4.1	10 51	11 19	5.1
22	M	4 10	4 29	p4.0	10 12	10 40	p5.2	22	T	5 33	5 56	p4.1	11 41	...	5.1
23	T	5 04	5 24	p4.1	11 06	11 33	p5.2	23	F	6 21	6 45	4.0	12 09	12 30	5.0
24	W	5 56	6 17	4.0	11 59	...	5.1	24	S	7 08	7 34	3.8	12 58	1 18	a4.9
25	T	6 48	7 11	3.9	12 26	12 51	a5.1	25	S	7 56	8 23	a3.7	1 46	2 07	4.6
26	F	7 39	8 04	a3.8	1 19	1 42	4.9	26	M	8 45	9 14	a3.4	2 35	2 57	4.4
27	S	8 31	8 58	a3.6	2 11	2 35	4.7	27	T	9 36	10 07	a3.2	3 26	3 49	4.1
28	S	9 24	9 54	a3.4	3 04	3 28	4.5	28	W	10 29	11 02	a3.0	4 19	4 44	3.9
29	M	10 18	10 50	a3.2	3 57	4 23	4.3	29	T	11 24	11 58	a3.0	5 13	5 39	3.8
30	T	11 13	11 47	a3.1	4 52	5 18	4.1	30	F	...	12 19	3.0	6 08	6 33	p3.9
31	W	...	12 08	3.0	5 47	6 12	4.0	31	S	12 51	1 10	p3.1	7 00	7 24	p4.0

The Kts. (knots) columns show the **maximum** predicted velocities of the stronger one of the Flood Currents and the stronger one of the Ebb Currents for each day.

The letter "a" means the velocity shown should occur **after** the **a.m.** Current Change. The letter "p" means the velocity shown should occur **after** the **p.m.** Current Change (even if next morning). No "a" or "p" means a.m. and p.m. velocities are the same for that day.

Avg. Max. Velocity: Flood 3.4 Kts., Ebb 4.6 Kts.

Max. Flood 3 hrs. after Flood Starts, ±10 min.

Max. Ebb 3 hrs. after Ebb Starts, ±10 min.

See pp. 22-29 for Current Change at other points.

2013 CURRENT TABLE
HELL GATE, NY (EAST RIVER)

40°46.7'N, 73°56.3'W Off Mill Rock

Daylight Saving Time   Daylight Saving Time

SEPTEMBER

DAY OF MONTH	DAY OF WEEK	NORTHEAST Flood Starts a.m.	p.m.	Kts.	SOUTHWEST Ebb Starts a.m.	p.m.	Kts.
1	S	1 41	1 58	p3.2	7 49	8 12	p4.2
2	M	2 26	2 42	p3.4	8 33	8 56	p4.4
3	T	3 09	3 24	p3.6	9 15	9 38	p4.6
4	W	3 47	4 02	p3.7	9 55	10 18	p4.7
5	T	4 24	4 40	p3.8	10 34	10 57	4.8
6	F	5 01	5 18	p3.9	11 12	11 37	4.9
7	S	5 37	5 57	p3.9	11 51	...	5.0
8	S	6 14	6 38	3.8	12 17	12 32	p5.0
9	M	6 54	7 23	a3.8	12 59	1 16	p4.9
10	T	7 39	8 12	a3.7	1 45	2 04	p4.8
11	W	8 30	9 09	a3.5	2 36	2 59	4.6
12	T	9 30	10 15	a3.4	3 34	4 02	p4.5
13	F	10 39	11 26	3.3	4 38	5 10	p4.4
14	S	11 53	...	3.4	5 46	6 19	p4.4
15	S	12 36	1 03	p3.5	6 53	7 25	p4.5
16	M	1 41	2 07	p3.7	7 54	8 26	p4.6
17	T	2 39	3 04	p3.9	8 51	9 21	4.8
18	W	3 32	3 57	p4.1	9 43	10 12	4.9
19	T	4 21	4 46	p4.1	10 32	11 00	a5.0
20	F	5 08	5 33	p4.1	11 19	11 47	a5.0
21	S	5 53	6 19	a4.0	...	12 05	4.9
22	S	6 37	7 04	3.8	12 32	12 50	4.8
23	M	7 21	7 49	a3.6	1 17	1 36	4.6
24	T	8 07	8 36	a3.4	2 03	2 22	p4.4
25	W	8 54	9 25	a3.2	2 51	3 12	4.1
26	T	9 45	10 18	a3.0	3 42	4 04	3.9
27	F	10 40	11 14	2.9	4 35	4 59	3.8
28	S	11 36	...	2.9	5 29	5 54	p3.8
29	S	12 08	12 30	p3.0	6 22	6 47	p3.9
30	M	1 00	1 20	p3.2	7 12	7 36	p4.1

OCTOBER

DAY OF MONTH	DAY OF WEEK	NORTHEAST Flood Starts a.m.	p.m.	Kts.	SOUTHWEST Ebb Starts a.m.	p.m.	Kts.
1	T	1 47	2 06	p3.4	7 58	8 22	p4.3
2	W	2 30	2 49	p3.6	8 41	9 05	4.5
3	T	3 12	3 32	p3.8	9 22	9 47	4.7
4	F	3 50	4 11	p3.9	10 02	10 28	a4.9
5	S	4 29	4 52	3.9	10 43	11 09	a5.0
6	S	5 08	5 34	3.9	11 24	11 52	a5.1
7	M	5 49	6 19	3.9	...	12 08	5.1
8	T	6 33	7 07	a3.9	12 37	12 55	p5.0
9	W	7 22	7 59	a3.7	1 25	1 46	p4.8
10	T	8 17	8 59	a3.6	2 19	2 44	p4.7
11	F	9 21	10 06	a3.4	3 19	3 48	p4.5
12	S	10 33	11 16	3.3	4 25	4 57	4.3
13	S	11 46	...	3.3	5 32	6 06	p4.3
14	M	12 24	12 55	p3.5	6 37	7 10	p4.4
15	T	1 27	1 56	p3.7	7 37	8 09	p4.6
16	W	2 23	2 51	p3.8	8 32	9 02	4.7
17	T	3 13	3 41	3.9	9 22	9 51	a4.9
18	F	4 01	4 28	3.9	10 09	10 36	a5.0
19	S	4 45	5 12	3.9	10 53	11 20	a5.0
20	S	5 28	5 55	a3.9	11 36	...	4.9
21	M	6 10	6 37	3.7	12 03	12 19	p4.8
22	T	6 52	7 19	a3.6	12 45	1 02	4.6
23	W	7 34	8 03	a3.4	1 28	1 45	p4.5
24	T	8 19	8 50	a3.2	2 13	2 31	p4.3
25	F	9 07	9 39	a3.0	3 00	3 20	4.1
26	S	9 59	10 32	2.9	3 50	4 12	p4.0
27	S	10 54	11 26	2.9	4 42	5 07	p4.0
28	M	11 49	...	2.9	5 35	6 00	4.0
29	T	12 18	12 42	p3.1	6 26	6 52	p4.2
30	W	1 07	1 31	p3.3	7 14	7 41	p4.4
31	T	1 53	2 18	p3.5	8 00	8 27	4.6

The Kts. (knots) columns show the **maximum** predicted velocities of the stronger one of the Flood Currents and the stronger one of the Ebb Currents for each day.

The letter "a" means the velocity shown should occur **after** the **a.m.** Current Change. The letter "p" means the velocity shown should occur **after** the **p.m.** Current Change (even if next morning). No "a" or "p" means a.m. and p.m. velocities are the same for that day.

Avg. Max. Velocity: Flood 3.4 Kts., Ebb 4.6 Kts.

Max. Flood 3 hrs. after Flood Starts, ±10 min.

Max. Ebb 3 hrs. after Ebb Starts, ±10 min.

At **City Island** the Current turns 2 hours before Hell Gate. At **Throg's Neck** the Current turns 1 hour before Hell Gate. At **Whitestone Pt.** the Current turns 35 min. before Hell Gate. At **College Pt.** the Current turns 20 min. before Hell Gate.

*Standard Time starts Nov. 3 at 2 a.m.   Standard Time

D A Y O F M O N T H	D A Y O F W E E K	NORTHEAST Flood Starts			SOUTHWEST Ebb Starts			D A Y O F M O N T H	D A Y O F W E E K	NORTHEAST Flood Starts			SOUTHWEST Ebb Starts		
		a.m.	**p.m.**	Kts.	a.m.	**p.m.**	Kts.			a.m.	**p.m.**	Kts.	a.m.	**p.m.**	Kts.
		NOVEMBER								**DECEMBER**					
1	F	2 37	3 03	p3.7	8 45	9 12	4.8	1	S	1 53	2 27	3.7	7 57	8 26	a5.1
2	S	3 19	3 48	p3.8	9 29	9 56	a5.0	2	M	2 41	3 17	3.8	8 47	9 16	a5.2
3	S	*3 03	*3 34	3.9	*9 13	*9 41	a5.2	3	T	3 32	4 08	a3.9	9 37	10 06	a5.3
4	M	3 46	4 19	3.9	9 59	10 27	a5.2	4	W	4 22	4 58	a3.9	10 28	10 57	a5.3
5	T	4 32	5 07	a4.0	10 46	11 16	a5.2	5	T	5 15	5 52	a3.9	11 21	11 50	a5.2
6	W	5 21	5 58	a3.9	11 36	...	5.1	6	F	6 10	6 47	a3.8	...	12 16	5.1
7	T	6 15	6 54	a3.7	12 07	12 30	p5.0	7	S	7 10	7 46	a3.6	12 46	1 13	4.9
8	F	7 14	7 54	a3.6	1 02	1 29	p4.8	8	S	8 12	8 48	a3.4	1 44	2 14	4.7
9	S	8 19	9 00	a3.4	2 03	2 32	4.5	9	M	9 18	9 51	a3.3	2 45	3 16	a4.6
10	S	9 29	10 07	a3.3	3 07	3 39	4.4	10	T	10 25	10 53	3.2	3 47	4 19	a4.5
11	M	10 39	11 12	3.3	4 12	4 45	4.4	11	W	11 28	11 52	3.2	4 48	5 20	a4.5
12	T	11 45	...	3.4	5 15	5 48	4.4	12	T	...	12 27	3.2	5 46	6 17	a4.5
13	W	12 12	12 44	p3.5	6 14	6 45	a4.6	13	F	12 47	1 20	3.3	6 40	7 09	a4.6
14	T	1 06	1 37	p3.6	7 08	7 37	a4.7	14	S	1 36	2 08	3.4	7 30	7 56	a4.7
15	F	1 56	2 26	3.7	7 57	8 24	a4.8	15	S	2 22	2 52	a3.5	8 16	8 40	a4.8
16	S	2 41	3 10	3.7	8 42	9 09	a4.9	16	M	3 05	3 33	3.5	8 58	9 22	a4.8
17	S	3 25	3 53	3.7	9 26	9 51	a4.9	17	T	3 45	4 13	3.5	9 39	10 02	a4.8
18	M	4 06	4 34	a3.7	10 07	10 31	a4.9	18	W	4 24	4 52	a3.5	10 19	10 41	a4.9
19	T	4 46	5 14	a3.6	10 48	11 12	a4.8	19	T	5 03	5 30	a3.5	10 58	11 20	a4.8
20	W	5 27	5 55	a3.5	11 28	11 52	a4.7	20	F	5 42	6 09	a3.4	11 38	11 59	a4.8
21	T	6 07	6 36	a3.4	...	12 09	4.6	21	S	6 21	6 48	a3.3	...	12 17	4.7
22	F	6 50	7 19	a3.2	12 34	12 52	4.5	22	S	7 01	7 29	a3.2	12 39	12 58	p4.7
23	S	7 34	8 04	a3.1	1 17	1 37	p4.4	23	M	7 44	8 11	a3.1	1 20	1 41	4.6
24	S	8 22	8 52	a3.0	2 03	2 24	4.3	24	T	8 31	8 57	3.0	2 04	2 28	4.5
25	M	9 13	9 43	2.9	2 51	3 15	4.2	25	W	9 23	9 47	3.0	2 51	3 19	a4.5
26	T	10 07	10 34	2.9	3 41	4 08	4.2	26	T	10 19	10 41	3.0	3 44	4 14	a4.5
27	W	11 02	11 25	p3.1	4 33	5 02	4.3	27	F	11 18	11 37	p3.2	4 40	5 11	a4.6
28	T	11 55	...	3.1	5 25	5 55	4.5	28	S	...	12 16	3.2	5 37	6 09	a4.7
29	F	12 15	12 47	p3.3	6 17	6 46	a4.7	29	S	12 33	1 13	3.4	6 35	7 06	a4.9
30	S	1 04	1 38	3.5	7 07	7 37	a4.9	30	M	1 29	2 08	a3.6	7 32	8 02	5.0
								31	T	2 24	3 02	a3.8	8 27	8 56	a5.2

The Kts. (knots) columns show the **maximum** predicted velocities of the stronger one of the Flood Currents and the stronger one of the Ebb Currents for each day.

The letter "a" means the velocity shown should occur **after** the **a.m.** Current Change. The letter "p" means the velocity shown should occur **after** the **p.m.** Current Change (even if next morning). No "a" or "p" means a.m. and p.m. velocities are the same for that day.

Avg. Max. Velocity: Flood 3.4 Kts., Ebb 4.6 Kts.

Max. Flood 3 hrs. after Flood Starts, ±10 min.

Max. Ebb 3 hrs. after Ebb Starts, ±10 min.

See pp. 22-29 for Current Change at other points.

2013 CURRENT TABLE
THE NARROWS, NY HARBOR
40°36.56'N, 74°02.77'W Mid-Channel

Standard Time | Standard Time

DAY OF MONTH	DAY OF WEEK	NORTH Flood Starts a.m.	p.m.	Kts.	SOUTH Ebb Starts a.m.	p.m.	Kts.	DAY OF MONTH	DAY OF WEEK	NORTH Flood Starts a.m.	p.m.	Kts.	SOUTH Ebb Starts a.m.	p.m.	Kts.
		JANUARY								**FEBRUARY**					
1	T	6 07	6 52	a1.6	...	12 08	2.0	1	F	7 30	7 51	p1.8	1 02	1 18	2.0
2	W	7 00	7 39	a1.7	12 44	12 57	p2.0	2	S	8 29	8 43	p1.8	1 52	2 07	1.9
3	T	7 58	8 30	p1.8	1 33	1 47	p2.0	3	S	9 33	9 40	p1.8	2 43	3 00	1.8
4	F	8 57	9 21	p1.9	2 23	2 38	p2.0	4	M	10 36	10 39	p1.8	3 39	4 00	a1.8
5	S	9 59	10 14	p2.0	3 16	3 32	1.9	5	T	11 39	11 40	p1.8	4 41	5 06	a1.8
6	S	11 00	11 08	p2.0	4 13	4 31	1.9	6	W	...	12 40	1.3	5 46	6 13	a1.9
7	M	...	12 01	1.6	5 13	5 34	2.0	7	T	12 41	1 37	a1.8	6 48	7 15	2.0
8	T	12 03	12 59	a2.1	6 12	6 35	a2.2	8	F	1 42	2 31	a1.9	7 45	8 12	a2.2
9	W	12 59	1 56	a2.1	7 09	7 32	a2.3	9	S	2 39	3 22	a2.1	8 39	9 06	a2.3
10	T	1 54	2 50	a2.2	8 03	8 28	a2.4	10	S	3 34	4 10	a2.1	9 30	9 58	a2.4
11	F	2 50	3 41	a2.3	8 56	9 22	a2.5	11	M	4 26	4 58	a2.1	10 21	10 50	a2.4
12	S	3 45	4 31	a2.3	9 48	10 16	a2.5	12	T	5 19	5 49	a2.0	11 12	11 44	a2.3
13	S	4 40	5 23	a2.2	10 40	11 12	a2.4	13	W	6 16	6 42	a1.8	...	12 05	2.2
14	M	5 38	6 18	a2.0	11 35	...	2.3	14	T	7 16	7 39	a1.7	12 40	1 00	2.0
15	T	6 40	7 18	a1.8	12 11	12 32	p2.2	15	F	8 20	8 36	a1.6	1 36	1 54	1.8
16	W	7 46	8 19	a1.7	1 11	1 30	p2.0	16	S	9 24	9 32	p1.5	2 31	2 49	1.7
17	T	8 53	9 19	1.6	2 11	2 27	p1.9	17	S	10 27	10 27	p1.4	3 27	3 46	a1.7
18	F	9 59	10 17	1.5	3 11	3 24	1.7	18	M	11 26	11 19	p1.3	4 25	4 46	a1.7
19	S	11 02	11 11	p1.5	4 13	4 25	1.7	19	T	...	12 20	1.2	5 23	5 45	a1.7
20	S	...	12 02	1.3	5 16	5 27	a1.7	20	W	12 08	1 09	a1.3	6 16	6 38	a1.8
21	M	12 01	12 59	a1.4	6 14	6 25	a1.8	21	T	12 54	1 52	1.3	7 02	7 23	a1.8
22	T	12 48	1 51	a1.4	7 03	7 15	a1.8	22	F	1 38	2 29	1.4	7 41	8 02	a1.9
23	W	1 31	2 35	a1.4	7 44	7 57	a1.8	23	S	2 19	3 01	1.5	8 17	8 38	a2.0
24	T	2 10	3 11	a1.4	8 17	8 33	a1.8	24	S	2 57	3 32	a1.7	8 51	9 12	2.0
25	F	2 45	3 40	a1.4	8 47	9 05	a1.8	25	M	3 33	4 02	a1.8	9 25	9 47	2.1
26	S	3 18	4 07	a1.5	9 17	9 37	a1.9	26	T	4 10	4 34	a1.9	10 01	10 24	2.1
27	S	3 51	4 33	a1.6	9 48	10 10	a1.9	27	W	4 49	5 08	p1.9	10 40	11 05	a2.2
28	M	4 26	5 03	a1.7	10 22	10 48	a2.0	28	T	5 31	5 47	p1.9	11 21	11 48	2.1
29	T	5 04	5 38	a1.7	11 01	11 29	a2.0								
30	W	5 47	6 17	1.7	11 43	...	2.1								
31	T	6 36	7 02	1.7	12 14	12 30	p2.1								

The Kts. (knots) columns show the **maximum** predicted velocities of the stronger one of the Flood Currents and the stronger one of the Ebb Currents for each day.

The letter "a" means the velocity shown should occur **after** the a.m. Current Change. The letter "p" means the velocity shown should occur **after** the p.m. Current Change (even if next morning). No "a" or "p" means a.m. and p.m. velocities are the same for that day.

Avg. Max. Velocity: Flood 1.7 Kts., Ebb 2.0 Kts.

Max. Flood 2 hrs. 25 min. after Flood Starts, ±30 min.

Max. Ebb 3 hrs. 15 min. after Ebb Starts, ±10 min.

At **The Battery, Desbrosses St., & Chelsea Dock** Current turns 1 1/2 hrs. after the Narrows. At **42nd St.** and the **George Washington Bridge**, the Current turns 1 3/4 hrs. after the Narrows. See pp. 22-29 for Current Change at other points.

2013 CURRENT TABLE
THE NARROWS, NY HARBOR
40°36.56'N, 74°02.77'W Mid-Channel

Daylight Time starts March 10 at 2 a.m.   **Daylight Saving Time**

DAY OF MONTH	DAY OF WEEK	CURRENT TURNS TO						DAY OF MONTH	DAY OF WEEK	CURRENT TURNS TO					
		NORTH Flood Starts			SOUTH Ebb Starts					NORTH Flood Starts			SOUTH Ebb Starts		
		a.m.	p.m.	Kts.	a.m.	p.m.	Kts.			a.m.	p.m.	Kts.	a.m.	p.m.	Kts.
1	F	6 18	6 30	p1.8	...	12 06	2.1	1	M	8 59	8 58	p1.6	2 06	2 32	a1.9
2	S	7 11	7 19	p1.8	12 36	12 54	a2.0	2	T	10 05	10 08	p1.4	3 00	3 29	a1.7
3	S	8 11	8 15	p1.7	1 25	1 45	a1.9	3	W	11 14	11 23	p1.3	3 58	4 33	a1.5
4	M	9 14	9 16	p1.6	2 17	2 39	a1.7	4	T	...	12 17	1.0	5 03	5 45	1.4
5	T	10 21	10 23	p1.5	3 14	3 40	a1.6	5	F	12 32	1 16	a1.3	6 14	6 57	1.5
6	W	11 25	11 31	p1.5	4 18	4 50	a1.6	6	S	1 36	2 11	1.3	7 20	8 00	1.7
7	T	...	12 26	1.2	5 26	6 00	1.6	7	S	2 35	3 01	1.5	8 18	8 54	p1.9
8	F	12 36	1 23	a1.5	6 32	7 05	1.8	8	M	3 28	3 47	1.6	9 09	9 41	2.0
9	S	1 37	2 16	a1.7	7 31	8 01	2.0	9	T	4 16	4 29	1.7	9 55	10 24	2.0
10	S	*3 33	*4 04	a1.8	*9 23	*9 52	2.1	10	W	5 01	5 08	1.7	10 39	11 05	2.0
11	M	4 24	4 49	a1.9	10 12	10 40	2.2	11	T	5 45	5 46	1.6	11 22	11 47	2.0
12	T	5 13	5 33	a1.9	10 59	11 28	a2.2	12	F	6 30	6 25	1.5	...	12 06	1.9
13	W	6 01	6 17	a1.8	11 47	...	2.2	13	S	7 19	7 08	p1.4	12 30	12 53	a1.9
14	T	6 52	7 04	a1.7	12 16	12 36	2.1	14	S	8 11	7 55	p1.4	1 15	1 42	a1.8
15	F	7 47	7 54	1.5	1 05	1 27	a2.0	15	M	9 06	8 49	p1.3	2 02	2 33	a1.7
16	S	8 46	8 47	1.4	1 56	2 19	a1.8	16	T	10 00	9 46	p1.3	2 50	3 23	a1.6
17	S	9 47	9 42	p1.4	2 47	3 11	a1.7	17	W	10 51	10 44	p1.4	3 39	4 15	a1.6
18	M	10 46	10 37	p1.3	3 38	4 05	a1.6	18	T	11 40	11 40	p1.4	4 31	5 10	a1.6
19	T	11 42	11 32	p1.3	4 31	5 01	a1.6	19	F	...	12 26	1.4	5 26	6 05	1.7
20	W	...	12 33	1.2	5 26	5 59	a1.6	20	S	12 34	1 10	p1.6	6 22	6 58	1.9
21	T	12 25	1 19	a1.3	6 21	6 53	a1.7	21	S	1 24	1 52	p1.7	7 14	7 46	p2.2
22	F	1 15	2 01	1.4	7 13	7 42	1.8	22	M	2 13	2 34	p2.0	8 03	8 31	p2.4
23	S	2 02	2 41	1.5	7 59	8 26	2.0	23	T	3 01	3 15	p2.2	8 48	9 14	p2.5
24	S	2 48	3 18	1.7	8 42	9 06	p2.2	24	W	3 46	3 55	p2.3	9 31	9 56	p2.6
25	M	3 30	3 54	p1.9	9 21	9 44	p2.3	25	T	4 31	4 35	p2.4	10 14	10 37	p2.5
26	T	4 11	4 29	p2.1	10 00	10 22	p2.4	26	F	5 15	5 15	p2.3	10 57	11 20	p2.5
27	W	4 52	5 04	p2.1	10 38	11 01	p2.4	27	S	6 01	5 59	p2.2	11 42	...	2.2
28	T	5 33	5 41	p2.1	11 19	11 42	2.3	28	S	6 51	6 47	p1.9	12 07	12 32	a2.3
29	F	6 16	6 21	p2.0	...	12 01	2.1	29	M	7 47	7 45	p1.7	12 57	1 26	a2.1
30	S	7 04	7 05	p1.9	12 26	12 47	a2.2	30	T	8 50	8 53	p1.5	1 52	2 25	a1.9
31	S	7 58	7 57	p1.7	1 14	1 38	a2.1								

The Kts. (knots) columns show the **maximum** predicted velocities of the stronger one of the Flood Currents and the stronger one of the Ebb Currents for each day.

The letter "a" means the velocity shown should occur **after** the **a.m.** Current Change. The letter "p" means the velocity shown should occur **after** the **p.m.** Current Change (even if next morning). No "a" or "p" means a.m. and p.m. velocities are the same for that day.

Avg. Max. Velocity: Flood 1.7 Kts., Ebb 2.0 Kts.

Max. Flood 2 hrs. 25 min. after Flood Starts, ±30 min.

Max. Ebb 3 hrs. 15 min. after Ebb Starts, ±10 min.

See pp. 22-29 for Current Change at other points.

2013 CURRENT TABLE
THE NARROWS, NY HARBOR
40°36.56'N, 74°02.77'W Mid-Channel
Daylight Saving Time　　　　　　　**Daylight Saving Time**

D A Y O F M O N T H	D A Y O F W E E K	NORTH Flood Starts			SOUTH Ebb Starts			D A Y O F M O N T H	D A Y O F W E E K	NORTH Flood Starts			SOUTH Ebb Starts		
		a.m.	p.m.	Kts.	a.m.	p.m.	Kts.			a.m.	p.m.	Kts.	a.m.	p.m.	Kts.
1	W	9 57	10 08	p1.3	2 49	3 26	a1.7	1	S	11 47	...	1.3	4 41	5 35	a1.6
2	T	11 03	11 23	p1.3	3 49	4 32	a1.5	2	S	12 21	12 44	p1.4	5 48	6 45	1.6
3	F	...	12 07	1.1	4 54	5 44	a1.5	3	M	1 24	1 38	p1.4	6 53	7 46	p1.7
4	S	12 31	1 03	1.2	6 03	6 55	p1.6	4	T	2 21	2 26	p1.5	7 51	8 37	p1.8
5	S	1 33	1 56	p1.3	7 09	7 56	p1.7	5	W	3 16	3 11	p1.5	8 42	9 19	p1.8
6	M	2 31	2 45	p1.5	8 06	8 47	p1.8	6	T	4 04	3 49	p1.5	9 26	9 55	p1.8
7	T	3 23	3 30	p1.6	8 55	9 31	p1.9	7	F	4 46	4 23	p1.4	10 04	10 26	p1.8
8	W	4 10	4 09	p1.6	9 39	10 09	p1.9	8	S	5 22	4 53	p1.4	10 40	10 56	p1.7
9	T	4 53	4 44	1.5	10 20	10 45	p1.9	9	S	5 55	5 22	p1.4	11 14	11 27	p1.7
10	F	5 33	5 17	p1.5	10 59	11 19	p1.8	10	M	6 26	5 55	p1.4	11 50	...	1.5
11	S	6 12	5 50	p1.5	11 38	11 56	p1.8	11	T	6 59	6 34	p1.4	12 01	12 30	a1.7
12	S	6 53	6 26	p1.4	...	12 20	1.6	12	W	7 36	7 21	p1.5	12 41	1 15	a1.8
13	M	7 36	7 09	p1.4	12 35	1 05	a1.7	13	T	8 18	8 15	p1.5	1 25	2 02	a1.8
14	T	8 21	8 00	p1.4	1 19	1 53	a1.7	14	F	9 04	9 12	p1.6	2 13	2 50	a1.9
15	W	9 09	8 57	p1.4	2 05	2 42	a1.7	15	S	9 52	10 11	1.6	3 02	3 40	a1.9
16	T	9 57	9 56	p1.5	2 53	3 32	a1.7	16	S	10 42	11 10	a1.8	3 53	4 33	1.9
17	F	10 45	10 55	p1.6	3 43	4 23	a1.7	17	M	11 32	...	1.9	4 47	5 28	2.0
18	S	11 33	11 51	1.6	4 36	5 17	1.8	18	T	12 08	12 22	p2.1	5 44	6 24	p2.2
19	S	...	12 20	1.8	5 32	6 12	2.0	19	W	1 04	1 12	p2.2	6 43	7 19	p2.3
20	M	12 46	1 06	p1.9	6 29	7 05	p2.2	20	T	2 00	2 02	p2.3	7 39	8 11	p2.5
21	T	1 38	1 52	p2.1	7 23	7 55	p2.4	21	F	2 54	2 52	p2.4	8 33	9 02	p2.6
22	W	2 30	2 37	p2.3	8 13	8 43	p2.6	22	S	3 46	3 43	p2.5	9 24	9 51	p2.6
23	T	3 20	3 22	p2.4	9 02	9 28	p2.7	23	S	4 36	4 34	p2.4	10 15	10 41	p2.6
24	F	4 09	4 07	p2.5	9 49	10 14	p2.6	24	M	5 26	5 27	p2.3	11 07	11 32	p2.5
25	S	4 57	4 53	p2.4	10 36	11 00	p2.5	25	T	6 17	6 23	p2.1	...	12 01	2.1
26	S	5 45	5 41	p2.2	11 25	11 49	p2.4	26	W	7 12	7 26	p1.9	12 26	1 00	a2.3
27	M	6 36	6 35	p2.0	...	12 17	2.0	27	T	8 12	8 34	p1.7	1 24	2 01	a2.1
28	T	7 32	7 37	p1.7	12 42	1 15	a2.2	28	F	9 15	9 45	p1.6	2 22	3 04	a2.0
29	W	8 35	8 48	p1.5	1 39	2 17	a2.0	29	S	10 19	10 55	1.5	3 21	4 07	a1.8
30	T	9 40	10 02	p1.4	2 38	3 20	a1.8	30	S	11 20	...	1.5	4 21	5 14	a1.7
31	F	10 45	11 14	1.3	3 39	4 25	a1.6								

The Kts. (knots) columns show the **maximum** predicted velocities of the stronger one of the Flood Currents and the stronger one of the Ebb Currents for each day.

The letter "a" means the velocity shown should occur **after** the **a.m.** Current Change. The letter "p" means the velocity shown should occur **after** the **p.m.** Current Change (even if next morning). No "a" or "p" means a.m. and p.m. velocities are the same for that day.

Avg. Max. Velocity: Flood 1.7 Kts., Ebb 2.0 Kts.
Max. Flood 2 hrs. 25 min. after Flood Starts, ±30 min.
Max. Ebb 3 hrs. 15 min. after Ebb Starts, ±10 min.

At **The Battery, Desbrosses St., & Chelsea Dock** Current turns 1 1/2 hrs. after the Narrows. At **42nd St.** and the **George Washington Bridge**, the Current turns 1 3/4 hrs. after the Narrows. See pp. 22-29 for Current Change at other points.

2013 CURRENT TABLE
THE NARROWS, NY HARBOR
40°36.56'N, 74°02.77'W Mid-Channel

Daylight Saving Time　　　　　　　　　**Daylight Saving Time**

JULY

DAY OF MONTH	DAY OF WEEK	NORTH Flood Starts a.m.	**p.m.**	Kts.	SOUTH Ebb Starts a.m.	**p.m.**	Kts.
1	M	12 01	12 18	p1.5	5 25	6 23	1.7
2	T	1 04	1 12	p1.4	6 30	7 25	p1.8
3	W	2 06	2 04	p1.4	7 32	8 19	p1.8
4	T	3 02	2 49	p1.4	8 26	9 02	p1.8
5	F	3 52	3 29	p1.4	9 11	9 38	p1.8
6	S	4 32	4 04	p1.4	9 49	10 07	p1.7
7	S	5 05	4 34	p1.3	10 22	10 34	p1.7
8	M	5 32	5 03	p1.4	10 52	11 02	p1.7
9	T	5 58	5 34	p1.5	11 24	11 34	p1.8
10	W	6 24	6 10	p1.5	...	12 01	1.6
11	T	6 56	6 52	p1.6	12 10	12 40	a1.8
12	F	7 33	7 41	p1.6	12 52	1 25	a1.9
13	S	8 17	8 35	1.6	1 38	2 12	a2.0
14	S	9 05	9 32	1.7	2 26	3 01	a2.0
15	M	9 55	10 32	a1.9	3 15	3 52	a2.0
16	T	10 48	11 33	a2.0	4 07	4 46	2.0
17	W	11 42	...	2.0	5 04	5 44	2.0
18	T	12 33	12 37	p2.1	6 06	6 44	p2.2
19	F	1 32	1 33	p2.1	7 08	7 42	p2.3
20	S	2 29	2 29	p2.2	8 07	8 38	p2.4
21	S	3 23	3 25	p2.3	9 03	9 31	p2.5
22	M	4 15	4 20	p2.3	9 56	10 22	p2.5
23	T	5 04	5 14	p2.3	10 49	11 14	p2.5
24	W	5 54	6 09	p2.1	11 43	...	2.3
25	T	6 46	7 09	p1.9	12 07	12 39	a2.4
26	F	7 43	8 13	p1.8	1 03	1 39	a2.3
27	S	8 44	9 20	a1.7	2 00	2 39	a2.1
28	S	9 46	10 29	a1.6	2 57	3 40	a1.9
29	M	10 47	11 35	a1.6	3 55	4 42	a1.8
30	T	11 46	...	1.5	4 57	5 48	1.7
31	W	12 39	12 41	p1.4	6 02	6 52	p1.8

AUGUST

DAY OF MONTH	DAY OF WEEK	NORTH Flood Starts a.m.	**p.m.**	Kts.	SOUTH Ebb Starts a.m.	**p.m.**	Kts.
1	T	1 40	1 33	p1.4	7 07	7 49	p1.8
2	F	2 36	2 22	p1.4	8 03	8 35	p1.8
3	S	3 27	3 06	p1.4	8 50	9 12	p1.8
4	S	4 05	3 42	p1.4	9 28	9 43	p1.8
5	M	4 36	4 15	p1.4	10 00	10 11	p1.8
6	T	5 01	4 45	p1.5	10 29	10 39	p1.8
7	W	5 25	5 16	p1.6	10 59	11 10	p1.9
8	T	5 50	5 50	p1.6	11 33	11 44	p2.0
9	F	6 20	6 29	p1.7	...	12 10	1.9
10	S	6 56	7 14	1.7	12 24	12 52	2.0
11	S	7 37	8 05	a1.8	1 07	1 38	a2.1
12	M	8 24	9 01	a1.8	1 54	2 27	a2.1
13	T	9 14	10 01	a1.9	2 43	3 17	a2.0
14	W	10 09	11 04	a1.9	3 34	4 10	p1.9
15	T	11 08	...	1.9	4 31	5 09	p1.9
16	F	12 07	12 10	p1.9	5 35	6 13	p1.9
17	S	1 08	1 12	p1.9	6 42	7 17	p2.0
18	S	2 06	2 13	p2.0	7 45	8 16	p2.2
19	M	3 01	3 12	p2.1	8 44	9 12	p2.3
20	T	3 53	4 07	p2.2	9 38	10 04	p2.4
21	W	4 42	5 01	p2.2	10 30	10 54	p2.4
22	T	5 29	5 53	p2.1	11 22	11 45	p2.4
23	F	6 19	6 48	p2.0	...	12 16	2.3
24	S	7 11	7 48	1.8	12 38	1 11	a2.3
25	S	8 08	8 52	a1.7	1 33	2 08	a2.1
26	M	9 07	9 59	a1.6	2 29	3 06	a1.9
27	T	10 08	11 05	a1.5	3 26	4 04	1.7
28	W	11 07	...	1.4	4 25	5 04	p1.7
29	T	12 08	12 05	1.3	5 29	6 07	p1.7
30	F	1 06	12 58	p1.3	6 33	7 05	p1.8
31	S	1 58	1 48	p1.3	7 30	7 55	p1.8

The Kts. (knots) columns show the **maximum** predicted velocities of the stronger one of the Flood Currents and the stronger one of the Ebb Currents for each day.

The letter "a" means the velocity shown should occur **after** the **a.m.** Current Change. The letter "p" means the velocity shown should occur **after** the **p.m.** Current Change (even if next morning). No "a" or "p" means a.m. and p.m. velocities are the same for that day.

Avg. Max. Velocity: Flood 1.7 Kts., Ebb 2.0 Kts.

Max. Flood 2 hrs. 25 min. after Flood Starts, ±30 min.

Max. Ebb 3 hrs. 15 min. after Ebb Starts, ±10 min.

See pp. 22-29 for Current Change at other points.

2013 CURRENT TABLE
THE NARROWS, NY HARBOR

40°36.56'N, 74°02.77'W Mid-Channel

Daylight Saving Time   Daylight Saving Time

SEPTEMBER

DAY OF MONTH	DAY OF WEEK	NORTH Flood Starts			SOUTH Ebb Starts		
		a.m.	**p.m.**	Kts.	a.m.	**p.m.**	Kts.
1	S	2 44	**2 33**	p1.4	8 18	**8 36**	p1.8
2	M	3 22	**3 14**	1.4	8 57	**9 11**	p1.9
3	T	3 55	**3 51**	p1.5	9 30	**9 42**	p1.9
4	W	4 23	**4 24**	p1.6	10 02	**10 14**	p2.0
5	T	4 50	**4 58**	p1.7	10 34	**10 46**	2.0
6	F	5 18	**5 33**	p1.8	11 07	**11 21**	2.1
7	S	5 49	**6 11**	a1.8	11 44	**11 59**	2.1
8	S	6 24	**6 54**	a1.9	...	**12 25**	2.1
9	M	7 04	**7 43**	a1.9	12 42	**1 10**	2.1
10	T	7 50	**8 38**	a1.8	1 29	**1 58**	2.0
11	W	8 42	**9 39**	a1.8	2 18	**2 48**	p1.9
12	T	9 41	**10 43**	a1.7	3 11	**3 42**	1.7
13	F	10 47	**11 48**	a1.6	4 08	**4 42**	p1.7
14	S	11 55	**...**	1.6	5 14	**5 48**	p1.7
15	S	12 50	**1 02**	p1.6	6 24	**6 56**	p1.8
16	M	1 47	**2 04**	p1.7	7 30	**7 58**	p2.0
17	T	2 41	**3 03**	p1.8	8 30	**8 54**	p2.1
18	W	3 32	**3 57**	p2.0	9 23	**9 45**	p2.3
19	T	4 19	**4 47**	p2.0	10 13	**10 33**	2.3
20	F	5 05	**5 37**	p2.0	11 01	**11 22**	2.3
21	S	5 50	**6 28**	a1.9	11 50	**...**	2.2
22	S	6 38	**7 23**	a1.8	12 11	**12 41**	a2.2
23	M	7 29	**8 23**	a1.6	1 04	**1 34**	a2.0
24	T	8 25	**9 27**	a1.5	1 59	**2 28**	1.8
25	W	9 24	**10 30**	a1.4	2 54	**3 21**	p1.7
26	T	10 24	**11 29**	1.3	3 51	**4 16**	p1.6
27	F	11 22	**...**	1.3	4 49	**5 14**	p1.6
28	S	12 22	**12 17**	p1.3	5 49	**6 11**	p1.7
29	S	1 10	**1 08**	1.3	6 45	**7 04**	p1.8
30	M	1 53	**1 55**	p1.4	7 34	**7 50**	p1.9

OCTOBER

DAY OF MONTH	DAY OF WEEK	NORTH Flood Starts			SOUTH Ebb Starts		
		a.m.	**p.m.**	Kts.	a.m.	**p.m.**	Kts.
1	T	2 31	**2 39**	1.5	8 17	**8 31**	p2.0
2	W	3 07	**3 20**	p1.7	8 55	**9 08**	p2.1
3	T	3 41	**4 00**	1.8	9 31	**9 44**	2.2
4	F	4 13	**4 37**	1.9	10 06	**10 21**	a2.3
5	S	4 46	**5 15**	a2.1	10 42	**10 58**	a2.3
6	S	5 20	**5 55**	a2.1	11 20	**11 38**	a2.3
7	M	5 57	**6 39**	a2.1	...	**12 02**	2.2
8	T	6 38	**7 28**	a2.0	12 22	**12 47**	p2.1
9	W	7 26	**8 24**	a1.8	1 10	**1 36**	p2.0
10	T	8 22	**9 26**	a1.7	2 02	**2 28**	p1.8
11	F	9 28	**10 31**	a1.5	2 58	**3 24**	p1.6
12	S	10 40	**11 35**	a1.4	3 57	**4 24**	p1.5
13	S	11 52	**...**	1.3	5 04	**5 31**	p1.5
14	M	12 36	**12 59**	p1.3	6 15	**6 40**	p1.6
15	T	1 32	**2 00**	p1.4	7 21	**7 42**	p1.8
16	W	2 24	**2 56**	p1.6	8 19	**8 37**	p2.0
17	T	3 13	**3 48**	p1.7	9 11	**9 27**	p2.1
18	F	3 59	**4 37**	1.8	9 57	**10 13**	2.1
19	S	4 42	**5 23**	a1.8	10 42	**10 59**	2.1
20	S	5 23	**6 10**	a1.8	11 26	**11 46**	a2.1
21	M	6 05	**7 00**	a1.7	...	**12 11**	2.0
22	T	6 51	**7 54**	a1.5	12 35	**12 58**	p1.9
23	W	7 41	**8 51**	a1.4	1 27	**1 48**	p1.8
24	T	8 37	**9 48**	a1.3	2 20	**2 38**	p1.7
25	F	9 36	**10 41**	a1.3	3 13	**3 29**	p1.6
26	S	10 35	**11 30**	1.3	4 06	**4 20**	p1.6
27	S	11 31	**...**	1.3	5 00	**5 14**	p1.7
28	M	12 16	**12 24**	p1.4	5 54	**6 08**	p1.8
29	T	12 58	**1 13**	1.5	6 45	**7 00**	p1.9
30	W	1 39	**2 01**	1.6	7 33	**7 47**	p2.1
31	T	2 19	**2 46**	a1.8	8 17	**8 31**	2.2

The Kts. (knots) columns show the **maximum** predicted velocities of the stronger one of the Flood Currents and the stronger one of the Ebb Currents for each day.

The letter "a" means the velocity shown should occur **after** the **a.m.** Current Change. The letter "p" means the velocity shown should occur **after** the **p.m.** Current Change (even if next morning). No "a" or "p" means a.m. and p.m. velocities are the same for that day.

Avg. Max. Velocity: Flood 1.7 Kts., Ebb 2.0 Kts.

Max. Flood 2 hrs. 25 min. after Flood Starts, ±30 min.

Max. Ebb 3 hrs. 15 min. after Ebb Starts, ±10 min.

At **The Battery, Desbrosses St., & Chelsea Dock** Current turns 1 1/2 hrs. after the Narrows. At **42nd St.** and the **George Washington Bridge**, the Current turns 1 3/4 hrs. after the Narrows. See pp. 22-29 for Current Change at other points.

2013 CURRENT TABLE
THE NARROWS, NY HARBOR

40°36.56'N, 74°02.77'W Mid-Channel

*Standard Time starts Nov. 3 at 2 a.m.   Standard Time

NOVEMBER

DAY OF MONTH	DAY OF WEEK	CURRENT TURNS TO						
		NORTH Flood Starts			SOUTH Ebb Starts			
		a.m.	p.m.	Kts.	a.m.	p.m.	Kts.	
1	F	2 58	3 31	a2.0	8 58	9 13	a2.4	
2	S	3 36	4 14	a2.2	9 38	9 54	a2.5	
3	S	*3 16	*3 57	a2.3	*9 18	*9 36	a2.5	
4	M	3 54	4 40	a2.3	9 58	10 19	a2.5	
5	T	4 35	5 26	a2.2	10 42	11 06	a2.4	
6	W	5 20	6 16	a2.0	11 29	11 57	a2.2	
7	T	6 12	7 13	a1.8	...	12 21	2.0	
8	F	7 14	8 16	a1.6	12 53	1 16	p1.8	
9	S	8 26	9 20	a1.4	1 52	2 13	p1.6	
10	S	9 40	10 23	a1.3	2 53	3 14	p1.5	
11	M	10 51	11 22	1.2	3 59	4 19	p1.5	
12	T	11 56	...	1.2	5 09	5 26	p1.6	
13	W	12 17	12 56	1.3	6 15	6 28	p1.7	
14	T	1 09	1 52	1.4	7 12	7 23	1.8	
15	F	1 57	2 43	1.5	8 01	8 12	a1.9	
16	S	2 41	3 30	a1.6	8 45	8 57	a1.9	
17	S	3 22	4 14	a1.6	9 25	9 40	a1.9	
18	M	4 00	4 56	a1.6	10 03	10 23	a1.9	
19	T	4 37	5 39	a1.5	10 42	11 07	a1.9	
20	W	5 17	6 24	a1.4	11 24	11 54	a1.8	
21	T	6 01	7 12	a1.4	...	12 08	1.7	
22	F	6 51	8 00	a1.3	12 43	12 55	p1.7	
23	S	7 47	8 47	a1.3	1 32	1 43	p1.7	
24	S	8 45	9 33	1.4	2 21	2 31	p1.7	
25	M	9 42	10 19	p1.5	3 10	3 22	p1.8	
26	T	10 37	11 04	p1.7	4 02	4 15	p1.9	
27	W	11 30	11 48	p1.8	4 55	5 09	p2.0	
28	T	...	12 21	1.7	5 47	6 02	2.1	
29	F	12 33	1 12	a2.0	6 37	6 53	2.3	
30	S	1 17	2 01	a2.2	7 23	7 41	a2.5	

DECEMBER

DAY OF MONTH	DAY OF WEEK	CURRENT TURNS TO						
		NORTH Flood Starts			SOUTH Ebb Starts			
		a.m.	p.m.	Kts.	a.m.	p.m.	Kts.	
1	S	2 01	2 49	a2.3	8 09	8 28	a2.6	
2	M	2 46	3 36	a2.4	8 53	9 14	a2.6	
3	T	3 32	4 23	a2.4	9 38	10 01	a2.6	
4	W	4 17	5 10	a2.3	10 24	10 51	a2.4	
5	T	5 08	6 01	a2.1	11 14	11 45	a2.3	
6	F	6 04	6 58	a1.9	...	12 08	2.1	
7	S	7 10	8 00	a1.6	12 43	1 05	p1.9	
8	S	8 21	9 03	a1.5	1 43	2 03	p1.7	
9	M	9 34	10 06	a1.4	2 45	3 02	p1.6	
10	T	10 43	11 05	1.3	3 50	4 05	1.5	
11	W	11 47	...	1.2	5 00	5 10	p1.6	
12	T	12 01	12 48	a1.3	6 06	6 14	1.6	
13	F	12 53	1 46	a1.4	7 04	7 11	a1.7	
14	S	1 42	2 40	a1.5	7 53	8 01	a1.8	
15	S	2 27	3 26	a1.5	8 35	8 46	a1.8	
16	M	3 06	4 07	a1.5	9 11	9 26	a1.8	
17	T	3 42	4 43	a1.4	9 45	10 04	a1.8	
18	W	4 15	5 18	a1.4	10 18	10 42	a1.7	
19	T	4 50	5 52	a1.4	10 53	11 21	a1.7	
20	F	5 28	6 29	a1.4	11 32	...	1.7	
21	S	6 12	7 08	a1.4	12 04	12 15	p1.8	
22	S	7 02	7 51	a1.4	12 49	1 00	p1.8	
23	M	7 57	8 36	1.5	1 36	1 47	p1.8	
24	T	8 54	9 23	p1.7	2 24	2 35	p1.9	
25	W	9 51	10 12	p1.9	3 13	3 26	p1.9	
26	T	10 48	11 01	p2.0	4 06	4 21	p2.0	
27	F	11 43	11 50	p2.1	5 01	5 19	2.1	
28	S	...	12 38	1.7	5 56	6 16	2.2	
29	S	12 40	1 32	a2.2	6 49	7 11	a2.4	
30	M	1 30	2 24	a2.3	7 40	8 03	a2.5	
31	T	2 21	3 14	a2.4	8 29	8 53	a2.6	

The Kts. (knots) columns show the **maximum** predicted velocities of the stronger one of the Flood Currents and the stronger one of the Ebb Currents for each day.

The letter "a" means the velocity shown should occur **after** the **a.m.** Current Change. The letter "p" means the velocity shown should occur **after** the **p.m.** Current Change (even if next morning). No "a" or "p" means a.m. and p.m. velocities are the same for that day.

Avg. Max. Velocity: Flood 1.7 Kts., Ebb 2.0 Kts.

Max. Flood 2 hrs. 25 min. after Flood Starts, ±30 min.

Max. Ebb 3 hrs. 15 min. after Ebb Starts, ±10 min.

See pp. 22-29 for Current Change at other points.

2013 HIGH & LOW WATER
THE BATTERY, NY HARBOR
40°42'N, 74°00.9'W

		JANUARY									FEBRUARY				
		Standard Time									Standard Time				
DAY OF MONTH	DAY OF WEEK	HIGH		LOW			DAY OF MONTH	DAY OF WEEK	HIGH		LOW				
		a.m.	Ht.	p.m.	Ht.	a.m.	p.m.			a.m.	Ht.	p.m.	Ht.	a.m.	p.m.
1	T	10 04	4.5	11 00	4.0	4 18	4 58	1	F	11 18	4.4	...	...	5 29	5 45
2	W	10 47	4.4	11 43	4.1	4 56	5 32	2	S	12 01	4.6	12 13	4.2	6 28	6 42
3	T	11 37	4.3	...	...	5 42	6 16	3	S	12 55	4.6	1 15	4.0	7 45	7 59
4	F	12 30	4.2	12 31	4.2	6 46	7 15	4	M	1 54	4.7	2 20	3.9	8 57	9 10
5	S	1 21	4.4	1 29	4.1	8 07	8 26	5	T	3 02	4.7	3 35	4.0	10 02	10 14
6	S	2 18	4.6	2 34	4.0	9 18	9 30	6	W	4 15	4.9	4 50	4.1	11 01	11 13
7	M	3 22	4.8	3 47	4.0	10 20	10 30	7	T	5 22	5.1	5 54	4.4	11 56	...
8	T	4 30	5.0	5 00	4.2	11 18	11 27	8	F	6 20	5.4	6 49	4.8	12 09	12 49
9	W	5 34	5.3	6 04	4.4	...	12 13	9	S	7 12	5.5	7 40	5.0	1 04	1 40
10	T	6 31	5.6	7 00	4.7	12 23	1 07	10	S	8 00	5.6	8 28	5.1	1 56	2 27
11	F	7 24	5.8	7 53	4.8	1 18	1 59	11	M	8 48	5.5	9 15	5.1	2 45	3 12
12	S	8 15	5.8	8 46	4.9	2 11	2 49	12	T	9 35	5.2	10 03	5.0	3 33	3 56
13	S	9 06	5.6	9 39	4.9	3 02	3 37	13	W	10 23	4.9	10 51	4.8	4 19	4 37
14	M	9 58	5.4	10 33	4.8	3 52	4 23	14	T	11 12	4.6	11 39	4.6	5 05	5 19
15	T	10 51	5.1	11 26	4.7	4 41	5 09	15	F	...	...	12 01	4.3	5 54	6 03
16	W	11 43	4.7	...	...	5 33	5 57	16	S	12 25	4.4	12 50	4.0	6 48	6 53
17	T	12 17	4.5	12 34	4.4	6 28	6 48	17	S	1 12	4.2	1 41	3.7	7 49	7 51
18	F	1 07	4.4	1 24	4.0	7 29	7 43	18	M	2 01	4.0	2 36	3.6	8 51	8 52
19	S	1 57	4.2	2 17	3.8	8 31	8 39	19	T	2 56	4.0	3 35	3.5	9 47	9 47
20	S	2 49	4.1	3 13	3.6	9 30	9 33	20	W	3 57	4.0	4 36	3.6	10 38	10 39
21	M	3 45	4.1	4 13	3.6	10 23	10 23	21	T	4 56	4.1	5 30	3.8	11 25	11 27
22	T	4 41	4.2	5 10	3.6	11 12	11 10	22	F	5 46	4.3	6 16	4.1	...	12 10
23	W	5 33	4.3	6 01	3.8	11 58	11 56	23	S	6 28	4.6	6 56	4.3	12 13	12 53
24	T	6 18	4.5	6 45	4.0	...	12 43	24	S	7 05	4.7	7 32	4.5	12 58	1 34
25	F	6 58	4.6	7 26	4.1	12 41	1 25	25	M	7 39	4.9	8 06	4.7	1 42	2 13
26	S	7 33	4.8	8 03	4.2	1 24	2 06	26	T	8 12	4.9	8 40	4.9	2 25	2 51
27	S	8 06	4.8	8 38	4.3	2 06	2 45	27	W	8 48	4.9	9 16	5.0	3 06	3 28
28	M	8 36	4.8	9 11	4.3	2 46	3 21	28	T	9 28	4.8	9 57	5.0	3 48	4 05
29	T	9 08	4.8	9 46	4.4	3 25	3 56								
30	W	9 45	4.7	10 25	4.5	4 03	4 30								
31	T	10 28	4.5	11 10	4.5	4 43	5 05								

Dates when Ht. of **Low** Water is below Mean Lower Low with Ht. of lowest given for each period and Date of lowest in ( ):

7th - 16th: -1.3' (12th)
26th - 31st: -0.4' (27th - 30th)

6th - 14th: -1.1' (10th - 11th)
24th - 28th: -0.5' (26th - 28th)

Average Rise and Fall 4.6 ft.

When a high tide exceeds avg. ht., the *following* low tide will be lower than avg.

2013 HIGH & LOW WATER
THE BATTERY, NY HARBOR
40°42'N, 74°00.9'W

*Daylight Time starts March 10 at 2 a.m.   Daylight Saving Time

DAY OF MONTH	DAY OF WEEK	MARCH HIGH a.m.	Ht.	p.m.	Ht.	LOW a.m.	p.m.	DAY OF MONTH	DAY OF WEEK	APRIL HIGH a.m.	Ht.	p.m.	Ht.	LOW a.m.	p.m.
1	F	10 14	4.7	10 45	5.0	4 31	4 43	1	M	12 26	5.3	1 05	4.5	7 06	7 17
2	S	11 07	4.5	11 39	5.0	5 19	5 28	2	T	1 27	5.2	2 08	4.4	8 12	8 30
3	S	...	...	12 07	4.3	6 18	6 27	3	W	2 32	5.0	3 14	4.4	9 22	9 43
4	M	12 37	4.9	1 09	4.2	7 28	7 42	4	T	3 37	4.9	4 20	4.5	10 24	10 47
5	T	1 40	4.8	2 16	4.1	8 39	8 56	5	F	4 46	4.8	5 26	4.7	11 21	11 46
6	W	2 49	4.8	3 29	4.1	9 44	10 01	6	S	5 51	4.9	6 25	5.0	...	12 13
7	T	4 02	4.8	4 41	4.4	10 43	11 00	7	S	6 47	5.0	7 16	5.2	12 40	1 03
8	F	5 09	5.0	5 42	4.7	11 37	11 56	8	M	7 37	5.1	8 01	5.4	1 32	1 49
9	S	6 07	5.2	6 35	5.0	...	12 28	9	T	8 22	5.1	8 42	5.5	2 20	2 34
10	S	*7 57	5.3	*8 22	5.2	12 49	*2 16	10	W	9 04	5.0	9 21	5.5	3 07	3 16
11	M	8 43	5.4	9 06	5.3	2 39	3 02	11	T	9 47	4.9	9 59	5.3	3 51	3 56
12	T	9 27	5.3	9 49	5.3	3 27	3 45	12	F	10 30	4.7	10 38	5.1	4 32	4 35
13	W	10 11	5.1	10 31	5.2	4 12	4 26	13	S	11 16	4.5	11 18	4.9	5 13	5 11
14	T	10 56	4.8	11 14	5.0	4 56	5 05	14	S	11 59	4.3	11 59	4.7	5 54	5 46
15	F	11 43	4.5	11 57	4.8	5 38	5 43	15	M	...	...	12 52	4.1	6 36	6 22
16	S	...	...	12 31	4.3	6 22	6 21	16	T	12 42	4.5	1 39	4.0	7 23	7 05
17	S	12 41	4.5	1 19	4.0	7 09	7 03	17	W	1 27	4.3	2 27	3.9	8 20	8 12
18	M	1 26	4.3	2 09	3.8	8 05	7 57	18	T	2 13	4.2	3 16	3.9	9 20	9 25
19	T	2 13	4.1	3 00	3.7	9 07	9 05	19	F	3 04	4.1	4 08	4.0	10 15	10 27
20	W	3 04	4.0	3 56	3.7	10 06	10 09	20	S	4 01	4.2	5 01	4.2	11 04	11 21
21	T	4 03	4.0	4 55	3.8	10 59	11 05	21	S	5 02	4.3	5 51	4.6	11 49	...
22	F	5 05	4.1	5 50	4.0	11 47	11 55	22	M	6 00	4.4	6 37	5.0	12 12	12 34
23	S	6 02	4.3	6 38	4.3	...	12 32	23	T	6 50	4.7	7 19	5.4	1 01	1 18
24	S	6 49	4.5	7 20	4.6	12 43	1 15	24	W	7 37	4.9	8 00	5.7	1 50	2 04
25	M	7 30	4.7	7 57	5.0	1 30	1 57	25	T	8 22	5.0	8 43	5.9	2 39	2 50
26	T	8 09	4.9	8 33	5.3	2 16	2 39	26	F	9 09	5.1	9 28	6.0	3 28	3 37
27	W	8 47	5.0	9 09	5.5	3 02	3 20	27	S	9 59	5.0	10 18	6.0	4 17	4 24
28	T	9 27	5.0	9 49	5.6	3 47	4 01	28	S	10 56	4.9	11 15	5.8	5 06	5 13
29	F	10 13	5.0	10 35	5.6	4 33	4 43	29	M	11 59	4.8	...	...	5 58	6 07
30	S	11 04	4.8	11 27	5.5	5 19	5 27	30	T	12 16	5.6	1 02	4.8	6 53	7 07
31	S	...	...	12 03	4.7	6 09	6 16								

Dates when Ht. of **Low** Water is below Mean Lower Low with Ht. of lowest given for each period and Date of lowest in ( ):

1st - 2nd: -0.4' (1st)   6th - 12th: -0.4' (10th)
8th - 14th -0.8' (11th)   24th - 30th: -0.7' (27th - 28th)
26th - 31st: -0.6' (28th - 29th)

Average Rise and Fall 4.6 ft.

When a high tide exceeds avg. ht., the *following* low tide will be lower than avg.

2013 HIGH & LOW WATER
THE BATTERY, NY HARBOR
40°42'N, 74°00.9'W

Daylight Saving Time   Daylight Saving Time

DAY OF MONTH	DAY OF WEEK	MAY HIGH a.m.	Ht.	HIGH p.m.	Ht.	LOW a.m.	LOW p.m.	DAY OF MONTH	DAY OF WEEK	JUNE HIGH a.m.	Ht.	HIGH p.m.	Ht.	LOW a.m.	LOW p.m.
1	W	1 19	5.4	2 03	4.7	7 55	8 16	1	S	2 59	4.9	3 41	5.0	9 31	10 08
2	T	2 20	5.1	3 03	4.7	8 59	9 26	2	S	3 57	4.6	4 37	5.0	10 26	11 06
3	F	3 22	4.9	4 05	4.8	10 01	10 31	3	M	4 57	4.5	5 34	5.1	11 18	...
4	S	4 24	4.8	5 05	4.9	10 56	11 28	4	T	5 54	4.4	6 24	5.2	12 01	12 04
5	S	5 25	4.7	6 02	5.1	11 47	...	5	W	6 47	4.4	7 10	5.3	12 48	12 49
6	M	6 22	4.7	6 52	5.3	12 21	12 34	6	T	7 35	4.4	7 51	5.3	1 36	1 34
7	T	7 13	4.7	7 36	5.4	1 11	1 20	7	F	8 19	4.5	8 30	5.3	2 21	2 18
8	W	7 59	4.8	8 17	5.5	1 59	2 04	8	S	9 01	4.5	9 06	5.3	3 05	3 00
9	T	8 42	4.7	8 54	5.5	2 45	2 46	9	S	9 44	4.4	9 42	5.2	3 46	3 41
10	F	9 24	4.7	9 31	5.4	3 28	3 27	10	M	10 27	4.4	10 17	5.0	4 26	4 19
11	S	10 07	4.6	10 07	5.2	4 10	4 06	11	T	11 11	4.3	10 52	4.9	5 04	4 56
12	S	10 51	4.4	10 44	5.0	4 50	4 44	12	W	11 55	4.2	11 27	4.7	5 41	5 31
13	M	11 38	4.3	11 23	4.8	5 29	5 19	13	T	...	...	12 36	4.2	6 16	6 07
14	T	...	...	12 25	4.2	6 08	5 54	14	F	12 06	4.6	1 15	4.3	6 53	6 50
15	W	12 03	4.6	1 10	4.1	6 48	6 31	15	S	12 48	4.5	1 53	4.4	7 33	7 50
16	T	12 44	4.5	1 53	4.1	7 34	7 22	16	S	1 34	4.4	2 34	4.6	8 25	9 06
17	F	1 27	4.4	2 35	4.1	8 28	8 36	17	M	2 25	4.4	3 21	4.8	9 25	10 13
18	S	2 14	4.3	3 19	4.3	9 24	9 47	18	T	3 23	4.3	4 15	5.0	10 23	11 12
19	S	3 05	4.3	4 07	4.5	10 16	10 46	19	W	4 28	4.3	5 15	5.4	11 18	...
20	M	4 04	4.3	5 00	4.8	11 05	11 40	20	T	5 38	4.4	6 14	5.7	12 08	12 12
21	T	5 08	4.4	5 53	5.2	11 53	...	21	F	6 44	4.6	7 11	6.0	1 03	1 07
22	W	6 10	4.6	6 44	5.6	12 33	12 42	22	S	7 43	4.9	8 05	6.2	1 58	2 03
23	T	7 07	4.8	7 33	5.9	1 25	1 32	23	S	8 38	5.1	8 58	6.3	2 51	2 59
24	F	8 00	4.9	8 21	6.2	2 18	2 24	24	M	9 34	5.2	9 52	6.2	3 43	3 53
25	S	8 52	5.1	9 11	6.2	3 10	3 16	25	T	10 32	5.2	10 49	6.0	4 34	4 46
26	S	9 47	5.1	10 05	6.2	4 01	4 08	26	W	11 32	5.2	11 48	5.7	5 23	5 39
27	M	10 47	5.1	11 03	6.0	4 51	5 00	27	T	...	...	12 31	5.2	6 13	6 34
28	T	11 49	5.0	...	...	5 42	5 55	28	F	12 45	5.4	1 26	5.2	7 05	7 34
29	W	12 05	5.7	12 50	5.0	6 36	6 53	29	S	1 40	5.1	2 19	5.1	8 00	8 38
30	T	1 05	5.5	1 49	5.0	7 32	7 58	30	S	2 33	4.8	3 12	5.0	8 57	9 41
31	F	2 02	5.2	2 45	5.0	8 32	9 05								

Dates when Ht. of **Low** Water is below Mean Lower Low with Ht. of lowest given for each period and Date of lowest in ( ):

24th - 30th: -0.8' (26th - 27th)   22nd - 28th: -0.9' (24th - 25th)

Average Rise and Fall 4.6 ft.

When a high tide exceeds avg. ht., the *following* low tide will be lower than avg.

2013 HIGH & LOW WATER
THE BATTERY, NY HARBOR
40°42'N, 74°00.9'W

		JULY								AUGUST					
		Daylight Saving Time								Daylight Saving Time					
DAY OF MONTH	DAY OF WEEK	HIGH				LOW		DAY OF MONTH	DAY OF WEEK	HIGH				LOW	
		a.m.	Ht.	p.m.	Ht.	a.m.	p.m.			a.m.	Ht.	p.m.	Ht.	a.m.	p.m.
1	M	3 27	4.5	4 05	5.0	9 53	10 40	1	T	4 51	4.0	5 18	4.8	11 02	11 54
2	T	4 24	4.3	4 59	4.9	10 45	11 33	2	F	5 50	4.1	6 12	4.8	11 51	...
3	W	5 24	4.1	5 54	5.0	11 34	...	3	S	6 44	4.2	7 00	5.0	12 42	12 38
4	T	6 19	4.2	6 42	5.0	12 23	12 20	4	S	7 30	4.4	7 41	5.1	1 26	1 23
5	F	7 10	4.2	7 26	5.1	1 10	1 05	5	M	8 12	4.5	8 19	5.2	2 09	2 07
6	S	7 55	4.3	8 06	5.2	1 55	1 50	6	T	8 51	4.6	8 52	5.2	2 50	2 50
7	S	8 38	4.4	8 43	5.2	2 39	2 34	7	W	9 27	4.7	9 24	5.2	3 29	3 32
8	M	9 19	4.5	9 18	5.2	3 20	3 16	8	T	10 02	4.8	9 54	5.1	4 06	4 11
9	T	9 59	4.5	9 51	5.1	4 00	3 56	9	F	10 36	4.8	10 26	5.0	4 40	4 49
10	W	10 39	4.5	10 23	5.0	4 37	4 34	10	S	11 11	4.9	11 04	4.8	5 13	5 27
11	T	11 18	4.4	10 55	4.9	5 12	5 10	11	S	11 51	4.9	11 50	4.7	5 44	6 09
12	F	11 56	4.5	11 32	4.7	5 45	5 47	12	M	...	...	12 36	5.0	6 18	7 00
13	S	...	...	12 33	4.5	6 16	6 27	13	T	12 43	4.5	1 26	5.1	7 02	8 09
14	S	12 15	4.6	1 12	4.7	6 49	7 19	14	W	1 41	4.4	2 21	5.2	8 08	9 24
15	M	1 04	4.5	1 56	4.8	7 33	8 32	15	T	2 43	4.3	3 23	5.2	9 28	10 30
16	T	1 58	4.4	2 46	5.0	8 37	9 45	16	F	3 53	4.3	4 31	5.4	10 38	11 30
17	W	2 57	4.3	3 43	5.2	9 49	10 49	17	S	5 08	4.5	5 41	5.6	11 39	...
18	T	4 04	4.3	4 48	5.4	10 53	11 48	18	S	6 18	4.8	6 44	5.8	12 26	12 37
19	F	5 18	4.4	5 54	5.6	11 52	...	19	M	7 17	5.1	7 39	6.0	1 19	1 33
20	S	6 28	4.6	6 56	5.9	12 44	12 50	20	T	8 10	5.4	8 30	6.1	2 11	2 28
21	S	7 29	4.9	7 52	6.1	1 39	1 47	21	W	9 00	5.6	9 19	6.0	3 00	3 20
22	M	8 25	5.2	8 45	6.2	2 32	2 43	22	T	9 50	5.7	10 08	5.8	3 48	4 10
23	T	9 19	5.4	9 37	6.2	3 23	3 37	23	F	10 40	5.6	10 59	5.5	4 33	4 59
24	W	10 13	5.4	10 30	6.0	4 12	4 29	24	S	11 31	5.5	11 51	5.1	5 17	5 47
25	T	11 08	5.4	11 25	5.7	5 00	5 20	25	S	...	...	12 22	5.3	6 01	6 38
26	F	...	...	12 04	5.4	5 47	6 12	26	M	12 44	4.8	1 11	5.1	6 46	7 33
27	S	12 20	5.3	12 57	5.3	6 34	7 07	27	T	1 36	4.5	2 01	4.9	7 37	8 33
28	S	1 13	5.0	1 48	5.1	7 24	8 07	28	W	2 28	4.2	2 50	4.7	8 34	9 35
29	M	2 05	4.6	2 38	5.0	8 19	9 10	29	T	3 22	4.1	3 43	4.6	9 34	10 32
30	T	2 57	4.3	3 29	4.8	9 15	10 10	30	F	4 19	4.0	4 40	4.6	10 30	11 23
31	W	3 52	4.1	4 23	4.8	10 11	11 04	31	S	5 18	4.1	5 37	4.7	11 22	...

Dates when Ht. of **Low** Water is below Mean Lower Low with Ht. of lowest given for each period and Date of lowest in ( ):

21st - 27th: -0.9' (24th)

19th - 24th: -0.8' (22nd)

Average Rise and Fall 4.6 ft.

When a high tide exceeds avg. ht., the *following* low tide will be lower than avg.

2013 HIGH & LOW WATER
THE BATTERY, NY HARBOR
40°42'N, 74°00.9'W

Daylight SavingTime — Daylight Saving Time

D A Y O F M O N T H	D A Y O F W E E K	SEPTEMBER HIGH a.m.	Ht.	HIGH p.m.	Ht.	LOW a.m.	LOW p.m.	D A Y O F M O N T H	D A Y O F W E E K	OCTOBER HIGH a.m.	Ht.	HIGH p.m.	Ht.	LOW a.m.	LOW p.m.
1	S	6 12	4.3	6 27	4.8	12 09	12 09	1	T	6 24	4.5	6 33	4.8	12 16	12 26
2	M	7 00	4.5	7 11	5.0	12 53	12 55	2	W	7 06	4.8	7 13	4.9	12 57	1 11
3	T	7 42	4.7	7 50	5.1	1 36	1 41	3	T	7 43	5.1	7 50	5.1	1 38	1 57
4	W	8 18	4.9	8 23	5.2	2 15	2 24	4	F	8 16	5.4	8 25	5.1	2 17	2 41
5	T	8 52	5.1	8 54	5.2	2 54	3 06	5	S	8 49	5.6	9 01	5.1	2 57	3 25
6	F	9 24	5.2	9 26	5.2	3 32	3 48	6	S	9 25	5.7	9 41	5.0	3 37	4 09
7	S	9 57	5.3	10 01	5.1	4 08	4 29	7	M	10 05	5.7	10 28	4.9	4 17	4 54
8	S	10 33	5.3	10 43	4.9	4 43	5 10	8	T	10 53	5.6	11 24	4.7	4 58	5 42
9	M	11 17	5.3	11 33	4.7	5 18	5 55	9	W	11 51	5.5	...	...	5 44	6 36
10	T	...	...	12 08	5.3	5 57	6 47	10	T	12 28	4.6	12 54	5.4	6 39	7 40
11	W	12 32	4.6	1 06	5.3	6 46	7 54	11	F	1 34	4.5	1 58	5.2	7 50	8 49
12	T	1 35	4.4	2 07	5.2	7 57	9 06	12	S	2 40	4.5	3 03	5.2	9 06	9 54
13	F	2 41	4.4	3 12	5.2	9 17	10 13	13	S	3 46	4.6	4 10	5.1	10 15	10 52
14	S	3 51	4.5	4 21	5.3	10 27	11 12	14	M	4 52	4.8	5 15	5.2	11 16	11 46
15	S	5 02	4.7	5 30	5.4	11 28	...	15	T	5 54	5.1	6 14	5.3	...	12 11
16	M	6 08	5.0	6 31	5.6	12 07	12 25	16	W	6 48	5.4	7 07	5.3	12 35	1 04
17	T	7 04	5.3	7 24	5.8	12 58	1 19	17	T	7 35	5.6	7 54	5.3	1 23	1 54
18	W	7 54	5.6	8 13	5.8	1 48	2 12	18	F	8 19	5.7	8 39	5.3	2 09	2 43
19	T	8 40	5.8	8 59	5.7	2 35	3 02	19	S	9 00	5.7	9 22	5.1	2 53	3 29
20	F	9 25	5.8	9 45	5.5	3 21	3 50	20	S	9 40	5.6	10 07	4.9	3 36	4 14
21	S	10 09	5.7	10 32	5.2	4 04	4 36	21	M	10 21	5.4	10 54	4.6	4 16	4 57
22	S	10 55	5.5	11 22	4.9	4 46	5 22	22	T	11 04	5.1	11 44	4.4	4 56	5 40
23	M	11 42	5.3	...	...	5 27	6 08	23	W	11 50	4.9	...	...	5 34	6 24
24	T	12 14	4.6	12 31	5.0	6 08	6 58	24	T	12 36	4.2	12 38	4.6	6 14	7 14
25	W	1 06	4.4	1 20	4.8	6 53	7 54	25	F	1 28	4.0	1 27	4.4	7 00	8 10
26	T	1 58	4.2	2 10	4.6	7 48	8 55	26	S	2 18	4.0	2 16	4.3	8 02	9 09
27	F	2 51	4.0	3 02	4.5	8 52	9 54	27	S	3 09	3.9	3 06	4.2	9 12	10 03
28	S	3 46	4.0	3 56	4.4	9 55	10 46	28	M	4 00	4.0	3 58	4.2	10 13	10 51
29	S	4 42	4.1	4 53	4.5	10 50	11 33	29	T	4 52	4.2	4 53	4.3	11 06	11 35
30	M	5 36	4.3	5 47	4.6	11 39	...	30	W	5 40	4.5	5 45	4.4	11 54	...
								31	T	6 24	4.8	6 32	4.6	12 17	12 42

Dates when Ht. of **Low** Water is below Mean Lower Low with Ht. of lowest given for each period and Date of lowest in ( ):

17th - 21st: -0.6' (19th)   16th - 20th: -0.4' (17th - 18th)

Average Rise and Fall 4.6 ft.

When a high tide exceeds avg. ht., the *following* low tide will be lower than avg.

126

2013 HIGH & LOW WATER
THE BATTERY, NY HARBOR
40°42'N, 74°00.9'W

*Standard Time starts Nov. 3 at 2 a.m.   **Standard Time**

DAY OF MONTH	DAY OF WEEK	NOVEMBER						DAY OF MONTH	DAY OF WEEK	DECEMBER					
		HIGH				LOW				HIGH				LOW	
		a.m.	Ht.	p.m.	Ht.	a.m.	p.m.			a.m.	Ht.	p.m.	Ht.	a.m.	p.m.
1	F	7 04	5.2	7 16	4.8	12 59	1 29	1	S	6 12	5.5	6 34	4.6	12 09	12 53
2	S	7 42	5.5	7 57	4.9	1 41	2 16	2	M	6 58	5.7	7 23	4.7	12 58	1 44
3	S	*7 21	5.8	*7 41	5.0	1 26	*2 05	3	T	7 46	5.9	8 14	4.8	1 50	2 35
4	M	8 01	5.9	8 26	4.9	2 10	2 51	4	W	8 34	5.9	9 08	4.8	2 40	3 24
5	T	8 47	5.9	9 17	4.8	2 56	3 39	5	T	9 29	5.8	10 09	4.7	3 31	4 14
6	W	9 39	5.8	10 18	4.7	3 43	4 29	6	F	10 29	5.6	11 12	4.7	4 23	5 05
7	T	10 40	5.6	11 24	4.6	4 34	5 23	7	S	11 31	5.3	...	...	5 19	6 01
8	F	11 44	5.4	...	...	5 31	6 22	8	S	12 14	4.7	12 31	5.0	6 22	7 00
9	S	12 29	4.6	12 48	5.2	6 38	7 27	9	M	1 13	4.7	1 30	4.8	7 30	8 01
10	S	1 31	4.6	1 49	5.0	7 51	8 30	10	T	2 11	4.7	2 28	4.5	8 37	9 00
11	M	2 33	4.7	2 52	4.8	8 59	9 28	11	W	3 09	4.7	3 28	4.3	9 39	9 54
12	T	3 34	4.8	3 54	4.8	10 00	10 21	12	T	4 08	4.8	4 29	4.2	10 35	10 44
13	W	4 34	5.0	4 53	4.7	10 55	11 10	13	F	5 03	4.9	5 25	4.2	11 27	11 31
14	T	5 27	5.2	5 47	4.8	11 47	11 57	14	S	5 53	5.0	6 15	4.3	...	12 16
15	F	6 15	5.4	6 35	4.8	...	12 36	15	S	6 37	5.0	7 00	4.3	12 17	1 02
16	S	6 57	5.5	7 19	4.7	12 42	1 23	16	M	7 17	5.1	7 43	4.3	1 02	1 47
17	S	7 37	5.5	8 02	4.7	1 27	2 09	17	T	7 55	5.0	8 24	4.3	1 45	2 29
18	M	8 15	5.3	8 45	4.5	2 09	2 52	18	W	8 31	4.9	9 06	4.2	2 26	3 10
19	T	8 53	5.2	9 29	4.4	2 50	3 33	19	T	9 08	4.8	9 49	4.1	3 05	3 48
20	W	9 32	5.0	10 16	4.2	3 29	4 14	20	F	9 44	4.6	10 33	4.0	3 43	4 25
21	T	10 13	4.7	11 05	4.0	4 06	4 54	21	S	10 20	4.4	11 16	3.9	4 18	5 01
22	F	10 57	4.5	11 54	3.9	4 43	5 36	22	S	10 57	4.3	11 57	3.9	4 53	5 36
23	S	11 41	4.3	...	...	5 21	6 22	23	M	11 36	4.1	...	...	5 30	6 14
24	S	12 41	3.9	12 25	4.2	6 09	7 14	24	T	12 35	3.9	12 18	4.0	6 19	7 00
25	M	1 25	3.9	1 10	4.1	7 17	8 10	25	W	1 15	4.0	1 06	3.9	7 34	8 01
26	T	2 10	4.0	1 58	4.0	8 28	9 02	26	T	1 59	4.1	1 59	3.8	8 47	9 01
27	W	2 57	4.1	2 51	4.0	9 28	9 50	27	F	2 51	4.3	3 01	3.8	9 48	9 57
28	T	3 46	4.4	3 50	4.1	10 21	10 36	28	S	3 50	4.6	4 10	3.9	10 45	10 50
29	F	4 37	4.7	4 49	4.2	11 12	11 22	29	S	4 51	5.0	5 17	4.1	11 39	11 44
30	S	5 25	5.1	5 44	4.4	...	12 03	30	M	5 48	5.3	6 15	4.4	...	12 32
								31	T	6 41	5.6	7 09	4.6	12 38	1 25

Dates when Ht. of **Low** Water is below Mean Lower Low with Ht. of lowest given for each period and Date of lowest in ( ):

   2nd - 7th: -0.5' (4th - 5th)   1st - 11th: -0.9' (3rd - 5th)
   12th - 18th: -0.3' (13th - 14th, 17th)   15th - 19th: -0.3' (16th - 18th)
                                       29th - 31st: -0.9' (31st)

Average Rise and Fall 4.6 ft.

When a high tide exceeds avg. ht., the *following* low tide will be lower than avg.

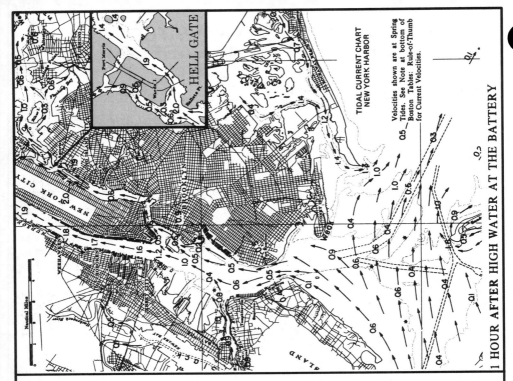

TIDAL CURRENT CHART
NEW YORK HARBOR

Velocities shown are at Spring
Tides. See Note at bottom of
Boston Tables: Rule-of-Thumb
for Current Velocities.

1 HOUR AFTER HIGH WATER AT THE BATTERY

NEW YORK BAY CURRENTS

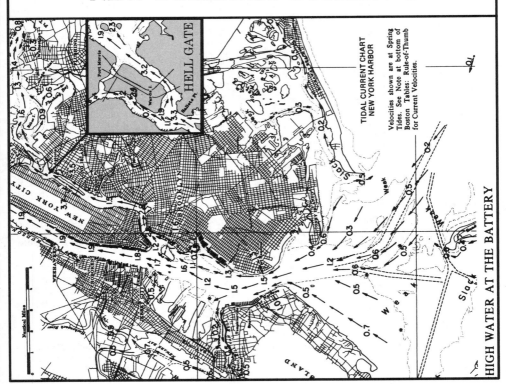

HELL GATE

TIDAL CURRENT CHART
NEW YORK HARBOR

Velocities shown are at Spring
Tides. See Note at bottom of
Boston Tables: Rule-of-Thumb
for Current Velocities.

HIGH WATER AT THE BATTERY

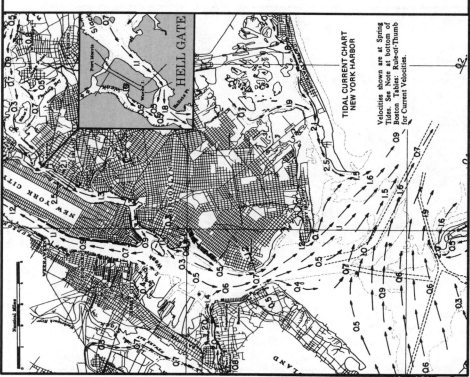

NEW YORK BAY CURRENTS

3 HOURS AFTER HIGH WATER AT THE BATTERY

2 HOURS AFTER HIGH WATER AT THE BATTERY

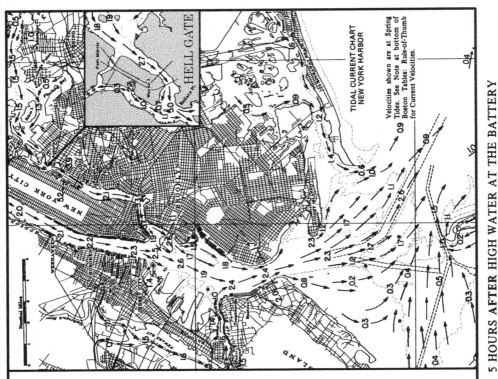

NEW YORK BAY CURRENTS

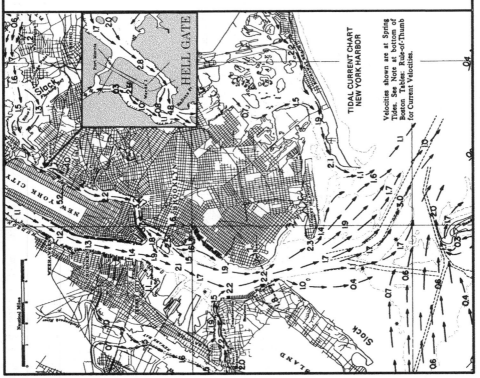

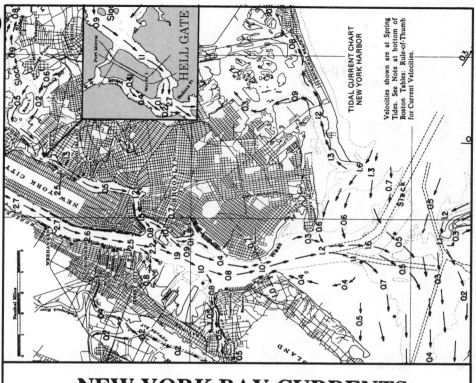

NEW YORK BAY CURRENTS

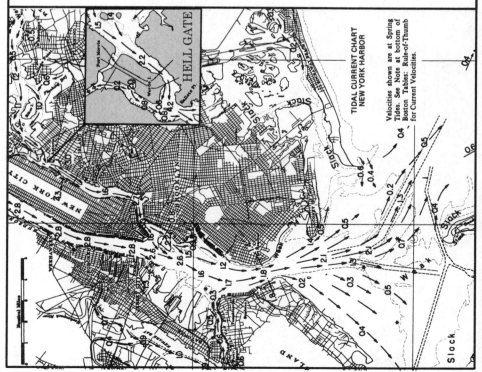

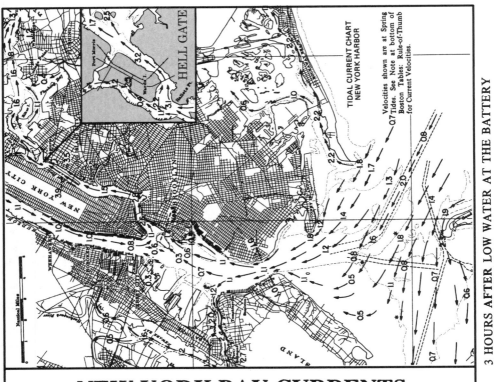

NEW YORK BAY CURRENTS

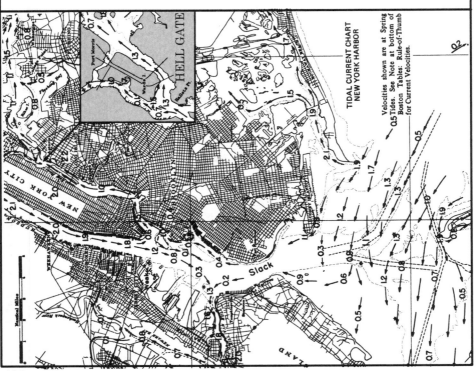

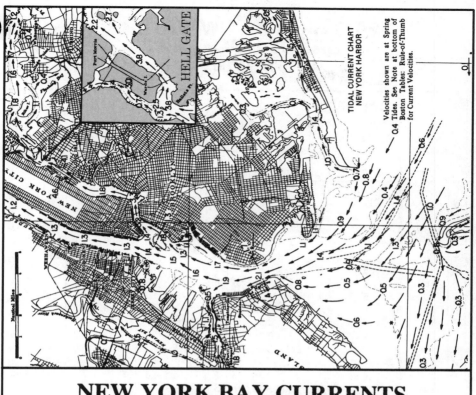

TIDAL CURRENT CHART
NEW YORK HARBOR

Velocities shown are at Spring
Tides. See Note at bottom of
Boston Tables: Rule-of-Thumb
for Current Velocities.

HELL GATE

NEW YORK BAY CURRENTS

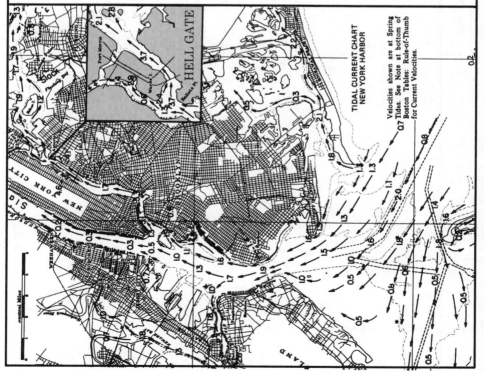

TIDAL CURRENT CHART
NEW YORK HARBOR

Velocities shown are at Spring
Tides. See Note at bottom of
Boston Tables: Rule-of-Thumb
for Current Velocities.

HELL GATE

2013 HIGH & LOW WATER
SANDY HOOK, NJ
40°28'N, 74°00.6'W

Standard Time   Standard Time

DAY OF MONTH	DAY OF WEEK	JANUARY						DAY OF MONTH	DAY OF WEEK	FEBRUARY					
		HIGH		LOW						HIGH		LOW			
		a.m.	Ht.	p.m.	Ht.	a.m.	p.m.			a.m.	Ht.	p.m.	Ht.	a.m.	p.m.
1	T	9 47	4.7	10 34	4.2	3 52	4 26	1	F	11 00	4.5	11 41	4.7	5 01	5 16
2	W	10 30	4.6	11 20	4.2	4 31	5 02	2	S	11 55	4.3	...	...	5 55	6 07
3	T	11 20	4.5	...	...	5 17	5 44	3	S	12 37	4.8	12 56	4.2	7 05	7 17
4	F	12 09	4.4	12 14	4.3	6 13	6 37	4	M	1 35	4.9	1 59	4.1	8 21	8 32
5	S	1 02	4.6	1 12	4.2	7 27	7 45	5	T	2 39	4.9	3 08	4.1	9 30	9 40
6	S	1 59	4.7	2 15	4.2	8 41	8 53	6	W	3 47	5.1	4 18	4.3	10 31	10 42
7	M	3 00	5.0	3 24	4.2	9 47	9 56	7	T	4 52	5.4	5 22	4.6	11 27	11 39
8	T	4 05	5.3	4 32	4.4	10 47	10 54	8	F	5 51	5.6	6 19	4.9	...	12 21
9	W	5 07	5.6	5 35	4.6	11 44	11 51	9	S	6 43	5.8	7 10	5.2	12 34	1 11
10	T	6 05	5.9	6 32	4.9	...	12 38	10	S	7 32	5.8	7 58	5.3	1 27	1 59
11	F	6 58	6.0	7 26	5.1	12 47	1 31	11	M	8 19	5.7	8 45	5.3	2 17	2 44
12	S	7 49	6.1	8 17	5.1	1 41	2 21	12	T	9 05	5.5	9 32	5.2	3 04	3 26
13	S	8 38	5.9	9 09	5.1	2 33	3 09	13	W	9 52	5.2	10 19	5.0	3 48	4 05
14	M	9 29	5.7	10 01	5.0	3 23	3 54	14	T	10 39	4.8	11 06	4.8	4 32	4 44
15	T	10 20	5.3	10 53	4.9	4 11	4 38	15	F	11 27	4.4	11 52	4.6	5 18	5 24
16	W	11 11	4.9	11 44	4.7	5 00	5 23	16	S	...	...	12 16	4.1	6 07	6 09
17	T	...	...	12 01	4.5	5 52	6 09	17	S	12 39	4.4	1 06	3.8	7 06	7 04
18	F	12 33	4.5	12 51	4.2	6 50	7 01	18	M	1 27	4.2	1 58	3.7	8 11	8 07
19	S	1 22	4.4	1 42	3.9	7 54	7 58	19	T	2 19	4.1	2 55	3.6	9 12	9 08
20	S	2 12	4.3	2 35	3.7	8 56	8 54	20	W	3 16	4.1	3 54	3.7	10 06	10 03
21	M	3 05	4.2	3 32	3.6	9 51	9 46	21	T	4 14	4.3	4 50	3.9	10 54	10 53
22	T	4 00	4.3	4 30	3.7	10 41	10 35	22	F	5 07	4.5	5 40	4.2	11 39	11 41
23	W	4 53	4.4	5 23	3.9	11 27	11 22	23	S	5 53	4.7	6 23	4.4	...	12 22
24	T	5 41	4.6	6 10	4.1	...	12 12	24	S	6 34	4.9	7 02	4.7	12 26	1 03
25	F	6 24	4.8	6 52	4.2	12 07	12 55	25	M	7 12	5.1	7 40	4.9	1 11	1 43
26	S	7 02	4.9	7 31	4.4	12 52	1 36	26	T	7 49	5.2	8 17	5.1	1 55	2 21
27	S	7 38	5.0	8 08	4.5	1 35	2 14	27	W	8 27	5.1	8 55	5.2	2 37	2 58
28	M	8 13	5.0	8 45	4.5	2 16	2 51	28	T	9 08	5.0	9 38	5.2	3 19	3 35
29	T	8 48	5.0	9 23	4.6	2 56	3 26								
30	W	9 26	4.9	10 04	4.6	3 35	4 00								
31	T	10 10	4.7	10 50	4.7	4 16	4 36								

Dates when Ht. of **Low** Water is below Mean Lower Low with Ht. of lowest given for each period and Date of lowest in ( ):

7th - 16th: -1.2' (12th - 13th)   6th - 14th: -1.1' (10th - 11th)
26th - 31st: -0.4' (28th - 30th)   24th - 28th: -0.5' (26th - 28th)

Average Rise and Fall 4.6 ft.

When a high tide exceeds avg. ht., the *following* low tide will be lower than avg.

2013 HIGH & LOW WATER
SANDY HOOK, NJ
40°28'N, 74°00.6'W

*Daylight Time starts March 10 at 2 a.m.

Daylight Saving Time

DAY OF MONTH	DAY OF WEEK	MARCH HIGH a.m.	Ht.	p.m.	Ht.	MARCH LOW a.m.	p.m.	DAY OF MONTH	DAY OF WEEK	APRIL HIGH a.m.	Ht.	p.m.	Ht.	APRIL LOW a.m.	p.m.
1	F	9 54	4.9	10 26	5.2	4 02	4 14	1	M	12 05	5.5	12 39	4.7	6 33	6 42
2	S	10 47	4.7	11 20	5.2	4 49	4 57	2	T	1 05	5.4	1 40	4.6	7 37	7 52
3	S	11 46	4.5	...	...	5 44	5 52	3	W	2 07	5.2	2 43	4.5	8 48	9 09
4	M	12 18	5.1	12 46	4.3	6 49	7 01	4	T	3 09	5.1	3 46	4.6	9 54	10 17
5	T	1 19	5.0	1 50	4.2	8 04	8 19	5	F	4 12	5.0	4 50	4.8	10 53	11 18
6	W	2 24	5.0	2 58	4.3	9 13	9 29	6	S	5 15	5.1	5 50	5.1	11 45	...
7	T	3 31	5.1	4 06	4.5	10 14	10 31	7	S	6 13	5.2	6 43	5.4	12 12	12 34
8	F	4 36	5.2	5 08	4.8	11 09	11 27	8	M	7 03	5.3	7 29	5.6	1 03	1 19
9	S	5 34	5.4	6 03	5.1	11 59	...	9	T	7 49	5.3	8 11	5.7	1 51	2 03
10	S	*7 25	5.6	*7 51	5.4	12 20	*1 47	10	W	8 33	5.2	8 51	5.7	2 37	2 44
11	M	8 12	5.6	8 36	5.5	2 10	2 33	11	T	9 15	5.1	9 30	5.5	3 20	3 23
12	T	8 56	5.5	9 19	5.5	2 58	3 15	12	F	9 57	4.9	10 09	5.3	4 01	4 01
13	W	9 40	5.3	10 01	5.4	3 42	3 55	13	S	10 41	4.6	10 48	5.1	4 40	4 37
14	T	10 24	5.0	10 43	5.2	4 25	4 32	14	S	11 26	4.4	11 29	4.8	5 19	5 12
15	F	11 09	4.7	11 25	5.0	5 05	5 09	15	M	...	...	12 14	4.2	5 58	5 50
16	S	11 55	4.4	...	...	5 46	5 45	16	T	12 13	4.6	1 02	4.0	6 41	6 32
17	S	12 09	4.7	12 44	4.1	6 29	6 24	17	W	12 59	4.5	1 50	4.0	7 33	7 29
18	M	12 55	4.5	1 33	3.9	7 19	7 12	18	T	1 47	4.3	2 40	4.0	8 35	8 41
19	T	1 42	4.3	2 24	3.8	8 21	8 17	19	F	2 39	4.3	3 32	4.1	9 36	9 49
20	W	2 33	4.2	3 17	3.8	9 26	9 27	20	S	3 34	4.3	4 25	4.3	10 29	10 47
21	T	3 28	4.2	4 14	3.9	10 24	10 28	21	S	4 33	4.4	5 18	4.7	11 16	11 39
22	F	4 26	4.2	5 11	4.1	11 14	11 22	22	M	5 30	4.6	6 08	5.1	...	12 01
23	S	5 24	4.4	6 02	4.4	...	12 01	23	T	6 23	4.9	6 55	5.5	12 29	12 46
24	S	6 15	4.7	6 48	4.8	12 11	12 43	24	W	7 12	5.1	7 39	5.9	1 19	1 32
25	M	7 00	4.9	7 29	5.1	12 59	1 26	25	T	7 59	5.2	8 23	6.2	2 09	2 19
26	T	7 43	5.1	8 09	5.5	1 46	2 08	26	F	8 47	5.3	9 10	6.3	2 59	3 06
27	W	8 24	5.3	8 49	5.7	2 32	2 49	27	S	9 37	5.2	9 59	6.2	3 48	3 54
28	T	9 06	5.3	9 31	5.8	3 18	3 31	28	S	10 31	5.1	10 54	6.0	4 37	4 44
29	F	9 52	5.2	10 17	5.8	4 03	4 13	29	M	11 30	5.0	11 52	5.8	5 28	5 35
30	S	10 42	5.0	11 08	5.7	4 50	4 57	30	T	...	...	12 31	4.9	6 22	6 33
31	S	11 38	4.8	...	...	5 39	5 45								

Dates when Ht. of **Low** Water is below Mean Lower Low with Ht. of lowest given for each period and Date of lowest in ( ):

1st - 2nd: -0.4' (1st)
8th - 14th: -0.8' (11th)
26th - 31st: -0.6' (28th - 29th)

6th - 12th: -0.4' (8th - 9th)
24th - 30th: -0.7' (27th - 28th)

Average Rise and Fall 4.6 ft.

When a high tide exceeds avg. ht., the *following* low tide will be lower than avg.

2013 HIGH & LOW WATER
SANDY HOOK, NJ
40°28'N, 74°00.6'W

Daylight Saving Time   Daylight Saving Time

DAY OF MONTH	DAY OF WEEK	MAY HIGH a.m.	Ht.	HIGH p.m.	Ht.	LOW a.m.	LOW p.m.	DAY OF MONTH	DAY OF WEEK	JUNE HIGH a.m.	Ht.	HIGH p.m.	Ht.	LOW a.m.	LOW p.m.
1	W	12 52	5.6	1 31	4.8	7 22	7 41	1	S	2 27	5.1	3 06	5.1	8 59	9 38
2	T	1 52	5.3	2 30	4.9	8 26	8 53	2	S	3 23	4.8	4 01	5.1	9 55	10 38
3	F	2 51	5.1	3 31	4.9	9 31	10 02	3	M	4 20	4.6	4 57	5.2	10 46	11 32
4	S	3 50	5.0	4 29	5.0	10 27	11 00	4	T	5 16	4.5	5 48	5.3	11 32	...
5	S	4 49	4.9	5 26	5.2	11 17	11 54	5	W	6 10	4.5	6 35	5.4	12 20	12 16
6	M	5 46	4.9	6 18	5.4	...	12 04	6	T	6 59	4.6	7 18	5.5	1 06	1 00
7	T	6 38	4.9	7 04	5.6	12 43	12 48	7	F	7 45	4.6	7 58	5.5	1 51	1 43
8	W	7 25	4.9	7 45	5.6	1 30	1 31	8	S	8 27	4.6	8 36	5.4	2 34	2 25
9	T	8 09	4.9	8 24	5.6	2 15	2 13	9	S	9 09	4.6	9 13	5.4	3 15	3 07
10	F	8 51	4.8	9 02	5.5	2 57	2 53	10	M	9 51	4.5	9 50	5.2	3 54	3 46
11	S	9 32	4.7	9 39	5.4	3 38	3 32	11	T	10 33	4.4	10 26	5.1	4 32	4 25
12	S	10 15	4.5	10 16	5.2	4 17	4 10	12	W	11 16	4.3	11 03	4.9	5 07	5 02
13	M	10 59	4.4	10 55	5.0	4 55	4 47	13	T	11 59	4.3	11 44	4.8	5 42	5 40
14	T	11 45	4.2	11 35	4.8	5 32	5 24	14	F	...	...	12 41	4.3	6 17	6 23
15	W	...	...	12 31	4.1	6 10	6 04	15	S	12 28	4.7	1 25	4.5	6 57	7 16
16	T	12 19	4.6	1 17	4.1	6 52	6 52	16	S	1 16	4.6	2 10	4.7	7 46	8 25
17	F	1 05	4.5	2 02	4.2	7 43	7 55	17	M	2 08	4.5	2 59	4.9	8 45	9 35
18	S	1 54	4.5	2 49	4.4	8 41	9 06	18	T	3 06	4.5	3 54	5.2	9 46	10 38
19	S	2 47	4.4	3 40	4.6	9 38	10 10	19	W	4 09	4.5	4 53	5.5	10 44	11 36
20	M	3 44	4.5	4 34	5.0	10 30	11 07	20	T	5 16	4.6	5 53	5.9	11 40	...
21	T	4 46	4.6	5 28	5.4	11 20	...	21	F	6 19	4.8	6 50	6.2	12 32	12 36
22	W	5 46	4.7	6 21	5.8	12 01	12 10	22	S	7 18	5.1	7 44	6.4	1 28	1 32
23	T	6 44	5.0	7 12	6.1	12 54	1 00	23	S	8 13	5.3	8 36	6.5	2 22	2 28
24	F	7 37	5.1	8 02	6.4	1 47	1 53	24	M	9 08	5.4	9 29	6.5	3 15	3 23
25	S	8 29	5.3	8 52	6.5	2 40	2 45	25	T	10 03	5.4	10 23	6.3	4 06	4 17
26	S	9 23	5.3	9 44	6.4	3 32	3 38	26	W	11 00	5.4	11 19	6.0	4 55	5 09
27	M	10 19	5.3	10 40	6.2	4 23	4 31	27	T	11 57	5.4	...	...	5 44	6 03
28	T	11 18	5.2	11 38	6.0	5 14	5 24	28	F	12 14	5.7	12 53	5.3	6 34	7 01
29	W	...	...	12 17	5.1	6 06	6 21	29	S	1 08	5.3	1 46	5.2	7 26	8 04
30	T	12 36	5.7	1 16	5.1	7 01	7 24	30	S	2 01	4.9	2 38	5.2	8 22	9 09
31	F	1 32	5.4	2 12	5.1	7 59	8 32								

Dates when Ht. of **Low** Water is below Mean Lower Low with Ht. of lowest given for each period and Date of lowest in ( ):

23rd - 30th: -0.8' (26th - 27th)   21st - 28th: -0.9' (25th)

Average Rise and Fall 4.6 ft.

When a high tide exceeds avg. ht., the *following* low tide will be lower than avg.

2013 HIGH & LOW WATER
SANDY HOOK, NJ
40°28'N, 74°00.6'W

Daylight Saving Time   **Daylight Saving Time**

D A Y O F M O N T H	D A Y O F W E E K	JULY HIGH a.m.	Ht.	HIGH p.m.	Ht.	LOW a.m.	LOW p.m.	D A Y O F M O N T H	D A Y O F W E E K	AUGUST HIGH a.m.	Ht.	HIGH p.m.	Ht.	LOW a.m.	LOW p.m.
1	M	2 53	4.6	3 29	5.1	9 17	10 10	1	T	4 12	4.1	4 39	4.8	10 26	11 24
2	T	3 47	4.4	4 22	5.0	10 10	11 04	2	F	5 09	4.1	5 33	4.9	11 16	...
3	W	4 45	4.3	5 16	5.1	11 00	11 54	3	S	6 05	4.3	6 24	5.1	12 12	12 05
4	T	5 40	4.3	6 05	5.1	11 46	...	4	S	6 54	4.4	7 07	5.2	12 55	12 50
5	F	6 33	4.3	6 51	5.2	12 40	12 31	5	M	7 37	4.6	7 47	5.3	1 38	1 35
6	S	7 20	4.4	7 34	5.3	1 24	1 16	6	T	8 18	4.8	8 24	5.4	2 19	2 19
7	S	8 04	4.5	8 13	5.4	2 08	2 00	7	W	8 56	4.9	8 59	5.4	2 58	3 01
8	M	8 45	4.6	8 50	5.4	2 49	2 43	8	T	9 32	4.9	9 33	5.3	3 35	3 41
9	T	9 25	4.6	9 25	5.3	3 29	3 24	9	F	10 08	5.0	10 08	5.2	4 10	4 20
10	W	10 04	4.6	9 59	5.2	4 05	4 03	10	S	10 46	5.0	10 47	5.0	4 43	4 59
11	T	10 43	4.6	10 34	5.0	4 40	4 41	11	S	11 28	5.1	11 32	4.9	5 15	5 40
12	F	11 23	4.6	11 13	4.9	5 13	5 19	12	M	...	...	12 15	5.1	5 51	6 28
13	S	11 59	4.7	11 57	4.8	5 45	5 59	13	T	12 25	4.7	1 07	5.2	6 34	7 29
14	S	...	...	12 48	4.8	6 20	6 48	14	W	1 23	4.6	2 03	5.3	7 32	8 43
15	M	12 46	4.7	1 35	4.9	7 03	7 51	15	T	2 24	4.5	3 03	5.4	8 49	9 55
16	T	1 40	4.6	2 27	5.1	8 01	9 05	16	F	3 31	4.5	4 08	5.5	10 02	10 59
17	W	2 39	4.5	3 24	5.3	9 11	10 14	17	S	4 40	4.6	5 15	5.8	11 07	11 56
18	T	3 44	4.5	4 27	5.6	10 18	11 15	18	S	5 47	4.9	6 17	6.0	...	12 06
19	F	4 54	4.6	5 31	5.8	11 20	...	19	M	6 48	5.3	7 12	6.2	12 50	1 03
20	S	6 01	4.8	6 32	6.1	12 13	12 19	20	T	7 42	5.6	8 03	6.3	1 42	1 58
21	S	7 02	5.1	7 28	6.4	1 09	1 16	21	W	8 32	5.8	8 52	6.3	2 32	2 51
22	M	7 58	5.4	8 21	6.5	2 03	2 13	22	T	9 21	5.9	9 40	6.1	3 19	3 41
23	T	8 51	5.6	9 12	6.4	2 55	3 08	23	F	10 09	5.8	10 29	5.7	4 04	4 29
24	W	9 44	5.7	10 03	6.2	3 44	4 00	24	S	10 58	5.7	11 19	5.3	4 46	5 16
25	T	10 37	5.6	10 55	5.9	4 31	4 51	25	S	11 48	5.5	...	...	5 28	6 04
26	F	11 30	5.6	11 48	5.5	5 17	5 41	26	M	12 10	5.0	12 37	5.2	6 10	6 55
27	S	...	...	12 23	5.4	6 02	6 34	27	T	1 01	4.6	1 26	5.0	6 56	7 53
28	S	12 40	5.2	1 14	5.3	6 49	7 31	28	W	1 52	4.4	2 15	4.8	7 49	8 57
29	M	1 32	4.8	2 04	5.1	7 40	8 34	29	T	2 45	4.2	3 06	4.7	8 51	9 57
30	T	2 23	4.5	2 53	5.0	8 35	9 36	30	F	3 40	4.1	4 00	4.7	9 52	10 51
31	W	3 16	4.3	3 45	4.9	9 32	10 33	31	S	4 37	4.1	4 56	4.7	10 46	11 38

Dates when Ht. of **Low** Water is below Mean Lower Low with Ht. of lowest given for each period and Date of lowest in ( ):

21st - 27th: -0.9' (24th)   19th - 24th: - 0.8' (22nd)

Average Rise and Fall 4.6 ft.

When a high tide exceeds avg. ht., the *following* low tide will be lower than avg.

2013 HIGH & LOW WATER
SANDY HOOK, NJ
40°28'N, 74°00.6'W

Daylight Saving Time · Daylight Saving Time

DAY OF MONTH	DAY OF WEEK	SEPTEMBER HIGH a.m.	Ht.	HIGH p.m.	Ht.	LOW a.m.	LOW p.m.	DAY OF MONTH	DAY OF WEEK	OCTOBER HIGH a.m.	Ht.	HIGH p.m.	Ht.	LOW a.m.	LOW p.m.
1	S	5 33	4.3	5 49	4.9	11 36	...	1	T	5 46	4.6	5 57	4.9	11 54	...
2	M	6 23	4.6	6 35	5.1	12 22	12 23	2	W	6 31	5.0	6 42	5.1	12 25	12 40
3	T	7 08	4.8	7 18	5.3	1 04	1 09	3	T	7 13	5.3	7 24	5.2	1 06	1 26
4	W	7 47	5.0	7 55	5.4	1 44	1 52	4	F	7 50	5.6	8 02	5.3	1 46	2 10
5	T	8 24	5.2	8 30	5.4	2 23	2 36	5	S	8 28	5.8	8 42	5.3	2 26	2 55
6	F	8 59	5.4	9 06	5.4	3 01	3 18	6	S	9 06	5.9	9 23	5.2	3 06	3 40
7	S	9 35	5.5	9 44	5.2	3 37	3 59	7	M	9 49	5.9	10 10	5.1	3 47	4 25
8	S	10 14	5.5	10 26	5.1	4 13	4 41	8	T	10 37	5.8	11 04	4.9	4 30	5 12
9	M	10 58	5.5	11 15	4.9	4 50	5 25	9	W	11 32	5.7	...	...	5 15	6 04
10	T	11 49	5.5	...	...	5 29	6 14	10	T	12 04	4.7	12 32	5.5	6 07	7 04
11	W	12 12	4.7	12 46	5.4	6 16	7 15	11	F	1 08	4.6	1 34	5.4	7 12	8 13
12	T	1 13	4.6	1 47	5.4	7 19	8 28	12	S	2 11	4.6	2 37	5.3	8 29	9 22
13	F	2 17	4.5	2 49	5.4	8 38	9 40	13	S	3 14	4.7	3 39	5.3	9 43	10 23
14	S	3 23	4.6	3 54	5.5	9 53	10 42	14	M	4 17	4.9	4 41	5.3	10 47	11 17
15	S	4 30	4.8	4 59	5.6	10 58	11 38	15	T	5 18	5.2	5 41	5.4	11 43	...
16	M	5 34	5.1	6 00	5.8	11 56	...	16	W	6 14	5.5	6 34	5.5	12 06	12 36
17	T	6 32	5.5	6 55	6.0	12 29	12 50	17	T	7 03	5.8	7 23	5.5	12 53	1 26
18	W	7 24	5.8	7 44	6.0	1 19	1 43	18	F	7 48	5.9	8 09	5.4	1 38	2 14
19	T	8 11	6.0	8 31	5.9	2 06	2 33	19	S	8 30	5.9	8 52	5.3	2 21	3 00
20	F	8 56	6.0	9 16	5.7	2 51	3 21	20	S	9 11	5.8	9 36	5.1	3 03	3 43
21	S	9 40	5.9	10 02	5.4	3 33	4 06	21	M	9 52	5.6	10 21	4.8	3 43	4 25
22	S	10 24	5.7	10 49	5.1	4 14	4 50	22	T	10 33	5.3	11 09	4.5	4 22	5 06
23	M	11 10	5.4	11 39	4.7	4 53	5 34	23	W	11 18	5.0	11 59	4.3	5 00	5 47
24	T	11 57	5.1	...	...	5 33	6 19	24	T	...	...	12 04	4.8	5 39	6 32
25	W	12 30	4.5	12 46	4.9	6 14	7 11	25	F	12 50	4.1	12 53	4.6	6 23	7 24
26	T	1 22	4.2	1 35	4.7	7 03	8 11	26	S	1 40	4.0	1 42	4.4	7 18	8 24
27	F	2 14	4.1	2 26	4.6	8 05	9 15	27	S	2 31	4.0	2 32	4.4	8 27	9 23
28	S	3 07	4.1	3 18	4.5	9 13	10 11	28	M	3 21	4.1	3 24	4.4	9 33	10 15
29	S	4 01	4.2	4 13	4.6	10 13	11 00	29	T	4 13	4.3	4 18	4.4	10 31	11 01
30	M	4 56	4.3	5 07	4.7	11 06	11 43	30	W	5 03	4.6	5 12	4.6	11 22	11 44
								31	T	5 51	5.0	6 03	4.8	...	12 10

Dates when Ht. of **Low** Water is below Mean Lower Low with Ht. of lowest given for each period and Date of lowest in ( ):

17th - 22nd: -0.6' (19th)

6th: -0.2'
16th - 20th: -0.4' (17th - 18th)

Average Rise and Fall 4.6 ft.

When a high tide exceeds avg. ht., the *following* low tide will be lower than avg.

2013 HIGH & LOW WATER
SANDY HOOK, NJ
40°28'N, 74°00.6'W

Standard Time starts Nov. 3 at 2 a.m.　　　　　　　　　　**Standard Time**

DAY OF MONTH	DAY OF WEEK	NOVEMBER HIGH a.m.	Ht.	HIGH p.m.	Ht.	LOW a.m.	LOW p.m.	DAY OF MONTH	DAY OF WEEK	DECEMBER HIGH a.m.	Ht.	HIGH p.m.	Ht.	LOW a.m.	LOW p.m.
1	F	6 36	5.4	6 50	4.9	12 26	12 58	1	S	5 49	5.7	6 11	4.8	...	12 22
2	S	7 18	5.7	7 35	5.1	1 09	1 45	2	M	6 37	6.0	7 02	4.9	12 27	1 14
3	S	*7 01	6.0	*7 21	5.1	1 55	*1 35	3	T	7 27	6.1	7 53	5.0	1 19	2 06
4	M	7 44	6.1	8 07	5.1	1 39	2 22	4	W	8 15	6.2	8 45	5.0	2 10	2 55
5	T	8 30	6.1	8 57	5.0	2 26	3 10	5	T	9 08	6.0	9 42	4.9	3 02	3 45
6	W	9 21	6.0	9 54	4.9	3 14	4 00	6	F	10 05	5.8	10 42	4.9	3 54	4 36
7	T	10 19	5.8	10 56	4.7	4 05	4 52	7	S	11 04	5.5	11 42	4.8	4 49	5 29
8	F	11 20	5.6	11 58	4.7	5 00	5 49	8	S	...	...	12 02	5.2	5 49	6 27
9	S	...	...	12 21	5.4	6 03	6 53	9	M	12 41	4.8	12 59	4.9	6 56	7 28
10	S	12 59	4.7	1 20	5.2	7 16	7 58	10	T	1 38	4.8	1 56	4.7	8 06	8 28
11	M	1 59	4.8	2 20	5.0	8 28	8 58	11	W	2 34	4.9	2 53	4.5	9 11	9 23
12	T	2 59	5.0	3 19	4.9	9 31	9 52	12	T	3 31	4.9	3 51	4.3	10 08	10 13
13	W	3 57	5.2	4 18	4.9	10 28	10 40	13	F	4 26	5.0	4 48	4.3	10 59	10 59
14	T	4 52	5.4	5 12	4.9	11 19	11 26	14	S	5 17	5.1	5 40	4.3	11 47	11 44
15	F	5 41	5.5	6 02	4.9	...	12 08	15	S	6 03	5.2	6 27	4.4	...	12 33
16	S	6 25	5.6	6 47	4.9	12 10	12 54	16	M	6 44	5.2	7 10	4.4	12 28	1 17
17	S	7 06	5.6	7 31	4.8	12 53	1 39	17	T	7 24	5.2	7 52	4.4	1 11	1 59
18	M	7 46	5.5	8 13	4.7	1 35	2 21	18	W	8 01	5.1	8 33	4.3	1 52	2 38
19	T	8 24	5.4	8 56	4.5	2 16	3 02	19	T	8 38	5.0	9 14	4.2	2 32	3 16
20	W	9 03	5.1	9 41	4.3	2 55	3 41	20	F	9 15	4.8	9 57	4.1	3 11	3 52
21	T	9 43	4.9	10 28	4.1	3 33	4 19	21	S	9 52	4.6	10 39	4.0	3 48	4 27
22	F	10 26	4.7	11 16	4.0	4 11	4 58	22	S	10 31	4.4	11 22	4.0	4 25	5 04
23	S	11 11	4.5	11 59	3.9	4 51	5 40	23	M	11 12	4.3	...	...	5 04	5 37
24	S	11 57	4.3	...	...	5 37	6 28	24	T	12 05	4.0	12 01	4.1	5 51	6 21
25	M	12 50	4.0	12 44	4.2	6 36	7 24	25	W	12 49	4.1	12 47	4.0	6 54	7 17
26	T	1 36	4.1	1 33	4.2	7 46	8 21	26	T	1 36	4.3	1 41	4.0	8 06	8 21
27	W	2 25	4.3	2 27	4.2	8 51	9 13	27	F	2 29	4.5	2 42	4.0	9 13	9 21
28	T	3 16	4.5	3 24	4.2	9 48	10 01	28	S	3 27	4.8	3 47	4.1	10 12	10 17
29	F	4 08	4.9	4 23	4.4	10 40	10 49	29	S	4 27	5.2	4 52	4.3	11 07	11 11
30	S	5 00	5.3	5 19	4.6	11 31	11 37	30	M	5 25	5.5	5 51	4.6	...	12 01
								31	T	6 19	5.9	6 46	4.8	12 06	12 55

Dates when Ht. of **Low** Water is below Mean Lower Low with Ht. of lowest given for each period and Date of lowest in ( ):

2nd - 7th: -0.5' (4th - 5th)　　　　　　1st - 9th: -0.9' (3rd - 5th)
12th - 18th: -0.3' (14th, 16th)　　　　15th - 18th: -0.2'
30th: -0.3'　　　　　　　　　　　　　29th - 31st: -0.9' (31st)

Average Rise and Fall 4.6 ft.

When a high tide exceeds avg. ht., the *following* low tide will be lower than avg.

2013 CURRENT TABLE
DELAWARE BAY ENTRANCE

38°46.85'N, 75°02.58'W

Standard Time   Standard Time

JANUARY

DAY OF MONTH	DAY OF WEEK	CURRENT TURNS TO					
		NORTHWEST Flood Starts			SOUTHEAST Ebb Starts		
		a.m.	p.m.	Kts.	a.m.	p.m.	Kts.
1	T	5 52	6 26	1.7	11 55	...	1.9
2	W	6 39	7 11	1.7	12 22	12 41	p1.9
3	T	7 33	8 02	p1.7	1 12	1 31	p1.8
4	F	8 32	8 57	p1.7	2 07	2 27	p1.8
5	S	9 36	9 57	p1.8	3 07	3 27	p1.8
6	S	10 43	10 59	p1.8	4 10	4 31	a1.8
7	M	11 49	...	1.6	5 14	5 35	1.8
8	T	12 01	12 52	a1.9	6 15	6 37	a1.9
9	W	1 00	1 50	a2.0	7 15	7 37	a2.0
10	T	1 57	2 45	a2.0	8 11	8 33	a2.1
11	F	2 53	3 38	a2.1	9 04	9 27	a2.1
12	S	3 46	4 28	a2.0	9 55	10 20	a2.1
13	S	4 38	5 17	a2.0	10 44	11 11	a2.1
14	M	5 30	6 05	a1.9	11 33	...	2.0
15	T	6 23	6 54	1.8	12 02	12 22	p1.9
16	W	7 17	7 44	1.7	12 54	1 12	1.8
17	T	8 12	8 35	p1.7	1 47	2 04	1.7
18	F	9 09	9 28	p1.7	2 41	2 58	1.7
19	S	10 07	10 22	p1.7	3 37	3 54	a1.7
20	S	11 04	11 15	p1.7	4 32	4 49	a1.7
21	M	11 58	...	1.5	5 25	5 44	a1.7
22	T	12 06	12 50	a1.7	6 16	6 35	a1.8
23	W	12 55	1 37	a1.8	7 04	7 22	a1.8
24	T	1 40	2 21	a1.8	7 47	8 06	a1.8
25	F	2 22	3 00	a1.8	8 27	8 45	a1.9
26	S	3 00	3 36	a1.8	9 04	9 22	a1.9
27	S	3 37	4 10	a1.8	9 39	9 57	a1.9
28	M	4 12	4 42	a1.8	10 13	10 33	a1.9
29	T	4 49	5 17	1.8	10 49	11 13	a2.0
30	W	5 30	5 55	1.8	11 29	11 56	a2.0
31	T	6 15	6 38	p1.9	...	12 13	2.0

FEBRUARY

DAY OF MONTH	DAY OF WEEK	CURRENT TURNS TO					
		NORTHWEST Flood Starts			SOUTHEAST Ebb Starts		
		a.m.	p.m.	Kts.	a.m.	p.m.	Kts.
1	F	7 07	7 28	p1.8	12 44	1 02	1.9
2	S	8 05	8 24	p1.8	1 38	1 57	1.8
3	S	9 12	9 28	p1.8	2 38	2 59	a1.8
4	M	10 21	10 35	p1.8	3 44	4 07	a1.8
5	T	11 32	11 44	p1.8	4 52	5 17	a1.8
6	W	...	12 38	1.6	5 59	6 26	a1.8
7	T	12 49	1 39	a1.9	7 03	7 29	a1.9
8	F	1 50	2 35	a1.9	8 01	8 27	a2.0
9	S	2 47	3 25	a2.0	8 54	9 19	a2.0
10	S	3 39	4 12	a2.0	9 43	10 08	a2.1
11	M	4 28	4 57	a2.0	10 29	10 54	a2.0
12	T	5 15	5 39	1.9	11 13	11 39	a2.0
13	W	6 01	6 22	p1.9	11 55	...	1.9
14	T	6 48	7 06	p1.8	12 24	12 39	1.8
15	F	7 37	7 52	p1.7	1 10	1 25	a1.8
16	S	8 28	8 41	p1.7	1 58	2 14	a1.7
17	S	9 23	9 35	p1.6	2 50	3 08	1.6
18	M	10 20	10 30	p1.6	3 44	4 05	a1.6
19	T	11 17	11 26	p1.6	4 40	5 02	a1.6
20	W	...	12 11	1.4	5 34	5 58	a1.7
21	T	12 19	1 02	a1.7	6 26	6 50	a1.7
22	F	1 09	1 47	a1.7	7 13	7 36	a1.8
23	S	1 54	2 28	1.7	7 56	8 18	a1.8
24	S	2 36	3 05	a1.8	8 36	8 56	a1.9
25	M	3 14	3 39	1.8	9 12	9 33	1.9
26	T	3 51	4 12	1.9	9 48	10 09	2.0
27	W	4 29	4 47	p2.0	10 25	10 49	2.0
28	T	5 10	5 26	p2.0	11 05	11 32	2.0

The Kts. (knots) columns show the **maximum** predicted velocities of the stronger one of the Flood Currents and the stronger one of the Ebb Currents for each day.

The letter "a" means the velocity shown should occur **after** the a.m. Current Change. The letter "p" means the velocity shown should occur **after** the p.m. Current Change (even if next morning). No "a" or "p" means a.m. and p.m. velocities are the same for that day.

Avg. Max. Velocity: Flood 1.8 Kts., Ebb 1.9 Kts.

Max. Flood 3 hrs. 5 min. after Flood Starts, ±15 min.

Max. Ebb 3 hrs. 5 min. after Ebb Starts, ±15 min.

See pp. 22-29 for Current Change at other points.

2013 CURRENT TABLE
DELAWARE BAY ENTRANCE
38°46.85'N, 75°02.58'W

*Daylight Time starts March 10 at 2 a.m.   Daylight Saving Time

DAY OF MONTH	DAY OF WEEK	NORTHWEST Flood Starts a.m.	p.m.	Kts.	SOUTHEAST Ebb Starts a.m.	p.m.	Kts.	DAY OF MONTH	DAY OF WEEK	NORTHWEST Flood Starts a.m.	p.m.	Kts.	SOUTHEAST Ebb Starts a.m.	p.m.	Kts.
		MARCH								**APRIL**					
1	F	5 56	**6 10**	p2.0	11 49	...	2.0	1	M	8 32	**8 42**	p1.8	1 55	**2 21**	a2.0
2	S	6 47	**7 00**	p1.9	12 20	**12 39**	a2.0	2	T	9 39	**9 54**	p1.7	2 57	**3 30**	a1.8
3	S	7 46	**8 00**	p1.8	1 14	**1 35**	a1.9	3	W	10 52	**11 12**	p1.6	4 07	**4 45**	a1.7
4	M	8 52	**9 06**	p1.7	2 15	**2 40**	a1.8	4	T	...	**12 02**	1.5	5 20	**6 00**	a1.7
5	T	10 05	**10 20**	p1.7	3 23	**3 52**	a1.7	5	F	12 26	**1 07**	p1.7	6 30	**7 08**	a1.8
6	W	11 18	**11 34**	p1.7	4 35	**5 08**	a1.7	6	S	1 33	**2 05**	p1.8	7 34	**8 08**	1.9
7	T	...	**12 25**	1.6	5 46	**6 18**	a1.8	7	S	2 32	**2 56**	p1.9	8 30	**9 01**	p2.0
8	F	12 42	**1 25**	a1.8	6 51	**7 21**	a1.9	8	M	3 25	**3 42**	p2.0	9 20	**9 47**	2.0
9	S	1 44	**2 19**	a1.9	7 49	**8 17**	a2.0	9	T	4 12	**4 24**	p2.0	10 05	**10 29**	2.0
10	S	*3 38	***4 07**	1.9	*9 40	***10 06**	2.0	10	W	4 55	**5 02**	p2.0	10 45	**11 07**	p2.0
11	M	4 28	**4 51**	p2.0	10 26	**10 51**	2.0	11	T	5 35	**5 38**	p1.9	11 21	**11 43**	p2.0
12	T	5 14	**5 31**	p2.0	11 09	**11 32**	2.0	12	F	6 12	**6 12**	p1.9	11 57	...	1.8
13	W	5 56	**6 10**	p1.9	11 48	...	1.9	13	S	6 50	**6 48**	p1.8	12 18	**12 33**	a1.9
14	T	6 37	**6 47**	p1.9	12 12	**12 26**	1.9	14	S	7 29	**7 27**	p1.7	12 54	**1 13**	a1.9
15	F	7 18	**7 26**	p1.8	12 51	**1 05**	a1.9	15	M	8 12	**8 12**	p1.6	1 34	**1 57**	a1.8
16	S	8 02	**8 08**	p1.7	1 31	**1 47**	a1.8	16	T	9 00	**9 04**	p1.6	2 19	**2 47**	a1.7
17	S	8 48	**8 55**	p1.7	2 15	**2 33**	a1.7	17	W	9 53	**10 02**	p1.5	3 10	**3 43**	a1.7
18	M	9 40	**9 48**	p1.6	3 03	**3 25**	a1.7	18	T	10 48	**11 03**	p1.5	4 04	**4 42**	a1.6
19	T	10 35	**10 45**	p1.5	3 55	**4 22**	a1.6	19	F	11 43	...	1.5	5 02	**5 41**	a1.6
20	W	11 33	**11 45**	p1.5	4 52	**5 22**	a1.6	20	S	12 03	**12 36**	p1.6	5 59	**6 36**	a1.7
21	T	...	**12 29**	1.4	5 49	**6 20**	a1.6	21	S	1 00	**1 24**	p1.7	6 52	**7 27**	1.7
22	F	12 42	**1 21**	a1.6	6 44	**7 14**	a1.7	22	M	1 52	**2 09**	p1.8	7 42	**8 13**	p1.9
23	S	1 36	**2 08**	1.6	7 35	**8 03**	1.7	23	T	2 40	**2 50**	p2.0	8 28	**8 57**	p2.0
24	S	2 25	**2 50**	1.7	8 21	**8 47**	1.8	24	W	3 25	**3 30**	p2.1	9 12	**9 39**	p2.1
25	M	3 09	**3 29**	p1.9	9 03	**9 27**	1.9	25	T	4 08	**4 10**	p2.1	9 54	**10 21**	p2.2
26	T	3 50	**4 05**	p2.0	9 43	**10 06**	2.0	26	F	4 52	**4 52**	p2.2	10 38	**11 05**	p2.2
27	W	4 30	**4 41**	p2.0	10 21	**10 45**	p2.1	27	S	5 38	**5 38**	p2.1	11 24	**11 52**	p2.2
28	T	5 10	**5 18**	p2.1	11 01	**11 26**	p2.1	28	S	6 27	**6 29**	p2.0	...	**12 15**	1.9
29	F	5 53	**6 00**	p2.1	11 43	...	2.0	29	M	7 22	**7 26**	p1.9	12 43	**1 11**	a2.1
30	S	6 40	**6 46**	p2.0	12 10	**12 29**	a2.1	30	T	8 22	**8 32**	p1.7	1 40	**2 14**	a2.0
31	S	7 32	**7 40**	p1.9	12 59	**1 22**	a2.1								

The Kts. (knots) columns show the **maximum** predicted velocities of the stronger one of the Flood Currents and the stronger one of the Ebb Currents for each day.

The letter "a" means the velocity shown should occur **after** the **a.m.** Current Change. The letter "p" means the velocity shown should occur **after** the **p.m.** Current Change (even if next morning). No "a" or "p" means a.m. and p.m. velocities are the same for that day.

Avg. Max. Velocity: Flood 1.8 Kts., Ebb 1.9 Kts.

Max. Flood 3 hrs. 5 min. after Flood Starts, ±15 min.

Max. Ebb 3 hrs. 5 min. after Ebb Starts, ±15 min.

See pp. 22-29 for Current Change at other points.

2013 CURRENT TABLE
DELAWARE BAY ENTRANCE

38°46.85'N, 75°02.58'W

Daylight Saving Time · Daylight Saving Time

		MAY CURRENT TURNS TO									JUNE CURRENT TURNS TO					
		NORTHWEST Flood Starts			SOUTHEAST Ebb Starts						NORTHWEST Flood Starts			SOUTHEAST Ebb Starts		
DAY OF MONTH	DAY OF WEEK	a.m.	p.m.	Kts.	a.m.	p.m.	Kts.	DAY OF MONTH	DAY OF WEEK	a.m.	p.m.	Kts.	a.m.	p.m.	Kts.
1	W	9 28	9 46	1.6	2 43	3 24	a1.8	1	S	11 15	11 51	a1.8	4 37	5 26	a1.8
2	T	10 36	11 01	1.6	3 51	4 37	a1.8	2	S	...	12 12	1.9	5 40	6 26	1.8
3	F	11 43	...	1.6	5 02	5 47	a1.7	3	M	12 54	1 07	p1.9	6 40	7 21	p1.9
4	S	12 12	12 43	p1.8	6 09	6 51	1.8	4	T	1 49	1 55	p2.0	7 34	8 10	p2.0
5	S	1 17	1 38	p1.9	7 10	7 48	1.9	5	W	2 40	2 40	p2.0	8 23	8 54	p2.0
6	M	2 14	2 28	p2.0	8 05	8 38	p2.0	6	T	3 27	3 22	p2.0	9 08	9 35	p2.0
7	T	3 05	3 13	p2.0	8 54	9 23	p2.0	7	F	4 09	4 00	p1.9	9 49	10 12	p1.9
8	W	3 51	3 54	p2.0	9 38	10 03	p2.0	8	S	4 48	4 36	p1.9	10 27	10 46	p1.9
9	T	4 33	4 31	p2.0	10 18	10 39	p2.0	9	S	5 24	5 10	p1.8	11 03	11 19	p1.9
10	F	5 12	5 06	p1.9	10 54	11 14	p1.9	10	M	5 59	5 45	p1.8	11 39	11 52	p1.9
11	S	5 48	5 39	p1.8	11 29	11 47	p1.9	11	T	6 34	6 22	p1.7	...	12 17	1.5
12	S	6 24	6 14	p1.8	...	12 04	1.6	12	W	7 11	7 04	p1.7	12 28	12 58	a1.9
13	M	7 00	6 52	p1.7	12 21	12 43	a1.9	13	T	7 50	7 51	1.6	1 08	1 44	a1.9
14	T	7 40	7 35	p1.6	12 59	1 26	a1.8	14	F	8 34	8 44	1.6	1 52	2 33	a1.9
15	W	8 24	8 25	p1.6	1 41	2 14	a1.8	15	S	9 21	9 42	a1.7	2 40	3 27	a1.8
16	T	9 12	9 21	1.5	2 28	3 08	a1.8	16	S	10 11	10 43	a1.7	3 33	4 22	a1.8
17	F	10 04	10 22	1.5	3 20	4 04	a1.7	17	M	11 03	11 45	a1.8	4 28	5 19	a1.8
18	S	10 57	11 23	a1.6	4 16	5 01	a1.7	18	T	11 56	...	1.9	5 26	6 15	1.8
19	S	11 49	...	1.7	5 12	5 57	a1.7	19	W	12 46	12 49	p2.0	6 24	7 09	p1.9
20	M	12 22	12 39	p1.8	6 08	6 50	1.8	20	T	1 43	1 42	p2.1	7 21	8 02	p2.0
21	T	1 18	1 27	p1.9	7 01	7 40	p1.9	21	F	2 39	2 34	p2.1	8 16	8 54	p2.0
22	W	2 10	2 13	p2.0	7 52	8 28	p2.0	22	S	3 32	3 26	p2.2	9 11	9 45	p2.2
23	T	3 00	2 59	p2.1	8 42	9 14	p2.1	23	S	4 24	4 18	p2.1	10 06	10 35	p2.2
24	F	3 48	3 44	p2.2	9 30	10 01	p2.2	24	M	5 16	5 13	p2.1	11 01	11 27	p2.2
25	S	4 37	4 32	p2.2	10 19	10 48	p2.2	25	T	6 08	6 09	p2.0	11 57	...	1.8
26	S	5 26	5 22	p2.1	11 11	11 38	p2.2	26	W	7 01	7 08	p1.9	12 19	12 55	a2.1
27	M	6 18	6 17	p2.0	...	12 05	1.8	27	T	7 55	8 10	1.8	1 13	1 55	a2.1
28	T	7 13	7 17	p1.9	12 31	1 04	a2.1	28	F	8 50	9 14	a1.8	2 09	2 56	a2.0
29	W	8 11	8 23	1.7	1 27	2 07	a2.0	29	S	9 46	10 19	a1.8	3 07	3 57	a1.9
30	T	9 12	9 33	a1.7	2 28	3 14	a1.9	30	S	10 42	11 22	a1.8	4 06	4 57	a1.8
31	F	10 14	10 44	a1.7	3 32	4 22	a1.8								

The Kts. (knots) columns show the **maximum** predicted velocities of the stronger one of the Flood Currents and the stronger one of the Ebb Currents for each day.
The letter "a" means the velocity shown should occur **after** the **a.m.** Current Change. The letter "p" means the velocity shown should occur **after** the **p.m.** Current Change (even if next morning). No "a" or "p" means a.m. and p.m. velocities are the same for that day.
Avg. Max. Velocity: Flood 1.8 Kts., Ebb 1.9 Kts.
Max. Flood 3 hrs. 5 min. after Flood Starts, ±15 min.
Max. Ebb 3 hrs. 5 min. after Ebb Starts, ±15 min.

See pp. 22-29 for Current Change at other points.

Daylight Saving Time   **Daylight Saving Time**

		JULY							AUGUST					
		CURRENT TURNS TO								CURRENT TURNS TO				
D A Y O F M O N T H	D A Y O F W E E K	NORTHWEST Flood Starts			SOUTHEAST Ebb Starts			D A Y O F M O N T H	D A Y O F W E E K	NORTHWEST Flood Starts			SOUTHEAST Ebb Starts	
		a.m.	p.m.	Kts.	a.m.	p.m.	Kts.			a.m.	p.m.	Kts.	a.m.	p.m.	Kts.
1	M	11 37	...	1.9	5 05	5 54	a1.8	1	T	12 44	12 44	p1.8	6 20	7 02	p1.8
2	T	12 22	12 30	p1.9	6 03	6 48	p1.8	2	F	1 37	1 34	p1.8	7 15	7 51	p1.8
3	W	1 20	1 21	p1.9	6 58	7 38	p1.9	3	S	2 28	2 21	p1.9	8 05	8 35	p1.9
4	T	2 11	2 07	p1.9	7 50	8 24	p1.9	4	S	3 12	3 04	p1.9	8 52	9 15	p1.9
5	F	2 58	2 51	p1.9	8 37	9 06	p1.9	5	M	3 53	3 44	p1.8	9 34	9 52	p1.9
6	S	3 42	3 31	p1.9	9 21	9 44	p1.9	6	T	4 30	4 21	p1.8	10 13	10 27	p1.9
7	S	4 22	4 09	p1.8	10 01	10 19	p1.9	7	W	5 04	4 57	p1.8	10 49	10 59	p2.0
8	M	4 59	4 45	p1.8	10 39	10 53	p1.9	8	T	5 36	5 32	p1.8	11 24	11 33	p2.0
9	T	5 34	5 20	p1.8	11 15	11 26	p1.9	9	F	6 08	6 10	1.8	...	12 02	1.7
10	W	6 07	5 56	p1.7	11 51	...	1.6	10	S	6 42	6 53	a1.8	12 09	12 42	a2.0
11	T	6 40	6 36	p1.7	12 01	12 30	a2.0	11	S	7 21	7 41	a1.9	12 48	1 27	a2.0
12	F	7 17	7 20	1.7	12 37	1 13	a2.0	12	M	8 05	8 35	a1.9	1 33	2 17	a2.0
13	S	7 57	8 10	a1.7	1 19	2 00	a2.0	13	T	8 55	9 37	a1.9	2 23	3 13	a1.9
14	S	8 41	9 06	a1.8	2 04	2 51	a1.9	14	W	9 51	10 45	a1.9	3 19	4 15	a1.8
15	M	9 30	10 07	a1.8	2 55	3 46	a1.9	15	T	10 54	11 56	a1.8	4 23	5 20	1.7
16	T	10 24	11 12	a1.9	3 50	4 44	a1.8	16	F	...	12 01	1.9	5 32	6 25	p1.8
17	W	11 21	...	1.9	4 50	5 44	1.8	17	S	1 05	1 07	p1.9	6 42	7 29	p1.9
18	T	12 18	12 20	p2.0	5 53	6 44	p1.9	18	S	2 09	2 10	p2.0	7 50	8 28	p2.0
19	F	1 22	1 19	p2.0	6 56	7 43	p2.0	19	M	3 07	3 09	p2.0	8 52	9 23	p2.1
20	S	2 22	2 18	p2.1	7 59	8 39	p2.0	20	T	3 59	4 04	p2.1	9 49	10 13	p2.1
21	S	3 19	3 15	p2.1	8 59	9 33	p2.1	21	W	4 48	4 57	p2.0	10 42	11 01	p2.2
22	M	4 13	4 11	p2.1	9 57	10 25	p2.2	22	T	5 35	5 47	p2.0	11 31	11 46	p2.1
23	T	5 04	5 05	p2.1	10 53	11 15	p2.2	23	F	6 19	6 36	1.9	...	12 20	1.9
24	W	5 54	6 00	p2.0	11 47	...	1.8	24	S	7 04	7 25	a1.9	12 31	1 07	a2.0
25	T	6 43	6 54	1.9	12 05	12 40	a2.1	25	S	7 48	8 17	a1.9	1 15	1 56	a1.9
26	F	7 32	7 50	a1.9	12 54	1 34	a2.1	26	M	8 35	9 10	a1.8	2 02	2 46	a1.8
27	S	8 22	8 48	a1.9	1 44	2 29	a2.0	27	T	9 24	10 07	a1.8	2 51	3 39	a1.7
28	S	9 13	9 47	a1.8	2 36	3 24	a1.9	28	W	10 17	11 06	a1.7	3 45	4 34	1.6
29	M	10 05	10 47	a1.8	3 30	4 21	a1.8	29	T	11 12	...	1.7	4 42	5 29	1.6
30	T	10 58	11 46	a1.8	4 26	5 16	1.7	30	F	12 05	12 07	p1.7	5 41	6 23	p1.7
31	W	11 52	...	1.8	5 23	6 11	1.7	31	S	1 00	1 00	p1.7	6 39	7 14	p1.7

The Kts. (knots) columns show the **maximum** predicted velocities of the stronger one of the Flood Currents and the stronger one of the Ebb Currents for each day.
The letter "a" means the velocity shown should occur **after** the **a.m.** Current Change. The letter "p" means the velocity shown should occur **after** the **p.m.** Current Change (even if next morning). No "a" or "p" means a.m. and p.m. velocities are the same for that day.
Avg. Max. Velocity: Flood 1.8 Kts., Ebb 1.9 Kts.
Max. Flood 3 hrs. 5 min. after Flood Starts, ±15 min.
Max. Ebb 3 hrs. 5 min. after Ebb Starts, ±15 min.

See pp. 22-29 for Current Change at other points.

2013 CURRENT TABLE
DELAWARE BAY ENTRANCE

38°46.85'N, 75°02.58'W

Daylight Saving Time   **Daylight Saving Time**

SEPTEMBER

DAY OF MONTH	DAY OF WEEK	NORTHWEST Flood Starts a.m.	NORTHWEST Flood Starts p.m.	NORTHWEST Flood Starts Kts.	SOUTHEAST Ebb Starts a.m.	SOUTHEAST Ebb Starts p.m.	SOUTHEAST Ebb Starts Kts.
1	S	1 51	1 50	p1.8	7 33	8 01	p1.8
2	M	2 38	2 36	p1.8	8 21	8 44	p1.9
3	T	3 20	3 19	p1.8	9 05	9 23	p1.9
4	W	3 57	3 57	p1.9	9 44	9 58	p2.0
5	T	4 31	4 33	p1.9	10 20	10 32	p2.0
6	F	5 02	5 09	p1.9	10 56	11 05	p2.0
7	S	5 34	5 46	a1.9	11 33	11 41	p2.1
8	S	6 09	6 28	a1.9	...	12 13	1.9
9	M	6 48	7 16	a2.0	12 21	12 58	a2.0
10	T	7 34	8 11	a1.9	1 06	1 49	a2.0
11	W	8 27	9 14	a1.9	1 58	2 46	a1.9
12	T	9 28	10 26	a1.8	2 57	3 51	a1.8
13	F	10 38	11 41	a1.8	4 06	5 01	p1.7
14	S	11 51	...	1.8	5 21	6 11	p1.7
15	S	12 51	1 01	p1.8	6 35	7 17	p1.8
16	M	1 55	2 05	p1.9	7 43	8 17	p2.0
17	T	2 51	3 03	p2.0	8 43	9 10	p2.1
18	W	3 42	3 56	p2.0	9 37	9 59	p2.1
19	T	4 28	4 44	2.0	10 26	10 43	p2.1
20	F	5 11	5 30	a2.0	11 11	11 25	p2.1
21	S	5 52	6 14	a2.0	11 55	...	1.9
22	S	6 32	6 58	a1.9	12 05	12 37	a2.0
23	M	7 13	7 44	a1.8	12 45	1 20	a1.9
24	T	7 56	8 33	a1.8	1 27	2 05	a1.8
25	W	8 42	9 26	a1.7	2 13	2 55	a1.7
26	T	9 34	10 23	a1.6	3 05	3 48	1.6
27	F	10 31	11 22	a1.6	4 02	4 44	p1.6
28	S	11 29	...	1.6	5 02	5 40	p1.6
29	S	12 18	12 25	p1.6	6 02	6 34	p1.7
30	M	1 11	1 18	p1.7	6 57	7 24	p1.8

OCTOBER

DAY OF MONTH	DAY OF WEEK	NORTHWEST Flood Starts a.m.	NORTHWEST Flood Starts p.m.	NORTHWEST Flood Starts Kts.	SOUTHEAST Ebb Starts a.m.	SOUTHEAST Ebb Starts p.m.	SOUTHEAST Ebb Starts Kts.
1	T	1 58	2 06	p1.8	7 47	8 09	p1.9
2	W	2 41	2 50	p1.8	8 31	8 49	p1.9
3	T	3 20	3 31	p1.9	9 12	9 27	p2.0
4	F	3 54	4 08	1.9	9 49	10 02	p2.0
5	S	4 27	4 46	a2.0	10 27	10 38	p2.1
6	S	5 01	5 25	a2.0	11 05	11 16	p2.1
7	M	5 39	6 08	a2.0	11 47	11 58	2.0
8	T	6 21	6 57	a2.0	...	12 33	2.0
9	W	7 10	7 54	a1.9	12 46	1 26	1.9
10	T	8 07	9 00	a1.8	1 41	2 26	1.8
11	F	9 14	10 12	a1.7	2 44	3 33	1.7
12	S	10 29	11 26	a1.7	3 58	4 46	p1.7
13	S	11 44	...	1.7	5 15	5 57	p1.7
14	M	12 35	12 54	p1.8	6 28	7 03	p1.9
15	T	1 36	1 56	p1.9	7 33	8 01	p2.0
16	W	2 30	2 52	1.9	8 30	8 53	p2.0
17	T	3 19	3 42	a2.0	9 20	9 40	p2.1
18	F	4 04	4 28	a2.0	10 06	10 22	2.0
19	S	4 45	5 11	a2.0	10 48	11 01	a2.0
20	S	5 23	5 52	a2.0	11 28	11 38	1.9
21	M	6 01	6 32	a1.9	...	12 06	1.8
22	T	6 38	7 13	a1.8	12 15	12 45	1.8
23	W	7 18	7 57	a1.7	12 54	1 26	1.7
24	T	8 02	8 46	a1.6	1 38	2 11	1.6
25	F	8 53	9 39	a1.6	2 28	3 02	p1.6
26	S	9 49	10 36	a1.5	3 23	3 57	p1.6
27	S	10 48	11 32	a1.5	4 22	4 54	p1.6
28	M	11 46	...	1.6	5 22	5 49	p1.7
29	T	12 25	12 41	p1.6	6 18	6 41	p1.7
30	W	1 13	1 32	p1.7	7 09	7 29	p1.8
31	T	1 58	2 19	1.8	7 55	8 13	p1.9

The Kts. (knots) columns show the **maximum** predicted velocities of the stronger one of the Flood Currents and the stronger one of the Ebb Currents for each day.
The letter "a" means the velocity shown should occur **after** the **a.m.** Current Change. The letter "p" means the velocity shown should occur **after** the **p.m.** Current Change (even if next morning). No "a" or "p" means a.m. and p.m. velocities are the same for that day.
Avg. Max. Velocity: Flood 1.8 Kts., Ebb 1.9 Kts.
Max. Flood 3 hrs. 5 min. after Flood Starts, ±15 min.
Max. Ebb 3 hrs. 5 min. after Ebb Starts, ±15 min.

See pp. 22-29 for Current Change at other points.

2013 CURRENT TABLE
DELAWARE BAY ENTRANCE
38°46.85'N, 75°02.58'W

*Standard Time starts Nov. 3 at 2 a.m.   Standard Time

Day of Month	Day of Week	NORTHWEST Flood Starts			SOUTHEAST Ebb Starts			Day of Month	Day of Week	NORTHWEST Flood Starts			SOUTHEAST Ebb Starts		
		NOVEMBER								**DECEMBER**					
		a.m.	**p.m.**	Kts.	a.m.	**p.m.**	Kts.			a.m.	**p.m.**	Kts.	a.m.	**p.m.**	Kts.
1	F	2 38	3 02	a1.9	8 38	8 54	p2.0	1	S	1 42	2 21	a2.0	7 51	8 07	2.0
2	S	3 16	3 43	a2.0	9 19	9 33	2.0	2	M	2 26	3 06	a2.1	8 37	8 53	a2.1
3	S	*2 55	*3 25	a2.1	*9 00	*9 13	a2.1	3	T	3 12	3 54	a2.1	9 23	9 40	a2.1
4	M	3 33	4 07	a2.1	9 41	9 55	a2.1	4	W	3 58	4 43	a2.1	10 11	10 30	a2.1
5	T	4 15	4 53	a2.1	10 26	10 41	a2.1	5	T	4 49	5 35	a2.0	11 02	11 25	a2.1
6	W	5 01	5 45	a2.0	11 15	11 33	a2.0	6	F	5 46	6 32	a1.9	11 57	...	2.0
7	T	5 54	6 43	a1.9	...	12 09	1.9	7	S	6 48	7 34	a1.8	12 25	12 56	p1.9
8	F	6 56	7 48	a1.8	12 31	1 10	1.8	8	S	7 56	8 38	a1.7	1 30	2 00	p1.8
9	S	8 06	8 58	a1.7	1 38	2 18	1.7	9	M	9 06	9 43	p1.7	2 38	3 07	1.7
10	S	9 20	10 08	a1.6	2 51	3 29	p1.7	10	T	10 16	10 45	p1.7	3 47	4 13	p1.8
11	M	10 34	11 13	1.7	4 05	4 38	p1.8	11	W	11 21	11 43	p1.8	4 52	5 15	1.8
12	T	11 41	...	1.7	5 14	5 42	p1.8	12	T	...	12 20	1.7	5 51	6 13	a1.9
13	W	12 12	12 41	1.8	6 16	6 40	1.9	13	F	12 36	1 14	a1.9	6 46	7 05	1.9
14	T	1 05	1 36	a1.9	7 10	7 31	2.0	14	S	1 25	2 04	a2.0	7 35	7 52	a2.0
15	F	1 53	2 25	a2.0	7 59	8 17	2.0	15	S	2 10	2 49	a2.0	8 19	8 35	a2.0
16	S	2 37	3 10	a2.0	8 44	8 59	a2.0	16	M	2 52	3 30	a1.9	8 59	9 15	a1.9
17	S	3 18	3 51	a2.0	9 24	9 38	a2.0	17	T	3 30	4 08	a1.9	9 36	9 51	a1.9
18	M	3 56	4 30	a1.9	10 01	10 14	a1.9	18	W	4 06	4 43	a1.8	10 11	10 26	a1.8
19	T	4 32	5 07	a1.8	10 37	10 49	a1.8	19	T	4 41	5 18	a1.8	10 45	11 02	a1.8
20	W	5 07	5 44	a1.8	11 13	11 27	a1.8	20	F	5 17	5 54	a1.7	11 20	11 41	a1.8
21	T	5 45	6 24	a1.7	11 51	...	1.7	21	S	5 56	6 32	a1.7	11 59	...	1.8
22	F	6 27	7 08	a1.6	12 08	12 33	p1.7	22	S	6 40	7 15	1.6	12 23	12 41	p1.8
23	S	7 14	7 56	a1.6	12 54	1 19	p1.7	23	M	7 29	8 01	1.6	1 10	1 27	p1.8
24	S	8 08	8 48	1.5	1 46	2 10	p1.7	24	T	8 22	8 51	1.6	2 00	2 18	p1.7
25	M	9 05	9 42	1.5	2 41	3 05	p1.7	25	W	9 20	9 43	p1.7	2 54	3 12	p1.7
26	T	10 04	10 34	p1.6	3 38	4 00	p1.7	26	T	10 19	10 36	p1.7	3 50	4 08	1.7
27	W	11 01	11 25	p1.7	4 34	4 54	p1.7	27	F	11 17	11 30	p1.8	4 46	5 04	1.7
28	T	11 55	...	1.6	5 28	5 46	p1.8	28	S	...	12 14	1.6	5 42	5 59	1.8
29	F	12 13	12 46	a1.8	6 18	6 35	p1.9	29	S	12 22	1 09	a1.9	6 35	6 53	a1.9
30	S	12 58	1 34	a1.9	7 05	7 21	a2.0	30	M	1 14	2 01	a2.0	7 27	7 46	a2.0
								31	T	2 05	2 52	a2.1	8 18	8 38	a2.1

The Kts. (knots) columns show the **maximum** predicted velocities of the stronger one of the Flood Currents and the stronger one of the Ebb Currents for each day.

The letter "a" means the velocity shown should occur **after** the a.m. Current Change. The letter "p" means the velocity shown should occur **after** the p.m. Current Change (even if next morning). No "a" or "p" means a.m. and p.m. velocities are the same for that day.

Avg. Max. Velocity: Flood 1.8 Kts., Ebb 1.9 Kts.

Max. Flood 3 hrs. 5 min. after Flood Starts, ±15 min.

Max. Ebb 3 hrs. 5 min. after Ebb Starts, ±15 min.

See pp. 22-29 for Current Change at other points.

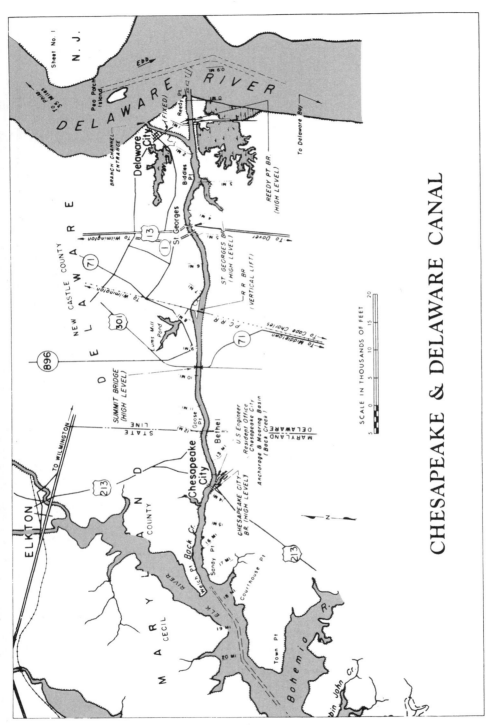

CHESAPEAKE & DELAWARE CANAL

See Chesapeake & Delaware Canal Current Tables, pp. 148-153

CHESAPEAKE & DELAWARE CANAL REGULATIONS

(Traffic Dispatcher is located at Chesapeake City and monitors Channel 13.)

Philadelphia District Engineer issues notices periodically showing available channel depths and navigation conditions.

Projected Channel dimensions are 35 ft. deep and 450 ft. wide. (The branch to Delaware City is 8 ft. deep and 50 ft. wide.) The distance from the Delaware River Ship Channel to the Elk River is 19.1 miles.

1. Traffic controls, located at Reedy Point and Old Town Point Wharf, flash green when Canal is open, flash red when it is closed.
2. Vessel identification and monitoring are performed by TV cameras at Reedy Point and Old Town Point Wharf.
3. The following vessels, tugs and tows are required to have radiotelephones:
   a. Power vessels of 300 gross tons and upward.
   b. Vessels of 100 gross tons and upward carrying 1 or more passengers for hire.
   c. Every towing vessel of 26 feet or over.
4. Vessels listed in 3. will not enter the Canal until radio communication is made with the dispatcher and clearance is received. Ships' captains will tell the dispatcher the estimated time of passing Reedy Point or Town Point. Communication is to be established on Channel 13 (156.65 MHz). Dispatcher also monitors Channel 16 (156.8 MHz) to respond to emergencies.
5. A westbound vessel must be able to pass Reedy Is. or Pea Patch Is. within 120 min. of receiving clearance; an eastbound vessel must be able to pass Arnold Point within 120 min. If passage is not made within these 120 min., a new clearance must be solicited. Vessels must also report to the dispatcher the time of passing the outer end of the jetties at Reedy Point and Old Town Point Wharf.
6. Vessels exceeding 800 feet are required to have operable bow thrusters.
7. Maximum combined extreme breadth of vessels meeting and overtaking each other is 190 feet.
8. Vessels of all types are required to travel at a safe speed to avoid damage by suction or wash to wharves, landings, other boats, etc. Operators of yachts, motorboats, etc. are cautioned that there are many large, deep-draft ocean-going and commercial vessels using the Canal. There is "no anchoring" in the canal at any time. Moor or anchor outside of Reedy Point, near Arnold Point, or in Chesapeake City Basin.
9. Vessels proceeding *with* the current shall have the right-of-way but all small pleasure craft shall relinquish the right-of-way to deeper draft vessels which have a limited maneuvering ability.
10. Vessels under sail will not be permitted in the Canal.
11. Vessels difficult to handle must use the Canal during daylight hours and must have tug assistance. They should clear Reedy Point Bridge (going east) or Chesapeake City Bridge (going west) before dark.

Anchorage and wharfage facilities for small vessels only are at Chesapeake City and permission to use them for more than 24 hours must be obtained from the dispatcher.

The **railroad bridge** has a clearance when closed of 45 ft. at MHW. The bridge monitors Channel 13 and gives 30 minutes notice prior to lowering.

The **five highway bridges** are high level and fixed.

Normal tide range is 5.4 ft. at Delaware R. end of the Canal and 2.6 ft. at Chesapeake City. Local mean low water at Courthouse Pt. is 2.5 ft. and decreases gradually eastward to 0.6 ft. at Delaware R. (See pp. 18 and 19 for times of High Water in this area.)
Note: A violent northeast storm may raise tide 4 to 5 ft. above normal in the Canal; a westerly storm may cause low tide to fall slightly below normal at Chesapeake City and as much as 4.0 ft. below normal at Reedy Point.

2013 CURRENT TABLE
CHESAPEAKE & DELAWARE CANAL
39°31.89'N, 75°49.65'W at Chesapeake City

Standard Time	Standard Time
JANUARY	**FEBRUARY**

DAY OF MONTH	DAY OF WEEK	CURRENT TURNS TO						DAY OF MONTH	DAY OF WEEK	CURRENT TURNS TO					
		EAST Flood Starts			WEST Ebb Starts					EAST Flood Starts			WEST Ebb Starts		
		a.m.	p.m.	Kts.	a.m.	p.m.	Kts.			a.m.	p.m.	Kts.	a.m.	p.m.	Kts.
1	T	6 28	6 48	p2.6	12 39	12 01	p2.4	1	F	7 43	7 48	p2.4	1 05	1 48	a2.3
2	W	7 18	7 30	p2.5	1 14	12 56	p2.2	2	S	8 41	8 35	p2.2	1 47	2 55	a2.3
3	T	8 11	8 14	p2.4	1 49	1 54	2.0	3	S	9 48	9 32	p2.1	2 34	4 10	a2.3
4	F	9 07	9 01	p2.3	2 29	3 01	a2.1	4	M	10 58	10 35	p2.1	3 30	5 24	a2.4
5	S	10 12	9 54	p2.2	3 13	4 18	a2.2	5	T	11 59	11 42	p2.1	4 34	6 32	a2.4
6	S	11 19	10 53	p2.1	4 03	5 35	a2.3	6	W	...	1 12	2.1	5 41	7 32	a2.5
7	M	...	12 24	2.0	4 57	6 47	a2.4	7	T	12 47	2 13	p2.3	6 49	8 27	a2.6
8	T	12 01	1 27	p2.2	5 54	7 53	a2.6	8	F	1 51	3 08	2.4	7 56	9 15	a2.7
9	W	12 56	2 28	p2.3	6 54	8 51	a2.7	9	S	2 52	3 58	2.5	8 58	10 01	a2.7
10	T	1 59	3 24	p2.5	7 56	9 43	a2.8	10	S	3 49	4 45	a2.6	9 57	10 44	a2.6
11	F	3 01	4 17	p2.6	8 57	10 32	a2.9	11	M	4 44	5 29	a2.6	10 52	11 26	a2.5
12	S	4 00	5 08	p2.6	9 57	11 18	a2.8	12	T	5 38	6 10	a2.5	11 47	...	2.3
13	S	4 58	5 55	p2.6	10 56	11 59	a2.7	13	W	6 29	6 48	a2.3	12 06	12 40	a2.2
14	M	5 55	6 40	2.5	11 54	...	2.5	14	T	7 17	7 23	a2.1	12 44	1 31	a2.2
15	T	6 50	7 21	2.3	12 47	12 51	p2.3	15	F	8 03	7 56	a1.9	1 19	2 22	a2.1
16	W	7 44	8 00	p2.2	1 29	1 47	a2.1	16	S	8 48	8 31	1.7	1 50	3 15	a2.0
17	T	8 37	8 37	p2.0	2 08	2 44	a2.0	17	S	9 34	9 12	p1.6	2 21	4 12	a1.9
18	F	9 32	9 14	p1.8	2 47	3 43	a2.0	18	M	10 22	10 00	1.5	2 55	5 08	a1.9
19	S	10 26	9 54	p1.7	3 24	4 44	a1.9	19	T	11 10	10 55	1.5	3 38	6 00	a1.9
20	S	11 18	10 38	p1.6	4 01	5 43	a1.9	20	W	11 58	11 50	1.6	4 30	6 47	a1.9
21	M	11 59	11 25	p1.5	4 38	6 38	a1.9	21	T	...	12 45	1.8	5 26	7 30	a2.0
22	T	...	12 49	1.6	5 16	7 29	a2.0	22	F	12 44	1 33	p2.0	6 24	8 10	a2.1
23	W	12 14	1 31	p1.7	5 59	8 15	a2.1	23	S	1 37	2 19	p2.1	7 23	8 47	a2.2
24	T	1 05	2 14	p1.9	6 46	8 56	a2.3	24	S	2 29	3 04	p2.3	8 19	9 21	a2.3
25	F	1 57	2 56	p2.1	7 37	9 34	a2.4	25	M	3 18	3 47	p2.4	9 13	9 55	a2.3
26	S	2 48	3 37	p2.3	8 29	10 09	a2.5	26	T	4 05	4 30	2.4	10 05	10 29	2.3
27	S	3 38	4 18	p2.4	9 20	10 43	a2.5	27	W	4 52	5 12	2.5	10 57	11 04	p2.4
28	M	4 26	5 00	p2.5	10 10	11 17	a2.5	28	T	5 40	5 55	2.5	11 50	11 43	p2.5
29	T	5 14	5 41	p2.6	11 01	11 51	a2.4								
30	W	6 02	6 22	p2.6	11 54	...	2.3								
31	T	6 52	7 04	p2.5	12 27	12 49	a2.2								

The Kts. (knots) columns show the **maximum** predicted velocities of the stronger one of the Flood Currents and the stronger one of the Ebb Currents for each day.

The letter "a" means the velocity shown should occur **after** the **a.m.** Current Change. The letter "p" means the velocity shown should occur **after** the **p.m.** Current Change (even if next morning). No "a" or "p" means a.m. and p.m. velocities are the same for that day.

Avg. Max. Velocity: Flood 2.0 Kts., Ebb 1.9 Kts.

Max. Flood 3 hrs. 10 min. after Flood Starts ±45 min.

Max. Ebb 2 hrs. 45 min. after Ebb Starts ±45 min.

See pp. 22-29 for Current Change at other points.

Note *from NOS: These predictions should be considered questionable. Caution is advised.*

2013 CURRENT TABLE
CHESAPEAKE & DELAWARE CANAL

39°31.89'N, 75°49.65'W at Chesapeake City

*Daylight Time starts March 10 at 2 a.m.   Daylight Saving Time

Day of Month	Day of Week	MARCH EAST Flood Starts a.m.	p.m.	Kts.	WEST Ebb Starts a.m.	p.m.	Kts.	Day of Month	Day of Week	APRIL EAST Flood Starts a.m.	p.m.	Kts.	WEST Ebb Starts a.m.	p.m.	Kts.
1	F	6 30	6 40	a2.5	...	12 47	1.9	1	M	9 08	9 06	a2.4	1 47	3 45	a2.6
2	S	7 23	7 26	a2.4	12 25	1 47	a2.5	2	T	10 11	10 11	a2.3	2 47	4 46	a2.5
3	S	8 22	8 19	a2.2	1 12	2 52	a2.5	3	W	11 20	11 23	a2.2	3 57	5 46	a2.4
4	M	9 27	9 18	2.1	2 05	4 01	a2.4	4	T	...	12 24	2.1	5 16	6 42	a2.2
5	T	10 39	10 27	a2.1	3 08	5 09	a2.4	5	F	12 30	1 24	2.1	6 34	7 32	a2.1
6	W	11 48	11 36	2.1	4 21	6 10	a2.3	6	S	1 34	2 20	a2.2	7 44	8 20	2.1
7	T	...	12 52	2.1	5 37	7 05	a2.3	7	S	2 35	3 10	a2.3	8 50	9 05	p2.3
8	F	12 42	1 50	2.2	6 48	7 55	a2.4	8	M	3 31	3 56	a2.4	9 49	9 46	p2.4
9	S	1 44	2 43	a2.4	7 55	8 41	a2.4	9	T	4 23	4 38	a2.4	10 42	10 24	p2.4
10	S	*3 43	*4 31	a2.5	*9 56	*10 25	a2.3	10	W	5 11	5 17	a2.4	11 33	10 59	p2.4
11	M	4 37	5 15	a2.6	10 52	11 05	p2.3	11	T	5 54	5 54	a2.3	-A-	12 21	1.6
12	T	5 29	5 56	a2.5	11 45	11 44	p2.3	12	F	6 34	6 30	a2.2	...	1 08	1.5
13	W	6 18	6 34	a2.4	...	12 36	1.9	13	S	7 11	7 07	a2.2	12 01	1 53	a2.3
14	T	7 04	7 10	a2.3	12 19	1 25	a2.3	14	S	7 45	7 46	a2.1	12 26	2 37	a2.3
15	F	7 46	7 45	a2.1	12 52	2 13	a2.3	15	M	8 18	8 28	a2.1	12 59	3 19	a2.3
16	S	8 24	8 19	a2.0	1 22	3 00	a2.2	16	T	8 55	9 15	a2.0	1 39	4 02	a2.2
17	S	9 00	8 57	a1.8	1 50	3 48	a2.1	17	W	9 37	10 09	a2.0	2 26	4 46	a2.1
18	M	9 39	9 40	a1.8	2 22	4 38	a2.0	18	T	10 26	11 09	a2.0	3 21	5 29	a2.0
19	T	10 23	10 33	a1.7	3 02	5 29	a2.0	19	F	11 20	...	2.0	4 27	6 11	a1.9
20	W	11 14	11 32	a1.8	3 52	6 16	a1.9	20	S	12 09	12 14	p2.0	5 41	6 50	1.8
21	T	...	12 07	1.8	4 54	7 00	a1.9	21	S	1 04	1 06	p2.1	6 52	7 28	p2.0
22	F	12 30	12 59	p1.9	6 02	7 41	a1.9	22	M	1 58	1 57	p2.2	7 58	8 06	p2.3
23	S	1 25	1 49	p2.0	7 08	8 19	a1.9	23	T	2 50	2 47	2.2	9 00	8 45	p2.5
24	S	2 18	2 39	p2.1	8 11	8 56	2.0	24	W	3 41	3 37	2.3	9 59	9 26	p2.6
25	M	3 09	3 27	2.2	9 11	9 32	p2.2	25	T	4 30	4 26	a2.5	10 55	10 08	p2.8
26	T	3 58	4 13	2.3	10 06	10 08	p2.4	26	F	5 20	5 15	a2.6	11 50	10 52	p2.9
27	W	4 46	4 58	a2.5	11 00	10 45	p2.5	27	S	6 12	6 06	a2.7	-B-	12 46	1.6
28	T	5 34	5 43	a2.6	11 53	11 24	p2.7	28	S	7 05	7 01	a2.7	...	1 42	1.6
29	F	6 23	6 29	a2.7	...	12 49	1.9	29	M	8 00	7 58	a2.6	12 34	2 36	a2.9
30	S	7 15	7 18	a2.6	12 06	1 47	a2.7	30	T	8 56	8 58	a2.5	1 34	3 30	a2.7
31	S	8 09	8 10	a2.5	12 54	2 45	a2.7								

A also at 11:29 p.m. 2.4   **B** also at 11:41 p.m. 2.9

The Kts. (knots) columns show the **maximum** predicted velocities of the stronger one of the Flood Currents and the stronger one of the Ebb Currents for each day.

The letter "a" means the velocity shown should occur **after** the a.m. Current Change. The letter "p" means the velocity shown should occur **after** the p.m. Current Change (even if next morning). No "a" or "p" means a.m. and p.m. velocities are the same for that day.

Avg. Max. Velocity: Flood 2.0 Kts., Ebb 1.9 Kts.

Max. Flood 3 hrs. 10 min. after Flood Starts ±45 min.

Max. Ebb 2 hrs. 45 min. after Ebb Starts ±45 min.

See pp. 22-29 for Current Change at other points.

Note from **NOS**: *These predictions should be considered questionable. Caution is advised.*

2013 CURRENT TABLE
CHESAPEAKE & DELAWARE CANAL

39°31.89'N, 75°49.65'W at Chesapeake City

Daylight Saving Time   Daylight Saving Time

		MAY						JUNE			
		CURRENT TURNS TO						CURRENT TURNS TO			
		EAST Flood Starts			WEST Ebb Starts			EAST Flood Starts			WEST Ebb Starts
DAY OF MONTH	DAY OF WEEK	a.m.	p.m.	Kts.	a.m.	p.m.	Kts.	DAY OF MONTH	DAY OF WEEK	a.m.	p.m.	Kts.	a.m.	p.m.	Kts.

DAY OF MONTH	DAY OF WEEK	a.m.	p.m.	Kts.	a.m.	p.m.	Kts.	DAY OF MONTH	DAY OF WEEK	a.m.	p.m.	Kts.	a.m.	p.m.	Kts.
1	W	9 55	10 03	a2.4	2 39	4 24	a2.5	1	S	11 20	...	2.1	4 59	5 33	p2.1
2	T	10 55	11 12	a2.3	3 52	5 18	a2.3	2	S	12 04	12 11	p2.0	6 11	6 20	p2.1
3	F	11 56	...	2.1	5 10	6 09	a2.1	3	M	1 07	12 59	p1.9	7 18	7 04	p2.2
4	S	12 20	12 50	p2.1	6 26	6 58	p2.1	4	T	2 03	1 44	a1.9	8 20	7 45	p2.3
5	S	1 23	1 42	2.0	7 34	7 43	p2.2	5	W	2 55	2 27	a1.9	9 17	8 22	p2.3
6	M	2 22	2 29	a2.1	8 38	8 26	p2.4	6	T	3 40	3 10	a2.0	10 08	8 56	p2.3
7	T	3 16	3 13	a2.2	9 36	9 05	p2.4	7	F	4 20	3 52	a2.0	10 54	9 29	p2.4
8	W	4 05	3 55	a2.2	10 28	9 41	p2.4	8	S	4 56	4 34	a2.1	11 36	10 02	p2.4
9	T	4 48	4 34	a2.2	11 16	10 12	p2.4	9	S	5 29	5 16	a2.2	-D-	12 16	1.3
10	F	5 27	5 12	a2.2	11 59	10 41	p2.4	10	M	6 03	6 01	a2.3	-E-	12 54	1.4
11	S	6 02	5 51	a2.2	-A-	12 46	1.3	11	T	6 38	6 47	a2.4	...	1 30	1.5
12	S	6 36	6 32	a2.3	-B-	1 28	1.3	12	W	7 15	7 35	a2.5	12 05	2 04	a2.5
13	M	7 09	7 16	a2.3	...	2 08	1.4	13	T	7 54	8 24	a2.5	12 55	2 37	a2.4
14	T	7 44	8 02	a2.3	12 25	2 45	a2.4	14	F	8 34	9 15	a2.4	1 48	3 11	a2.2
15	W	8 22	8 51	a2.3	1 11	3 22	a2.3	15	S	9 16	10 11	a2.4	2 45	3 48	a2.0
16	T	9 03	9 44	a2.3	2 03	3 59	a2.2	16	S	10 02	11 12	a2.3	3 48	4 28	p2.0
17	F	9 48	10 42	a2.2	3 00	4 39	a2.0	17	M	10 53	...	2.2	5 01	5 12	p2.2
18	S	10 38	11 42	a2.2	4 05	5 19	1.9	18	T	12 14	-F-	1.8	6 17	5 58	p2.3
19	S	11 31	...	2.2	5 20	6 00	p2.0	19	W	1 14	12 42	p2.1	7 30	6 46	p2.5
20	M	12 40	12 24	p2.2	6 34	6 41	p2.2	20	T	2 13	1 39	p2.2	8 38	7 37	p2.7
21	T	1 36	1 16	p2.2	7 44	7 23	p2.4	21	F	3 11	2 38	2.2	9 40	8 31	p2.8
22	W	2 31	2 09	p2.2	8 50	8 06	p2.6	22	S	4 07	3 39	a2.4	10 36	9 28	p2.9
23	T	3 25	3 03	a2.3	9 51	8 53	p2.8	23	S	5 01	4 38	a2.6	11 27	10 27	p3.0
24	F	4 18	3 58	a2.5	10 48	9 42	p2.9	24	M	5 54	5 37	a2.7	-G-	12 17	1.6
25	S	5 10	4 53	a2.6	11 43	10 33	p3.0	25	T	6 46	6 36	a2.7	...	1 05	1.8
26	S	6 03	5 49	a2.7	-C-	12 37	1.5	26	W	7 36	7 35	a2.7	12 27	1 51	a2.8
27	M	6 57	6 48	a2.8	...	1 29	1.6	27	T	8 23	8 34	a2.6	1 30	2 36	a2.6
28	T	7 50	7 47	a2.7	12 27	2 18	a2.9	28	F	9 10	9 34	a2.4	2 33	3 21	a2.4
29	W	8 42	8 48	a2.6	1 30	3 07	a2.7	29	S	9 55	10 37	a2.2	3 37	4 07	p2.1
30	T	9 34	9 51	a2.4	2 37	3 55	a2.5	30	S	10 41	11 41	a2.0	4 43	4 53	p2.1
31	F	10 27	10 58	a2.3	3 46	4 44	a2.2								

A also at 11:11 p.m. 2.4   **B** also at 11:45 p.m. 2.5   **C** also at 11:28 p.m. 3.0
D also at 10:39 p.m. 2.5   **E** also at 11:20 p.m. 2.5   **F** also at 11:47 a.m. 2.2
G also at 11:26 p.m. 2.9

The Kts. (knots) columns show the **maximum** predicted velocities of the stronger one of the Flood Currents and the stronger one of the Ebb Currents for each day.
The letter "a" means the velocity shown should occur **after** the **a.m.** Current Change. The letter "p" means the velocity shown should occur **after** the **p.m.** Current Change (even if next morning). No "a" or "p" means a.m. and p.m. velocities are the same for that day.
Avg. Max. Velocity: Flood 2.0 Kts., Ebb 1.9 Kts.
Max. Flood 3 hrs. 10 min. after Flood Starts ±45 min.
Max. Ebb 2 hrs. 45 min. after Ebb Starts ±45 min.

See pp. 22-29 for Current Change at other points.

    Note *from NOS: These predictions should be considered questionable. Caution is advised.*

Daylight Saving Time   Daylight Saving Time

		JULY									AUGUST					
		CURRENT TURNS TO									CURRENT TURNS TO					
		EAST Flood Starts			WEST Ebb Starts						EAST Flood Starts			WEST Ebb Starts		
DAY OF MONTH	DAY OF WEEK	a.m.	p.m.	Kts.	a.m.	p.m.	Kts.	DAY OF MONTH	DAY OF WEEK	a.m.	p.m.	Kts.	a.m.	p.m.	Kts.
1	M	11 28	...	1.9	5 51	5 39	p2.0	1	T	12 54	12 21	1.5	7 24	6 12	p1.9
2	T	12 41	12 14	p1.7	6 55	6 22	p2.0	2	F	1 39	1 10	1.5	8 15	6 54	p2.0
3	W	1 36	1 00	1.6	7 55	7 01	p2.1	3	S	2 22	2 00	a1.7	9 00	7 39	p2.1
4	T	2 23	1 44	a1.7	8 50	7 37	p2.1	4	S	3 01	2 48	a1.8	9 40	8 28	p2.2
5	F	3 06	2 30	a1.8	9 39	8 14	p2.2	5	M	3 40	3 36	a2.0	10 16	9 18	p2.3
6	S	3 44	3 16	a1.9	10 22	8 53	p2.3	6	T	4 19	4 23	a2.2	10 49	10 08	p2.4
7	S	4 20	4 02	a2.0	11 01	9 35	p2.4	7	W	4 59	5 09	a2.3	11 21	10 57	p2.4
8	M	4 55	4 48	a2.2	11 36	10 19	p2.5	8	T	5 38	5 55	a2.4	11 53	11 47	p2.4
9	T	5 31	5 33	a2.3	11 59	11 06	p2.5	9	F	6 18	6 42	a2.5	...	12 26	2.2
10	W	6 09	6 20	a2.5	...	12 44	1.7	10	S	6 58	7 30	a2.5	12 37	1 00	2.3
11	T	6 47	7 08	a2.5	12 01	1 17	a2.5	11	S	7 39	8 19	a2.5	1 30	1 37	p2.3
12	F	7 27	7 56	a2.6	12 45	1 49	a2.4	12	M	8 21	9 12	a2.4	2 26	2 17	p2.3
13	S	8 06	8 46	a2.5	1 37	2 23	a2.2	13	T	9 06	10 12	a2.2	3 27	3 02	p2.3
14	S	8 47	9 40	a2.4	2 33	3 00	p2.1	14	W	9 58	11 21	a2.1	4 37	3 54	p2.3
15	M	9 32	10 40	a2.3	3 35	3 42	p2.2	15	T	11 00	...	2.0	5 51	4 55	p2.4
16	T	10 21	11 46	a2.2	4 46	4 29	p2.3	16	F	12 30	12 07	p2.0	6 59	6 04	p2.4
17	W	11 18	...	2.1	6 04	5 22	p2.4	17	S	1 36	1 14	p2.1	8 00	7 13	p2.5
18	T	12 52	12 19	p2.1	7 16	6 20	p2.5	18	S	2 39	2 18	p2.3	8 55	8 22	p2.6
19	F	1 55	1 21	p2.1	8 22	7 20	p2.6	19	M	3 36	3 21	p2.5	9 44	9 28	p2.6
20	S	2 56	2 25	2.2	9 21	8 23	p2.8	20	T	4 29	4 20	p2.6	10 30	10 29	p2.6
21	S	3 54	3 28	2.4	10 14	9 26	p2.8	21	W	5 18	5 16	p2.7	11 14	11 28	p2.5
22	M	4 48	4 28	2.5	11 02	10 28	p2.8	22	T	6 04	6 11	p2.7	11 57	...	2.3
23	T	5 39	5 26	2.6	11 48	11 28	p2.8	23	F	6 48	7 05	p2.6	12 24	12 39	2.4
24	W	6 28	6 24	2.6	...	12 33	2.0	24	S	7 29	7 57	2.3	1 20	1 20	p2.3
25	T	7 15	7 21	2.6	12 27	1 17	a2.7	25	S	8 09	8 46	2.1	2 14	1 59	p2.2
26	F	7 59	8 17	a2.5	1 27	2 01	a2.4	26	M	8 47	9 34	a1.9	3 08	2 37	p2.1
27	S	8 41	9 13	a2.3	2 25	2 43	2.2	27	T	9 25	10 23	a1.7	4 02	3 12	p2.0
28	S	9 21	10 09	a2.1	3 23	3 25	p2.1	28	W	10 08	11 11	1.5	4 58	3 49	p1.8
29	M	10 02	11 07	a1.9	4 24	4 07	p2.0	29	T	10 57	11 59	p1.5	5 54	4 31	p1.8
30	T	10 45	11 59	1.5	5 26	4 49	p1.9	30	F	11 50	...	1.4	6 45	5 21	p1.8
31	W	11 32	...	1.6	6 27	5 30	p1.9	31	S	12 44	12 43	a1.6	7 31	6 17	p1.8

The Kts. (knots) columns show the **maximum** predicted velocities of the stronger one of the Flood Currents and the stronger one of the Ebb Currents for each day.

The letter "a" means the velocity shown should occur **after** the **a.m.** Current Change. The letter "p" means the velocity shown should occur **after** the **p.m.** Current Change (even if next morning). No "a" or "p" means a.m. and p.m. velocities are the same for that day.

Avg. Max. Velocity: Flood 2.0 Kts., Ebb 1.9 Kts.

Max. Flood 3 hrs. 10 min. after Flood Starts ±45 min.

Max. Ebb 2 hrs. 45 min. after Ebb Starts ±45 min.

See pp. 22-29 for Current Change at other points.

Note *from NOS: These predictions should be considered questionable. Caution is advised.*

2013 CURRENT TABLE
CHESAPEAKE & DELAWARE CANAL

39°31.89'N, 75°49.65'W at Chesapeake City

Daylight Saving Time   Daylight Saving Time

D A Y O F M O N T H	D A Y O F W E E K	SEPTEMBER CURRENT TURNS TO — EAST Flood Starts a.m.	**p.m.**	Kts.	WEST Ebb Starts a.m.	**p.m.**	Kts.	D A Y O F M O N T H	D A Y O F W E E K	OCTOBER CURRENT TURNS TO — EAST Flood Starts a.m.	**p.m.**	Kts.	WEST Ebb Starts a.m.	**p.m.**	Kts.
1	S	1 28	**1 34**	a1.7	8 12	**7 13**	p1.9	1	T	1 23	**2 01**	a1.9	7 56	**7 55**	p1.9
2	M	2 13	**2 24**	a1.9	8 50	**8 10**	p2.1	2	W	2 11	**2 51**	2.1	8 31	**8 54**	a2.1
3	T	2 58	**3 14**	2.0	9 25	**9 06**	p2.1	3	T	2 59	**3 41**	p2.3	9 06	**9 50**	a2.3
4	W	3 41	**4 00**	2.2	9 58	**9 59**	p2.2	4	F	3 45	**4 27**	p2.4	9 42	**10 43**	a2.5
5	T	4 23	**4 47**	2.3	10 31	**10 50**	2.2	5	S	4 30	**5 13**	p2.5	10 18	**11 35**	a2.6
6	F	5 05	**5 33**	p2.5	11 03	**11 41**	a2.3	6	S	5 15	**6 01**	p2.6	10 56	**...**	2.7
7	S	5 47	**6 19**	p2.5	11 38	**...**	2.5	7	M	6 01	**6 50**	p2.6	12 29	**-A-**	1.8
8	S	6 29	**7 07**	2.5	12 32	**12 15**	p2.5	8	T	6 49	**7 41**	p2.6	1 24	**12 23**	p2.8
9	M	7 13	**7 57**	2.4	1 27	**12 55**	p2.6	9	W	7 40	**8 36**	p2.4	2 20	**1 14**	p2.7
10	T	7 58	**8 50**	2.3	2 23	**1 40**	p2.6	10	T	8 35	**9 35**	p2.3	3 16	**2 11**	p2.6
11	W	8 48	**9 50**	p2.2	3 23	**2 31**	p2.5	11	F	9 36	**10 39**	p2.2	4 14	**3 16**	p2.4
12	T	9 44	**10 59**	p2.1	4 28	**3 29**	p2.4	12	S	10 44	**11 46**	p2.1	5 12	**4 33**	p2.3
13	F	10 51	**...**	2.0	5 35	**4 39**	p2.3	13	S	11 55	**...**	2.0	6 08	**5 54**	p2.1
14	S	12 09	**12 02**	2.0	6 36	**5 57**	p2.3	14	M	12 48	**1 02**	p2.2	6 59	**7 10**	p2.1
15	S	1 15	**1 09**	2.1	7 32	**7 13**	p2.3	15	T	1 46	**2 04**	p2.3	7 48	**8 19**	2.1
16	M	2 15	**2 12**	p2.4	8 23	**8 23**	p2.4	16	W	2 39	**3 04**	p2.5	8 35	**9 22**	a2.3
17	T	3 12	**3 13**	p2.5	9 10	**9 28**	p2.4	17	T	3 29	**4 00**	p2.5	9 19	**10 20**	a2.5
18	W	4 03	**4 10**	p2.6	9 55	**10 27**	2.3	18	F	4 15	**4 51**	p2.5	10 01	**11 14**	a2.5
19	T	4 49	**5 04**	p2.7	10 37	**11 23**	a2.4	19	S	4 58	**5 39**	p2.5	10 40	**11 59**	a2.5
20	F	5 33	**5 56**	p2.6	11 18	**...**	2.5	20	S	5 39	**6 24**	p2.4	11 16	**...**	2.5
21	S	6 15	**6 46**	p2.5	12 17	**12 01**	p2.5	21	M	6 20	**7 04**	p2.3	12 56	**12 01**	p2.4
22	S	6 56	**7 33**	p2.3	1 10	**12 36**	p2.4	22	T	7 01	**7 40**	p2.2	1 43	**12 21**	p2.3
23	M	7 35	**8 15**	p2.1	2 01	**1 11**	p2.3	23	W	7 41	**8 13**	p2.1	2 27	**12 53**	p2.2
24	T	8 14	**8 54**	p1.9	2 50	**1 43**	p2.1	24	T	8 23	**8 46**	p2.0	3 09	**1 30**	p2.1
25	W	8 53	**9 32**	p1.8	3 38	**2 16**	p2.0	25	F	9 07	**9 22**	p2.0	3 50	**2 13**	p2.0
26	T	9 37	**10 12**	p1.7	4 27	**2 53**	p1.9	26	S	9 57	**10 05**	p2.0	4 30	**3 05**	p1.9
27	F	10 27	**10 57**	p1.7	5 15	**3 39**	p1.8	27	S	10 53	**10 54**	p2.0	5 10	**4 07**	p1.8
28	S	11 23	**11 45**	p1.7	6 00	**4 38**	p1.8	28	M	11 50	**11 45**	p2.0	5 49	**5 19**	1.7
29	S	...	**12 18**	1.5	6 42	**5 46**	p1.8	29	T	...	**12 45**	1.7	6 26	**6 31**	a1.8
30	M	12 35	**1 10**	a1.8	7 20	**6 52**	p1.8	30	W	12 36	**1 38**	a2.1	7 03	**7 38**	a2.1
								31	T	1 26	**2 29**	a2.1	7 40	**8 41**	a2.3

A also at 11:38 a.m. 2.8

The Kts. (knots) columns show the **maximum** predicted velocities of the stronger one of the Flood Currents and the stronger one of the Ebb Currents for each day.

The letter "a" means the velocity shown should occur **after** the a.m. Current Change. The letter "p" means the velocity shown should occur **after** the p.m. Current Change (even if next morning). No "a" or "p" means a.m. and p.m. velocities are the same for that day.

Avg. Max. Velocity: Flood 2.0 Kts., Ebb 1.9 Kts.

Max. Flood 3 hrs. 10 min. after Flood Starts ±45 min.

Max. Ebb 2 hrs. 45 min. after Ebb Starts ±45 min.

See pp. 22-29 for Current Change at other points.

   Note *from NOS: These predictions should be considered questionable. Caution is advised.*

CHESAPEAKE & DELAWARE CANAL
39°31.89'N, 75°49.65'W at Chesapeake City

*Standard Time starts Nov. 3 at 2 a.m.   **Standard Time**

		NOVEMBER							DECEMBER				
DAY OF MONTH	**DAY OF WEEK**	CURRENT TURNS TO						**DAY OF MONTH**	**DAY OF WEEK**	CURRENT TURNS TO			
		EAST Flood Starts			WEST Ebb Starts					EAST Flood Starts			WEST Ebb Starts
		a.m.	**p.m.**	Kts.	a.m.	**p.m.**	Kts.			a.m.	**p.m.**	Kts.	a.m.	**p.m.**	Kts.
1	F	2 15	3 20	2.2	8 18	9 40	a2.5	1	S	1 30	2 54	p2.3	7 24	9 25	a2.8
2	S	3 05	4 09	p2.4	8 58	10 35	a2.7	2	M	2 26	3 45	p2.5	8 13	10 19	a2.9
3	S	*2 56	*3 59	p2.5	*8 40	*10 29	a2.8	3	T	3 23	4 37	p2.6	9 04	11 10	a2.9
4	M	3 45	4 47	p2.6	9 24	11 23	a2.9	4	W	4 18	5 29	p2.7	9 58	11 59	a3.0
5	T	4 36	5 38	p2.7	10 11	...	2.9	5	T	5 15	6 21	p2.7	10 55	...	2.9
6	W	5 30	6 31	p2.7	12 17	-A-	1.5	6	F	6 14	7 12	p2.6	12 49	12 01	p2.8
7	T	6 26	7 25	p2.6	1 09	12 01	p2.8	7	S	7 14	8 03	p2.5	1 36	1 02	p2.6
8	F	7 25	8 20	p2.5	2 00	1 03	p2.6	8	S	8 16	8 55	p2.4	2 23	2 10	p2.3
9	S	8 27	9 19	p2.3	2 52	2 12	p2.4	9	M	9 21	9 49	p2.2	3 11	3 23	p2.1
10	S	9 35	10 19	p2.2	3 44	3 29	p2.2	10	T	10 30	10 42	p2.1	4 01	4 38	a2.1
11	M	10 45	11 17	2.1	4 36	4 48	p2.0	11	W	11 36	11 33	p2.0	4 51	5 48	a2.2
12	T	11 51	...	2.1	5 26	6 02	a2.1	12	T	...	12 38	2.0	5 39	6 54	a2.2
13	W	12 11	12 53	p2.3	6 13	7 09	a2.3	13	F	12 23	1 35	p2.0	6 24	7 56	a2.3
14	T	1 02	1 52	p2.3	6 59	8 12	a2.4	14	S	1 11	2 26	p2.1	7 08	8 51	a2.3
15	F	1 50	2 46	p2.3	7 43	9 09	a2.5	15	S	1 58	3 11	p2.1	7 48	9 39	a2.4
16	S	2 37	3 34	p2.3	8 24	10 01	a2.5	16	M	2 44	3 49	p2.1	8 25	10 23	a2.3
17	S	3 20	4 18	p2.3	9 02	10 49	a2.5	17	T	3 28	4 24	p2.1	9 00	11 03	a2.3
18	M	4 03	4 56	p2.3	9 36	11 35	a2.4	18	W	4 10	4 56	p2.2	9 36	11 41	a2.4
19	T	4 44	5 31	p2.2	10 08	...	2.4	19	T	4 53	5 28	p2.3	10 14	...	2.4
20	W	5 26	6 04	p2.2	12 17	-B-	1.3	20	F	5 36	6 02	p2.4	12 15	-E-	1.5
21	T	6 09	6 35	p2.2	12 56	-C-	1.4	21	S	6 21	6 37	p2.4	12 48	-F-	1.6
22	F	6 52	7 09	p2.2	1 32	12 01	p2.3	22	S	7 07	7 14	p2.4	1 19	12 33	p2.2
23	S	7 37	7 45	p2.2	2 07	12 48	p2.1	23	M	7 55	7 54	p2.4	1 50	1 27	p2.0
24	S	8 26	8 26	p2.2	2 41	1 42	p2.0	24	T	8 47	8 36	p2.3	2 23	2 26	a2.0
25	M	9 21	9 11	p2.2	3 16	2 44	1.8	25	W	9 45	9 23	p2.2	3 00	3 35	a2.1
26	T	10 19	10 01	p2.2	3 53	3 55	a1.9	26	T	10 47	10 15	p2.2	3 42	4 50	a2.2
27	W	11 17	10 53	p2.2	4 33	5 10	a2.0	27	F	11 47	11 10	p2.1	4 28	6 03	a2.3
28	T	-D-	12 13	1.8	5 13	6 20	a2.2	28	S	...	12 45	1.9	5 17	7 11	a2.4
29	F	...	1 08	2.0	5 55	7 26	a2.4	29	S	12 07	1 43	2.1	6 07	8 14	a2.6
30	S	12 36	2 01	2.2	6 38	8 29	a2.6	30	M	1 05	2 39	p2.3	7 01	9 09	a2.7
								31	T	2 06	3 33	p2.4	7 58	10 00	a2.9

A also at 11:03 a.m. 2.9 **B** also at 10:40 a.m. 2.4 **C** also at 11:17 a.m. 2.3
D also at 11:45 p.m. 2.2 **E** also at 10:56 a.m. 2.4 **F** also at 11:42 a.m. 2.3

The Kts. (knots) columns show the **maximum** predicted velocities of the stronger one of the Flood Currents and the stronger one of the Ebb Currents for each day.
The letter "a" means the velocity shown should occur **after** the **a.m.** Current Change. The letter "p" means the velocity shown should occur **after** the **p.m.** Current Change (even if next morning). No "a" or "p" means a.m. and p.m. velocities are the same for that day.
Avg. Max. Velocity: Flood 2.0 Kts., Ebb 1.9 Kts.
Max. Flood 3 hrs. 10 min. after Flood Starts ±45 min.
Max. Ebb 2 hrs. 45 min. after Ebb Starts ±45 min.

See pp. 22-29 for Current Change at other points.

Note *from NOS: These predictions should be considered questionable. Caution is advised.*

Upper Chesapeake Bay Currents

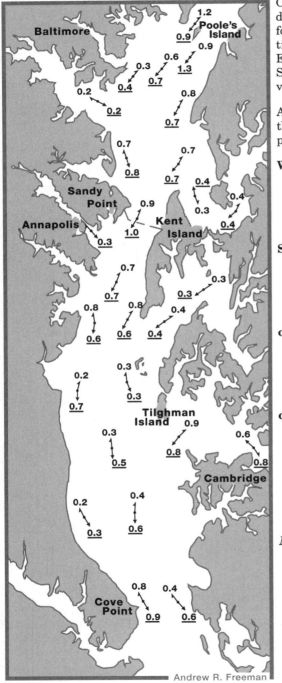

On this Current Diagram, the arrows denote maximum velocities. Refer to the four areas listed below for the specific times. Double-headed arrows are for Ebb and the velocities are <u>underlined</u>. Single-headed arrows are for Flood and velocities and <u>not</u> underlined.

All times below are in hours and relate to the time of **High Water at Baltimore**, pp. 156-159.

West of Pooles Island:
Flood begins 3 1/2 before
Flood max. 1 1/2 before (1.2 kts.)
Ebb begins 2 1/2 after
Ebb max. 4 1/2 after (0.9 kts.)

Sandy Point:
Flood begins 3 1/2 before
Flood max. 1 1/2 before (0.9 kts.)
Ebb begins 1 1/2 after
Ebb max. 4 1/2 after (1.0 kts.)

off Tilghman Island:
Flood begins 5 1/2 before
Flood max. 3 1/2 before (0.3 kts.)
Ebb begins 1/2 after
Ebb max. 3 1/2 after (0.7 kts.)

off Cove Point:
Flood begins 6 1/2 before
Flood max. 4 1/2 before (0.9 kts.)
Ebb begins 1/2 before
Ebb max. 1 1/2 after (0.8 kts.)

Note:
From the beginning of the Flood Current at Cove Point until the Ebb Current begins off Baltimore, a north-bound vessel will have over 8 hours of fair current. A vessel bound southward from Sandy Point can expect only 4 hours of fair current.

154

Relationship of High Water and Ebb Current

Many people wonder why the times of High Water and the start of Ebb Current at the mouths of bays and inlets are not simultaneous. (See p. 6, Why Tides and Currents Often Behave Differently.) The twelve diagrams below show the hourly stages of the Tide in the Ocean and a Bay connected by a narrow Inlet.

Picture the rising Tide, borne by the Flood Current, as a long wave. The wave enters the inlet and the crest reaches its maximum height in or at the inlet. But, the body of water inside the inlet - in the bay - has yet to be filled and the Flood Current continues to pour water through the inlet for a good period after the crest has already passed the inlet. The Ebb Current will not start until the level of the water in the ocean is lower than the water in the bay.

This does not necessarily apply to the mouths of small bays with wide entrances. The narrowness of the inlet and the size of the bay are the controlling factors.

1.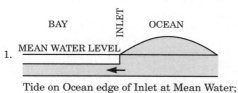

Tide on Ocean edge of Inlet at Mean Water;
Tide rising in Bay; Current Flooding.

7.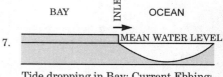

Tide dropping in Bay; Current Ebbing;
Mean Water at Ocean edge of Inlet.

2.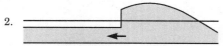

Tide rising in Bay; Current Flooding;
Crest approaching Inlet.

8.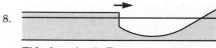

Tide dropping in Bay;
Current Ebbing.

3.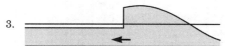

Tide rising in Bay; Current Flooding;
Crest approaching Inlet.

9.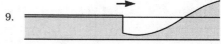

Tide dropping in Bay;
Current Ebbing.

4.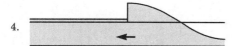

Tide rising in Bay; Current Flooding;
Crest at Inlet (High Water at Inlet).

10.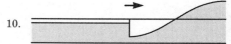

Tide dropping in Bay; Current Ebbing;
Low Water at Ocean edge of Inlet.

5.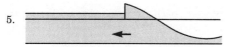

Tide rising in Bay; Current Flooding;
Crest has passed Inlet.

11.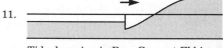

Tide dropping in Bay; Current Ebbing;
Tide rising at Ocean edge of Inlet.

6.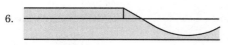

High Water in Bay;
Ebb Current about to start.

12.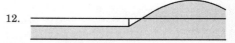

Low Water in Bay;
Flood Current about to start.

2013 HIGH WATER
BALTIMORE, MD
At Ft. McHenry 39°16'N, 76°34.7'W

Standard Time   Standard Time   *Daylight Time starts
March 10 at 2 a.m.

D A Y O F M O N T H	D A Y O F W E E K	JANUARY a.m.	Ht.	p.m.	Ht.	D A Y O F W E E K	FEBRUARY a.m.	Ht.	p.m.	Ht.	D A Y O F W E E K	MARCH a.m.	Ht.	p.m.	Ht.	D A Y O F M O N T H
1	T	8 57	0.7	9 19	1.1	F	10 07	1.0	10 21	0.9	F	8 53	1.3	9 16	1.0	1
2	W	9 43	0.8	10 00	1.1	S	11 01	1.1	11 11	0.8	S	9 43	1.3	10 04	0.9	2
3	T	10 35	0.8	10 46	1.0	S	...	...	12 01	1.1	S	10 39	1.3	10 59	0.9	3
4	F	11 28	0.9	11 34	0.9	M	12 07	0.7	1 03	1.1	M	11 38	1.3	11 56	0.9	4
5	S	...	...	12 27	1.0	T	1 07	0.7	2 09	1.2	T	...	...	12 43	1.3	5
6	S	12 27	0.8	1 28	1.1	W	2 11	0.7	3 15	1.2	W	12 59	0.9	1 52	1.3	6
7	M	1 25	0.7	2 30	1.2	T	3 14	0.7	4 18	1.2	T	2 03	0.9	3 00	1.3	7
8	T	2 25	0.7	3 31	1.3	F	4 14	0.8	5 16	1.3	F	3 06	1.0	4 03	1.3	8
9	W	3 27	0.7	4 31	1.3	S	5 12	0.9	6 08	1.2	S	4 05	1.1	4 59	1.3	9
10	T	4 27	0.7	5 28	1.4	S	6 06	0.9	6 56	1.2	S	*6 00	1.2	*6 48	1.2	10
11	F	5 25	0.7	6 22	1.4	M	6 58	1.0	7 41	1.2	M	6 52	1.2	7 33	1.2	11
12	S	6 21	0.8	7 14	1.3	T	7 49	1.0	8 23	1.1	T	7 41	1.3	8 14	1.2	12
13	S	7 15	0.8	8 03	1.3	W	8 39	1.1	9 04	1.0	W	8 27	1.3	8 54	1.1	13
14	M	8 09	0.9	8 50	1.2	T	9 29	1.1	9 46	0.9	T	9 12	1.4	9 34	1.0	14
15	T	9 04	0.9	9 35	1.1	F	10 20	1.0	10 28	0.8	F	9 57	1.3	10 14	1.0	15
16	W	9 59	0.9	10 20	1.0	S	11 12	1.0	11 14	0.8	S	10 41	1.3	10 57	0.9	16
17	T	10 57	0.9	11 05	0.9	S	...	...	12 08	1.0	S	11 27	1.3	11 42	0.9	17
18	F	11 56	0.9	11 51	0.8	M	12 03	0.7	1 07	1.0	M	...	...	12 16	1.2	18
19	S	...	...	12 57	0.9	T	12 57	0.7	2 07	1.0	T	12 32	0.9	1 09	1.1	19
20	S	12 41	0.7	1 59	0.9	W	1 53	0.7	3 05	1.0	W	1 26	0.9	2 07	1.1	20
21	M	1 33	0.6	2 58	1.0	T	2 50	0.7	3 57	1.0	T	2 22	0.9	3 05	1.1	21
22	T	2 27	0.6	3 52	1.0	F	3 43	0.8	4 42	1.0	F	3 19	1.0	4 01	1.1	22
23	W	3 20	0.6	4 39	1.0	S	4 32	0.8	5 22	1.1	S	4 12	1.1	4 50	1.1	23
24	T	4 12	0.6	5 21	1.0	S	5 17	0.9	5 59	1.1	S	5 01	1.1	5 35	1.2	24
25	F	5 00	0.6	5 58	1.1	M	5 59	0.9	6 35	1.1	M	5 47	1.2	6 18	1.2	25
26	S	5 44	0.7	6 32	1.1	T	6 41	1.0	7 12	1.1	T	6 31	1.3	6 59	1.2	26
27	S	6 26	0.7	7 06	1.1	W	7 23	1.1	7 50	1.1	W	7 14	1.5	7 41	1.2	27
28	M	7 07	0.7	7 40	1.1	T	8 07	1.2	8 31	1.0	T	7 58	1.6	8 25	1.1	28
29	T	7 48	0.8	8 16	1.1						F	8 44	1.6	9 10	1.1	29
30	W	8 31	0.8	8 55	1.0						S	9 32	1.7	9 59	1.1	30
31	T	9 18	0.9	9 36	1.0						S	10 23	1.7	10 52	1.1	31

Dates when Ht. of **Low** Water is below Mean Low with Ht. of lowest given for each period and Date of lowest in ( ):

1st: -0.2'   1st - 18th: -0.5' (7th - 10th)   1st - 12th: -0.2'
3rd - 31st: -0.6' (10th - 12th)   22nd - 27th: -0.2'

Average Rise and Fall 1.1 ft.

When a high tide exceeds avg. ht., the *following* low tide will be lower than avg.

2013 HIGH WATER
BALTIMORE, MD
At Ft. McHenry 39°16'N, 76°34.7'W

Daylight Saving Time   Daylight Saving Time   Daylight Saving Time

DAY OF MONTH	DAY OF WEEK	APRIL a.m.	Ht.	p.m.	Ht.	DAY OF WEEK	MAY a.m.	Ht.	p.m.	Ht.	DAY OF WEEK	JUNE a.m.	Ht.	p.m.	Ht.	DAY OF MONTH
1	M	11 19	1.6	11 49	1.1	W	...	...	12 02	1.7	S	1 33	1.6	1 36	1.5	1
2	T	...	...	12 19	1.5	T	12 42	1.3	1 04	1.6	S	2 35	1.7	2 33	1.4	2
3	W	12 51	1.1	1 25	1.5	F	1 47	1.4	2 09	1.5	M	3 36	1.8	3 29	1.3	3
4	T	1 54	1.2	2 33	1.4	S	2 49	1.5	3 09	1.4	T	4 31	1.8	4 21	1.2	4
5	F	2 58	1.2	3 39	1.3	S	3 50	1.6	4 07	1.3	W	5 20	1.9	5 12	1.2	5
6	S	3 59	1.3	4 40	1.3	M	4 46	1.7	4 59	1.3	T	6 05	1.9	6 01	1.1	6
7	S	4 56	1.4	5 33	1.3	T	5 37	1.8	5 47	1.2	F	6 45	1.9	6 47	1.1	7
8	M	5 49	1.5	6 20	1.3	W	6 23	1.8	6 32	1.2	S	7 23	1.9	7 32	1.2	8
9	T	6 38	1.6	7 04	1.2	T	7 05	1.9	7 15	1.2	S	7 58	1.9	8 16	1.2	9
10	W	7 23	1.6	7 45	1.2	F	7 44	1.9	7 57	1.2	M	8 32	1.8	8 58	1.2	10
11	T	8 05	1.7	8 25	1.1	S	8 21	1.8	8 39	1.2	T	9 07	1.8	9 41	1.3	11
12	F	8 46	1.6	9 05	1.1	S	8 57	1.8	9 22	1.2	W	9 42	1.8	10 25	1.3	12
13	S	9 25	1.6	9 46	1.1	M	9 33	1.7	10 05	1.2	T	10 20	1.7	11 10	1.3	13
14	S	10 05	1.6	10 30	1.1	T	10 11	1.7	10 51	1.2	F	11 00	1.6	11 57	1.4	14
15	M	10 46	1.5	11 16	1.1	W	10 51	1.6	11 38	1.3	S	11 43	1.6	...	...	15
16	T	11 30	1.4	...	...	T	11 35	1.6	...	...	S	12 47	1.5	12 30	1.5	16
17	W	12 05	1.1	12 17	1.4	F	12 28	1.3	12 22	1.5	M	1 39	1.6	1 22	1.4	17
18	T	12 57	1.1	1 09	1.3	S	1 20	1.4	1 12	1.4	T	2 32	1.7	2 18	1.3	18
19	F	1 52	1.2	2 04	1.3	S	2 13	1.5	2 05	1.4	W	3 26	1.9	3 17	1.2	19
20	S	2 46	1.3	3 00	1.3	M	3 05	1.6	3 00	1.3	T	4 19	2.0	4 19	1.2	20
21	S	3 39	1.4	3 53	1.3	T	3 56	1.7	3 56	1.3	F	5 13	2.1	5 19	1.2	21
22	M	4 29	1.5	4 44	1.2	W	4 47	1.9	4 52	1.2	S	6 06	2.2	6 19	1.2	22
23	T	5 16	1.6	5 33	1.2	T	5 36	2.0	5 47	1.2	S	6 59	2.2	7 17	1.3	23
24	W	6 03	1.7	6 22	1.2	F	6 25	2.1	6 42	1.2	M	7 52	2.2	8 15	1.4	24
25	T	6 49	1.8	7 10	1.2	S	7 15	2.1	7 37	1.2	T	8 44	2.1	9 12	1.4	25
26	F	7 35	1.9	8 00	1.2	S	8 06	2.1	8 33	1.3	W	9 35	2.0	10 10	1.5	26
27	S	8 23	2.0	8 51	1.2	M	8 58	2.1	9 29	1.3	T	10 26	1.9	11 09	1.6	27
28	S	9 14	2.0	9 45	1.2	T	9 51	2.0	10 27	1.4	F	11 17	1.7	...	...	28
29	M	10 06	1.9	10 41	1.2	W	10 46	1.9	11 27	1.5	S	12 10	1.6	12 08	1.6	29
30	T	11 02	1.8	11 40	1.3	T	11 42	1.7	...	...	S	1 11	1.7	12 59	1.4	30
31						F	12 29	1.5	12 39	1.6						31

Dates when Ht. of **Low** Water is below Mean Low with Ht. of lowest given for each period and Date of lowest in ( ):

Average Rise and Fall 1.1 ft.

When a high tide exceeds avg. ht., the *following* low tide will be lower than avg.

2013 HIGH WATER
BALTIMORE, MD
At Ft. McHenry 39°16'N, 76°34.7'W

Daylight Saving Time   Daylight Saving Time   Daylight Saving Time

DAY OF MONTH	DAY OF WEEK	JULY a.m.	Ht.	p.m.	Ht.	DAY OF WEEK	AUGUST a.m.	Ht.	p.m.	Ht.	DAY OF WEEK	SEPTEMBER a.m.	Ht.	p.m.	Ht.	DAY OF MONTH
1	M	2 13	1.8	1 53	1.3	T	3 37	1.8	3 09	1.2	S	4 37	1.8	4 35	1.3	1
2	T	3 13	1.8	2 48	1.2	F	4 29	1.8	4 08	1.2	M	5 19	1.8	5 27	1.4	2
3	W	4 09	1.9	3 45	1.2	S	5 17	1.8	5 05	1.2	T	5 59	1.8	6 15	1.4	3
4	T	4 59	1.9	4 39	1.1	S	5 57	1.8	5 55	1.3	W	6 33	1.8	6 57	1.5	4
5	F	5 43	1.9	5 31	1.1	M	6 34	1.8	6 42	1.3	T	7 07	1.7	7 37	1.6	5
6	S	6 24	1.9	6 21	1.2	T	7 08	1.8	7 25	1.4	F	7 42	1.7	8 17	1.7	6
7	S	7 01	1.9	7 07	1.2	W	7 41	1.8	8 06	1.4	S	8 18	1.7	8 57	1.8	7
8	M	7 35	1.9	7 51	1.2	T	8 13	1.8	8 46	1.5	S	8 57	1.6	9 40	1.9	8
9	T	8 09	1.8	8 34	1.3	F	8 47	1.8	9 27	1.6	M	9 39	1.5	10 26	1.9	9
10	W	8 41	1.8	9 15	1.3	S	9 23	1.7	10 09	1.6	T	10 26	1.4	11 17	2.0	10
11	T	9 15	1.8	9 57	1.4	S	10 02	1.6	10 54	1.7	W	11 18	1.4	...	...	11
12	F	9 51	1.7	10 40	1.5	M	10 45	1.5	11 43	1.8	T	12 12	2.0	12 16	1.3	12
13	S	10 29	1.7	11 25	1.5	T	11 34	1.4	...	...	F	1 12	2.0	1 20	1.3	13
14	S	11 11	1.6	...	...	W	12 36	1.9	12 28	1.3	S	2 16	2.0	2 28	1.3	14
15	M	12 14	1.6	12 01	1.5	T	1 34	2.0	1 30	1.3	S	3 21	1.9	3 35	1.4	15
16	T	1 06	1.8	12 50	1.4	F	2 35	2.0	2 36	1.3	M	4 22	1.9	4 38	1.5	16
17	W	2 01	1.9	1 48	1.3	S	3 37	2.0	3 42	1.3	T	5 18	1.9	5 37	1.6	17
18	T	2 58	2.0	2 51	1.2	S	4 38	2.0	4 47	1.4	W	6 08	1.8	6 33	1.7	18
19	F	3 56	2.0	3 56	1.2	M	5 36	2.0	5 48	1.5	T	6 54	1.8	7 25	1.8	19
20	S	4 54	2.1	5 00	1.2	T	6 29	2.0	6 45	1.6	F	7 38	1.7	8 14	1.9	20
21	S	5 50	2.1	6 01	1.3	W	7 18	2.0	7 40	1.7	S	8 20	1.6	9 02	1.9	21
22	M	6 45	2.1	7 00	1.4	T	8 04	1.9	8 34	1.8	S	9 02	1.5	9 49	1.9	22
23	T	7 37	2.1	7 57	1.5	F	8 48	1.8	9 26	1.8	M	9 44	1.4	10 36	1.9	23
24	W	8 26	2.0	8 53	1.6	S	9 32	1.7	10 18	1.8	T	10 28	1.4	11 24	1.8	24
25	S	9 14	1.9	9 49	1.7	S	10 15	1.6	11 11	1.8	W	11 16	1.3	...	...	25
26	F	10 01	1.8	10 46	1.7	M	11 00	1.5	11 59	1.8	T	12 14	1.8	12 08	1.3	26
27	S	10 47	1.7	11 43	1.7	T	11 47	1.4	...	...	F	1 07	1.7	1 05	1.2	27
28	S	11 34	1.5	...	...	W	1 00	1.8	12 39	1.3	S	2 01	1.7	2 06	1.2	28
29	M	12 42	1.8	12 22	1.4	T	1 57	1.8	1 37	1.2	S	2 55	1.6	3 07	1.3	29
30	T	1 41	1.8	1 14	1.3	F	2 54	1.8	2 37	1.2	M	3 45	1.6	4 04	1.3	30
31	W	2 40	1.8	2 10	1.2	S	3 48	1.8	3 38	1.3						31

Dates when Ht. of **Low** Water is below Mean Low with Ht. of lowest given for each period and Date of lowest in ( ):

Average Rise and Fall 1.1 ft.

When a high tide exceeds avg. ht., the *following* low tide will be lower than avg.

2013 HIGH WATER
BALTIMORE, MD
At Ft. McHenry 39°16'N, 76°34.7'W

Daylight Saving Time   *Standard Time starts
Nov. 3 at 2 a.m.   Standard Time

DAY OF MONTH	DAY OF WEEK	OCTOBER				DAY OF WEEK	NOVEMBER				DAY OF WEEK	DECEMBER				DAY OF MONTH
		a.m.	Ht.	p.m.	Ht.		a.m.	Ht.	p.m.	Ht.		a.m.	Ht.	p.m.	Ht.	
1	T	4 30	1.6	4 56	1.4	F	5 05	1.3	5 54	1.6	S	4 15	0.9	5 10	1.6	1
2	W	5 11	1.6	5 43	1.5	S	5 50	1.3	6 37	1.7	M	5 07	0.9	5 59	1.6	2
3	T	5 51	1.6	6 27	1.6	S	*5 37	1.2	*6 23	1.8	T	6 01	0.9	6 50	1.7	3
4	F	6 29	1.6	7 07	1.7	M	6 23	1.2	7 07	1.9	W	6 53	0.9	7 40	1.7	4
5	S	7 08	1.5	7 48	1.8	T	7 12	1.1	7 55	1.9	T	7 48	0.9	8 32	1.6	5
6	S	7 50	1.5	8 30	1.9	W	8 04	1.1	8 46	1.9	F	8 45	0.9	9 25	1.5	6
7	M	8 33	1.4	9 15	2.0	T	8 58	1.1	9 40	1.8	S	9 44	1.0	10 20	1.4	7
8	T	9 20	1.4	10 04	2.0	F	9 57	1.1	10 37	1.7	S	10 46	1.0	11 14	1.3	8
9	W	10 11	1.3	10 56	2.0	S	11 00	1.1	11 37	1.6	M	11 52	1.0	...	...	9
10	T	11 07	1.3	11 53	1.9	S	...	...	12 06	1.2	T	12 10	1.2	12 59	1.1	10
11	F	...	...	12 09	1.3	M	12 37	1.5	1 14	1.3	W	1 05	1.1	2 05	1.2	11
12	S	12 55	1.9	1 14	1.3	T	1 36	1.4	2 20	1.3	T	1 59	0.9	3 08	1.2	12
13	S	1 59	1.8	2 22	1.4	W	2 32	1.3	3 22	1.4	F	2 52	0.9	4 04	1.3	13
14	M	3 01	1.7	3 28	1.4	T	3 24	1.2	4 18	1.5	S	3 43	0.8	4 55	1.3	14
15	T	4 00	1.7	4 31	1.6	F	4 13	1.2	5 09	1.6	S	4 32	0.8	5 40	1.4	15
16	W	4 53	1.6	5 28	1.7	S	4 59	1.1	5 55	1.6	M	5 19	0.7	6 21	1.3	16
17	T	5 42	1.6	6 21	1.7	S	5 43	1.0	6 37	1.6	T	6 03	0.7	6 59	1.3	17
18	F	6 27	1.5	7 10	1.8	M	6 26	1.0	7 17	1.6	W	6 46	0.7	7 35	1.3	18
19	S	7 10	1.4	7 55	1.8	T	7 08	1.0	7 56	1.6	T	7 28	0.7	8 10	1.2	19
20	S	7 52	1.3	8 39	1.8	W	7 51	0.9	8 34	1.5	F	8 10	0.7	8 44	1.2	20
21	M	8 34	1.3	9 21	1.8	T	8 34	0.9	9 13	1.5	S	8 53	0.7	9 20	1.2	21
22	T	9 16	1.2	10 03	1.8	F	9 20	0.9	9 53	1.4	S	9 38	0.8	9 57	1.1	22
23	W	10 00	1.2	10 46	1.7	S	10 08	0.9	10 34	1.3	M	10 26	0.8	10 36	1.1	23
24	T	10 47	1.1	11 30	1.6	S	11 00	0.9	11 17	1.3	T	11 16	0.8	11 18	1.0	24
25	F	11 38	1.1	...	...	M	11 55	1.0	...	...	W	...	...	12 10	0.9	25
26	S	12 17	1.6	12 33	1.1	T	12 03	1.2	12 52	1.0	T	12 05	0.9	1 05	1.0	26
27	S	1 07	1.5	1 32	1.1	W	12 50	1.1	1 48	1.1	F	12 56	0.8	2 01	1.1	27
28	M	1 57	1.5	2 31	1.2	T	1 40	1.1	2 41	1.2	S	1 51	0.7	2 57	1.2	28
29	T	2 46	1.4	3 28	1.3	F	2 31	1.0	3 32	1.3	S	2 49	0.7	3 53	1.3	29
30	W	3 33	1.4	4 21	1.4	S	3 23	1.0	4 22	1.5	M	3 47	0.7	4 47	1.4	30
31	T	4 20	1.4	5 09	1.5						T	4 44	0.7	5 41	1.4	31

Dates when Ht. of **Low** Water is below Mean Low with Ht. of lowest given for each period and Date of lowest in (   ):

1st - 6th: -0.3' (3rd - 5th)
11th - 20th: -0.3' (14th - 17th)
25th - 31st: -0.5' (30th - 31st)

Average Rise and Fall 1.1 ft.

When a high tide exceeds avg. ht., the *following* low tide will be lower than avg.

2013 HIGH WATER
MIAMI HARBOR ENTRANCE, FL
25°45.8'N, 80°07.8'W

DAY OF MONTH	DAY OF WEEK	JANUARY a.m.	Ht.	p.m.	Ht.	DAY OF WEEK	FEBRUARY a.m.	Ht.	p.m.	Ht.	DAY OF WEEK	MARCH a.m.	Ht.	p.m.	Ht.	DAY OF MONTH
1	T	11 01	2.3	11 19	2.2	F	11 58	2.2	...	...	F	10 53	2.4	11 29	2.4	1
2	W	11 41	2.3	...	...	S	12 37	2.1	12 46	2.1	S	11 39	2.3	...	...	2
3	T	12 07	2.1	12 25	2.2	S	1 37	2.1	1 44	2.0	S	12 22	2.3	12 31	2.2	3
4	F	12 59	2.1	1 12	2.2	M	2 41	2.1	2 50	2.0	M	1 19	2.2	1 30	2.1	4
5	S	1 58	2.1	2 08	2.1	T	3 50	2.1	4 01	2.1	T	2 24	2.2	2 38	2.1	5
6	S	3 03	2.2	3 10	2.1	W	4 58	2.2	5 09	2.2	W	3 33	2.2	3 50	2.1	6
7	M	4 10	2.3	4 17	2.2	T	5 59	2.4	6 12	2.3	T	4 40	2.3	4 59	2.2	7
8	T	5 14	2.4	5 22	2.3	F	6 54	2.5	7 09	2.5	F	5 41	2.4	6 01	2.4	8
9	W	6 14	2.6	6 23	2.4	S	7 44	2.6	8 01	2.6	S	6 35	2.5	6 56	2.5	9
10	T	7 09	2.7	7 20	2.6	S	8 31	2.7	8 50	2.6	S	*8 23	2.6	*8 46	2.6	10
11	F	8 01	2.8	8 14	2.7	M	9 15	2.6	9 37	2.6	M	9 08	2.6	9 32	2.7	11
12	S	8 50	2.8	9 06	2.7	T	9 58	2.6	10 22	2.5	T	9 50	2.6	10 15	2.6	12
13	S	9 38	2.8	9 56	2.6	W	10 39	2.4	11 06	2.4	W	10 30	2.5	10 56	2.6	13
14	M	10 24	2.7	10 46	2.6	T	11 20	2.3	11 50	2.2	T	11 08	2.4	11 36	2.5	14
15	T	11 09	2.6	11 35	2.4	F	...	...	12 01	2.1	F	11 46	2.3	...	...	15
16	W	11 55	2.4	...	...	S	12 36	2.0	12 43	2.0	S	12 16	2.3	12 24	2.2	16
17	T	12 26	2.2	12 41	2.2	S	1 25	1.9	1 31	1.8	S	12 58	2.2	1 04	2.0	17
18	F	1 17	2.1	1 29	2.0	M	2 20	1.8	2 25	1.7	M	1 43	2.0	1 49	1.9	18
19	S	2 12	1.9	2 20	1.9	T	3 20	1.7	3 26	1.7	T	2 33	1.9	2 41	1.8	19
20	S	3 11	1.9	3 15	1.8	W	4 21	1.8	4 29	1.7	W	3 30	1.9	3 42	1.8	20
21	M	4 10	1.8	4 12	1.8	T	5 18	1.9	5 27	1.8	T	4 32	1.9	4 47	1.8	21
22	T	5 06	1.9	5 08	1.8	F	6 08	2.0	6 18	2.0	F	5 31	1.9	5 50	1.9	22
23	W	5 57	2.0	6 00	1.9	S	6 52	2.1	7 05	2.1	S	6 25	2.1	6 45	2.1	23
24	T	6 42	2.1	6 47	2.0	S	7 34	2.2	7 49	2.2	S	7 13	2.2	7 35	2.3	24
25	F	7 24	2.2	7 31	2.1	M	8 14	2.3	8 31	2.4	M	7 58	2.3	8 22	2.4	25
26	S	8 04	2.3	8 13	2.1	T	8 52	2.4	9 14	2.4	T	8 41	2.4	9 07	2.6	26
27	S	8 43	2.3	8 54	2.2	W	9 31	2.4	9 56	2.5	W	9 23	2.5	9 52	2.7	27
28	M	9 20	2.3	9 35	2.2	T	10 11	2.4	10 41	2.5	T	10 05	2.6	10 37	2.7	28
29	T	9 58	2.3	10 16	2.2						F	10 49	2.6	11 24	2.7	29
30	W	10 36	2.3	10 59	2.2						S	11 35	2.6	...	...	30
31	T	11 15	2.2	11 46	2.2						S	12 14	2.7	12 24	2.5	31

Dates when Ht. of **Low** Water is below Mean Low with Ht. of lowest given for each period and Date of lowest in ( ):

6th - 17th: -0.8' (11th - 12th)   1st - 15th: -0.7' (9th - 11th)   1st - 15th: -0.5' (1st, 11th - 13th)
25th - 31st: -0.3' (26th - 31st)   24th - 28th: -0.3' (25th - 28th)   26th - 31st: -0.5' (28th - 30th)

Average Rise and Fall 2.5 ft.

When a high tide exceeds avg. ht., the *following* low tide will be lower than avg.

2013 HIGH WATER
MIAMI HARBOR ENTRANCE, FL
25°45.8'N, 80°07.8'W

		Daylight Saving Time					Daylight Saving Time					Daylight Saving Time				
DAY OF MONTH	DAY OF WEEK	APRIL				DAY OF WEEK	MAY				DAY OF WEEK	JUNE				DAY OF MONTH
		a.m.	Ht.	p.m.	Ht.		a.m.	Ht.	p.m.	Ht.		a.m.	Ht.	p.m.	Ht.	
1	M	1 07	2.6	1 19	2.4	W	1 49	2.6	2 11	2.4	S	3 22	2.4	4 00	2.3	1
2	T	2 05	2.5	2 21	2.3	T	2 49	2.5	3 16	2.4	S	4 19	2.3	5 02	2.3	2
3	W	3 09	2.4	3 30	2.3	F	3 51	2.4	4 24	2.4	M	5 17	2.3	6 01	2.3	3
4	T	4 14	2.3	4 39	2.3	S	4 51	2.4	5 28	2.4	T	6 09	2.2	6 53	2.3	4
5	F	5 19	2.4	5 47	2.4	S	5 49	2.4	6 27	2.5	W	6 58	2.2	7 40	2.4	5
6	S	6 18	2.4	6 47	2.5	M	6 42	2.4	7 19	2.5	T	7 44	2.2	8 23	2.4	6
7	S	7 11	2.5	7 40	2.6	T	7 30	2.4	8 05	2.6	F	8 26	2.2	9 03	2.4	7
8	M	7 59	2.5	8 27	2.7	W	8 14	2.4	8 48	2.6	S	9 06	2.2	9 42	2.4	8
9	T	8 42	2.6	9 11	2.7	T	8 54	2.4	9 27	2.6	S	9 46	2.2	10 20	2.4	9
10	W	9 23	2.5	9 51	2.7	F	9 33	2.4	10 06	2.5	M	10 25	2.2	10 57	2.4	10
11	T	10 01	2.5	10 30	2.6	S	10 10	2.3	10 43	2.5	T	11 05	2.2	11 35	2.3	11
12	F	10 38	2.4	11 08	2.5	S	10 48	2.3	11 21	2.4	W	11 45	2.1	...	...	12
13	S	11 15	2.3	11 47	2.4	M	11 27	2.2	...	...	T	12 14	2.3	12 27	2.1	13
14	S	11 52	2.2	...	...	T	12 01	2.3	12 07	2.1	F	12 53	2.2	1 12	2.1	14
15	M	12 26	2.3	12 32	2.1	W	12 40	2.3	12 50	2.1	S	1 35	2.2	2 02	2.0	15
16	T	1 08	2.2	1 16	2.0	T	1 23	2.2	1 38	2.0	S	2 20	2.1	2 56	2.1	16
17	W	1 55	2.1	2 07	2.0	F	2 09	2.1	2 31	2.0	M	3 09	2.1	3 56	2.1	17
18	T	2 46	2.0	3 04	1.9	S	2 58	2.1	3 29	2.0	T	4 05	2.1	4 58	2.2	18
19	F	3 42	2.0	4 07	2.0	S	3 52	2.1	4 30	2.1	W	5 05	2.2	6 00	2.4	19
20	S	4 40	2.0	5 10	2.1	M	4 47	2.1	5 31	2.2	T	6 06	2.3	7 00	2.5	20
21	S	5 36	2.1	6 08	2.2	T	5 44	2.2	6 29	2.4	F	7 06	2.4	7 57	2.7	21
22	M	6 29	2.2	7 02	2.4	W	6 39	2.3	7 25	2.6	S	8 05	2.5	8 51	2.8	22
23	T	7 18	2.4	7 53	2.6	T	7 33	2.5	8 18	2.8	S	9 01	2.7	9 43	2.9	23
24	W	8 06	2.5	8 42	2.8	F	8 26	2.6	9 10	2.9	M	9 56	2.7	10 34	2.9	24
25	T	8 53	2.6	9 30	2.9	S	9 19	2.7	10 01	2.9	T	10 50	2.7	11 24	2.9	25
26	F	9 40	2.7	10 19	2.9	S	10 11	2.7	10 52	2.9	W	11 44	2.7	...	...	26
27	S	10 29	2.7	11 08	2.9	M	11 05	2.7	11 43	2.9	T	12 14	2.8	12 39	2.6	27
28	S	11 19	2.7	11 59	2.8	T	...	...	12 01	2.7	F	1 05	2.7	1 34	2.5	28
29	M	...	...	12 13	2.6	W	12 36	2.8	12 57	2.6	S	1 56	2.5	2 31	2.4	29
30	T	12 53	2.7	1 10	2.5	T	1 30	2.7	1 56	2.5	S	2 48	2.3	3 30	2.3	30
31						F	2 25	2.5	2 57	2.4						31

Dates when Ht. of **Low** Water is below Mean Low with Ht. of lowest given for each period and Date of lowest in ( ):

1st: -0.3'	7th - 10th: -0.2'	6th - 8th: -0.2'
7th - 12th: -0.3' (8th - 11th)	22nd - 29th: -0.7' (25th - 26th)	19th - 29th: -0.7' (22nd - 24th)
23rd - 30th: -0.6' (26th - 27th)		

Average Rise and Fall 2.5 ft.

When a high tide exceeds avg. ht., the *following* low tide will be lower than avg.

161

2013 HIGH WATER
MIAMI HARBOR ENTRANCE, FL
25°45.8'N, 80°07.8'W

		Daylight Saving Time JULY					Daylight Saving Time AUGUST					Daylight Saving Time SEPTEMBER				
DAY OF MONTH	DAY OF WEEK	a.m.	Ht.	p.m.	Ht.	DAY OF WEEK	a.m.	Ht.	p.m.	Ht.	DAY OF WEEK	a.m.	Ht.	p.m.	Ht.	DAY OF MONTH
1	M	3 43	2.2	4 30	2.2	T	4 54	2.1	5 46	2.2	S	6 10	2.3	6 48	2.5	1
2	T	4 38	2.1	5 28	2.2	F	5 50	2.1	6 38	2.2	M	7 00	2.5	7 32	2.6	2
3	W	5 33	2.1	6 23	2.2	S	6 43	2.1	7 26	2.3	T	7 48	2.6	8 15	2.7	3
4	T	6 24	2.1	7 11	2.2	S	7 30	2.2	8 07	2.4	W	8 30	2.7	8 53	2.8	4
5	F	7 13	2.1	7 56	2.3	M	8 15	2.3	8 47	2.5	T	9 12	2.8	9 32	2.8	5
6	S	7 58	2.1	8 37	2.3	T	8 57	2.4	9 26	2.5	F	9 53	2.9	10 10	2.9	6
7	S	8 41	2.2	9 16	2.4	W	9 38	2.5	10 04	2.6	S	10 35	2.9	10 49	2.8	7
8	M	9 22	2.2	9 55	2.4	T	10 19	2.5	10 41	2.6	S	11 18	2.9	11 29	2.8	8
9	T	10 02	2.2	10 32	2.4	F	10 59	2.5	11 18	2.6	M	...	...	12 04	2.9	9
10	W	10 42	2.2	11 09	2.4	S	11 41	2.5	11 56	2.5	T	12 13	2.8	12 54	2.8	10
11	T	11 23	2.2	11 47	2.4	S	...	...	12 25	2.5	W	1 02	2.7	1 50	2.8	11
12	F	...	...	12 04	2.2	M	12 36	2.5	1 13	2.5	T	1 59	2.6	2 51	2.7	12
13	S	12 24	2.3	12 48	2.2	T	1 21	2.4	2 06	2.4	F	3 04	2.6	3 57	2.7	13
14	S	1 04	2.3	1 35	2.2	W	2 13	2.4	3 07	2.4	S	4 14	2.7	5 03	2.8	14
15	M	1 47	2.2	2 28	2.2	T	3 14	2.4	4 13	2.5	S	5 23	2.8	6 05	2.9	15
16	T	2 36	2.2	3 28	2.2	F	4 22	2.4	5 20	2.6	M	6 27	2.9	7 01	3.0	16
17	W	3 33	2.2	4 32	2.3	S	5 31	2.5	6 23	2.7	T	7 25	3.1	7 52	3.1	17
18	T	4 37	2.2	5 37	2.4	S	6 37	2.7	7 20	2.8	W	8 17	3.2	8 40	3.2	18
19	F	5 44	2.3	6 40	2.5	M	7 37	2.8	8 13	3.0	T	9 06	3.3	9 24	3.2	19
20	S	6 48	2.5	7 38	2.7	T	8 32	3.0	9 03	3.1	F	9 52	3.3	10 07	3.2	20
21	S	7 49	2.6	8 33	2.8	W	9 24	3.1	9 50	3.1	S	10 37	3.2	10 49	3.1	21
22	M	8 46	2.8	9 24	2.9	T	10 14	3.1	10 35	3.1	S	11 20	3.1	11 30	2.9	22
23	T	9 41	2.8	10 13	3.0	F	11 02	3.0	11 20	3.0	M	...	...	12 03	3.0	23
24	W	10 33	2.9	11 01	2.9	S	11 49	2.9	...	...	T	12 12	2.8	12 47	2.8	24
25	T	11 25	2.8	11 49	2.8	S	12 03	2.8	12 36	2.8	W	12 55	2.6	1 34	2.6	25
26	F	...	...	12 16	2.7	M	12 48	2.7	1 24	2.6	T	1 43	2.5	2 25	2.5	26
27	S	12 36	2.7	1 07	2.6	T	1 33	2.5	2 14	2.5	F	2 36	2.4	3 20	2.5	27
28	S	1 23	2.5	1 59	2.4	W	2 22	2.4	3 08	2.3	S	3 35	2.4	4 18	2.5	28
29	M	2 12	2.4	2 54	2.3	T	3 16	2.3	4 06	2.3	S	4 36	2.4	5 14	2.5	29
30	T	3 03	2.2	3 51	2.2	F	4 14	2.2	5 05	2.3	M	5 35	2.5	6 06	2.6	30
31	W	3 57	2.1	4 50	2.1	S	5 14	2.3	5 59	2.4						31

Dates when Ht. of **Low** Water is below Mean Low with Ht. of lowest given for each period and Date of lowest in ( ):

18th - 27th: -0.6' (21st - 23rd)   18th - 23rd: -0.3' (19th - 21st)

Average Rise and Fall 2.5 ft.

When a high tide exceeds avg. ht., the *following* low tide will be lower than avg.

2013 HIGH WATER
MIAMI HARBOR ENTRANCE, FL
25°45.8'N, 80°07.8'W

| Daylight Saving Time | *Standard Time starts Nov. 3 at 2 a.m. | Standard Time |

DAY OF MONTH	DAY OF WEEK	OCTOBER				DAY OF WEEK	NOVEMBER				DAY OF WEEK	DECEMBER				DAY OF MONTH
		a.m.	Ht.	p.m.	Ht.		a.m.	Ht.	p.m.	Ht.		a.m.	Ht.	p.m.	Ht.	
1	T	6 28	2.7	6 52	2.7	F	7 31	3.0	7 42	2.9	S	6 54	2.9	7 00	2.8	1
2	W	7 16	2.8	7 36	2.9	S	8 18	3.1	8 27	3.0	M	7 44	3.0	7 51	2.9	2
3	T	8 02	3.0	8 19	2.9	S	*8 06	3.2	*8 14	3.0	T	8 35	3.1	8 43	2.9	3
4	F	8 45	3.1	8 59	3.0	M	8 52	3.3	9 00	3.1	W	9 23	3.1	9 35	2.9	4
5	S	9 28	3.2	9 40	3.1	T	9 40	3.3	9 49	3.1	T	10 14	3.1	10 29	2.9	5
6	S	10 12	3.2	10 22	3.1	W	10 30	3.2	10 42	3.0	F	11 05	3.0	11 25	2.8	6
7	M	10 58	3.2	11 07	3.0	T	11 23	3.1	11 38	2.9	S	11 59	2.9	...	...	7
8	T	11 46	3.2	11 56	3.0	F	...	...	12 19	3.0	S	12 24	2.7	12 54	2.8	8
9	W	...	...	12 38	3.1	S	12 40	2.9	1 17	2.9	M	1 26	2.6	1 51	2.6	9
10	T	12 49	2.9	1 35	3.0	S	1 45	2.8	2 18	2.9	T	2 30	2.6	2 50	2.5	10
11	F	1 50	2.8	2 36	2.9	M	2 52	2.8	3 20	2.8	W	3 35	2.5	3 50	2.5	11
12	S	2 56	2.8	3 40	2.9	T	3 58	2.8	4 19	2.8	T	4 36	2.5	4 46	2.4	12
13	S	4 06	2.8	4 44	2.9	W	4 59	2.9	5 15	2.8	F	5 32	2.6	5 39	2.4	13
14	M	5 14	2.9	5 44	3.0	T	5 53	3.0	6 05	2.9	S	6 22	2.6	6 27	2.4	14
15	T	6 15	3.1	6 39	3.1	F	6 43	3.0	6 51	2.9	S	7 07	2.6	7 11	2.4	15
16	W	7 11	3.2	7 29	3.1	S	7 27	3.0	7 34	2.8	M	7 48	2.6	7 52	2.4	16
17	T	8 01	3.3	8 15	3.2	S	8 09	3.0	8 14	2.8	T	8 27	2.6	8 31	2.4	17
18	F	8 47	3.3	8 59	3.1	M	8 49	3.0	8 53	2.7	W	9 04	2.6	9 09	2.4	18
19	S	9 30	3.3	9 40	3.1	T	9 27	2.9	9 32	2.7	T	9 41	2.5	9 48	2.3	19
20	S	10 12	3.2	10 20	3.0	W	10 05	2.8	10 11	2.6	F	10 18	2.5	10 28	2.2	20
21	M	10 52	3.1	10 59	2.9	T	10 44	2.7	10 52	2.5	S	10 55	2.4	11 09	2.2	21
22	T	11 33	3.0	11 39	2.8	F	11 24	2.6	11 36	2.4	S	11 33	2.3	11 52	2.1	22
23	W	...	...	12 14	2.8	S	...	...	12 07	2.5	M	...	...	12 13	2.2	23
24	T	12 21	2.6	12 57	2.7	S	12 23	2.3	12 52	2.4	T	12 39	2.1	12 56	2.1	24
25	F	1 07	2.5	1 44	2.6	M	1 16	2.3	1 41	2.4	W	1 32	2.1	1 44	2.1	25
26	S	1 58	2.5	2 35	2.5	T	2 13	2.3	2 33	2.3	T	2 31	2.1	2 39	2.1	26
27	S	2 55	2.4	3 29	2.5	W	3 13	2.3	3 27	2.4	F	3 33	2.1	3 38	2.1	27
28	M	3 55	2.4	4 25	2.5	T	4 12	2.4	4 22	2.4	S	4 36	2.3	4 40	2.2	28
29	T	4 55	2.5	5 18	2.6	F	5 08	2.6	5 16	2.5	S	5 36	2.4	5 40	2.3	29
30	W	5 51	2.7	6 08	2.7	S	6 02	2.8	6 08	2.6	M	6 32	2.6	6 38	2.5	30
31	T	6 43	2.8	6 56	2.8						T	7 25	2.7	7 34	2.6	31

Dates when Ht. of **Low** Water is below Mean Low with Ht. of lowest given for each period and Date of lowest in ( ):

2nd - 6th: -0.4' (3rd - 5th)
28th - 31st: -0.6' (31st)

Average Rise and Fall 2.5 ft.

When a high tide exceeds avg. ht., the *following* low tide will be lower than avg.

163

A Great Gamefish, Too Good to Lose

by Lou Tabory

I caught my first striper nearly 60 years ago at Compo Beach in the western end of Long Island Sound. Since then I have been fortunate enough to fish for stripers all over the East Coast. There was a time when these great fish were plentiful from Maine down to the Carolinas. Fishing was not always easy, but in good locations there was the possibility of taking a nice fish on every outing. In my home waters of Long Island Sound a shore-caught 20-pound fish was a good catch. But when I started fishing Rhode Island, Nantucket and Cape Cod I found that 30- to 40-pound fish were not out of the question. And the lifetime catch that every surf angler dreams about, a 50-pound striper, was possible on the next cast.

In their early history striped bass were a fickle fish, their numbers rising and falling for no apparent reason. From the 1940s to the 1960s striper numbers fluctuated, but by 1962 there was a distinct population increase and it continued for about 10 years. From 1962 to 1970 both the numbers of fish and young of the year increased substantially, continuing into the early 1970s. In 1973 the landings were the largest in modern times. In this period sport fishing for stripers was at an all-time high, especially for catching big fish along the beaches. These were the boom years that many anglers, plus fish management, thought would never end.

Stripers are my favorite gamefish because they exist in so many different water types. Few other fish can even swim along beaches with heavy rolling surf, but stripers thrive in this environment. Yet they will also roam way up on shallow, clear water flats, at times feeding in 18 inches of water. Even big fish venture up into little creeks, and stripers are kings of large estuaries in the Northeast. They feed in a variety of foods, from tiny spawning cinder worms and small sand eels to menhaden weighing nearly 3 pounds. Their love of small foods and shallow water make them the perfect gamefish for fly and light spin tackle anglers, yet stripers will crash a big surface plug or live herring, delighting the big plug and live bait angler as well. Because of their diversified feeding habits and their ability to survive in so many water types, they are the perfect sport fish.

Striper anglers are an interesting group, almost a cult that worships a nocturnal fish with feeding habits that are unlike many other species. It truly is a fish that has changed anglers' lives. Sensible people become crazed once the fishing season begins. I know anglers that refuse to fish in daylight, believing that stripers feed only at night. Actually fishing at night is not unusual for the diehard fishing enthusiast. There was a time in my life when I fished entire weekends without sleep. These activities have caused people to lose their jobs, even their spouses, while searching for that big fish. Few other species create such hysteria; perhaps it is because stripers are available to so many anglers. From Maine to the Carolinas no other gamefish creates so much excitement for so many anglers.

In the '60s, '70s, and early '80s there were many big fish. I fished mostly on Cape Cod and spent some time on Nantucket, but other locations also had great runs of fish. I never saw the massive runs of big fish along the outer Cape beaches that one writer described in Saltwater Sportsman as the Last Hurrah. A friend who happened to witness the aftermath of one of these runs said that the beach was covered with huge fish. And some anglers were actually unhappy because they only took to 30 pounds. The quest for action like this made Cape Cod and the Islands fall gathering locations for surf anglers in beach buggies, filling the hotels and rental cottages. Many beaches were packed with anglers, some having traveled over 1000 miles looking for that pot of gold.

Around the early to mid-'80s, while fishing Cape Cod outer beaches I met several commercial shore anglers. They became friends and were good, hard fishermen, sharing with me some excellent fishing information. They told stories of how in the early to mid-'70s they could fill the back of a pickup truck with 20- to 40-pound stripers in one night's fishing. That's how good the fishing was at that time. I also thought that there would be a time when taking too many fish might someday affect the striper fishery. But by the early '80s, perhaps even sooner, the decline had started with the young of the year counts reaching record lows by 1981. Not long after, the fishery began to collapse; then the grim moratorium years set in.

After the collapse The Atlantic Striped Bass Conservation Act helped improve the fishery. It took strict rules for all anglers, but fish numbers increased; the recovery seemed solid and continued to improve. There were fewer large fish, but fishing for small to mid-size stripers was excellent in the late '90s. However, from the mid-'90s on, as fish numbers increased, fishing regulations became more liberal.

By 2006 to 2007 I noticed a drop in fish numbers but thought it might be lack of bait along the shore. However, each season since has produced fewer stripers and a dwindling number of anglers along the beaches. Is it due to changes in the fish's habits, too many seals, or decreasing fish numbers? Whatever it is, the once productive striper fishing along the beaches of Cape Cod and the Islands is rapidly declining. There are still some fish offshore and in the vast rips south of Monomoy down east to the rips off Nantucket. And there is still some good beach fishing off New York and New Jersey. Perhaps unpredictability is what the fishery experiences from time to time. If the trend continues, we must take a hard look. Only time will tell. The striped bass is our most important gamefish.

Lou Tabory has been an outdoor writer for over 40 years, with articles in all the significant fishing publications. He has authored five books on saltwater flyfishing, including Inshore Fly Fishing. He has fished northeast waters for almost 60 years and is considered one of the early pioneers of Northeast fly fishing. He continues to work full time in the outdoor field. This article represents his experiences and his views on the striped bass fishery. – Eds.

Striped Bass - printed with permission of the artist Dann Jacobus, www.dannjacobus.com

CHARACTERISTICS OF LIGHT SIGNALS
(see footnote on next page for abbreviations used.)

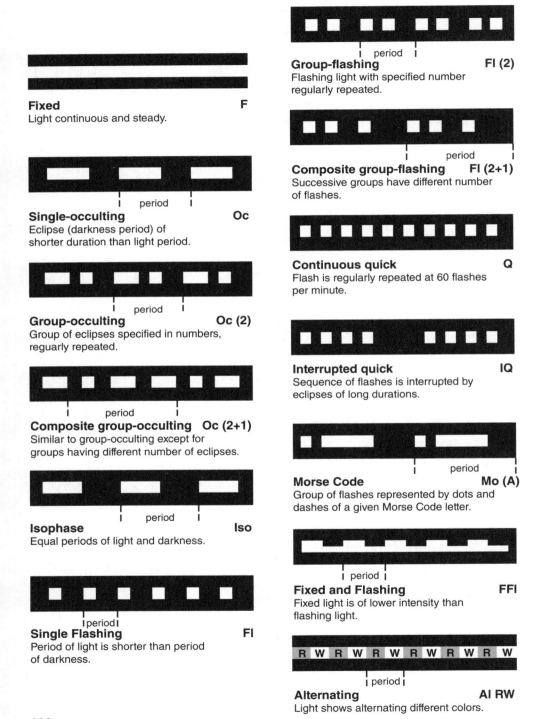

Fixed F
Light continuous and steady.

Single-occulting Oc
Eclipse (darkness period) of
shorter duration than light period.

Group-occulting Oc (2)
Group of eclipses specified in numbers,
reguarly repeated.

Composite group-occulting Oc (2+1)
Similar to group-occulting except for
groups having different number of eclipses.

Isophase Iso
Equal periods of light and darkness.

Single Flashing Fl
Period of light is shorter than period
of darkness.

Group-flashing Fl (2)
Flashing light with specified number
regularly repeated.

Composite group-flashing Fl (2+1)
Successive groups have different number
of flashes.

Continuous quick Q
Flash is regularly repeated at 60 flashes
per minute.

Interrupted quick IQ
Sequence of flashes is interrupted by
eclipses of long durations.

Morse Code Mo (A)
Group of flashes represented by dots and
dashes of a given Morse Code letter.

Fixed and Flashing FFl
Fixed light is of lower intensity than
flashing light.

Alternating Al RW
Light shows alternating different colors.

LIGHTS, FOG SIGNALS and OFFSHORE BUOYS

NOVA SCOTIA, EAST COAST

North Canso Lt., W. side of N. entr. to Strait of Canso – Fl. W. ev. 3 s., Obscured S. of 120°, Ht. 36.7 m. (120'), Rge. 13 mi., (45-41-29.8N/61-29-18.1W)

Cranberry Is. Lt., off Cape Canso, S. part of Is. – Fl. W. ev. 15 s., 2 Horns 2 bl. ev. 60 s., Horns point 066° and 141°, Ht. 16.9 m. (56'), Rge. 21 mi., Racon (B), (45-19-29.6N/60-55-38.2W)

White Head Is. Lt., SW side of Is. – Fl. W. ev. 5 s., Horn 1 bl. ev. 30 s., Horn points 190°, Ht. 18.2 m. (60'), Rge. 12 mi., (45-11-49.1N/61-08-10.8W)

Country Is. Lt., S. side of Is. – Fl. W. ev. 20 s., Ht. 16.5 m. (54'), Rge. 10 mi., (45-05-59.8N/61-32-31.9W)

Liscomb Is. Lt., near Cranberry Pt. – Fl. W. ev. 10 s., Horn 1 bl. ev. 30 s., Ht. 21.9 m. (72'), Rge. 14 mi., (44-59-15.8N/61-57-58.4W)

Beaver Is. Lt., E. end of Is. – Fl. W. ev. 7 s., Horn 1 bl. ev. 60 s., Horn points 144°, Ht. 19.9 m. (66'), Rge. 14 mi., (44-49-29.2N/62-20-16W)

Ship Harbour Lt., on Wolfes Pt. – LFl. G. ev. 6 s., Ht. 18.2 m. (60'), Rge. 4 mi., (44-44-55.4N/62-45-23.6W)

Owls Head Lt., at end of head – Fl. W. ev. 4 s., Ht. 25.8 m. (84'), Rge. 6 mi., (44-43-14.6N/62-47-59.5W)

Egg Is. Lt., center of Is. – LFl. W. ev. 6 s., Ht. 23.8 m. (78'), Rge. 14 mi., (44-39-52.7N/62-51-48.4W)

Jeddore Rock Lt., summit of rock – LFl. W. ev. 12 s., Ht. 29.5 m. (97'), Rge. 8 mi., (44-39-47.1N/63-00-37.3)

Bear Cove Lt. & Bell By. "H6," NE of cove, Q. R., Racon (N), Red, (44-32-36.3N/63-31-19.6W)

Sambro Harbor Lt. & Wh. By. "HS," S. of SW breaker, Halifax Hbr. app. – Mo(A)W ev. 6 s., RWS, (44-24-30N/63-33-36.5W)

Chebucto Head Lt., on summit, Halifax Hbr. app. – Fl. W. ev. 20 s., Horn 2 bl. ev. 60 s., Horn points 113°, Ht. 47.8 m. (157'), Rge. 10 mi., Racon (Z), (44-30-26.6N/63-31-21.8W)

Halifax Alpha Lt. & Wh. By. "HA," Halifax app. – Mo(A)W ev. 6 s., RWS, (44-21-45N/63-24-15W)

Sambro Is. Lt., center of Is. – Fl. W. ev. 6 s., Ht. 42.7 m. (145'), Rge. 23 mi., (44-26-12N/63-33-48W)

Ketch Harbour Lt. By. "HE 19," Ketch Harbour entr. – Fl. G. ev 4 s., Green (44-28-19.6N/63-32-16W)

Betty Is. Lt., on Brig Pt. – Fl. W. ev. 15 s., Horn 1 bl. ev. 60 s., Ht. 19.2 m. (63'), Rge. 13 mi., (44-26-19.7N/63-46-00.4W)

Pearl Is. Lt., off St. Margaret's & Mahone Bays – Fl. W. ev. 10 s., Ht. 19.0 m. (63'), Rge. 8 mi., (44-22-57.2N/64-02-54W)

East Ironbound Is. Lt., center of Is. – Iso. W. ev. 6 s., Ht. 44.5 m. (147'), Rge. 13 mi., (44-26-22.4N/64-04-59.7W)

Abbreviations: **Alt.**, Alternating; **App.**, Approach; **By.**, Buoy; **Ch.**, Channel; **Entr.**, Entrance; **ev.**, every; **F.**, Fixed; **fl.**, flash; **Fl.**, Flashing; **Fl(2)**, Group Flashing; **LFl.**, 2 s. flash.; **G.**, Green; **Hbr.**, Harbor or Harbour; **Ht.**, height; **Is.**, Island; **Iso.**, Isophase (Equal interval); **Iso. W.**, Isophase White (Red sector(s) of Lights warn of dangerous angle of approach. Bearings and ranges are <u>from</u> the observer <u>to</u> the aid.); **Jct.**, Junction; **Keyed**, Fog signal is radio activated. During times of reduced visibility, within ½ mile of the fog signal, turn VHF marine radio to channel 83A and 81A as alternate. Key microphone 5–10 times consecutively to activate fog signal for 45 minutes. **Lt.**, Light; **Ltd.**, Lighted.; **mi.**, miles; **Mo(A)** Morse Code "A," **Mo(U)**, Morse Code "U"; **Oc.**, Occulting; **Pt.**, Point; **Q.**, Quick (Flashing); **RaRef.**, Radar Reflector; **R.**, Red; **rge.**, range; **RWS**, R.&W. Stripes; **RWSRST**, RWS with R. Spherical Topmarks; **s.**, seconds; **Wh.**, Whistle; **W.**, White; **Y.**, Yellow

---

Notices To Mariners: Keep informed of important changes. Visit www.navcen.uscg.gov/lnm/ to receive Local Notices to Mariners via email. When reporting discrepancies in navigational aids, contact nearest C.G. unit and give official name of the aid.

Table for Converting Seconds to Decimals of a Minute, p. 262, for standard GPS input of Lat/Lon.

See pp. 207-209 for Atlantic Coast DGPS Stations and Racon Information.   **167**

FISH TRAPS, South of Newport - What Boaters Need to Know

by Greg Wolf and Miles Wheeler

Crew members with the Point Trap Co. based at Sakonnet Point, RI.

Many local boaters know to steer clear of the fish trap areas south of the Sakonnet River and Newport. After all, this method of fishing has been in operation for over 100 years. Unfortunately because floating fish traps are unique to these waters, few outsiders have any real understanding of the fish traps.

The traps are set in fixed locations, usually within one-half mile from shore, and are designed to catch fish on their migratory routes. The leader, 1500 ft. in length and designed to guide fish into the trap, goes perpendicularly from shore into the trap. The trap consists of the wings that create a wide opening, an intermediate area called the kitchen, and finally the parlor, from which the fish are harvested. Nozzles between the chambers make it easy for fish to enter and difficult to exit. The traps are constructed of small mesh twine, with corks to keep them afloat, and 1" to 2" line connecting a framework of steel barrels and, on the bottom, 900 lb. anchors. Each of the 20 or more anchors is marked by a buoy. This is a maze of barrels, buoys, and floats in which too many careless boaters have found themselves.

The trap companies harvest these traps daily using steel-hulled vessels ("steamers") that tow three double-ended aluminum workboats and a skiff. To haul a trap the steamer secures to the offshore end of the parlor, and the workboats surround the remaining three sides. The parlor is then closed. At this point the men in the workboats, working by hand, slowly bring up the sides of the trap. The crew then pulls up the bottom of the trap, forming a trough alongside the steamer. The fish are then bailed from this trough using a bull net that is guided by lines on winches. The bull net can lift approximately 800 lbs. of fish with each bail.

During the big scup run which usually goes on for a month or so each spring, it is not uncommon for the trap companies to bring in 60,000 lbs. each day of scup and other mixed fish. Because the traps are constructed of one-inch mesh, fish are not "gilled." Fish can be held in the traps for weeks at a time, if necessary, with only minimal mortality. Unwanted catch such as stingrays, sharks, sunfish, and undersize stripers are released. Each year the three primary trap companies at Sakonnet and Newport (and one company which operates out of Point Judith) sell millions of pounds of whole fish to wholesalers. The trap season runs from mid-April until October. Traps may be in place at any time during the season as conditions allow; they are pulled occasionally for maintenance.

Fishing by rod and reel is not permitted within 100 yards of the traps. All boaters are advised to stay far away. Pleasure boats cause extensive damage to the traps almost daily each summer, which requires the men to work extra hours to make repairs. If by error of judgment or navigation a boat gets caught in a floating fish trap, the boat owner will be liable for any damages to the trap. More importantly, getting caught by prop or rudder in a floating fish trap is extremely dangerous. There is no safe or easy way out. These areas are labeled and marked in magenta, outlined by long and short dashes, on government and most other charts. Please use extreme caution when navigating close to the designated fish trap areas.

East Point Island Lt., Mahone Bay – F.G., Ht. 9.6 m. (31'), Rge. 7 mi., (44-20-59.2N/64-12-15W)

Cross Is. Lt., E. Pt. of Is. – Fl. W. ev. 10 s., Ht. 24.9 m. (82'), Rge. 10 mi., (44-18-43.7N/64-10-06.4W)

West Ironbound Is. Lt., Entr. to La Have R. – Fl. W. ev. 12 s., Ht. 24.3 m. (80'), Rge. 8 mi., (44-13-43.7N/64-16-28W)

Mosher Is. Lt., W. side Entr. to La Have R. – F.W., Horn 1 bl. ev. 20 s., Ht. 23.3 m. (77'), Rge. 13 mi., (44-14-14.6N/64-18-59.1W)

Cherry Cove Lt., betw. Little Hbr. & Back Cove – Iso. G. ev. 4 s., Horn 1 bl. ev. 30 s., Horn points 055°46', Ht. 6.7 m. (22'), Rge. 8 mi., (44-09-29.8N/64-28-53.3W)

Medway Head Lt., W. side entr. to Pt. Medway – Fl. W. ev. 12 s., Ht. 24.2 m. (80'), Rge. 11 mi., (44-06-10.6N/64-32-23.3W)

Western Head Lt., W. side entr. to Liverpool Bay – Fl. W. ev. 15 s., Horn 1 bl. ev. 60 s., Horn points 104°, Ht. 16.8 m. (55'), Rge. 15 mi., (43-59-20.8N/64-39-44.5W)

Lockeport Lt., on Gull Rock, entr. to hbr. – LFl. W. ev. 15 s., Horn 1 bl. ev. 30 s., Ht. 16.7 m. (56'), Rge. 12 mi., (43-39-18.3N/65-05-55.9W)

Cape Roseway Lt., near SE Pt. of McNutt Is. – Fl. W. ev. 10 s., Ht. 33.1 m. (109'), Rge. 10 mi., (43-37-21.4N/65-15-50W)

Cape Negro Is. Lt., on SE end of Is. – Fl(2) W. ev. 15 s., Horn 1 bl. ev. 60 s., Ht. 28.3 m. (92'), Rge. 10 mi., (43-30-26.2N/65-20-44.2W)

The Salvages Lt., SE end of Is. – LFl. W. ev. 12 s., Horn 3 bl. ev. 60 s., Ht. 15.6 m. (51'), Rge. 10 mi., (43-28-08.1N/65-22-44W)

Baccaro Point Lt., E. side entr. to Barrington Bay – Mo(D)W 10 ev. s., Horn 1 bl. ev. 20 s., Horn points 200°, Ht. 15.0 m. (49'), Rge. 15 mi., (43-26-59N/65-28-15W)

Cape Sable Lt., on cape – Fl. W. ev. 5 s., Horn 1 bl. ev. 60 s., Horn points 150°, Ht. 29.7 m. (97'), Rge. 18 mi., Racon (C), (43-23-24N/65-37-16.9W)

West Head Lt., Cape Sable Is. – F.R., Horn 2 bl. ev. 60 s., Horn points 254°, Ht. 15.6 m. (51'), Rge. 5 mi., (43-27-23.8N/65-39-16.9W)

Outer Island Lt., on S. Pt. of Outer Is. – Fl. W. ev. 10 s., Ht. 13.7 m. (46'), Rge. 10 mi., (43-27-23.2N/65-44-36.2W)

Seal Is. Lt., S. Pt. of Is. – Fl. W. ev. 10 s., Horn 3 bl. ev. 60 s., Horn points 183°, Ht. 33.4 m. (110'), Rge. 19 mi., (43-23-40N/66-00-51W)

NOVA SCOTIA, WEST COAST

Peases Is. Lt., S. Pt. of one of the Tusket Is. – Fl. W. ev. 6 s., Horn 2 bl. ev. 60 s., Ht. 16 m. (53'), Rge. 9 mi., (43-37-42.6N/66-01-34.9W)

Cape Forchu Lt., E. Cape S. Pt. Yarmouth Sd. – LFl. W. ev. 12 s., Ht. 34.5 m. (113'), Rge. 12 mi., Racon (B), (43-47-38.8N/66-09-19.3W)

Lurcher Shoal Bifurcation Light By. "NM," W. of SW shoal – Fl.(2+1) R. ev. 6 s., Racon (K), R.G.R. marked "NM," (43-48-57.2N/66-29-58W)

Cape St. Marys Lt., E. side of Bay – Fl. W. ev. 5 s., Horn 1 bl. ev. 60 s., Horn points 251° 30', Ht. 31.8 m (105'), Rge. 13 mi., (44-05-09.2N/66-12-39.6W)

Brier Is. Lt., on W. side of Is. R. & W. Tower – Fl(3) W. ev. 18 s., 2 Horns 2 bl. ev. 60 s., Horns point 270° and 315°, Ht. 22.2 m. (72'), Rge. 14 mi., (44-14-55N/66-23-32W)

Boars Head Lt., W. side of N. entr. to Petit Passage – Fl. W. ev. 5 s., Horn 3 bl. ev. 60 s., Horn points 315°, Ht. 28.0 m. (91'), Rge. 16 mi., (44-24-14.5N/66-12-55W)

Prim Pt. Lt., Digby Gut, W. Pt. of entr. to Annapolis Basin – Iso. W. ev. 6 s., Horn 1 bl. ev. 30 s., Horn points 318°, Ht. 24.8 m. (82'), Rge. 12 mi., (44-41-28N/65-47-10.8W)

Ile Haute Lt., on highest Pt. – Fl. W. ev. 4 s., Rge. 7 mi., Ht. 112 m. (367'), (45-15-03.3N/65-00-19.8W)

NEW BRUNSWICK COAST

Cape Enrage Lt., at pitch of cape – Fl. G. ev. 6 s., Horn 3 bl. ev. 60 s., Horn points 220°, Ht. 40.7 m. (134'), Rge. 10 mi., (45-35-38.1N/64-46-47.7W)

For abbreviations see footnote p. 167

FISHING and BAROMETRIC PRESSURE

It is impossible to fish and not pay attention. The activity is intrinsically compelling, full of possibility and visions of hauling in "the big one." Along with its lures, for both catcher and catch, fishing rewards those who are experienced and prepared. We look for the right gear, the right place, the right water and weather. As for weather, a frequently debated question is the role, if any, of barometric pressure. Is that "fishing barometer" reliable?

"Although there is little scientific data on the subject, all fishermen seem to have a personal theory on changes in barometric pressure, fish feeding behavior, and successful fishing. Popular fishing lore holds that: (1) fishing is more productive just before a weather front arrives (with changing barometric pressure) and (2) fishing is usually slow just after a weather front passes through. (3) Fish feed better when the pressure is rising than when the pressure is falling. (4) Fishing is relatively poor when the barometric pressure is very high or very low."[1]

So, do changes in pressure affect fish behavior? With all due respect to those experienced fishermen who may disagree, the scientific answer is that it isn't the pressure change they respond to. Here's why. Simply put, even a drastic change in atmospheric pressure cannot equal the pressure changes experienced by fish as they rise or descend in the water column. A one-inch change in the weight of the atmosphere, say from 30.50 to 29.50 inches of mercury (on your barometer that could be almost a quarter-circle), is a very considerable change, which often takes one or more days, even with a storm arriving or departing. This is about the same change in pressure as what a fish feels when changing depth by about one foot.[2] Since most fish move up and down repeatedly in the water column, and atmospheric pressure usually changes only slowly, fish would not be able to detect the relatively subtle pressure changes above the surface.

What fish clearly can detect are the effects of changing pressure: water turbulence (wind and wave action, tidal currents), level of light or dark, precipitation, and for some, maybe air temperature if it affects water temperature. An approaching storm, with falling pressure, can bring darkening skies, turbulent wave action, and stronger currents, and these effects can certainly change the way fish behave, but it is not directly from the changing pressure: it is from the weather and ocean effects of that change - a subtle but important distinction.

So if you have a "fishing barometer" and its pointer indicates "good fishing," look for the specific weather and water conditions present in your fishing area rather than counting on barometric pressure alone to tell the story!

---

[1] *Beyond the Moon,* James G. McCully, 2008, World Scientific Publishing Co., p. 193
   A comprehensive, well-illustrated source for all your questions about tide. – Ed.
[2] *The Barometer Handbook*, David Burch, 2009, Starpath Publications, p. 121
   Everything to know about barometers and pressure measurement. – Ed.

Quaco Lt., tower on head – Fl. W. ev. 10 s., Horn 1 bl. ev. 30 s., Horn points 130°, Ht. 26.0 m. (86'), Rge. 21 mi., (45-19-25.3N/65-32-08.8W)

Cape Spencer Lt., pitch of cape – Fl. W. ev. 11 s., Horn 3 bl. ev. 60 s., Horn points 165°, Ht. 61.6 m. (203'), Rge. 14 mi., (45-11-42.5N/65-54-35.5W)

Partridge Is. Lt., highest pt. of Is., Saint John Harbour – Fl. W. ev. 7.5 s., Ht. 35.3 m. (116'), Rge. 19 mi., (45-14-21N/66-03-13.8W)

Musquash Head Lt., E. side entr. to Musquash Hbr. – Fl. W. ev. 3 s., Horn 1 bl. ev. 60 s., Horn points 180°, Ht. 35.1 m. (116'), Rge. 20 mi., (45-08-37.1N/66-14-14.2W)

Pt. Lepreau Lt., on point – Fl. W. ev. 5 s., Horn 3 bl. ev. 60 s., Horn points 190°, Ht. 25.5 m. (84'), Rge. 14 mi., (45-03-31.7N/66-27-31.3W)

Pea Pt. Lt., E. side entr. to Letang Hbr. – F.W. visible 251° thru N & E to 161°, Horn 2 bl. ev. 60 s., Horn points 180°, Ht. 17.2 m. (56'), Rge. 12 mi., (45-02-20.4N/66-48-28.2W)

Head Harbour Lt., outer rock of E. Quoddy Head – F.R., Horn 1 bl. ev. 60 s., Horn points 116°, Ht. 17.6 m. (58'), Rge. 13 mi., (44-57-28.6N/66-54-00.2W)

Swallowtail Lt., NE Pt. of Grand Manan – Oc. W. ev. 6 s., Horn 1 bl. ev. 20 s., Horn points 100°, Ht. 37.1 m. (122'), Rge. 12 mi., (44-45-51.1N/66-43-57.5W)

Great Duck Is. Lt., S. end of Is. – Fl. W. ev. 10 s., Horn 1 bl. ev. 60 s., Horn points 120°, Ht. 15.3 m. (50'), Rge. 18 mi., (44-41-03.5N/66-41-34.3W)

Southwest Head Lt., S. end of Grand Manan – Fl. W. ev. 10 s., Horn 1 bl. ev. 60 s., Horn points 240°, Ht. 47.5 m. (156'), Rge. 16 mi., (44-36-02.9N/66-54-19.8W)

Gannet Rock Lt., S. of Grand Manan – Fl. W. ev. 5 s., Horn 3 bl. ev. 60 s., Horn omni-directional, Ht. 28.2 m. (93'), Rge. 19 mi., Racon (G), (44-30-37.1N/66-46-52.9W)

Machias Seal Is. Lt., On Is. summit – Fl. W. ev. 3 s., Horn 2 bl. ev. 60 s. Horn Points 065°, Ht. 25 m. (83'), Rge. 17 mi., (44-30-07N/67-06-04W)

MAINE

West Quoddy Head Lt., Entr. Quoddy Roads – Fl(2) W. ev. 15 s., Horn 2 bl. ev. 30 s., Ht. 83', Rge. 18 mi., (44-48-54N/66-57-02W)

Libby Island Lt., Entr. Machias Bay – Fl(2) W. ev. 20 s., Horn 1 bl. ev. 15 s., Ht. 91', Rge. 18 mi., (44-34-06N/67-22-03W)

Moose Peak Lt., E. end Mistake Is. – Fl. W. ev. 30 s., Horn 2 bl. ev. 30 s., Ht. 72', Rge. 20 mi., (44-28-28N/67-31-55W)

Petit Manan Lt., E. Pt. of Is. – Fl. W. ev. 10 s., Horn 1 bl. ev. 30 s., Ht. 123', Rge. 19 mi., (44-22-03N/67-51-52W)

Prospect Harbor Point Lt. – Fl. R. ev. 6 s., (2 W. sect.), Ht. 42', Rge. R. 7 mi., W. 9 mi., ltd. 24 hrs., (44-24-12N/68-00-47W)

Mount Desert Lt., 20 mi. S. of island – Fl. W. ev. 15 s., Horn 2 bl. ev. 30 s., Ht. 75', Rge. 20 mi., (43-58-07N/68-07-42W)

Great Duck Island Lt., S. end of island – Fl. R. ev. 5 s., Horn 1 bl. ev. 15 s., Ht. 67', Rge. 19 mi., (44-08-31N/68-14-45W)

Frenchman Bay Ltd. By. "FB," Fl. (2+1) R. ev. 6 s., Rge. 4 mi., R&G Bands, Racon (B), (44-19-21N/68-07-24W)

Egg Rock Lt., Frenchman Bay – Fl. R. ev. 5 s., Horn 2 bl. ev. 30 s., Ht. 64', Rge. 18 mi., (44-21-14N/68-08-18W)

Baker Island Lt., SW Entr. Somes Sound – Fl. W. ev. 10 s., Ht. 105', Rge. 10 mi., (44-14-28N/68-11-56W)

Bass Harbor Head Lt., SW Pt. Mt. Desert Is. – Oc. R. ev. 4 s., Ht. 56', Rge. 13 mi., ltd. 24 hrs., (44-13-19N/68-20-14W)

Blue Hill Bay Lt. #3, on Green Is. – Fl. G. ev. 4 s., Ht. 25', Rge. 5 mi., SG on tower, (44-14-55N/68-29-52W)

Burnt Coat Harbor Lt. – Oc. W. ev. 4 s., Ht. 75', Rge. 9 mi., (44-08-03N/68-26-50W)

For abbreviations see footnote p. 167

Fishing Adrift: Know the Flow

By Zach Harvey

Nowhere is the strength of the ebbing or flooding tide more critical than in drift fishing, where we ride the current over productive bottom structure in search of striped bass, fluke and an array of other game- and food-fish. Unfortunately, too often we find ourselves bobbing around in tight circles, or zipping over our target area too fast, or on the change of a tide, seeing mill-pond sea conditions give way to the washing machine.

Conditions and location   Armed with a marine forecast I trust, the Eldridge, and a good chart, I can often anticipate favorable fishing grounds (read: the sum of a spot and the conditions affecting it), even on some days that leave most of the fleet tied fast to the pilings. The first key to the conditions mix is understanding the overall movements of water that affect your area with some careful study of the current charts contained herein. In certain winding inlets, for example, the tide will flood for two or three hours after the tide has peaked out front. There's always a push of water somewhere, and where there's moving water, there are feeding fish.

The right mix   In drift fishing, the name of the game is movement over ground. In general, I'll take a so-so piece of bottom with perfect drift over a great spot with none. On days when the wind runs 180 degrees against a tide, we struggle to get much speed over structure, and our catch rate plummets. So we quickly rule out areas where wind will buck tide, creating not only no drift, but ugly sea conditions, like a steep chop, as the forces duke it out. In other situations, wind and tide aligned can send the boat streaking along, the heaviest of our sinkers failing to pin a bait to bottom. In most cases - at least for those of us who fish when we choose - these scenarios are predictable to a degree. So, consulting the current charts and tables to understand the direction and timing of tidal flow, I would time my departure to coincide with a certain tide change or wind shift that will set up the right drift conditions. With the diversity of drift "angles" at our disposal, it's possible to target a piece of bottom with favorable drift conditions.

A sequence of locations   In other scenarios, I can identify areas that will see running tide earlier or later, timing my route to minimize the impact of slack tides. At places like Block Island or the Vineyard, which are affected by numerous tidal influences, we can take advantage of playing the sequence in current change at different locations.

Real vs. ideal   When Mother Nature serves up an absolute dud in the drift-conditions department, we can also use the Eldridge for damage control, maybe noting a piece of water where we can minimize the impact of a "wrong" wind. When tides are weak on the quarters of the moon, we can try to arrive on the grounds when a meager charge of tide will be backed up by the breeze, giving us the quick, linear drift we need to catch lethargic stripers during the brief window of their feed.

Prediction is a slippery piece of the fishing puzzle. But we can, thanks to this book, learn to predict theoretically perfect drift scenarios and ultimately narrow the search considerably. That is the real trick. Knowing the conditions and getting a feel for the all-important timing can make the difference between chasing the fishing headlines and living in them.

Zach Harvey is a freelance writer, editor, illustrator, photographer, and fisherman. He lives in Wakefield, RI with his wife, Sarah, and daughter, Kaya.

Halibut Rocks Lt., Jericho Bay – Fl. W. ev. 6 s., Horn 1 bl. ev. 10 s., Ht. 25′, Rge. 6 mi., NR on tower, (44-08-03N/68-31-32W)

Eggemoggin Ltd. Bell By. "EG" – Mo(A)W, Rge. 5 mi., RWSRST, (44-19-13N/68-44-34W)

Eggemoggin Reach Bell By. "ER" – RWSRST, (44-18-00N/68-46-29W)

Crotch Island Lt. #21, Deer Is. Thorofare – Fl. G. ev. 4 s., Ht. 20′, Rge. 5 mi., SG on tower, (44-08-46N/68-40-39W)

Saddleback Ledge Lt., Isle au Haut Bay – Fl. W. ev. 6 s., Horn 1 bl. ev. 10 s., Ht. 54′, Rge. 9 mi., (44-00-52N/68-43-35W)

Isle Au Haut Lt., Isle au Haut Bay – Fl. R. ev. 4 s., W. Sect. 034°-060°, Ht. 48′, Rge. R. 6 mi., W. 8 mi., (44-03-53N/68-39-05W)

Deer Island Thorofare Lt., W. end of thorofare – Fl. W. ev. 6 s., Horn 1 bl. ev. 15 s., Ht. 52′, Rge. 8 mi., (44-08-04N/68-42-12W)

Goose Rocks Lt., E. Entr. Fox Is. Thorofare – Fl. R. ev. 6 s., W. Sect. 301°-304°, Horn 1 bl. ev. 10 s., Ht. 51′, Rge. R. 11 mi., W. 12 mi., (44-08-08N/68-49-50W)

Eagle Island Lt., E. Penobscot Bay – Fl. W. ev. 4 s., Ht. 106′, Rge. 9 mi., (44-13-04N/68-46-04W)

Green Ledge Lt. #4, E. Penobscot Bay – Fl. R. ev. 6 s., Ht. 31′, Rge. 5 mi., TR on tower, (44-17-25N/68-49-42W)

Heron Neck Lt., E. Entr. Hurricane Sound – F.R., W. Sect. 030°-063°, Horn 1 bl. ev. 30 s., Ht. 92′, Rge. R. 7 mi., W. 9 mi., (44-01-30N/68-51-44W)

Matinicus Rock Lt., Penobscot Bay App. – Fl. W. ev. 10 s., Horn 1 bl. ev. 15 s., Ht. 90′, Rge. 20 mi., (43-47-00N/68-51-18W)

Grindel Pt. Lt., West Penobscot Bay – Fl. W. ev. 4 s., Ht. 39′, Rge. 4 mi., (44-16-53N/68-56-35W)

Two-Bush Island Lt., Two-Bush Ch. – Fl. W. ev. 5 s., R. Sect. 061°-247°, Horn 1 bl. ev. 15 s., Ht. 65′, Rge. W. 21 mi., R. 15 mi., (43-57-51N/69-04-26W)

Two Bush Island Ltd. Wh. By. "TBI" – Mo(A)W, Rge. 6 mi., RWS, (43-58-17N/69-00-16W)

Whitehead Lt., W. side of S. entr. Muscle Ridge Ch. – Oc.G. ev. 4 s., Horn 2 bl. ev. 30 s., Ht. 75′, Rge. 6 mi., (43-58-43N/69-07-27W)

Owl's Head Lt., S. side Rockland Entr. – F.W., Horn 2 bl. ev. 20 s., Ht. 100′, Rge. 16 mi., Obscured from 324°-354° by Monroe Island, ltd. 24 hrs., (44-05-32N/69-02-38W)

Rockland Harbor Breakwater Lt., S. end of breakwater – Fl. W. ev. 5 s., Horn 1 bl. ev. 15 s., Ht. 39′, Rge. 17 mi., (44-06-15N/69-04-39W)

Lowell Rock Lt. #2, Rockport Entr. – Fl. R. ev. 6 s., Ht. 25′, Rge. 5 mi., TR on spindle, (44-09-46N/69-03-37W)

Browns Head Lt., W. Entr. Fox Is. Thorofare – F. W., 2 R. Sect. 001°-050° and 061°-091°, Horn 1 bl. ev. 10 s., Ht. 39′, Rge. R. 11 mi., F.W. 14 mi., ltd. 24 hrs., (44-06-42N/68-54-34W)

Curtis Island Lt., S. side Camden Entr. – Oc.G. ev. 4 s., Ht. 52′, Rge. 6 mi., (44-12-05N/69-02-56W)

Northeast Point Lt. #2, Camden Entr. – Fl. R. ev. 4 s., Ht. 20′, Rge. 5 mi., TR on white tower, (44-12-31N/69-02-47W)

Dice Head Lt., N. side Entr. to Castine – Fl. W. ev. 6 s., Ht. 134′, Rge. 11 mi., White tower, (44-22-58N/68-49-08W)

Fort Point Lt., W. side Entr. to Penobscot R. – F.W., Horn 1 bl. ev. 10 s., Ht. 88′, Rge. 15 mi., ltd. 24 hrs., (44-28-02N/68-48-42W)

Marshall Point Lt., E. side of Pt. Clyde Hbr. S. Entr. – F.W., Horn 1 bl. ev. 10 s., Ht. 30′, Rge. 13 mi., ltd. 24 hrs., (43-55-03N/69-15-41W)

Marshall Point Ltd. By. "MP" – Mo(A)W, Rge. 6 mi., RWSRST, (43-55-18N/69-10-52W)

For abbreviations see footnote p. 167

MAINE YACHT CENTER
A Perfect Place to Refuel, Refit, and Relax

Located in Casco Bay, minutes from downtown Portland

MARINA FACILITIES

- Calm, quiet, and protected
- 80 seasonal slips
- Transient berths for yachts to 150′ with three-phase 100 amp service
- Customer lounge area with new heads, showers and laundry facilities
- Gas and diesel

SERVICE FACILITIES

- **80-Ton Travelift**
- Climate-controlled paint and varnish building
- 35,000 square feet of new heated indoor storage
- Certified, dedicated technicians and craftsmen providing the full range of boat yard services

100 Kensington Street • Portland, Maine
207.842.9000 • www.maineyacht.com

Monhegan Island Lt., Penobscot Bay – Fl. W. ev. 15 s., Ht. 178', Rge. 20 mi., (43-45-53N/69-18-57W)

Manana Island Sound Signal Station, Penobscot Bay – Horn 2 bl. ev. 60 s., (43-45-48N/69-19-36W)

Franklin Is. Lt., Muscongus Bay – Fl. W. ev. 6 s., Ht. 57', Rge. 8 mi., (43-53-31N/69-22-29W)

Pemaquid Pt. Lt., W. side Muscongus Bay Entr. – Fl. W. ev. 6 s., Ht. 79', Rge. 14 mi., (43-50-12N/69-30-21W)

Ram Is. Lt., Fisherman Is. Passage S. side – Iso. R. ev. 6 s., 2 W. Sect. 258°-261° and 030°-046°, Covers fairways, Horn 1 bl. ev. 30 s., Ht. 36', Rge. W. 11 mi., R. 9 mi., W. 9 mi. (43-48-14N/69-35-57W)

Burnt Is. Lt., Boothbay Hbr. W. side Entr. – Fl. R. ev. 6 s., 2 W. Sect. 307°-316° and 355°-008°, Covers fairways. Horn 1 bl. ev. 10 s., Ht. 61', Rge. W. 8 mi., R. 6 mi., (43-49-31N/69-38-25W)

The Cuckolds Lt., Boothbay – Fl(2) W. ev. 6 s., Keyed (VHF 83A) Horn 1 bl. ev. 15 s., Ht. 59', Rge. 12 mi., (43-46-46N/69-39-00W)

Seguin Lt., 2 mi. S. of Kennebec R. mouth – F.W., Horn 2 bl. ev. 20 s., Ht. 180', Rge. 18 mi., (43-42-27N/69-45-29W)

Hendricks Head Lt., Sheepscot R. mouth E. side – F.W., R. Sect. 180°-000°, Ht. 43', Rge. R. 7 mi., F.W. 9 mi., (43-49-21N/69-41-23W)

Pond Is. Lt., Kennebec R. mouth W. side – Iso. W. ev. 6 s., Horn 2 bl. ev. 30 s., Ht. 52', Rge. 9 mi., (43-44-24N/69-46-13W)

Perkins Is. Lt., Kennebec R. – Fl. R. ev. 2.5 s., 2 W. Sect. 018° – 038°, 172° – 188°, Covers fairways, Ht. 41', Rge. R. 5 mi., W. 6 mi., (43-47-12N/69-47-07W)

Squirrel Pt. Lt., Kennebec R. – Iso. R. ev. 6 s., W. Sect. 321° - 324°, Covers fairway, Ht. 25', Rge. R. 7 mi., W. 9 mi., (43-48-59N/69-48-09W)

Fuller Rock Lt., off Cape Small – Fl. W. ev. 4 s., Ht. 39', Rge. 6 mi., NR on tower, (43-41-45N/69-50-01W)

White Bull Ltd. Gong By. "WB" – Mo(A)W, Rge. 6 mi., RWS, (43-42-49N/69-55-13W)

Whaleboat Island Lt., Broad Sd., Casco Bay – Fl. W. ev. 6 s., Ht. 47', Rge. 6 mi., NR on tower, (43-44-31N/70-03-40W)

Cow Island Ledge Lt., Portland to Merepoint – Fl. W. ev. 6 s., Ht. 23', Rge. 8 mi., RaRef., NR on spindle, (43-42-11N/70-11-19W)

Halfway Rock Lt., midway betw. Cape Small Pt. and Cape Eliz. – Fl. R. ev. 5 s., Horn 2 bl. ev. 30 s., Ht. 76', Rge. 19 mi., (43-39-21N/70-02-12W)

Portland Ltd. Wh. By. "P", Portland Hbr. App. – Mo(A)W, Rge. 6 mi., Racon (M), RWSRST, (43-31-36N/70-05-28W)

Ram Island Ledge Lt., N. side of Portland Hbr. Entr. – Fl. (2) W. ev. 6 s., Horn 1 bl. ev. 10 s., Ht. 77', Rge. 8 mi., (43-37-53N/70-11-15W)

Cape Elizabeth Lt., S. of Portland Hbr. Entr. – Fl(4) W. ev. 15 s., Horn 2 bl. ev. 60 s., Ht. 129', Rge. 15 mi., ltd. 24 hrs., (43-33-58N/70-12-00W)

Portland Head Lt., SW side Portland Hbr. Entr. – Fl. W. ev. 4 s., Horn 1 bl. ev. 15 s., Ht. 101', Rge. 24 mi., ltd. 24 hrs., (43-37-23N/70-12-28W)

Spring Pt. Ledge Lt., Portland main ch. W. side – Fl. W. ev. 6 s., 2 R. Sect., 2 W. Sectors 331°-337° and 074°-288°, Horn 1 bl. ev. 10 s., Ht. 54', Rge. R. 10 mi., W. 12 mi., ltd. 24 hrs., (43-39-08N/70-13-26W)

Wood Island Lt., S. Entr. Wood Is. Hbr. N. side – Alt. W. and G. ev. 10 s., Horn 2 bl. ev. 30 s., Ht. 71', Rge. W. 18 mi., G. 16 mi., (43-27-25N/70-19-45W)

Goat Is. Lt., Cape Porpoise Hbr. Entr. – Fl. W. ev. 6 s., Horn 1 bl. ev. 15 s., Ht. 38', Rge. 12 mi., (43-21-28N/70-25-30W)

Cape Neddick Lt., On N. side of Nubble – Iso. R. ev. 6 s., Horn 1 bl. ev. 10 s., Ht. 88', Rge. 13 mi., (43-09-55N/70-35-28W)

Jaffrey Point Lt. #4 – Fl. R. ev. 4 s., Ht. 22', rge. 5 mi., TR on tower, (43-03-18N/70-42-49W)

For abbreviations see footnote p. 167

When cruising Buzzards Bay, visit our full-service loft for

FAST SAIL REPAIRS

· 24 hour turn-around in most cases.
· Furling system trouble-shooting.
· Local pick-up & delivery -- *FREE.*
· New sails & sail washing.
· Custom canvas fabrication & repair.

508-563-3080

est. 1976

4B Long Hill Road
Cataumet, MA 02534
www.capecodsailmakers.com

SQUETEAGUE
S A I L M A K E R S

Barden's Boat Yard, Inc.
est. 1927

Your full service boat yard on beautiful Sippican Harbor!

Winter Storage • Fiberglass & Carpentry Repairs
Engine Replacements • Moorings
Summer Dry Dock Service • Launch Service • Fuel

Authorized Yanmar Dealer
Authorized Helix Mooring Installer

2 Island Wharf Road, Marion, MA • 508-748-0250
bardensboatyard@comcast.net • www.bardensboatyard.com

LIGHTS, FOG SIGNALS and OFFSHORE BUOYS – Maine (cont.)

Boon Is. Lt., 6.5 mi. off coast – Fl. W. ev. 5 s., Horn 1 bl. ev. 10 s., Ht. 137', Rge. 19 mi., (43-07-17N/70-28-35W)

York Harbor Ltd. Bell By. "YH" – Mo(A)W, Rge. 5 mi., RWSRST, (43-07-45N/70-37-01W)

NEW HAMPSHIRE

Whaleback Lt., Portsmouth Entr. NE side –Fl(2) W. ev. 10 s., Keyed (VHF 83A) Horn 2 bl. ev. 30 s., Ht. 59', Rge. 11 mi., (43-03-32N/70-41-47W)

Portsmouth Harbor Lt. (New Castle), on Fort Point – F. G., Horn 1 bl. ev. 10 s., Ht. 52', Rge. 12 mi., (43-04-16N/70-42-31W)

Rye Harbor Entr. Ltd. Wh. By. "RH" – Mo(A)W, Rge. 6 mi., RWSRST, (42-59-38N/70-43-45W)

Isles Of Shoals Lt., 5.5 mi. off coast – Fl. W. ev. 15 s., Horn 1 bl. ev. 30 s., Ht. 82', Rge. 14 mi., (42-58-02N/70-37-24W)

MASSACHUSETTS

Newburyport Harbor Lt., N. end of Plum Is. – Oc.(2) G. ev. 15 s., Obscured from 165°-192° and 313°-344°, Ht. 50', Rge. 10 mi., (42-48-55N/70-49-08W)

Merrimack River Entr. Ltd. Wh. By. "MR"– Mo(A)W, Rge. 4 mi., RWSRST, (42-48-34N/70-47-03W)

Ipswich Lt., Ipswich Entr. S. side – Oc.W. ev. 4 s., Ht. 30', Rge. 5 mi., NR on tower, (42-41-07N/70-45-58W)

Rockport Breakwater Lt. #6, W. side Entr. Rockport inner hbr. – Fl. R. ev. 4 s., Ht. 32', Rge. 5 mi., TR on tower, (42-39-39N/70-36-43W)

Annisquam Harbor Lt., E. side Entr. – Fl. W. ev. 7.5 s., R. Sector 180°-217°, Horn 2 bl. ev. 60 s., Ht. 45', Rge. R. 11 mi., W. 14 mi., (42-39-43N/70-40-53W)

Straitsmouth Lt., Rockport Entr. S. side – Fl. G. ev. 6 s., Horn 1 bl. ev. 15 s., Ht. 46', Rge. 6 mi., (42-39-44N/70-35-17W)

Cape Ann Lt., E. side Thacher Is. – Fl. R. ev. 5 s., Horn 2 bl. ev. 60 s., Ht. 166', Rge. 17 mi., (42-38-12N/70-34-30W)

Eastern Point Ltd. Wh. By. #2 – Fl. R. ev. 4 s., Rge. 3 mi., Red, (42-34-14N/70-39-50W)

Eastern Point Lt., Gloucester Entr. E. side – Fl. W. ev. 5 s., Ht. 57', Rge. 20 mi., ltd. 24 hrs., (42-34-49N/70-39-52W)

Gloucester Breakwater Lt., W. end – Oc.R. ev. 4 s., Horn 1 bl. ev. 10 s., Ht. 45', Rge. 6 mi., (42-34-57N/70-40-20W)

Bakers Island Lt., Salem Ch. – Alt. Fl. W. and R. ev. 20 s., Horn 1 bl. ev. 30 s., Ht. 111', Rge. R. 14 mi., W. 16 mi., (42-32-11N/70-47-09W)

Hospital Point Range Front Lt., Beverly Cove W. side – F.W., Ht. 70', (42-32-47N/70-51-21W)

The Graves Ltd. Wh. By. #5 – Fl. G. ev. 4 s., Rge. 4 mi., Green, (42-22-33N/70-51-28W)

Marblehead Lt., N. point Marblehead Neck – F.G., Ht. 130', Rge. 7 mi., (42-30-19N/70-50-01W)

The Graves Lt., Boston Hbr. S. Ch. Entr. – Fl(2) W. ev. 12 s., Horn 2 bl. ev. 20 s., Ht. 98', Rge. 15 mi., (42-21-54N/70-52-09W)

Boston App. Ltd. By. "BG"– Mo(A)W, Rge. 6 mi., RWSRST, (42-23-27N/70-51-29W)

Deer Island Lt., President Roads, Boston Hbr. – Alt. W. and R. ev. 10 s., R. Sect. 198°-222°, Obscured 112°-186°, Horn 1 bl. ev. 10 s., Ht. 53', Rge. R. 11 mi., (42-20-23N/70-57-16W)

Deer Island Danger Lt., On south end of spit – F.R., R. Sect. 198°-222°, Ht. 15', Rge. 6 mi., (42-20-23N/70-57-16W)

Long Island Head Lt., President Roads, Boston Hbr. – Fl. W. ev. 2.5 s., Ht. 120', Rge. 6 mi., (42-19-49N/70-57-28W)

Boston Ltd. Wh. By. "B", Boston Hbr. Entr. – Mo(A)W, Rge. 6 mi., Racon (B), RWSRST, (42-22-42N/70-46-58W)

For abbreviations see footnote p. 167

177

The Best Marina on the Best Island

Marinalife named Nantucket Boat Basin the Best Transient Marina
in the U.S. two years running. And *National Geographic* named
Nantucket The Best Island in the World in 2012.
Enjoy a world-class travel experience, from ship to shore.

240 SLIPS | COMPLETE AMENITIES | CONCIERGE SERVICE
AWARD-WINNING RESTAURANTS | LUXURY SPA ACCESS

800.NAN-BOAT   nantucketboatbasin.com   Open year round

NANTUCKET. UNFORGETTABLE STAYS.
Nantucket Island Resorts owns a unique collection of premier hotels, cottages, island residences, and a marina.

WHITE ELEPHANT • WHITE ELEPHANT HOTEL VILLAGE | RESIDENCES & INN • THE WAUWINET
JARED COFFIN HOUSE • THE COTTAGES & LOFTS • NANTUCKET BOAT BASIN

nantucketislandresorts.com

Marinalife Best Transient Marina in the U.S. 2010, 2011

Boston App. Ltd. By. "BF" (NOAA) –Fl(4) Y. ev. 20 sec, Rge. 7 mi., Yellow, (42-20-44N/70-39-04W)

Boston North Ch.Entr. Ltd. Wh. By. "NC" – Mo(A)W, Rge. 6 mi., RWSRST, Racon (N), (42-22-32N/70-54-18W)

Minots Ledge Lt., Boston Hbr. Entr. S. side – Fl(1+4+3) W. ev. 45 s., Horn 1 bl. ev. 10 s., Ht. 85', Rge. 10 mi., (42-16-11N/70-45-33W)

Boston Lt., SE side Little Brewster Is. – Fl. W. ev. 10 s., Horn 1 bl. ev. 30 s., Ht. 102', Rge. 27 mi., (42-19-41N/70-53-24W) *See article pg. 215.*

Scituate App. Ltd. Gong By. "SA"– Mo(A)W, Rge. 6 mi., RWSRST, (42-12-08N/70-41-49W)

Plymouth Lt. (Gurnet), N. side Entr. to hbr. – Fl(3) W. ev. 30 s., R. Sect. 323°-352°, Horn 2 bl. ev. 15 s., Ht. 102', Rge. R. 15 mi., W. 17 mi., (42-00-13N/70-36-02W)

Race Point Lt., NW Point of Cape Cod – Fl. W. ev. 10 s., Obscured 220°-292°, Ht. 41', (42-03-44N/70-14-35W)

Wood End Lt., Entr. to Provincetown – Fl. R. ev. 10 s., Horn 1 bl. ev. 30 s., Ht. 45', Rge. 13 mi., (42-01-17N/70-11-37W)

Long Point Lt., Provincetown Entr. SW side – Oc.G. ev. 4 s., Horn 1 bl. ev. 15 s., Ht. 36', Rge. 8 mi., (42-01-59N/70-10-07W)

Mary Ann Rocks Ltd. Wh. By. #12 – Fl. R. ev. 2.5 s., Rge. 4 mi., Red, (41-55-07N/70-30-22W)

Cape Cod Canal App. Ltd. Bell By. "CC" – Mo(A)W, Rge. 4 mi., RWSRST, (41-48-53N/70-27-39W)

Cape Cod Canal Breakwater Lt. #6, E. Entr. – Fl. R. ev. 5 s., Horn 1 bl. ev. 15 s., Ht. 43', Rge. 15 mi., (41-46-47N/70-29-23W)

Highland Lt., NE side of Cape Cod – Fl. W. ev. 5 s., Ht. 170', Rge. 18 mi., ltd. 24 hrs., (42-02-22N/70-03-39W)

Nauset Beach Lt., E. side of Cape Cod – Alt. W. R. ev. 10 s., (Tides divide and run in opposite directions abreast of light), Ht. 120', (41-51-36N/69-57-12W)

Chatham Beach Ltd. Wh. By. "C" – Mo(A)W, Rge. 4 mi., RWSRST, (41-39-12N/69-55-30W)

Chatham Lt., W. side of hbr. – Fl(2)W. ev. 10 s., Ht. 80', Rge. 24 mi., ltd. 24 hrs., (41-40-17N/69-57-01W)

Chatham Inlet Bar Guide Lt., Fl. Y. ev. 2.5 s., Ht. 62', Rge. 11 mi., (41-40-18N/69-57-00W)

Hyannis Harbor App. Ltd. Bell By. "HH" – Mo(A)W, Rge. 6 mi., RWSRST, (41-35-57N/70-17-22W)

Pollock Rip Ch. Ltd. By. #8 – Fl. R. ev. 6 s., Rge. 3 mi., Red, (41-32-43N/69-58-56W)

Cape Wind Meteorological Lt. Tower "MT"– Fl.Y. ev. 6 s., (41-28-20N/70-18-53W)

Nantucket Lt., (Great Point), Nantucket, N. end of Is., – Fl. W. ev. 5 s., R. sect. 084°-106° (Covers Cross Rip & Tuckernuck Shoals), Ht. 71', Rge. W. 14 mi., R. 12 mi., (41-23-25N/70-02-54W)

Sankaty Head Lt., E. end of Is. – Fl. W. ev. 7.5 s., Ht. 158', Rge. 24 mi., (41-17-04N/69-57-58W)

Nantucket Sound Ltd. Wh. By. "NS"– Mo(A)W, Rge. 4 mi., RWSRST, (41-27-43N/70-23-42W)

Nantucket East Breakwater Lt. #3, Outer Entr. to hbr. – Fl. G. ev. 4 s., Horn 1 bl. ev. 10 s., Ht. 30', Rge. 12 mi., (41-18-37N/70-06-59W)

Brant Point Lt., Hbr. Entr. W. side – Oc.R. ev. 4 s., Horn 1 bl. ev. 10 s., Ht. 26', Rge. 10 mi., (41-17-24N/70-05-25W)

Cape Poge Lt., NE point of Chappaquiddick Is. – Fl. W. ev. 6 s., Ht. 65', Rge. 9 mi., (41-25-10N/70-27-08W)

Muskeget Ch. Ltd. Wh. By. "MC" – Mo(A)W, Rge. 4 mi., RWSRST, (41-15-00N/70-26-10W)

For abbreviations see footnote p. 167

MARTHA'S VINEYARD SHIPYARD

We are a full-service boatyard, offering complete marine services
to sail and power boats, including:

- **Marine Supply Store** (Dyer dinghies, Charts, Ice)
- **Travelift** hauling up to 20 tons
- **Repairs to:** Engines - Pumping - Rigging -
  Electronics - Hull, Keel and Deck - Sails
- **Expert painting** and varnishing, including Awlgrip
- **Boat Storage**, inside and outside
- **Authorized** Yanmar, Yamaha, Hinckley Service
  and Johnson/Evinrude parts
- **Vanguard** Laser and Sunfish Dealer
- **Zodiac** Inflatables
- **Transportation**

164 BEACH ROAD, P.O. BOX 1119
VINEYARD HAVEN, MA 02568
Telephone: (508) 693-0400
FAX 693-4100

Now also in Edgartown, May - September
45 Dock Street, (508) 627-6000

www.mvshipyard.com

We monitor VHF channels 16, 9, 73

Member: American Boat Builders & Repairers Association

Tisbury
Wharf
company

Martha's Vineyard Island • Vineyard Haven Harbor

- Fuel prices competitive with mainland
- Dockage for ships up to 200'
- Shell fuel and lubricants
- Marine railway 50 tons
- Bunkering service upon request
- Towing and salvage
- Water, ice: blocks/cubes

144 Beach Road   P.O. Box 1317   Tisbury, MA 02568
Tel: 508 693-9300   Fax: 508 696-8436   www.tisburywharf.com

Edgartown Harbor Lt., Inner end of hbr. W. side – Fl. R. ev. 6 s., Ht. 45', Rge. 5 mi., (41-23-27N/70-30-11W)

East Chop Lt., E. side Vineyard Haven Hbr. Entr. – Iso. G. ev. 6 s., Ht. 79', Rge. 9 mi., (41-28-13N/70-34-03W)

West Chop Lt., W. side Vineyard Haven Hbr. Entr. – Oc.W. ev. 4 s., R. Sect. 281°-331° (covers Squash Meadow and Norton Shoals), Horn 1 bl. ev. 30 s., Ht. 84', Rge. R. 10 mi., W. 14 mi., (41-28-51N/70-35-59W)

Nobska Point Lt., Woods Hole E. Entr. – Fl. W. ev. 6 s., R. Sect. 263°-289° (covers Hedge Fence and L'hommedieu Shoal), Horn 2 bl. ev. 30 s., Ht. 87', Rge. R. 11 mi., W. 13 mi., ltd 24 hrs., (41-30-57N/70-39-18W)

Tarpaulin Cove Lt., SE side Naushon Is. – Fl. W. ev. 6 s., Ht. 78', Rge. 9 mi., (41-28-08N/70-45-27W)

Menemsha Creek Entr. Jetty Lt. #3 – Fl. G. ev. 4 s., Ht. 25', Rge. 5 mi., (41-21-16N/70-46-07W)

Gay Head Lt., W. point of Martha's Vineyard – Alt. W. and R. ev. 15 s., Ht. 170', Rge. W. 24 mi., R. 20 mi., Obscured 342°-359° by Nomans Land, ltd. 24 hrs., (41-20-54N/70-50-06W)

Cuttyhunk East Entr. Ltd. Bell By. "CH" – Mo(A)W, Rge. 5 mi., RWSRST, (41-26-34N/70-53-22W)

BUZZARDS BAY

Canapitsit Ch. Entr. Bell By. "CC", – RWSRST, (41-25-01N/70-54-23W)

Narragansett - Buzzards Bay App. Ltd. Wh. By. "A" – Mo(A)W, Rge. 6 mi., Racon (N), RWSRST, (41-06-00N/71-23-22W)

Buzzards Bay Entr. Lt., W. Entr. – Fl. W. ev. 2.5 s., Horn 2 bl. ev. 30 s., Ht. 67', Rge. 17 mi., Racon (B), (41-23-49N/71-02-05W)

Dumpling Rocks Lt. #7, off Round Hill Pt. – Fl. G. ev. 6 s., Ht. 52', Rge. 8 mi., (41-32-18N/70-55-17W)

Buzzards Bay Midch. Ltd. Bell By. "BB" (east of Wilkes Ledge) – Mo(A)W, Rge. 4 mi., RWSRST, (41-30-33N/70-49-54W)

New Bedford West Barrier Lt. – Q.G., Horn 1 bl. ev. 10 s., Ht. 48', Rge. 8 mi., (41-37-27N/70-54-22W)

New Bedford East Barrier Lt. – Q. R., Ht. 48', Rge. 5 mi., (41-37-29N/70-54-19W)

Padanaram Breakwater Lt. #8 – Fl. R. ev. 4 s., Ht. 25', Rge. 5 mi., (41-34-27N/70-56-21W)

Butler Flats Lt. – Fl. W. ev. 4 s., Ht. 25', (41-36-12N/70-53-40W)

Cleveland East Ledge Lt., Cape Cod Canal App. E. side of S. Entr. – Fl. W. ev. 10 s., Horn 1 bl. ev. 15 s., Ht. 74', Rge. 15 mi., Racon (C), (41-37-51N/70-41-39W)

Ned Point Lt. – Iso. W. ev. 6 s., Ht. 41', Rge. 12 mi., (41-39-03N/70-47-44W)

Westport Harbor Entr. Lt. #7, W. side – Fl. G. ev. 6 s., Ht. 35', Rge. 9 mi., (41-30-27N/71-05-17W)

Westport Harbor App. Ltd. Bell By. "WH", Mo(A)W, Rge. 4 mi., RWSRST, (41-29-15N/71-04-04W)

RHODE ISLAND

Sakonnet River Entr. Ltd. Wh. By. "SR" – Mo(A)W, Rge. 4 mi., RWSRST, (41-25-45N/71-13-23W)

Sakonnet Lt. – Fl. W. ev. 6 s., R. sect. 195°-350°, Ht. 58', Rge. W. 7 mi., R. 5 mi., (41-27-11N/71-12-09W)

Sakonnet Breakwater Lt. #2, Entr. to hbr. – Fl. R. ev. 4 s., Ht. 34', Rge. 8 mi., (41-28-00N/71-11-42W)

Narragansett Bay Entr. Ltd. Wh. By. "NB" – Mo(A)W, Rge. 6 mi., Racon (B), RWSRST, (41-23-00N/71-23-21W)

Beavertail Lt. – Narrag. Bay E. passage – Fl. W. ev. 10 s., Obscured 175°-215°, Horn 1 bl. ev. 30 s., Ht. 64', Rge. 15 mi., ltd. 24 hrs., (41-26-58N/71-23-58W)

For abbreviations see footnote p. 167

CROSBY YACHT YARD, INC.
www.crosbyyacht.com

Crosby Yacht Yard has been in the business of boat building and repair since the early 1800's. Located on Cape Cod in scenic Osterville, we are a 150 slip full service marina specializing in wood and fiberglass vessel restorations. Shops include a 35,000 square foot storage and repair building with radiant heat.

Crosby Yacht Yard is the custom builder of the 24' Crosby Striper, Hawk 29', Canyon 30', Wianno Senior, and 21' and 26' Yacht Club Launches. We offer transient dockage and moorings, Ship Store, Fuel Dock, Showers, and "The Islander" restaurant. Shopping, the Post Office and Banks are all within walking distance.

CROSBY YACHT YARD SERVICES

Yacht Sales and Certified Professional Yacht Brokerage: New and Pre-Owned

Sailboat Rigging: Installation & service, re-rigging and conversions

Marine Electronics: Installation all types

Carpentry: Full shop from small repairs to new construction, restorations and furniture

Paint Shop: Specialty - Varnish finishes & maintenance, refinish and restoration

Engine Repair and Maintenance: Cummins, Mercruiser, Mercury Yamaha, Yanmar & Westerbeke

Hauling: 70 Ton Travel Lift

AUTHORIZED DEALER FOR:
- Topaz - 33' to 40'
- Scout Boats - 13' to 35'

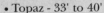   

CROSBY YACHT YARD, INC.
~ Established 1850 ~
72 Crosby Circle, Osterville, MA 02655
Phone:508-428-6900 / Fax: 508-428-0323
Toll Free: 877-491-9759 / VHF Channel 9
Email:contact@crosbyyacht.com

Castle Hill Lt. – Iso R. 6 s., Horn 1 bl. ev. 10 s., Ht. 40′, Rge. 12 mi., (41-27-44N/71-21-47W)

Fort Adams Lt. #2, Narrag. Bay E. passage – Fl. R. ev. 6 s., Horn 1 bl. ev. 15 s., Ht. 32′, Rge. 7 mi., (41-28-54N/71-20-12W)

Newport Harbor Lt., N. end of breakwater – F.G., Ht. 33′, Rge. 11 mi., (41-29-36N/71-19-38W)

Rose Is. Lt., Fl W. ev. 6 s., Ht. 48′, (41-29-44N/71-20-34W)

Prudence Is. Lt. (Sandy Pt.), Narrag. Bay E. passage – Fl. G. ev. 6 s., Ht. 28′, Rge. 6 mi., (41-36-21N/71-18-13W)

Hog Island Shoal Lt., N. side Entr. to Mt. Hope Bay – Iso. W. ev. 6 s., Keyed (VHF 83A) Horn 2 bl. ev. 30 s., Ht. 54′, Rge. 12 mi., (41-37-56N/71-16-24W)

Musselbed Shoals Lt.#6A, Mt. Hope Bay Ch. – Fl. R. ev. 6 s., Ht. 26′, Rge. 6 mi., (41-38-11N/71-15-36W)

Castle Is. Lt. #2, N. of Hog Is. – Fl. R. ev. 6 s., Ht. 26′, Rge. 3 mi., (41-39-14N/71-17-10W)

Bristol Harbor Lt. #4 – F.R., Ht. 25′, Rge. 11 mi., (41-39-58N/71-16-42W)

Conimicut Lt., Providence R. App. – Fl. W. ev. 2.5 s., R. Sect. 322°-349°, Horn 2 bl. ev. 30 s., Ht. 58′, Rge. W. 8 mi., R. 5 mi., (41-43-01N/71-20-42W)

Bullock Point Lt. "BP", Prov. R. – Oc.W. ev. 4 s., Ht. 29′, Rge. 6 mi., (41-44-16N/71-21-51W)

Pomham Rocks Lt., Prov. R. – F.R., Ht. 67′, Rge. 6 mi., (41-46-39N/71-22-10W)

Providence River Ch. Lt. #42, off rock – Iso. R. ev. 6 s., Ht. 31′, Rge. 4 mi., (41-47-39N/71-22-47W)

Mt. Hope Bay Jct. Ltd. Gong By. "MH" – Fl(2+1) R. 6 s., Rge., 3 mi., R. & G. Bands, (41-39-32N/71-14-03W)

Borden Flats Lt., Mt. Hope Bay – Fl. W. ev. 2.5 s., Horn 1 bl. ev. 10 s., Ht. 47′, Rge. 11 mi., (41-42-16N/71-10-28W)

Wickford Harbor Lt. #1, Narrag. Bay W. passage – Fl. G. ev. 6 s., Ht. 40′, Rge. 6 mi., (41-34-24N/71-26-13W)

Warwick Lt., Greenwich Bay App. – Oc.G. ev. 4 s., Horn 1 bl. ev. 15 s., Ht. 66′, Rge. 12 mi., ltd. 24 hrs., (41-40-02N/71-22-42W)

Point Judith Lt., Block Is. Sd. Entr. – Oc(3)W. ev. 15 s., Horn 1 bl. ev. 15 s., Ht. 65′, Rge. 16 mi., (41-21-40N/71-28-53W)

Block Island North Lt., N. end of Is. – Fl. W. ev. 5 s., Ht. 58′, (41-13-39N/71-34-33W)

Block Island Southeast Lt., SE end of Is. – Fl. G. ev. 5 s., Horn 1 bl. ev. 30 s., Ht. 261′, Rge. 20 mi., ltd. 24 hrs., (41-09-10N/71-33-04W)

Block Island Breakwater Lt. #3, – F. G., Keyed (VHF 83A) Horn 2 bl. ev. 30 s., Ht. 27′, Rge. 11 mi., (41-10-38N/71-33-15W)

Pt. Judith Harbor of Refuge W. Entr. Lt. #3 – Fl. G. ev. 6 s., Horn 1 bl. ev. 30 s., Ht. 35′, Rge. 5 mi., (41-21-56N/71-30-53W)

Watch Hill Lt., Fishers Is. Sd. E. Entr. – Alt. W. and R. ev. 5 s., Horn 1 bl. ev. 30 s., Ht. 61′, Rge. 14 mi., ltd. 24 hrs., (41-18-14N/71-51-30W)

FISHERS ISLAND SOUND

Latimer Reef Lt., Fishers Is. Sd. main ch. – Fl. W. ev. 6 s., Bell 2 strokes ev. 15 s., Ht. 55′, Rge. 9 mi., (41-18-16N/71-56-00W)

N. Dumpling Lt., Fishers Is. Sd. main ch. – F.W., Horn 1 bl. ev. 30 s., R. Sect. 257°-023°, Ht. 94′, Rge. R. 7 mi., F.W. 9 mi., (41-17-17N/72-01-10W)

Stonington Outer Breakwater Lt. #4 – Fl. R. ev. 4 s., Horn 1 bl. ev. 10 s., Ht. 46′, Rge. 5 mi., (41-19-00N/71-54-28W)

LONG ISLAND SOUND, NORTH SIDE

Race Rock Lt., SW end of Fishers Is. – Fl. R. ev. 10 s., Horn 2 bl. ev. 30 s., Ht. 67′, Rge. 16 mi., (41-14-37N/72-02-50W)

For abbreviations see footnote p. 167

Preston's, founded in 1880, is the oldest chandlery in continuous operation in the United States. Here are charts for the entire East Coast, navigation equipment and a full stock of marine supplies for power and sail.

Figureheads, ships' wheels & copper lights, marine pictures and hosts of decorative marine items are in The Ship and Sea Gallery. There is also a mail-order showroom filled with the nautical items found in their catalogue.

PRESTON'S
Main Street Wharf
Greenport, Long Island, N.Y. 11944

One of Long Island's most spectacular stores   631-477-1990

Come in and tie up at our docks

Moor, store & maintain in the Heart of Narragansett Bay

- Dockage for any size vessel & 160 all-inclusive moorings; pristine heads & showers, unlimted launch service
- Wireless internet, courtesy shuttle, alongside pump-out
- 10 acres of secure inland inside and outside storage
- State-of-the-art work facilities; paint & refit professionals
- ABYC certified technicians with current training certificates; Repower specialists, mechanical and electrical upgrades
- 7000 sq. ft. Ship's Store & Chandlery

CONANICUT
MARINE SERVICES INC.

nannidiesel   EVINRUDE   YAMAHA   WESTERBEKE   HONDA MARINE   YANMAR

20 Narragansett Avenue, Jamestown, RI 02835 | VHF 71 | 401.423.1556
www.CONANICUTMARINA.com

Bartlett Reef Lt., S. end of reef – Fl. W. ev. 6 s., Keyed (VHF 79A may change to 83A) Horn 2 bl. ev. 60 s., Ht. 35′, Rge. 8 mi., (41-16-28N/72-08-14W)

New London Ledge Lt., W. side of Southwest ledge –Fl(3) W. ev. 30 s., Horn 2 bl. ev. 20 s., Ht. 58′, Rge. 17 mi., (41-18-21N/72-04-39W)

New London Harbor Lt., W. side Entr. – Iso. W. ev. 6 s., R. Sect. 000°-041°, Ht. 89′, Rge. R. 14 mi., W. 17 mi., (41-19-00N/72-05-23W)

Saybrook Breakwater Lt., W. jetty – Fl. G. ev. 6 s., Horn 1 bl. ev. 30 s., Ht. 58′, Rge. 14 mi., (41-15-48N/72-20-34W)

Lynde Pt. Lt., Conn. R. mouth W. side – F.W., Ht. 71′, Rge. 14 mi., (41-16-17N/72-20-35W)

Twenty-Eight Foot Shoal Ltd. Wh. By. "TE" – Fl(2+1) R. ev. 6 s., , Rge. 4 mi., Racon (T), R&G Bands, (41-09-16N/72-30-25W)

Falkner Is. Lt., off Guilford Hbr. – Fl. W. ev. 10 s., Ht. 94′, Rge. 13 mi., (41-12-43N/72-39-13W)

Branford Reef Lt., SE Entr. New Haven – Fl. W. ev. 6 s., Ht. 22′, Rge. 7 mi., (41-13-17N/72-48-19W)

New Haven Hbr. Ltd. Wh. By. "NH" – Mo(A)W, Rge. 4 mi., RWSRST, (41-12-07N/72-53-47W)

Southwest Ledge Lt., E. side Entr. New Haven – Fl. R. ev. 5 s., Horn 1 bl. ev. 15 s., Ht. 57′, Rge. 14 mi., (41-14-04N/72-54-44W)

New Haven Lt. – Fl. W. ev. 4 s., Ht. 27′, Rge. 7 mi., (41-13-16N/72-56-32W)

Stratford Pt. Lt., W. side Entr. Housatonic R. –Fl(2)W. ev. 20 s., Ht. 52′, Rge. 16 mi., (41-09-07N/73-06-12W)

Stratford Shoal Lt., Middle Ground – Fl. W. ev. 5 s., Horn 1 bl. ev. 15 s., Ht. 60′, Rge. 13 mi., (41-03-35N/73-06-05W)

Tongue Pt. Lt., at Bridgeport Breakwater – Fl. G. ev. 4 s., Ht. 31′, Rge. 5 mi., (41-10-00N/73-10-39W)

Penfield Reef Lt., S. side Entr. to Black Rock – Fl. R. ev. 6 s., Horn 1 bl. ev. 15 s., Ht. 51′, Rge. 15 mi., (41-07-02N/73-13-20W)

Peck Ledge Lt., E. App. to Norwalk – Fl. G. ev. 2.5 s., Ht. 61′, Rge. 5 mi., (41-04-39N/73-22-11W)

Greens Ledge Lt., W. end of ledge – Alt. Fl. W. and R. ev. 24 s., Horn 2 bl. ev. 20 s., Ht. 62′, Rge. W. 18 mi., R. 15 mi., (41-02-30N/73-26-38W)

Stamford Harbor Ledge Obstruction Lt., on SW end of Harbor Ledge – Fl. W. ev. 4 s., (41-00-49N/73-32-34W)

Great Captain Is. Lt., SE Pt. of Is. – Alt. W. R. ev. 12 s., Horn 1 bl. ev. 15 s., Ht. 62′, Rge. 17 mi., (40-58-57N/73-37-23W)

Larchmont Harbor Lt. #2, East Entr. – Fl. R. ev. 4 s., Ht. 26′, Rge. 4 mi., (40-55-05N/73-43-52W)

LONG ISLAND SOUND, SOUTH SIDE

Little Gull Is. Lt., E. Entr. L.I. Sd. – Fl(2) W. ev. 15 s., Ht. 91′, Rge. 18 mi., (41-12-23N/72-06-25W)

Plum Gut Lt. – Fl. W. ev. 2.5 s., Ht. 21′ Rge. 5 mi., (41-10-26N/72-12-42W)

Plum Island Ltd. Wh. By. "PI" – Mo(A)W, Rge. 4 mi., RWSRST, (41-13-17N/72-10-48W)

Plum Is. Hbr. West Dolphin Lt., W. end of Is. – Fl. G., Ht. 12′, Rge. 6 mi., Horn 1 bl. ev. 10 s., (Maintained by U.S. Agr. Dept.), (41-10-17N/72-12-24W)

Orient Pt. Lt., outer end of Oyster Pond Reef – Fl. W. ev. 5 s., Horn 2 bl. ev. 30 s., Ht. 64′, Rge. 17 mi., (41-09-48N/72-13-25W)

Horton Pt. Lt., NW point of Horton Neck – Fl. G. ev. 10 s., Ht. 103′, Rge. 14 mi., (41-05-06N/72-26-44W)

Mattituck Breakwater Lt. "MI" – Fl. W. ev. 4 s., Ht. 25′, Rge. 6 mi., (41-00-55N/72-33-40W)

Old Field Pt. Lt. – Alt. Fl. R. and Fl. G. ev. 24 s., Ht. 74′, Rge. 14 mi., (40-58-37N/73-07-07W)

For abbreviations see footnote p. 167

NEW YORK NAUTICAL

We Cover the New York Waterfront

WORLD-WIDE GOVERNMENT CHARTS & PUBLICATIONS
CHELSEA MARINE CLOCKS * SEXTANTS * BAROMETERS
DIVIDERS, PARALLEL RULERS, ETC. * BINOCULARS
WEATHER INSTRUMENTS * EVERYTHING FOR THE NAVIGATOR

Maritime Bookstore

WE ALSO OFFER AN EXTENSIVE SELECTION
OF DISTINCTIVE NAUTICAL GIFTS

158 Duane Street, New York, NY 10013

Telephone: (212) 962-4522 • FAX: (212) 406-8420
Email: sales@newyorknautical.com
www.newyorknautical.com

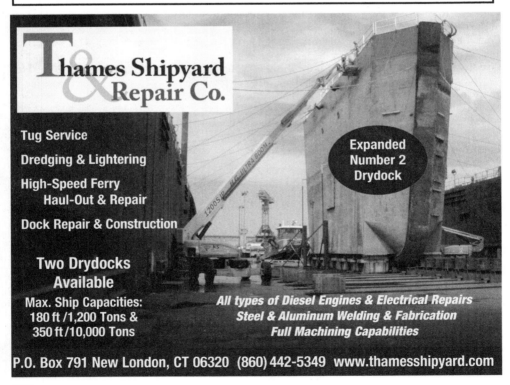

Thames Shipyard & Repair Co.

Tug Service

Dredging & Lightering

High-Speed Ferry Haul-Out & Repair

Dock Repair & Construction

Expanded Number 2 Drydock

Two Drydocks Available

Max. Ship Capacities:
180 ft /1,200 Tons &
350 ft /10,000 Tons

All types of Diesel Engines & Electrical Repairs
Steel & Aluminum Welding & Fabrication
Full Machining Capabilities

P.O. Box 791 New London, CT 06320 (860) 442-5349 www.thamesshipyard.com

Eatons Neck Lt., E. side Entr. Huntington Bay – F. W., Horn 1 bl. ev. 30 s., Ht. 144′, Rge. 18 mi., (40-57-14N/73-23-43W)

Cold Spring Hbr. Lt., on Pt. of shoal – F.W., R. Sect. 039°-125°, Ht. 37′, Rge. W. Sect. 8 mi., R. Sect. 6 mi., (40-54-51N/73-29-35W)

Glen Cove Breakwater Lt. #5, E. side Entr. to hbr. – Fl. G. ev. 4 s., Ht. 24′, Rge. 5 mi., (40-51-43N/73-39-37W)

Port Jefferson App. Ltd. Wh. By. "PJ" – Mo(A)W, Rge. 4 mi., RWSRST, (40-59-16N/73-06-27W)

Huntington Harbor Lt. – Iso. W. ev. 6 s., Horn 1 bl. ev. 15 s., Ht. 42′, Rge. 9 mi., (40-54-39N/73-25-52W)

LONG ISLAND, OUTSIDE

Montauk Point Ltd. Wh. By. "MP" – Mo(A)W, Rge. 4 mi., Racon (M), RWSRST, (41-01-48N/71-45-40W)

Montauk Pt. Lt., E. end of L.I. – Fl. W. ev. 5 s., Horn 1 bl. ev. 15 s., Ht. 168′, Rge. 18 mi., (41-04-15N/71-51-26W)

Montauk Hbr. Entr. Ltd. Bell By. "M" – Mo(A)W, Rge. 6 mi., (41-05-07N/71-56-23W)

Shinnecock Inlet App. Ltd. Wh. By. "SH" – Mo(A)W, Rge. 4 mi., RWSRST, (40-49-00N/72-28-35W)

Moriches Inlet App. Ltd. Wh. By. "M" – Mo(A)W, Rge. 6 mi., RWS, (40-44-08N/72-45-12W)

Shinnecock Lt., W. side of Inlet – Fl(2) W. ev. 15 s., Ht. 75′, Rge. 11 mi., (40-50-31N/72-28-42W)

Jones Inlet Lt., end of breakwater – Fl. W. ev. 2.5 s., Ht. 33′, Rge. 6 mi., (40-34-24N/73-34-32W)

Jones Inlet Ltd. Wh. By. "JI" – Mo(A)W, Rge. 4 mi., RWSRST, (40-33-37N/73-35-13W)

E. Rockaway Inlet Ltd. Bell By. "ER" – Mo(A)W, Rge. 5 mi., RWSRST, (40-34-17N/73-45-49W)

Fire Is. Lt., 5.5 mi. E. of inlet – Fl. W. ev. 7.5 s., Ht. 167′, ltd. 24 hrs., (40-37-57N/73-13-07W)

Rockaway Point Breakwater Lt. #4, end of breakwater – Fl. R. ev. 4 s., Ht. 34′, Rge. 5 mi., (40-32-25N/73-56-27W)

NEW YORK HARBOR & APPROACHES

Execution Rocks Lt. – Fl. W. ev. 10 s., Ht. 62′, Rge. 15 mi., Racon (X), (40-52-41N/73-44-16W)

Hart Is. Lt. #46, off S. end of Is. – Fl. R. ev. 4 s., Ht. 23′, Rge. 6 mi., (40-50-42N/73-46-00W)

Stepping Stones Lt., outer end of reef – Oc.G. ev. 4 s., Ht. 46′, Rge. 8 mi., (40-49-28N/73-46-29W)

Throgs Neck Lt., Fort Schuyler – F. R., Ht. 60′, Rge. 11 mi., (40-48-16N/73-47-26W)

Whitestone Pt. Lt. #1, East R. main ch. – Q.G., Ht. 56′, Rge. 3 mi., (40-48-06N/73-49-10W)

Kings Pt. Lt. – (Private Aid), Iso. W. ev. 2 s., (40-48-42N/73-45-48W)

Hell Gate Lt. #15, East R. Hallets Pt. – Fl. G. ev. 2.5 s., Ht. 33′, Rge. 4 mi., (40-46-41N/73-56-05W)

Mill Rock South Lt. #16, East R., main ch. – Fl. R. ev. 4 s., Ht. 37′, Rge. 4 mi., (40-46-46N/73-56-22W)

Governors Is. Extension Lt., SW Pt. of Is. – F. R., Horn 1 bl. ev. 15 s., Ht. 47′, Rge. 9 mi., (40-41-09N/74-01-35W)

Governors Is. Lt. #2 – NW pt of Is. – 2 F.R. arranged vertically, Lower Lt. Obscured from 240°-243°, 254°-256°, 264°-360°, Horn 2 bl. ev. 20 s., Ht. 75′, Rge. 7 mi., (40-41-35N/74-01-11W)

For abbreviations see footnote p. 167

NEB
New England Boatworks

Rhode Island's best protected marina. Come visit & see what experienced boat owners have enjoyed for years!

❖ Top Rated, full service Marina & Boatyard ❖ Professional service staff – small jobs to major refits
❖ Located: Narragansett Bay, East Passage, 5 Mi North of Newport bridge ❖ Pool ❖ WiFi
❖ Modern Shower & Rest Room Facilities ❖ Restaurant – Melville Grille ❖ Ship's Store
❖ Haulout to 88 Tons – 15' draft ❖ Repairs, Repower, Refit ❖ Fuel, Pump-out, Laundry

One Lagoon Road, Portsmouth, RI 02871 Tel: 401.683.4000
information@NEBoatworks.com www.NEBoatworks.com

We'll steer your diesel power decisions the way you steer your boat.

You wouldn't take risks when it comes to navigation. So when you consider the right engine for long term perform-ance and reliability, we'll help you make the right decisions. At Mack Boring, we do more than just sell equipment. We're staffed with experts in product specification, application engineering, service and parts, so that when you have a propulsion issue, you get straight answers and solid solutions.

So whether you are building a new boat, repowering or dealing with a performance problem, count on us to steer you right.

MACK BORING
& PARTS COMPANY
Reliable Power. Everywhere.
Since 1922
3 locations: NJ, MA, NC
www.mackboring.com
800-622-5364

YANMAR.
Diesel Engines 14 to 900 hp

Ask about our nationally recognized diesel engine maintenance seminars.

Verrazano-Narrows Bridge Sound Signal – (Private Aid), 2 Horns on bridge 1 bl. ev. 15 s., (none given)

Coney Is. Lt., N.Y. Hbr. main ch. – Fl. R. ev. 5 s., Ht. 75′, Rge. 16 mi., ltd. 24 hrs., (40-34-36N/74-00-42W)

Romer Shoal Lt., N.Y. Hbr. S. App. – Fl(2) W. ev. 15 s., Horn 2 bl. ev. 30 s., Ht. 54′, Rge. 15 mi., (40-30-47N/74-00-49W)

West Bank (Range Front) Lt., Ambrose Ch. outer sect. – Iso. W. ev. 6 s., R. Sect. 004°-181° and W from 181° - 004°, Horn 2 bl. ev. 20 s., Ht. 69′, ltd. 24 hrs., (40-32-17N/74-02-34W)

Staten Island (Range Rear) Lt., Ambrose Ch. outer sect. – F. W. , Visible on range line only, Ht. 231′, ltd. 24 hrs., (40-34-34N/74-08-28W)

Old Orchard Shoal Lt., N.Y. Hbr. – Fl. W. ev. 6 s., R. Sect. 087°-203°, Ht. 51′, Rge. W. 7 mi., R. 5 mi., (40-30-44N/74-05-55W)

Sandy Hook Lt. – F. W., Ht. 88′, Rge. 19 mi., ltd. 24 hrs., (40-27-42N/74-00-07W)

Sandy Hook Ch. (Range Front) Lt. – Q. W., G., and R. sectors, Red from 063°-073° and Green from 300.5°-315.5°, Ht. 44′, Rge. 5 mi., Racon (C), (40-29-15N/73-59-35W)

Southwest Spit Jct. Ltd. Gong By. "SP" – Fl(2+1) R. ev. 6 s., Rge. 3 mi., R. & G. Bands, (40-28-46N/74-03-18W)

Sandy Hook Pt. Lt. – Iso W. ev. 6 s., Ht. 38′, Rge. 13 mi., Horn 1 bl. ev. 10 s., "NB" on Skeleton Tower, (40-28-15N/74-01-07W)

Scotland Ltd. Wh. By. "S", Sandy Hook Ch. App. – Mo(A)W, Rge. 7 mi., Racon (M), RWSRST, (40-26-33N/73-55-01W)

Nantucket Traffic Lane Ltd. Wh. By. "NA" – Fl.Y. ev. 6 s., Rge. 7 mi., Racon (N), Yellow, (40-25-42N/73-11-28W)

Ambrose Ch. Ltd. Wh. By. "A" – Mo(A)W, Rge. 7 mi., Racon (N), RWSRST, (40-27-28N/73-50-12W)

NEW JERSEY

Highlands Lt. – Oc. W. ev. 10 s., Obscured 334°-140°, (40-23-48N/73-59-09W)

Atlantic Highlands Breakwater Lt. – Fl. W. ev. 4 s., Ht. 33′, Rge. 7 mi., (40-25-07N/74-01-10W)

Kill Van Kull Ch. Jct. Ltd. Wh. By. "KV"– Fl (2+1) R. ev. 6 s., Rge. 3 mi., R. & G. Bands, Racon (K), (40-39-02N/74-03-51W)

Kill Van Kull Ch. Jct. Ltd. By. "A"– Fl (2+1) G. ev. 6 s., Rge. 3 mi., G. & R. Bands (40-38-45N/74-10-07W)

Kill Van Kull Ch. East Jct. Ltd. By. "E"– Fl (2+1) G. ev. 6 s., Rge. 3 mi. G. & R. Bands (40-38-31N/74-09-15W)

Manasquan Inlet Lt. #3 - Fl. G. ev. 6 s., Horn 1 bl. ev. 30 s., Ht. 35′ Rge. 8 mi., (40-06-01N/74-01-54W)

Shark River Inlet Ltd. Wh. By. "SI" – Mo(A)W, Rge. 6 mi., RWSRST, (40-11-09N/74-00-03W)

Barnegat Inlet S. Breakwater Lt. #7 – Q. G., Ht. 37′, Rge. 8 mi., Horn 1 bl. ev. 30 s., (39-45-26N/74-05-36W)

Barnegat Ltd. By. "B" – Fl. Y. ev. 6 s., Rge. 7 mi., Racon (B), Yellow, (39-45-48N/73-46-04W)

Barnegat Inlet Outer Ltd. Wh. By. "BI" – Mo(A)W, Rge. 6 mi., RWSRST, (39-44-28N/74-03-51W)**Little Egg Inlet Outer Ltd. Wh. By. "LE"** – Mo(A)W, Rge. 6 mi., RWSRST, (39-27-56N/74-16-27W)**Brigantine Inlet Wreck Ltd. By. "WR2"** (100 yards, 090° from wreck) – Q. R., Rge. 5 mi., Red, (39-24-48N/74-13-47W)

Great Egg Harbor Inlet Outer Ltd. Wh. By. "GE" – Mo(A)W, Rge. 5 mi., RWSRST, (39-16-14N/74-31-56W)

Hereford Inlet Lt., S. side – Fl. W. ev. 10 s., Ht. 57′, Rge. 24 mi., (39-00-24N/74-47-28W)

Five Fathom Bank Ltd. By. "F", Delaware Bay Entr. – Fl. Y. ev. 2.5 s., Rge. 6 mi., Racon (M), Yellow, (38-46-49N/74-34-32W)

For abbreviations see footnote p. 167

There is no substitute for paper charts and guides.
There is no substitute for Maptech.®

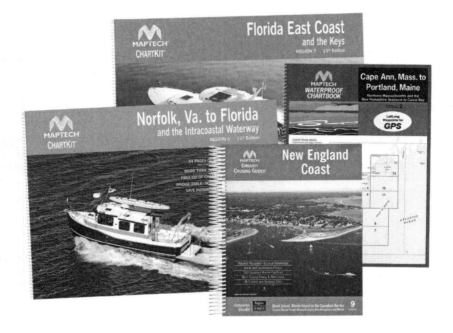

SAFE, RELIABLE AND EASY TO USE

Our product family includes ChartKit,® Embassy Cruising Guides, waterproof chartbooks, waterproof charts, and waterproof inland lakes and waterways maps.

- **ChartKit®** - Get the big picture. Go beyond the limits of digital screens with our large, 17" x 22" charts.
- **Embassy Cruising Guide** - The perfect ChartKit® companion and the most comprehensive guide available.
- **Waterproof Chartbooks** - Full-size charts in a conveniently sized book, printed on tough, tear-resistant waterproof pages.

Purchase at your local marine dealer or bookstore.

1-888-839-5551 | www.maptech.com

Cape May Lt. – Fl. W. ev. 15 s., Ht. 165', Rge. 24 mi., (38-55-59N/74-57-37W)

NEW JERSEY, DELAWARE AND MARYLAND

Delaware Ltd. By. "D", Del. Bay – Fl. Y. ev. 6 s., Rge. 7 mi., Racon (K), Yellow, (38-27-18N/74-41-47W)

Delaware Traffic Lane Ltd. By. "DA" – Fl. Y. ev. 2.5 s., Rge. 6 mi., Yellow, (38-32-45N/74-46-56W)

Delaware Traffic Lane Ltd. By. "DB" – Fl. Y. ev. 4 s., Rge. 6 mi., Yellow, (38-38-12N/74-52-11W)

Delaware Traffic Lane Ltd. By. "DC" – Fl. Y. ev. 2.5 s., Rge. 7 mi., Yellow, (38-43-47N/74-57-33W)

Brown Shoal Lt. – Fl. W. ev. 2.5 s., Ht. 23', Rge. 7 mi., Racon (B), (38-55-21N/75-06-01W)

Brandywine Shoal Lt., Del. Bay main ch. 9 mi. from S. end of shoal – Fl. W. ev. 10 s., R. Sect. 151°-338°, Horn 1 bl. ev. 15 s. (Mar. 15 - Dec. 15), Ht. 60', Rge. W. 19 mi., R. 13 mi., (38-59-10N/75-06-47W)

Harbor of Refuge Lt., Del. Bay main ch., S. end of breakwater – Fl. W. ev. 10 s., 2 R. Sect. 325°-351° and 127°-175°, Horn 2 bl. ev. 30 s., Ht. 72', Rge. W. 19 mi., R. 16 mi., (38-48-52N/75-05-33W)

Fourteen Foot Bank Lt., Del. Bay main ch. W. side – Fl. W. ev. 9 s., R. Sect. 332.5°-151°, Horn 1 bl. ev. 30 s., Ht. 59', Rge. W. 13 mi., R. 10 mi., (39-02-54N/75-10-56W)

Miah Maull Shoal Lt., Del Bay main ch. – Oc. W. ev. 4 s., R. Sect. 137.5°-333°, Horn 1 bl. ev. 10 s., (Mar. 15-Dec. 15). Ht. 59', Rge. W. 15 mi., R. 12 mi., Racon (M), (39-07-36N/75-12-31W)

Elbow of Cross Ledge Lt., Del. Bay main ch. – Iso. W. ev. 6 s., Horn 2 bl. ev. 20 s., (Mar. 15-Dec. 15), Ht. 61', Rge. 15 mi., (39-10-56N/75-16-06W)

Ship John Shoal Lt., Del. Bay main ch. – Fl. W. ev. 5 s., R. Sect. 138°-321.5°, Horn 1 bl. ev. 15 s. (Mar. 15 - Dec. 15), Ht. 50', Rge. W. 16 mi., R. 12 mi., Racon (O), (39-18-19N/75-22-36W)

Egg Island Point Lt. – Fl. W. ev. 4 s., Ht. 27', Rge. 7 mi., (39-10-21N/75-07-55W)

Ben Davis Pt. Lt. "BD" – Fl. W. ev. 6 s., Ht. 30', Rge. 6 mi., (39-17-27N/75-17-18W)

Old Reedy Is. Lt. – Iso. W. ev. 6 s., R. Sect. 353°-014°, Ht. 20', Rge. W. 8 mi., R. 6 mi., (39-30-03N/75-34-08W)

Fenwick Is. Lt. – Oc.W. ev. 13 s., Ht. 83', (Rge. none given), (38-27-06N/75-03-18W)

Ocean City Inlet Jetty Lt., on end of jetty – Iso. W. ev. 6 s., Ht. 38', Rge. 6 mi., (38-19-27N/75-05-06)

VIRGINIA

Assateague Lt., S. side of Is. – Fl(2) W. ev. 5 s., Ht. 154', Rge. 22 mi., (37-54-40N/75-21-22W)

Wachapreague Inlet Ltd. Wh. By. "W" – Mo(A)W, Rge. 6 mi., RWSRST, (37-34-54N/75-33-37W)

Quinby Inlet Ltd. Wh. By. "Q" – Mo(A)W, Rge. 5 mi., RWSRST, (37-28-06N/75-36-05W)

Great Machipongo Inlet Ltd. Wh. By. "GM" – Mo(A)W, Rge. 5 mi., RWSRST, (37-23-36N/75-39-06W)

Great Machipongo Inlet Lt. #5, S. side – Fl. G. ev. 4 s., Ht. 15', Rge. 4 mi., (37-21-40N/75-44-06W)

Cape Charles Lt., N. side of Entr. to Ches. Bay – Fl. W. ev. 5 s., Ht. 180', Rge. 18 mi., (37-07-23N/75-54-23W)

For abbreviations see footnote p. 167

Distance Table in Nautical Miles
*Approximate

Bar Harbor to
Halifax, N.S.	259
Yarmouth, N.S.	101
Saint John, N.B.	122
Machiasport	52
Rockland	62
Boothbay Harbor	86
Portland	115
Marblehead	169

Rockland to
Boothbay Harbor	42
Belfast	22
Bucksport	33

Boothbay Harbor to
Kennebec River	11
Monhegan	15
Portland	36

Portland Ltd. Buoy "P" to
Biddeford	17
Portsmouth	54
Cape Cod Light	99
Cape Cod Canal (E. Entr.)	118
Pollock Rip Slue	141

Portsmouth (Whaleback) to
York River	7
Biddeford Pool	30
Newburyport Entr.	15
Gloucester – via Annisquam	28

Gloucester to
Boston	26
Scituate	26
Plymouth	43
Cape Cod Canal (E. Entr.)	52
Provincetown	45

Marblehead to
Portsmouth	43
Biddeford Pool	68
Portland	87
Boothbay Harbor	104
Rockland	133
Plymouth	38
Cape Cod Canal (E. Entr.)	47

Boston (Commonwealth Pier)
Marblehead	17
Isles of Shoals	52
Portsmouth	58
Portland	95
Kennebec River	107
Boothbay Harbor	116
Rockland	149
North Haven	148
Bangor	194
St. John, N.B.	286
Halifax, N.S.	380
Cohasset	14
Cape Cod Canal, E. Entr.	50
Provincetown	50
Vineyard Haven	77
New Bedford	81
Fall River	107
Newport	122
New London	140
New York	234

**Western Entr., Cape Cod Canal to
East Entrance	8
Woods Hole	15
Quicks Hole	20
New Bedford	24
Newport	50
New London	83

Woods Hole to
Hyannis	19
Chatham	32
Cuttyhunk	14
Marion	11

Vineyard Haven to
Edgartown	9
Marblehead – around Cape	114
Canal – via Woods Hole	20
Newport	45
New London	77
New Haven	114
South Norwalk	140
City Island	153

*Each distance is by the shortest route that safe navigation permits between the two ports concerned.

**Western entr., The beginning of the "land cut" at Bourne Neck, 7.3 nautical miles up the channel from Cleveland Ledge Lt.

Continued p. 194

Chesapeake Lt., off Entr. to Ches. Bay – Fl(2) W. ev. 15 s., Horn 1 bl. ev. 10 s., Ht. 117', Rge. 19 mi., Racon (N), (36-54-17N/75-42-46W)

Chesapeake Bay Entr. Ltd. Wh. By. "CH" – Mo(A)W, Rge. 7 mi., Racon (C), RWSRST, (36-56-08N/75-57-27W)

Cape Henry Lt., S. side of Entr. to Ches. Bay – Mo (U) W ev. 20 s., R. Sect. 154°-233°, Ht. 164', Rge. W. 17 mi., R. 15 mi., (36-55-35N/76-00-26W)

CHESAPEAKE BAY

Thimble Shoal Lt., Thimble Shoal Ch. – Fl. W. ev. 10 s., Ht. 55', Rge. 18 mi., (37-00-52N/76-14-23W)

Worton Pt. Lt., Fl. W. ev. 6 s., Ht. 93' Rge. 6 mi., (39-19-06N/76-11-11W)

Old Point Comfort Lt., N. side Entr. to Hampton Roads – Fl(2) R. ev. 12 s., W. Sect. 265°-038°, Ht. 54', Rge. W. 16 mi., R. 14 mi., (37-00-06N/76-18-23W)

York Spit Lt., N. side Entr. to York R. – On pile, Fl. W. ev. 6 s., Ht. 30', Rge. 8 mi., (37-12-35N/76-15-15W)

Wolf Trap Lt., Ches. Ch. – Fl. W. ev. 15 s., Ht. 52', Rge. 14 mi., (37-23-26N/76-11-22W)

Stingray Pt. Lt., Ches. Ch. – Fl. W. ev. 4 s., Ht. 34', Rge. 9 mi., (37-33-41N/76-16-12W)

Windmill Pt. Lt., Ches. Ch. – On pile. Fl. W. ev. 6 s., 2 R. Sectors 293°-082° and 091.5°-113°, Ht. 34', Rge. W. 9 mi., R. 7 mi., (37-35-49N/76-14-10W)

Tangier Sound Lt., Ches. Ch. – Fl. W. ev. 6 s., R. Sect. 115°-193°, Ht. 45', Rge. W. 12 mi., R. 9 mi., (37-47-17N/75-58-24W)

Smith Pt. Lt., Ches. Ch. – Fl. W. ev. 10 s., Ht. 52', Rge. 15 mi., (37-52-48N/76-11-01W)

Point Lookout Lt., Ches. Ch. – Fl(2) W. ev. 5 s., Ht. 39', Rge. 8 mi., (38-01-30N/76-19-25W)

Holland Is. Bar Lt., Ches. Ch. – Fl. W. ev. 2.5 s., Horn 1 bl. ev. 30 s. (operates continuously Sept. 15 - June 1), Ht. 37', Rge. 7 mi., (38-04-07N/76-05-45W)

Point No Point Lt., Ches. Ch. – Fl. W. ev. 6 s., Ht. 52', Rge. 9 mi., (38-07-41N/76-17-25W)

Hooper Is. Lt., Ches. Ch. – Fl. W. ev. 6 s., Horn 1 bl. ev. 30 s. (operates continuously Sept. 15 - June 1), Ht. 63', Rge. 9 mi., (38-15-23N/76-14-59W)

Drum Pt. Lt.#4, Ches. Ch. – Fl. R. ev. 2.5 s., Ht. 17', Rge. 5 mi., (38-19-08N/76-25-15W)

Cove Pt. Lt., Ches. Ch. – Fl. W. ev. 10 s., Ht. 45', Rge. 12 mi., Obscured from 040°-110°, ltd. 24 hrs, (38-23-11N/76-22-54W)

Bloody Point Bar Lt., Ches. Ch. – Fl. W. ev. 6 s., 2 R. Sectors 003°-022° and 183°-202°, Ht. 54', Rge. W. 9 mi., R. 7 mi., (38-50-02N/76-23-30W)

Thomas Pt. Shoal Lt., Ches. Ch. – Fl. W. ev. 5 s., 2 R. Sectors 011°-051.5° and 096.5°-202°, Horn 1 bl. ev. 15 s., Ht. 43', Rge. W. 16 mi., R. 11 mi., (38-53-56N/76-26-09W)

Sandy Pt. Shoal Lt., Ches. Ch. – Fl. W. ev. 6 s., Ht. 51', Rge. 9 mi., (39-00-57N/76-23-04W)

Baltimore Lt. – Fl. W. ev. 2.5 s., R. Sector 082°- 160°, Ht. 52', Rge. W. 7 mi., R. 5 mi., (39-03-33N/76-23-56W)

Wm. P. Lane, Jr. Bridge West Ch. Fog Signal, on main ch. span – Horn 1 bl. ev. 15 s., 5 s. bl., Horn Points 017° & 197°, (38-59-36N/76-22-53W)

Wm. P. Lane, Jr. Bridge East Ch. Fog Signal, on main ch. span – Horn 1 bl. ev. 20 s., 2 s. bl., (38-59-18N/76-21-30W)

NORTH CAROLINA

Currituck Beach Lt. – Fl. W. ev. 20 s., Ht. 158', Rge. 18 mi., (36-22-37N/75-49-47W)

Bodie Is. Lt. – Fl(2) W. ev. 30 s., Ht. 156', Rge. 18 mi., (35-49-07N/75-33-48W)

Oregon Inlet Jetty Lt. – Iso. W. ev. 6 s., Ht. 28', Rge. 7 mi., (35-46-26N/75-31-30W)

Cape Hatteras Lt., – Fl. W. ev. 7.5 s., Ht. 192', Rge. 24 mi., (35-15-02N/75-31-44W)

Hatteras Inlet Lt. – Iso. W. ev. 6 s., Ht. 48', Rge. 10 mi., (35-11-52N/75-43-56W)

Ocracoke Lt., on W. part of island – F.W., Ht. 75', Rge. 15 mi., (35-06-32N/75-59-10W)

For abbreviations see footnote p. 167

Distance Table in Nautical Miles

Continued from p. 192   *Approximate

Nantucket Entr. Bell NB to
Boston – around Cape.............. 105
Boston – via Canal 94
Chatham 23
Edgartown.................................... 23
Hyannis 21
Woods Hole................................... 30
Cape Cod Canal (W. Entr.) 45
Newport... 71

New Bedford (State Pier) to
Woods Hole................................... 14
Newport... 38
New London 74
New York (Gov. Is.)................. 166

Newport to
Providence.................................... 21
Stonington.................................... 34
New London 48
New Haven 84
City Island 122

Block Island (FR Horn) to
Nantucket 79
Vineyard Haven...................... 52
Cleveland Ledge Lt.................. 50
New Bedford 44
Newport 22
Race Point Lt............................... 21
New London 29

New London to
Greenport..................................... 25
New Haven.................................... 49
Bridgeport 60
City Island 86

Port Jefferson to
Larchmont..................................... 30
So. Norwalk................................... 15
Milford... 14
Old Saybrook................................ 43
New London 53

City Island to
Governors Island 17
Execution Rocks............................ 3

Execution Rocks to
Port Chester 8
Stamford....................................... 12
Oyster Bay Harbor 14
So. Norwalk................................... 19
Bridgeport 29

Port Jefferson........................... 30
Milford... 37
New Haven.................................... 49
Conn. River 69
Mystic 84
Montauk Point 87

New York (Battery) to
Jones Inlet.................................... 34
Fire Island Inlet...................... 47
Moriches Inlet............................ 74
Shinnecock Inlet...................... 88
Montauk Point 117
Keyport... 22
Asbury Park 35
Manasquan 40
Little Egg Inlet 81
Atlantic City................................ 97
Philadelphia............................ 235
Chesapeake Lt. Stn............... 247
Cape Henry Lt. 262
Norfolk 288
Baltimore 418

Brielle-Manasquan to
E. Rockaway Inlet.................... 32
Jones Inlet.................................. 35
Fire Island Inlet...................... 45
Montauk Point 117
Barnegat Inlet............................ 21
Atlantic City................................ 51

Delaware Breakwater to
Reedy Pt. Entr. (C&D Canal) .. 51
Annapolis – via Canal.............. 97
Norfolk 167
New York 150
New London 242
Providence................................ 275
New Bedford 278
Boston (outside) 399
Portland (outside) 443

Old Point Comfort to
Baltimore 163
Philadelphia............................ 240
New York 276
New London 363
Providence................................ 392
New Bedford 397
Boston (outside) 512
Portland..................................... 553

Cape Lookout Lt., on N. pt. of cape – Fl. W. ev. 15 s., Ht. 156′, Rge. 25 mi., (34-37-22N/76-31-28W)

Beaufort Inlet Ch. Ltd. Wh. By. "BM" – Mo(A)W, Rge. 6 mi., Racon (M), RWSRST, (34-34-49N/76-41-33W)

New River Inlet Ltd. Wh. By. "NR" – Mo(A)W, Rge. 6 mi., RWSRST, (34-31-02N/77-19-33W)

Oak Is. Lt., on SE pt. of island – Fl(4) W. ev. 10 s., Ht. 169′, Rge. 24 mi., (33-53-34N/78-02-06W)

Cape Fear River Entr. Ltd. Wh. By. "CF" – Mo(A)W, Rge. 6 mi., Racon (C), RWSRST, (33-46-17N/78-03-02W)

SOUTH CAROLINA

Little River Inlet Entr. Ltd. Wh. By. "LR" – Mo(A)W, Rge. 5 mi., RWSRST, (33-49-49N/78-32-27W)

Little River Inlet North Jetty Lt. #2 – Fl. R. ev. 4 s., Ht. 24′, Rge. 5 mi., (33-50-31N/78-32-39W)

Winyah Bay Ltd. Wh. By. "WB" – Mo(A)W, Rge. 6 mi., RWSRST, (33-11-37N/79-05-11W)

Georgetown Lt., E. side Entr. to Winyah Bay – Fl(2) W. ev. 15 s., Ht. 85′, Rge. 15 mi., (33-13-21N/79-11-06W)

Charleston Entr. Ltd. By. "C" – Mo(A)W, Rge. 6 mi., Racon (K), RWSRST, (32-37-05N/79-35-30W)

Charleston Lt., S. side of Sullivans Is. – Fl(2) W. ev. 30 s., Ht. 163′, Rge. 26 mi., (32-45-29N/79-50-36W)

GEORGIA

Tybee Lt., NE end of Is. – F. W., Ht. 144′, Rge. 19 mi., ltd. 24 hrs., (32-01-20N/80-50-44W)

Tybee Lighted Buoy "T" – Mo(A)W, Rge. 6 mi., Racon (G), RWSRST, (31-57-52N/80-43-10W)

St. Simons Ltd. By. "STS" – Mo(A)W, Rge. 6 mi., Racon (B), RWSRST, (31-02-49N/81-14-25W)

St. Simons Lt., N. side Entr. to St. Simons Sd. – F. Fl. W. ev. 60 s., Ht. 104′, Rge. F. W. 18 mi., Fl. W. 23 mi., (31-08-03N/81-23-37W)

FLORIDA

Amelia Is. Lt., 2 mi. from N. end of Is. – Fl. W. ev. 10 s., R. Sect. 344°-360°, Ht. 107′, Rge. W. 23 mi., R. 19 mi., (30-40-23N/81-26-33W)

St. Johns Lt., on shore – Fl(4) W. ev. 20 s., Obscured 179°-354°, Ht. 83′, Rge. 19 mi., (30-23-10N/81-23-53W)

St. Johns Ltd. By. "STJ" – Mo(A)W, Rge. 6 mi., Racon (M), RWSRST, (30-23-35N/81-19-08W)

St. Augustine Lt., N. end of Anastasia Is. – F. Fl. W. ev. 30 s., Ht. 161′, Rge. F. W. 19 mi., Fl. W. 24 mi., (29-53-08N/81-17-19W)

Ponce De Leon Inlet Lt., S. side on inlet – Fl(6) W. ev. 30 s., Ht. 159′, (29-04-50N/80-55-41W)

Cape Canaveral Lt., on Cape – Fl(2) W. ev. 20 s., Ht. 137′, Rge. 24 mi., (28-27-37N/80-32-36W)

Sebastian Inlet N. Jetty Lt. – Fl. W. ev. 4 s., R. Sect. 104°-154°, Ht. 27′, Rge. W. 5 mi., R. 4 mi., (27-51-41N/80-26-51W)

Jupiter Inlet Lt., N. side of inlet – Fl(2) W. ev. 30 s., Obscured 231°-234°, Ht. 146′, Rge. 25 mi., (26-56-55N/80-04-55W)

Hillsboro Inlet Entr. Lt., N. side of inlet – Fl. (2) W. ev. 20 s., Obscured 114°-119°, Ht. 136′, Rge. 28 mi., (26-15-33N/80-04-51W)

Port Everglades Ltd. By. "PE" - Mo(A)W, Rge. 7 mi., Racon (T), RWSRST, (26-05-30N/80-04-46W)

For abbreviations see footnote p. 167

SHIPYARD COMPANIES, INC.

FULL SERVICE SHIPYARD & MARINA

FIRST IN EXPERIENCE

FIRST IN SERVICE

FIRST CHOICE FOR YOUR YACHT

WWW.FAIRHAVENSHIPYARD.COM
50 FORT STREET & 32 WATER STREET
FAIRHAVEN, MASSACHUSETTS 02719
PHONE: (508) 999-1600 FAX: (508) 999-1650

Miami Ltd. By. "M" – E. end of Miami Beach, Mo(A)W, Rge. 7 mi., Racon (M), RWSRST, (25-46-06N/80-05-00W)

Fowey Rocks Lt., Hawk Ch. – Fl. W. ev. 10 s., 2 R. Sect., W. Sectors 188°-359° and 022°-180°, R. in intervening sectors, Ht. 110′, Rge. W. 15 mi., R. 10 mi. Racon (O), (25-35-26N/80-05-48W)

Carysfort Reef Lt., outer line of reefs – Fl(3) W. ev. 60 s., 3 W. Sectors 211°-018° and 049°-087° and 145°-184°, R. in intervening sectors, Ht. 100′, Rge. W. 15 mi., R. 13 mi., Racon (C), (25-13-19N/80-12-41W)

Alligator Reef Lt., outer line of reefs – Fl(4) W. ev. 60 s., 2 R. sectors 223°-249° and 047°-068°, Ht. 136′, Rge. W. 16 mi., R. 13 mi., Racon (G), (24-51-06N/80-37-08W)

Sombrero Key Lt., outer line of reefs – Fl(5) W. ev. 60 s., 3 W. Sectors 222°-238° and 264°-066° and 094°-163°, R. in intervening sectors, Ht. 142′, Rge. W. 15 mi., R. 12 mi., Racon (M), (24-37-40N/81-06-39W)

American Shoal Lt., outer line of reefs – Fl(3) W. ev. 15 s., W. sectors 270°-067° and 125°-242°, Obscured 90°-125°, R. in intervening sectors, Ht. 109′, Rge. R. 10 mi., Racon (Y), (24-31-30N/81-31-10W)

Sand Key Lt., Fl(2) W. ev. 15 s., 2 Red Sectors 072°-086° and 248°-270°, Ht. 109′, Rge. W. 14 mi., R. 11 mi., Racon (N), (24-27-14N/81-52-39W)

Dry Tortugas Lt., on Loggerhead Key – Fl. W. ev. 20 s., Ht. 151′, Rge. 20 mi., Racon (K), (24-38-00N/82-55-14W)

BERMUDA – APPROACH LIGHTS FROM SEAWARD

North Rock Beacon – Fl(4)W. ev. 20 s., Ht. 70′, Rge. 12 mi., RaRef, (32-28.5N/64-46.1W)

North East Breaker Beacon – Fl. W. ev. 2.5 s., Ht. 45′, Rge. 12 mi., Racon (N), RaRef, (Red tower on red tripod base reading "Northeast," (32-28.7N/64-41.0W)

Kitchen Shoal Beacon – Fl(3)W. ev. 15 s., Ht. 45′, Rge. 12 mi., RaRef, RWS, Red "Kitchen" on White background, (32-26.1N/64-37.6W)

Eastern Blue Cut Beacon – Fl. W. Mo(U) ev. 10 s., Ht. 60′, Rge. 12 mi., RaRef, B&W Tower "Eastern Blue Cut" on white band, (32-23.9N/64-52.6W)

Chub Heads – Q. Fl(9) W. ev. 15 s., Ht. 60′, Rge. 12 mi., RaRef, Yellow and Black Horizontal Stripe Tower with "Chub Heads" in White on Black Central band, Racon (C), (32-17.2N/64-58.9W)

Mills Breaker By. – Q. Fl(3)W. ev. 5 s., Black "Mills" on yellow background, (32-23.9N/64-36.9W)

Spit By. – Q. Fl(3) W. ev. 10 s., Black "Spit" on yellow, (32-22.7N/64-38.5W)

Sea By. –Mo(A)W ev. 6 s., RWS, Red "SB" in white on side, (32-22.9N/64-37.1W)

St. David's Is. Lt. – F. R. and G. Sectors below Fl(2) W. ev. 20 s., Ht. 212′, Rge. W. 15 mi., R. and G. 20 mi., (32-21.8N/64-39.1W) Your bearing from seaward of G. Sector is 221°-276° True; remaining Sector is R. and partially obscured by land 044°-135° True.

Kindley Field Aero Beacon – Alt. W and G.; 1 White, 1 Green (rotating Aero Beacon), Ht. 140′, Rge. 15 mi., (32-21.95N/64-40.55W)

Gibbs Hill Lighthouse – Fl. W. ev. 10 s., Ht. 354′, Rge. 26 mi., (32-15.2N/64-50.1W)

☆ Note: The information in this volume has been compiled from U. S. Government sources and others, and carefully checked. The Publishers cannot assume any liability for errors, omissions, or changes.

Foregoing information checked to date, September, 2012. See page 4 for free Supplement in May 2013.

Heaving the Lead

In tidal water where depths were doubtfully marked on the chart, or in thick weather off shore, soundings were made to determine the ship's position. The leadsman stood in the fore channels and swung the lead. [Aft] in the main and mizzen channels were other men who held the line as it led aft to the stern, where the mate stood by the line tub. The leadsman called, "All ready there?" to the next man, the mate shouted "Heave!" and the lead went spinning forward. Each man let go as the line tautened, and the mate grasped the line as it ran from the tub, and made the sounding. If the lead struck bottom before it reached him, one of the others took the sounding and called the marks. Markers on the line indicated the depth in fathoms, and an "arming" of tallow in the end of the lead showed the nature of the bottom.

reprinted from Sail Ho! Windjammer Sketches Alow and Aloft, by Gordon Grant, 1931, William Farquhar Payson, Inc., NY

Traditional markings for Leadlines

2 fathoms – a 2-ended scrap of leather	**13 fathoms** – a piece of thick blue serge
3 fathoms – a 3-ended scrap of leather	**15 fathoms** – a piece of white calico
5 fathoms – a scrap of white calico	**17 fathoms** – a piece of red wool bunting
7 fathoms – a strip of red wool bunting	**20 fathoms** – a cord with 2 knots
10 fathoms – leather with a round hole	**30 fathoms** – a cord with 3 knots

The NANTUCKET SOUNDER™, a modern equivelent of the lead line, is available from Robert E. White Instruments, Inc.

See our ad on p. 222, or see it online at www.robertwhite.com Click on Yestertech.

TIDAL HEIGHTS and DEPTHS

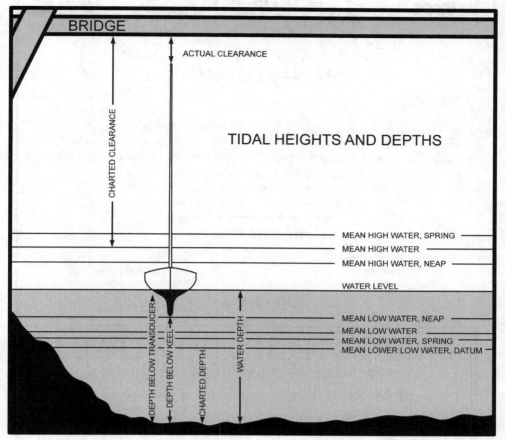

Mean High Water, Spring - the mean of high water heights of spring tides
Mean High Water - the mean of all high water heights; the charted clearance of bridges is measured from this height
Mean High Water, Neap - the mean of high water heights of neap tides
Mean Low Water, Neap - the mean of low water heights of neap tides
Mean Low Water - the mean of all low water heights
Mean Low Water, Spring - the mean of low water heights of spring tides
Mean Lower Low Water Datum - the mean of lower low water heights; charted depths originate from this reference height or datum

---

Spring Tides - tides of increased range, occurring twice a month, around the times of the new and full moons
Neap Tides - tides of decreased range, occurring twice a month, around the times of the half moons
Diurnal Inequality - the difference in height of the two daily low waters or the two daily high waters, a result of the moon's (and to a lesser extent the sun's) changing declination above and below the Equator

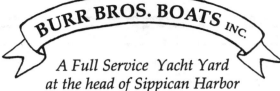

BURR BROS. BOATS INC.

A Full Service Yacht Yard
at the head of Sippican Harbor

Awlgrip Shop   50 Ton Travelift
Varnish Experts   28 Ton Hydraulic Crane
Custom Electrical & Charging Systems   Custom Fiberglass & Composite Specialist
Aluminum & Stainless Steel Fabrication   Factory Trained Inboard & Outboard Mechanics
Complete Rigging Shop & Furling Gear Service   Full Electronic Department & Installation Service

60,000 Sq. Ft. of Inside Storage Including 3 Heated Sheds
Complete Carpentry Shop with Custom Interior Workmanship
Gas and Diesel   WiFi and Showers

Come Sail With Us

Main Yard Address: (508) 748-0541 Main Office
309 Front Street   (508) 748-0963 Fax
Marion, MA 02738   www.burrbros.com.

VHF Channel 68

YESTERTECH* HOSPITAL

* Old technology which worked well, was built to last, and is therefore still useful.

FREE ESTIMATES – 1-YEAR GUARANTEE - EXPERT SERVICE

Clocks - We service Chelsea, Seth Thomas, and other ship's bell clocks and non-striking clocks, from cleaning and lubrication to installation of new parts.

Barometers and Barographs - We can calibrate aneroid barometers and barographs, replace cracked glass, and repair or replace aneroid movements. Large inventory of charts, pens, recorder ink for most makes.

Sextants - From simple tune-up to full restoration, we specialize in the repair, cleaning, and adjustment of all makes of sextants: all Plath models, Tamaya, Astra, Freiberger, and most English sextants. Large parts inventory, mirror resilvering/replacement.

Compasses - Expert service on Ritchie and Danforth compasses, including overhaul and restoration.

ROBERT E. WHITE INSTRUMENTS INC.
www.robertwhite.com   whiteinstruments@gmail.com
617-482-8460
For all mail and packages shipped by US Postal Service:
P. O Box 775, Medfield, MA 02052
For shipping only by UPS, FedEx, etc.: 11 Pound Street, Medfield, MA 02052

The Tide Cycle Simplified: The Rule of Twelfths

Since the average interval between high and low is just over six hours, we can divide the cycle into six segments of one hour each. On average the tide rises or falls approximately according to the fractions at right:

1st hour - 1/12
2nd hour - 2/12
3rd hour - 3/12
4th hour - 3/12
5th hour - 2/12
6th hour - 1/12

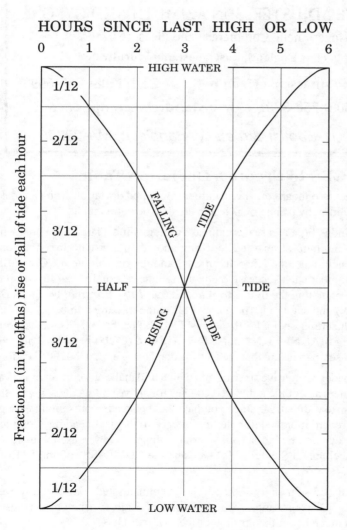

HOURS SINCE LAST HIGH OR LOW

Mean tidal heights by the hour at five ports				
9.6	3.5	4.6	5.2	6.9
8.8	3.2	4.2	4.8	6.3
7.2	2.6	3.4	3.9	5.2
Boston	Newport	New York	Charleston	Savannah
4.8	1.8	2.3	2.6	3.5
2.4	0.9	1.2	1.3	1.7
0.8	0.3	0.4	0.4	0.6
0.0	0.0	0.0	0.0	0.0

ANDREWS COMPASS SERVICE
Professional Compass Adjuster
Serving The New Bedford Fleet Since 1983

FACTORY AUTHORIZED
SALES/SERVICE FOR:
DANFORTH/WHITE   RITCHIE
DIRIGO   PLASTIMO   SUUNTO
C-PLATH   SESTREL   CASSENS & PLATH

FULL SERVICE ADJUSTER: SUN AZIMUTH AND GYRO
Serving Government, Commercial and Pleasure Craft
In Southern New England, East Coast and Worldwide

Email: andrewscompass@verizon.net   Cell: (508) 965-6599
Local / Fax: (508) 758-3001   www.andrewscompass.com

Ray Andrews, 11 Baptist Street., Mattapoisett, MA 02739

Using GPS to Create a Deviation Table

Most compasses are subject to onboard magnetic influences, called deviation. You can make your compass more trustworthy by using your GPS to create a deviation table.

Choose a day when the wind is light and sea as calm as possible. Find a large open area with little or no current and a minimum of boat traffic. Bring aboard an assistant. In a notebook create two columns: in pencil, label the left column GPS and the right column COMPASS. Down the right column, number each successive line using intervals of 15° [24 lines] up to 360°. You can concentrate on noting the four *Cardinal* and four *Inter Cardinal* headings (N, NE, E, SE, S, SW, W, NW) and safely interpolate and fill in the missing numbers for every 15°. Note that the Default setting on a GPS display is **TRUE**. For this exercise, make sure that your GPS is displaying **MAGNETIC- C**ourse **O**ver **G**round (COG) heading. This may require going into the GPS setup to insure that the COG is displaying a MAGNETIC heading.

Choose a speed which provides responsive steering and which will make any current or leeway a negligible factor. Proceed on any of the numbered courses for at least 30 seconds, giving the GPS time to report a consistent direction. Once you have held a steady course long enough to get a repeated reading, record it in the left column. Proceed to the next heading. Completing the circle results in a deviation table for your steering compass. Now, erase the penciled column headings and relabel the GPS column TO GO, and the COMPASS column STEER. *Example: TO GO 094°, STEER 090°.*

A deviation table admittedly falls far short of the ideal of a compensated compass; however, such a table will allow you to use your compass with a measure of confidence before an adjuster comes aboard. And that is much better than trying to steer by your GPS.

See p. 203 for how to adjust your compass.

Using GPS to Adjust Your Compass

Nothing can equal the expert services of a professional Compass Adjuster, but if these services are not available, the following information can help you adjust a compass yourself.

As you used the GPS to create a Deviation Table (see p. 202), you can also use it to correct your steering compass to eliminate deviation.

Built-in Correctors - Most modern compasses are fitted with a magnetic corrector system attached inside the bottom of the compass or the binnacle cylinder. Such "B.I.C.'s" (Built-in Correctors) are easy to use and are capable of removing virtually all the deviations of a well-located compass. B.I.C.'s consist of two horizontal shafts, slotted at each end, one running *Athwartship* (port and starboard) and one running *Fore and Aft*. On each shaft are magnets. When these magnets are horizontal, they are in a neutral position. When a shaft is rotated to any angle, the magnets create correction. The usual B.I.C. can remove up to about 15° of deviation. The shaft which runs *Athwartship* corrects on **North and South** headings, and has zero effect on East and West. The *Fore and Aft* shaft corrects on **East and West** headings, and has zero effect on North and South.

Getting Started - Pick a quiet day and a swinging area with calm conditions. Have someone with a steady hand at the helm and the engine ticking over enough so there is good steering control. It is important to hold a steady heading for at least 30-45 seconds. You are looking at your GPS, and you are equipped with a non-magnetic screwdriver.

Adjusting your compass:

1. As steadily as possible steer within +/- 5° of a cardinal heading, let's say North. Slowly and with a non-magnetic screwdriver rotate the *Athwartship* B.I.C. until the compass reads the same as the GPS, creating zero error on North.
2. Turn 90° right to the next cardinal heading, let's say East. Turn the *Fore/Aft* B.I.C. to remove all of the existing error so the compass matches your GPS on East.
3. Turn 90° right to South. Compare your compass to the GPS. If the error is zero, move to step **#4**. If you have error, you will split the difference: if you have two (2) degrees of error, turn the *Athwartship* B.I.C. so you only have one (1) degree of error.
4. Turn 90° right to West. Compare your compass to the GPS. If the error is zero, move to step **#5**. If you have error, you will split the difference: if you have two (2) degrees of error, turn the *Fore/Aft* B.I.C. so you only have one (1) degree of error.
5. Return to North and confirm that you either have zero error, or if you had error on South and you split the difference to create an error of 1°, you have the same 1° of error on North.
6. Return to East and confirm that you either have zero error, or if you had error on West and you split the difference to create an error of 1°, you have the same 1° of error on East.

Check for deviation all around - Compare the steering compass to your GPS at least every 45° on all the cardinal (N, E, S, W) and intercardinal (NE, SE, SW, NW) points. If the steering compass reads too little (lower number of degrees), the deviation is Easterly on that heading, and the number of degrees must be subtracted when steering that magnetic course. If the steering compass reads too much (higher number of degrees), the deviation is Westerly on that heading, and the number of degrees must be added when steering that magnetic course.

Checking for Misalignment - After checking 8 headings, add up the total of Easterly deviations, subtract the total of Westerly, and divide by 8. The result tells you the amount by which your compass is misaligned. Let's say it is 1° Easterly. This means your lubbers line is off to port 1°. If you rotate the compass 1° clockwise, all your Easterly deviations will be reduced by 1°, your Westerly deviations will be increased by 1°, and your 0 deviations will become 1° Westerly. You will now find the total of your Easterly deviations is the very same as your Westerly total. You have eliminated misalignment error. Now you can trust your compass!

A Chelsea clock. It's about time.

Representing Chelsea's full line of clocks, starting at about $100,
and their finest Ship's Bell series, above (8 ½", 6", and 4 ½" dials).

ROBERT E. WHITE INSTRUMENTS, INC.
www.robertwhite.com
1-617-482-8460

The Ship's Bell Code

Telling time by ship's bell has a romantic background that goes back hundreds of years. It is based in the workday routine of the ship's crew. A ship at sea requires a constant watch throughout the whole twenty-four hours of the day. To divide the duty, the day is broken up into six watches of four hours each and the crew into three divisions, or watches.

Each division of the crew stands two four-hour watches a day. In order to rotate the duty, so that a division does not have to stand the same watch day in and day out, the 4 to 8 watch in the afternoon is divided into two watches known as the dog watches.

The Mid-Watch - Midnight to 4 A.M.	*The 1st Dog Watch* - 4 P.M. to 6 P.M.
The Morning Watch - 4 A.M. to 8 A.M.	*The 2nd Dog Watch* - 6 P.M. to 8 P.M.
The Forenoon Watch - 8 A.M. to 12 Noon	*The First Watch* - 8 P.M. to Midnight
The Afternoon Watch - 12 Noon to 4 P.M.	

To apprise the crew of the time, the ship's bell was struck by the watch officer at half hour intervals, the first half hour being one bell, the first hour two bells, hour and a half three bells, and so on up to eight bells, denoting time to relieve the watch. By this method of timekeeping eight bells marks 4, 8, or 12 o'clock.

8 Bells	4:00	8:00	12:00
1 Bell	4:30	8:30	12:30
2 Bells	5:00	9:00	1:00
3 Bells	5:30	9:30	1:30
4 Bells	6:00	10:00	2:00
5 Bells	6:30	10:30	2:30
6 Bells	7:00	11:00	3:00
7 Bells	7:30	11:30	3:30

Courtesy of Chelsea Clock Co., Chelsea, MA

What Your Marine GPS Can and Cannot Do

Marine GPS is a tremendous aid to today's boater. Most current GPS receivers include charting so a boater can not only determine position, but can also see chart information that pertains to the area around that position - buoys, depth, land masses, etc., all on one screen. In addition to waypoint and route navigation, GPS can do much more. But it also has some limitations. Here are a few of each.

What GPS can do

Marine GPS can pinpoint the spot where a person falls overboard. Simply press the MOB (man overboard) button. The GPS automatically saves the position and turns on the "Go To" function giving bearing and distance to that position. The one who is watching the person overboard should continue to do so. The GPS can help guide the boat back and aid the spotter if visual contact is lost.

GPS can find optimal sail trim by watching how the SOG (speed over ground) changes after adjusting sheets, travelers, etc. Don't forget to note the SOG before you start making changes.

GPS can find optimal trim tab setting. With the engine rpms set to a certain speed, watch the GPS readings of SOG as the trim tab angles are gradually changed.

GPS can determine effect of the current. Assuming the boat's knotmeter is correct, then the difference between the GPS reading of SOG and the knotmeter is the positive or negative effect of the current on your boat. Only if you are heading directly into or away from the current will this difference be the current's actual speed.

GPS can determine leeway. If your compass heading averages 150°, but your COG (course over ground) is 155°, then your leeway is 5° to starboard, and your heading should change to 145°. Do not confuse the GPS compass screen with a compass. GPS indicates the direction your boat is traveling; a compass indicates the direction your boat is pointing. Current and wind effects can make these very different values, especially at low boat speeds.

GPS can find compass deviation. (1) If you can hold a steady compass course for a period of time, and (2) if your GPS is set to read Magnetic, then the difference between what your compass has been reading and the GPS reading is the approximate deviation of your magnetic compass on that heading. Deviation will be different on other headings.

GPS can act as an anchor watch. Most have drift alarms, where you can set the drift distance above which the GPS alarm will go off. Make sure the drift distance will allow for anticipated anchor rode swing if current or wind shift.

What GPS cannot do

GPS cannot warn you of navigation dangers. Unless you have entered waypoints of hazards such as shoals, rocks, etc., your GPS will blindly point you to the next waypoint, possibly over impassable terrain.

GPS cannot tell you if you are on a collision course with another vessel. Keep watch at all times.

GPS will not normally warn you when you're off course. Some GPS have cross-track error alarms. They must be activated and set independently of your "Go To." The "highway" display on your screen may be most helpful for staying on a determined course.

GPS cannot tell you it's not working properly. If it loses adequate satellite contact, suffers battery failure, or experiences some other malfunction, you won't know unless you check it and compare the information displayed to what you should expect it to be.

GPS cannot recall your last position if it loses power. Plot its positions periodically, so when the power fails, you will know a recent position for dead-reckoning plotting.

Warning:

Your GPS cannot function optimally without your checking and possibly resetting the manufacturer's default settings. Recommended settings, if any, are underlined here. The Map Datum (probably WGS-84) must agree with your charts; Nautical or statute miles; True or Magnetic North; Degrees, minutes, and either tenths of minutes or seconds; GMT or local time; 24-hour or 12-hour clock; Grid preference should be Latitude and Longitude.

MARINA BAY
BOSTON HARBOR'S
Flagship Marina

New England's Premier Full Service Marina and Waterfront Complex
www.marinabayboston.com

Summer Dockage:
Transient & Seasonal

Winter Storage:
Inside, Land or In Water

Amenities:
Concierge Service
Parking & Security
Laundry & Showers
Free Wireless internet
35 Ton Marine Travel Lift

Security:
On site staff, electronic gate access and video surveillance

Full Boat Service & Repair:
Certified for Mercruiser, Mercury, Kohler, Yanmar

888-624-1259
VHF Channel 10
333 Victory Road,
North Quincy, MA 02171
email: marinabay@flagshipmarinas.com

Put Your Sea Time to Work
with a USCG Captain's License

OUPV/100 Ton Master License Courses

Since 1891, Massachusetts Maritime Academy has trained mariners for a career at sea. Be a part of our tradition of excellence with an OUPV/100 Ton Master License course.

- USCG Exam onsite - no need to travel to regional exam centers
- Assistance Towing Endorsement exam offered
- Convenient evening or daytime options
- STCW and Commercial Maritime Training Courses available

Call today for a complete training schedule.
It DOES matter where you go to school!

Center for Maritime & Professional Training
101 Academy Drive, Buzzards Bay, MA 02532
508 830 5005 • cmt@maritime.edu • www.maritime.edu/cmt

ATLANTIC COAST DGPS STATIONS

Revised as of September, 2012

	kHz	Rate	Signal Strength		Lat.N.	Lon.W.
CANADA						
Western Head, NS	312	200 bps			43-59	64-40
Hartlen Point, NS	298	200 bps			44-36	63-27
Fox Island, NS	307	200 bps			45-20	61-05
Pt. Escuminiac, NB	319	200 bps			47-04	64-48
Partridge Is., NB	295	200 bps			45-14	66-03
UNITED STATES			microvolts/meter (uV)			
Penobscot, ME	290	200 bps	100uV	at 435 km	44-27.10	68-46.33
Brunswick, ME	316	100 bps	75uV	at 322 km	43-53.4	69-56.8
Acushnet, MA	306	200 bps	100uV	at 370 km	41-44.57	70-53.19
Moriches Pt, NY	293	100 bps	75uV	at 241 km	40-47.40	72-44.83
Sandy Hook, NJ	286	200 bps	100uV	at 185 km	40-28.29	74-00.71
Reedy Point, DE	309	200 bps	100uV	at 113 km	39-33.69	75-34.19
Hagerstown, MD	307	100 bps	75uV	at 250 km	39-33.19	77-42.79
Annapolis, MD	301	200 bps	100uV	at 290 km	39-00.65	76-36.36
Driver, VA	289	100 bps	75uV	at 241 km	36-57.48	76-33.44
New Bern, NC	294	100 bps	75uV	at 259 km	35-10.50	77-02.91
Kensington, SC	292	100 bps	75uV	at 200 km	33-28.86	79-20.58
Savannah, GA	319	100 bps	75uV	at 298 km	32-08.40	81-42.00
Cape Canaveral, FL	289	100 bps	75uV	at 371 km	28-27.62	80-32.74
Card Sound, FL	314	200 bps	100uV	at 261 km	25-25.90	80-27.09
Key West, FL	286	100 bps	75uV	at 204 km	24-34.94	81-39.18
BERMUDA						
St. David's Head	323	BSD		150	32-22.0	64-39.0

These stations are land-based receivers and transmitters for Differential GPS (DGPS). The carrier of these Radiobeacons is modulated with a GPS correction (differential) signal, which may be used to greatly improve the accuracy of GPS. Mariners should see no degradation in the usability of the radiobeacon signal for direction finding although a warbling of the identification signal may be noticed. Correction broadcasts are changing from Type 1 format to Type 9-3. Your equipment may need upgrading. For an automated status report of GPS broadcasts: call NAVCEN (703) 313-5900 x5907.

Please see our May 2013 Free Supplement for further updates. To order see p. 4.
*For further information visit U.S.C.G. Navigation Centers website at **http://www.navcen.uscg.gov** or Canadian CG at **http://www.ccg-gcc.gc.ca/eng/CCG/DGPS_Beacon_Information***

Looking for Old ELDRIDGEs

Some folks just can't let old publications go. Are you among them? If so, your collection may be worth something. We are looking to add to our library of ELDRIDGEs.

Here are the years we are looking for.

1875 – 1926, 1930, 1935, 1936, 1938 – 1954

We are offering a choice of either one free new ELDRIDGE or $10.00 for each old copy accepted by us. If you have any old copies from the years listed above, in fair or better condition and with covers intact, please <u>contact us before shipping</u> by email at ebb2flood@gmail.com, or by phone at 617-482-8460.

Thank you, the Publishers

PARKER'S BOAT YARD

Located on Cape Cod in beautiful, picturesque
Red Brook Harbor, Cataumet, MA 02534
(508) 563-9366 • Fax (508) 563-3899
www.parkersboatyard.com
email: pby@verizon.net

VHF Channel 69

Hauling • Storage • Rigging

Repairs • Restoration

AWLGRIP Refinishing

Brokerage • Marine Store • CNG

Gas • Diesel • Showers • Ice

Dealers for: Westerbeke
Yanmar · Universal · Volvo

"TURMOIL"

Transient & Seasonal Moorings
Slips Available · Pumpout Available
Launch Service · Dining Nearby

Your most convenient stopover for passages
through Cape Cod Canal.

"Where yachtsmen return for friendly, expert service"

RACONS

RACONS are Radar Beacons operating in the marine radar frequency bands, 2900-3100 MHz (s-band) and 9300-9500 MHz (x-band). When triggered by a vessel's radar signal they provide a bearing by sending a coded reply (e.g. "T": –). This signal received takes the form of a single line or narrow sector extending radially towards the circumference of the radarscope from a point slightly beyond the spot formed by the echo from the lighthouse, buoy, etc. at the Racon site. Thus may be measured to the point at which the Racon coded flash begins. (The figure obtained will be a few hundred feet greater than the actual distance of the ship from the Racon due to the slight response delay in the Racon apparatus.)

Hours of transmission are continuous and coverage is all around the horizon unless otherwise stated. Their ranges depend on the effective range of the ship's radar and on the power and elevation of the Racon apparatus. Under conditions of abnormal radio activity, reliance should only be put on a Racon flash that is consistent and when the ship is believed to be within the area of the Racon's quoted range. Mariners are advised to turn off the interference controls of their radar when wishing to receive a Racon signal or else the signal may not come through to the ship.

See p. 209 for list of Racons.

ATLANTIC COAST RACONS

Location	RACON SITE	SIGNAL	LAT. N	LONG. W
NS	Cranberry Islands	− • • • (B)	45-19-29.6	60-55-38.2
	Bear Cove Lt. & Bell By "H6"	− • (N)	44-32-36.3	63-31-19.6
	Chebucto Head	− − • • (Z)	44-30-26.6	63-31-21.8
	Cape Sable	− • − • (C)	43-23-24	65-37-16.9
	Cape Forchu	− • • • (B)	43-47-38.8	66-09-19.3
	Lurcher Shoal Bifurcation Lt. By. "NM"	− • − (K)	43-48-57	66-29-58
NB	St. John Harbour. Lt. & Wh. By. "J"	− • (N)	45-12-55.3	66-02-36.9
	Gannet Rock	− − • (G)	44-30-37.1	66-46-52.9
ME	Frenchman Bay Ltd. By. "FB"	− • • • (B)	44-19-21	68-07-24
	Portland Ltd. Wh. By. "P"	− − (M)	43-31-36	70-05-28
MA	Boston Ltd. Wh. By. "B"	− • • • (B)	42-22-42	70-46-58
	Boston North Ch.Entr. Ltd. Wh. By. "NC"	− • (N)	42-22-32	70-54-18
	Cleveland East Ledge Lt.	− • − • (C)	41-37-51	70-41-39
	Buzzards Bay Entr. Lt., Horn	− • • • (B)	41-23-49	71-02-05
RI	Narrag. Bay Entr. Ltd. Wh. By. "NB"	− • • • (B)	41-23-00	71-23-21
	Narrag.-Buzz. Bay Appr. Ltd. Wh. By. "A"	− • (N)	41-06-00	71-23-22
	Newport - Pell Bridge Fog Signal	− • (N)	41-30-18	71-20-55
CT	Twenty-Eight Ft. Sh. Ltd. Wh. By. "TE"	− (T)	41-09-16	72-30-25
NY	Ambrose Ch. Ltd. Wh. By. "A"	− • (N)	40-27-28	73-50-12
	Tappen Zee Bridge	− − • • (Z)	41-04-12	73-52-47
	Kill van Kull Ch. Ltd. Jct. By. "KV"	− • − (K)	40-39-02	74-03-51
	Montauk Pt. Ltd. Wh. By. "MP"	− − (M)	41-01-48	71-45-40
	Southwest Ledge Ltd. Wh. By. #2	− • • • (B)	41-06-23	71-40-14
	Nantucket Traffic Lane Ltd. Wh. By. "NA"	− • (N)	40-25-42	73-11-28
	Execution Rocks Lt.	− • • − (X)	40-52-41	73-44-16
	Hudson Canyon Traffic Lane Ltd. Wh. By. "HA"	− • − • (C)	40-07-36	73-21-22
NJ	Scotland Ltd. Wh. By. "S"	− − (M)	40-26-33	73-55-01
	Sandy Hook Ch. Rge. Front Lt.	− • − • (C)	40-29-15	73-59-35
	Barnegat Ltd. By. "B"	− • • • (B)	39-45-48	73-46-04
DE	Del. Bay Appr. Ltd. Wh. By. "CH"	− • − (K)	38-46-14	75-01-20
	Del. Ltd. By. "D"	− • − (K)	38-27-18	74-41-47
	Del. River, Pea Patch Is.	− • • − (X)	39-36-42	75-34-54
	Five Fathom Bank Ltd. By. "F"	− − (M)	38-46-49	74-34-32
	Brown Shoal Lt.	− • • • (B)	38-55-21	75-06-01
	Miah Maull Shoal Lt.	− − (M)	39-07-36	75-12-31
	Ship John Shoal Lt.	− − − (O)	39-18-19	75-22-36
VA	Chesapeake Light Tower	− • (N)	36-54-17	75-42-46
	Chesapeake Bay Ent. Ltd. Wh. By. "CH"	− • − • (C)	36-56-08	75-57-27
	Ches. Ch. Ltd. By. #78	− − • − (Q)	38-33-19	76-25-39
	Ches. Ch. Ltd. Bell By. #68	− • • − (X)	37-59-53	76-11-49
	Ches. Ch. Ltd. By. #42	− − − (O)	37-25-37	76-05-07
NC	Beaufort Inlet Ch. Ltd. Wh. By. "BM"	− − (M)	34-34-49	76-41-33
	Cape Fear River Ent. Ltd. Wh. By. "CF"	− • − • (C)	33-46-17	78-03-02
SC	Charleston Entr. Ltd. By. "C"	− • − (K)	32-37-05	79-35-30
GA	Tybee Ltd. By. "T"	− − • (G)	31-57-52	80-43-10
	St. Simons Ltd. By. "STS"	− • • • (B)	31-02-49	81-14-25
FL	St. Johns Ltd. By. "STJ"	− − (M)	30-23-35	81-19-08
	Port Everglades Ltd. By. "PE"	− (T)	26-05-30	80-04-46
	Miami Ltd. By. "M"	− − (M)	25-46-06	80-05-00
	Fowey Rocks Lt.	− − − (O)	25-35-26	80-05-48
	Carysfort Rf. Lt.	− • − • (C)	25-13-19	80-12-41
	Alligator Rf. Lt.	− − • (G)	24-51-06	80-37-08
	Sombrero Key Lt.	− − (M)	24-37-40	81-06-39
	American Shoal Lt.	− • − − (Y)	24-31-30	81-31-10
	Sand Key Lt.	− • (N)	24-27-14	81-52-39
	Dry Tortugas Lt.	− • − (K)	24-38-00	82-55-14
Bermuda	North East Breaker Beacon	− • (N)	32-28.7	64-41.0
	Chub Heads Beacon	− • − • (C)	32-17.2	64-58.9

Range: Canada under 10 mi., US under 16 mi. **See p. 208** *for more on RACONS.*

DIAL-A-BUOY SERVICE
SEA-STATE & WEATHER CONDITIONS BY TELEPHONE

If you are planning a coastwise voyage, you can rely on a number of sources for weather. A possible source is **Dial-A-Buoy**, offering reports of conditions at numerous coastal and offshore locations along the Atlantic Coast, as well as the coasts of the Gulf of Mexico, the Pacific, and the Great Lakes. In all there over 100 buoy and 60 Coastal-Marine Automated Network (C-MAN) stations. The system is operated by the National Data Buoy Center (NDBC), with headquarters at the Stennis Space Center in Mississippi. The NDBC is part of the National Weather Service (NWS).

The reports from offshore buoys include wind speed, gusts, and direction, wave heights and periods, water temperature, and barometric pressure as recorded within the last hour or so. Reports from land stations cover wind speed and direction, temperature and pressure; some land stations also add water temperature, visibility, and dew point.

The value of this information is apparent. Say someone in your boating party is susceptible to seasickness, and the Dial-A-Buoy report says wave heights are six feet with a period (interval) of eight seconds. Maybe that person would rather stay ashore and experience the gentler motion of a rocking chair. (Wave heights of six feet with a period of twenty seconds, on the other hand, might be tolerable.) Surfers, too, can benefit greatly from wave height reports. Likewise, since actual conditions frequently differ dramatically from forecasts, someone sailing offshore might be interested to know that a Data Buoy ahead is reporting squalls, giving time to shorten sail. And bathers and fishermen might gain from hearing the water temperature reports.

On the next page, we give the station or buoy identifier, location name, and lat/long in degrees and hundredths, as provided by the NWS. To find the station or buoy locations and identifiers using the Internet, you can see maps with station identifiers at **www.ndbc.noaa.gov/**. To find locations by telephone, you can enter a latitude and longitude to receive the locations and identifiers of the closest stations.

To access Dial-A-Buoy using any touch-tone or cell phone, here are the steps:

1. Call 888-701-8992.
2. If you know the identifier of the station or buoy, press 1. Press 2 to get station locations by entering the approximate lat/long of the area you want.
3. Enter the five-digit (or character) station identifier. To enter a Character press the key containing the character.
4. Press 1 to confirm that your entry was correct.
5. If, after hearing the latest report, you wish to hear a forecast for that same location, press 2 then 1. You can jump to the forecast before the end of the station report by pressing 2 then 1 during the reading of the station conditions.
6. If you want to hear the report for another station, press 2 then 2.
7. You do not have to wait for the prompts. For example, you can press "1440271" as soon as you begin to hear the welcome message to hear the report from station 44027.

NOTE: In some cases a buoy may become temporarily unavailable. You should try again later to see if it has come back online. Please be aware that stations that may be adrift and not at the stated location are not reported via the telephone feature. This information is only available on the website by typing in the station identifier at: www.ndbc.noaa.gov/dial.shtml

DIAL-A-BUOY and C-MAN STATION LOCATIONS

Station ID	Location Name	Latitude	Longitude
44027	JONESPORT, ME	44.27N	67.31W
MDRM1	MT DESERT ROCK, ME	43.97N	68.13W
MISM1	MATINICUS ROCK, ME	43.78N	68.86W
44007	PORTLAND, ME	43.53N	70.14W
44005	GULF OF MAINE	43.20N	69.13W
IOSN3	ISLE OF SHOALS, NH	42.97N	70.62W
44013	BOSTON, MA	42.35N	70.65W
BUZM3	BUZZARDS BAY, MA	41.40N	71.03W
44018	E. CAPE COD, MA	42.13N	69.63W
44011	GEORGES BANK, MA	41.11N	66.60W
44017	MONTAUK POINT, NY	40.69N	72.05W
44008	NANTUCKET, MA	40.50N	69.25W
ALSN6	AMBROSE LIGHT, NY	40.45N	73.80W
44025	LONG ISLAND, NY	40.25N	73.17W
TPLM2	THOMAS POINT, MD	38.90N	76.44W
44004	HOTEL, NJ	38.48N	70.43W
44009	DELAWARE BAY, NJ	38.46N	74.70W
CHLV2	CHESAPEAKE LIGHT, VA	36.91N	75.71W
44014	VIRGINIA BEACH, VA	36.61N	74.84W
DUKN7	DUCK PIER, NC	36.18N	75.75W
41025	DIAMOND SHOALS	35.01N	75.40W
41001	E. HATTERAS, NC	34.56N	72.63W
CLKN7	CAPE LOOKOUT, NC	34.62N	76.53W
41013	FRYING PAN SHOAL, NC	33.44N	77.74W
41004	EDISTO, SC	32.50N	79.10W
41002	S. HATTERAS, SC	31.86N	74.84W
41008	GRAYS REEF, GA	31.40N	80.87W
41012	ST. AUGUSTINE, FL	30.04N	80.53W
SAUF1	ST AUGUSTINE, FL	29.86N	81.27W
41010	CANAVERAL EAST, FL	28.91N	78.47W
41009	CANAVERAL, FL	28.52N	80.17W
LKWF1	LAKE WORTH, FL	26.61N	80.03W
FWYF1	FOWEY ROCKS, FL	25.59N	80.10W
MLRF1	MOLASSES REEF, FL	25.01N	80.38W
LONF1	LONG KEY, FL	24.84N	80.86W
SMKF1	SOMBRERO KEY, FL	24.63N	81.11W
SANF1	SAND KEY, FL	24.45N	81.88W

Most stations have added the ability to access information via RSS feed using your Internet browser. For information regarding how to use this feature please go to: www.ndbc.noaa.gov/rss_access.shtml

MATTAPOISETT BOATYARD, INC.

Since 1962

In the Heart of Buzzards Bay

WESTERBEKE
Marine Engine Products

YANMAR marine

Universal Motors

- Complete yacht repairs
- Expert mechanics
- Minor/major fiberglass or carpentry
- Transient moorings & launch service
- 35 ton lift
- Inland Storage/Repair Facility

32 NED'S POINT RD • MATTAPOISETT, MA 02739 • www.mattapoisettboatyard.com

508-758-3812

Edgartown Marine

Relax. We'll take care of your boat.

- Full Service Year Round Boat Yard on Martha's Vineyard
- Boat Detailing, Bottom Painting & Custom Lettering
- Engine Winterizing & Spring Tune Ups
- Inside & Outside Boat Storage
- Authorized Yamaha & Mercury Dealer For Sales & Service
- Authorized Parts Dealer for Johnson, Evinrude, Bombardier, and all Major Brands

- Only Travel Lift On Edgartown Harbor
- Certified Mechanics
- Complete Marine Services
- Boat Hauling & Launching

Visiting Boaters: ask the launch to drop you at "North Wharf" (Fuel & dinghy dock at Morse Street)
Morse Ship's Store: *Ice & Snacks, Water Toys, Marine Supplies, PFD's, Oil, MV Info, Gifts & More*

32 Herring Creek Road
508.627.6500 - Service
(Year Round Ship's Store)

1 Morse Street
508.627.4388 - Storage and Travel Lift
(Seasonal Store - Memorial Day through Labor Day)

www.edgartownmarine.com

IALA BUOYAGE SYSTEM

Lateral Aids marking the sides of channels seen when entering from Seaward

Port Side - Odd Numbers

G "9"
Fl G 4sec
Lighted Buoy -
Green Light only

C "7"
Can Buoy -
Unlighted

Daymark
SG

G
"1"

Port- hand aids are Green, some with Flashing Green Lights.
Daymarks:
1st letter "S" = Square
2nd letter "G" = color Green

Starboard Side - Even Numbers

R "8"
Fl R 4sec
Lighted Buoy -
Red Light only

N "6"
Nun Buoy -
Unlighted

Daymark
TR

R
"2"

Starboard-hand aids remain Red, some with Flashing Red Lights.
Daymarks:
1st letter "T" = Triangle
2nd letter "R"= color Red

Safe Water Aids Marking Mid-Channels & Fairways - No Numbers - May Be Lettered:

RW "E"
Mo (A)
Lighted
White Light

RW
SP "G"
Spherical Buoy -
Unlighted

Daymark
MR

RW
"A"

Red and White replaces Black and White. Buoys are spherical; or have a Red spherical topmark. Flashing White Light only: Mo (A).
Daymarks:
1st letter "M" = Octagon
2nd letter "R" = color Red

Preferred Channel Aids - Mark Bifurcations - No Numbers - Preferred Ch. to Starboard (Aid to Port):

GR "M"
CGpFl G
Lighted Buoy -
Green Light only

GR
C "F"
Can Buoy -
Unlighted

Daymark
JG

GR
"A"

Green replaces Black. Flashing Light (Red or Green) is Composite Gp. Fl. (2 + 1).
Daymarks:
1st letter "J" = Square or Triangle
2nd letter "R" or "G" is color of top band

Preferred CH. to Port (Aid to Starboard):

RG "D"
CGpFl R
Lighted Buoy -
Red Light only

RG
N "L"
Nun Buoy -
Unlighted

Daymark
JR

RG
"B"

Note: **ISOLATED DANGER BUOYS, Black and Red with two Black spherical topmarks** - no numbers, may be lettered (if lighted, white light only, Fl (2) 5s). Stay Clear. **SPECIAL AIDS BUOYS will be all YELLOW** (if lighted, with yellow light only, Fixed Flashing): Anchorage Areas, Fish Net Areas, Spoil Grounds, Military Exercise Zones, Dredging Buoys (where conventional markers would be confusing), Ocean Data Systems, some Traffic Separations Zone Mid-Channel Buoys.

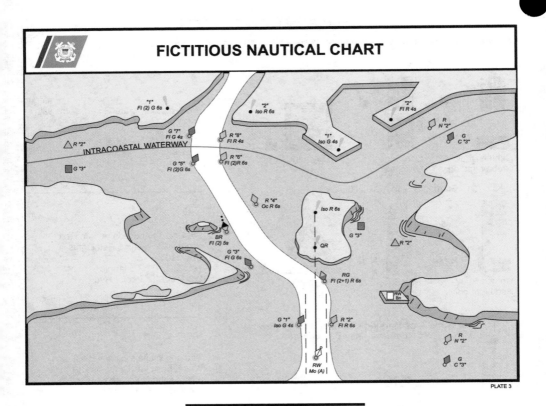

FICTITIOUS NAUTICAL CHART

PLATE 3

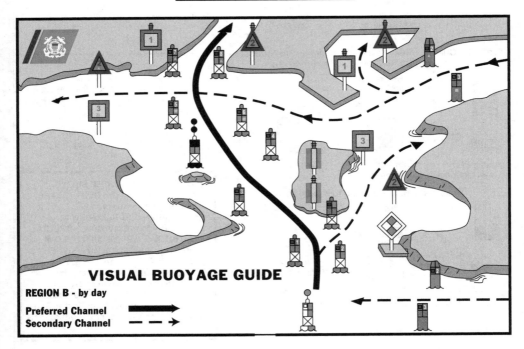

VISUAL BUOYAGE GUIDE

REGION B - by day

Preferred Channel
Secondary Channel

Photo by Jeremy D'Entremont, www.lighthouse.cc

Boston Light

Marking a main entrance to New England's most active port, the first Boston Light was a stone tower constructed in 1716. It was the first lighthouse built in North America. To pay for the structure a tonnage tax of one penny per ton was levied on vessels entering or leaving Boston. Destroyed by the British in the Revolutionary War, the light tower was rebuilt in 1783, making it the second oldest after Sandy Hook, NJ. Its location is 42°19'41N, 070°53'24W on Little Brewster Island, a granite outcrop of about three acres. Outbuildings include a residence, fog signal building, cistern, oil house, and boathouse.

The tower is constructed of masonry and rubble stone, and is lined with brick. The walls are seven and a half feet thick at the base, tapering to two and a half feet at the top. Its height was originally 75 feet, but in 1856 the height was increased, so that the height of the light is now 102 feet above sea level. Electrified in 1948 and automated in 1998, the light has an intensity of 1.8 million candlepower, and it shines through a second-order Fresnel lens. With a range of 27 nautical miles, it flashes white every 10 seconds. The foghorn's signal is a single blast every 30 seconds.

A very colorful history surrounds this landmark, including its capture by the British, various marine disasters occurring close by, valiant rescues by keepers, and even its use by one keeper to make "imported" Spanish cigars. Boston Light Station was designated a National Historic Landmark in 1964. Although the light is automated, it remains staffed by a civilian lightkeeper, Sally Snowman, who is assisted by volunteer watchstanders from the U.S. Coast Guard Auxiliary. As such it is the last manned light in the United States.

It is open only for guided tours, and reservations are recommended. Call 617-223-8666 for information on the 3½ hour public cruises to the island, offered from June 15th to September 30th, on Fridays, Saturdays, and Sundays.

Concordia Boatyard
- Skilled, Long-Tenured Professionals
- Highest Quality Work
- Lower Prices Fall 2012
- Excellent Work Spaces & Clean Indoor Sheds
- 14 Acre Facility
- 155 Moorings in Padanaram Harbor

Concordia Yacht Sales
- Hand In Hand With Quality Service
- Showroom Quality Storage Spaces
- Moorings In Padanaram Harbor
- Quality Honest Brokerage

Concordia Yawl
- 103 Built From 1938 To 1966
- Most Built By A&R (Germany)
- Designed Sold & Commissioned By Concordia Company
- Concordia Currently Maintains 12-15 Yawls Annually

Concordia Company
300 Gulf Road
South Dartmouth, MA 02748

Phone: (508) 999-1381
Yacht Sales: (508) 742-5884
E-mail: conco@concordiaboats.com

Yacht Flags and How To Fly Them

U.S. Ensign: 8 a.m. to sundown only. Not flown while racing.
   At the stern staff of all vessels at anchor, or under way by power or sail.
   At the leech of the aftermost sail, approximately 2/3 of the leech above the clew.
   When the aftermost sail is gaff-rigged, the Ensign is flown immediately below the peak of the gaff.

U.S. Power Squadron Ensign: 8 a.m. to sundown when flown at the stern staff in place of the U.S. Ensign; otherwise, day and night from the starboard spreader. In either case it is flown only when a Squadron member is in command.

Club Burgee: Day and night. Not flown while racing.
   At the bow staff of power vessels with one mast.
   At the main peak of yawls, ketches, sloops, cutters, and catboats.
   At the fore peak of schooners and power vessels with two masts.

Private Signal: Day and night.
   At the bow staff of power vessels without a mast.
   At the masthead of power and sailing vessels with one mast.
   At the mizzen peak of yawls and ketches.
   At the main peak of schooners and power vessels with two masts.

Flag Officers' Flags: Day and night. Flown in place of the private signal on all rigs except single-masted sailboats, when it is flown in place of the club burgee at the masthead.

Union Jack: 8 a.m. to sundown, only at anchor, and only on Sundays, holidays, or occasions for dressing ship, at the bow staff. Sailboats without a bow staff may fly it from the forestay a few feet above the stem head.

International Signal Flags and Morse Code

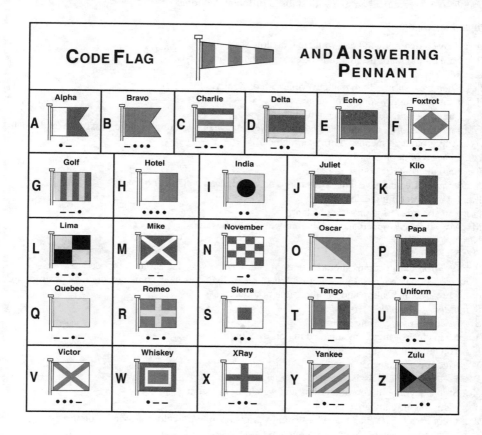

Code Flag AND **Answering Pennant**

A Alpha • —	**B** Bravo — • • •	**C** Charlie — • — •	**D** Delta — • •	**E** Echo •	**F** Foxtrot • • — •
G Golf — — •	**H** Hotel • • • •	**I** India • •	**J** Juliet • — — —	**K** Kilo — • —	
L Lima • — • •	**M** Mike — —	**N** November — •	**O** Oscar — — —	**P** Papa • — — •	
Q Quebec — — • —	**R** Romeo • — •	**S** Sierra • • •	**T** Tango —	**U** Uniform • • —	
V Victor • • • —	**W** Whiskey • — —	**X** XRay — • • —	**Y** Yankee — • — —	**Z** Zulu — — • •	

Numeral Pennants

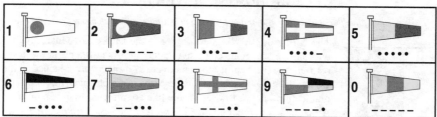

1 • — — — —	2 • • — — —	3 • • • — —	4 • • • • —	5 • • • • •
6 — • • • •	7 — — • • •	8 — — — • •	9 — — — — •	0 — — — — —

Repeaters

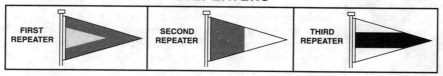

FIRST REPEATER   SECOND REPEATER   THIRD REPEATER

217

THE INTERNATIONAL CODE OF SIGNALS

The Code comprises 40 flags: 1 Code Flag; 26 letters; 10 numerals; 3 repeaters. With this Code it is possible to converse freely at sea with ships of different countries.

Single Flag Signals

A :: I have a diver down; keep well clear at slow speed.

B :: I am taking in, or discharging, or carrying dangerous goods.

C :: Yes

D :: Keep clear of me; I am maneuvering with difficulty.

E :: I am altering my course to starboard.

F :: I am disabled; communicate with me.

G :: I require a pilot. (When made by fishing vessels when operating in close proximity on the fishing grounds it means; "I am hauling nets.")

H :: I have a pilot on board.

I :: I am altering my course to port.

J :: I am on fire and have dangerous cargo on board; keep well clear of me.

K :: I wish to communicate with you.

L :: You should stop your vessel instantly.

M :: My vessel is stopped and making no way through water.

N :: No

O :: Man overboard.

P :: *In harbor*; All persons should report on board as the vessel is about to proceed to sea.
  At sea; It may be used by fishing vessels to mean "My nets have come fast upon an obstruction."

Q :: My vessel is healthy and I request free pratique.

R :: *nothing currently assigned*

S :: My engines are going astern.

T :: Keep clear of me; I am engaged in pair trawling.

U :: You are running into danger.

V :: I require assistance.

W :: I require medical assistance.

X :: Stop carrying out your intentions and watch for my signals.

Y :: I am dragging my anchor.

Z :: I require a tug. (When made by fishing vessels operating in close proximity on the fishing grounds it means : "I am shooting nets.")

FLAGS SHOWING "DIVER DOWN"

There are two flags that may be flown to indicate diving operations, and each has a distinct meaning.

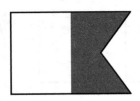

The **Alpha or "A" flag**, according to the U.S. Coast Guard, is to be flown on small vessels engaged in diving operations (1) whenever these vessels are restricted in their ability to maneuver (2) if divers are attached to the vessel. Generally, only vessels to which the divers are physically connected by communication lines, air hoses, or the like are affected by this requirement. The Alpha flag is a signal intended to *protect the vessel from collision*.

In sports diving, where divers are usually free-swimming, the Alpha flag does not have to be shown. The Coast Guard encourages the use of the traditional sports diver flag. The **sports diver flag** is an unofficial signal that, through custom, has come to be used to *protect the diver in the water*. To be most effective, the sports diver flag should be exhibited on a float in the water to mark the approximate location of the diver. Restrictions for nearby vessels vary from state to state, but typically they include a zone of 100' radius around the flag where no other boats are allowed, and a second larger zone in which speed is limited.

U.S. STORM SIGNALS

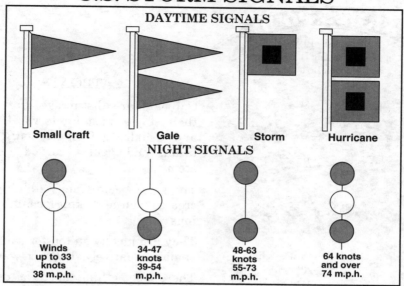

DAYTIME SIGNALS

Small Craft   Gale   Storm   Hurricane

NIGHT SIGNALS

Winds up to 33 knots 38 m.p.h.

34-47 knots 39-54 m.p.h.

48-63 knots 55-73 m.p.h.

64 knots and over 74 m.p.h.

The above signals are displayed regularly on Light Vessels, at Coast Guard shore stations, and at many principal lighthouses. Each Coast and Geodetic Survey Chart lists those locations which appear within the area covered by that chart.

When the Rain before the Wind,
    Topsail Sheets and Halliards Mind,
But when the Wind before the Rain,
    Then you may set sail again.

Rain before 7

Clear before 11

Distance of Visibility

Given the curvature of the earth, can you see a 200' high headland from 20 miles away? (Answer below.) How far you can see depends on visibility, which we will assume here to be ideal, and the heights above water of your eye and the object.

To find the theoretical maximum distance of visibility, use the Table below. First, using your height of eye above water (say, 8'), the Table shows that at that height, your horizon is 3.2 n.m. away. Then, from our Lights, Fog Signals and Offshore Buoys (pp. 167-197), your chart, or the Light List, find the height of the object (say, 200'). The Table shows that object can be seen 16.2 n.m. from sea level. Add the two distances: 3.2 + 16.2 = 19.4 n.m. *Answer: not quite!* (Heights below in feet, distance in nautical miles)

Ht.	Dist.	Ht.	Dist.	Ht.	Dist.	Ht.	Dist.	Ht.	Dist.
4	2.3	30	6.3	80	10.3	340	21.1	860	33.6
6	2.8	32	6.5	90	10.9	380	22.3	900	34.4
8	3.2	34	6.7	100	11.5	420	23.5	1000	36.2
10	3.6	36	6.9	120	12.6	460	24.6	1400	42.9
12	4.0	38	7.1	140	13.6	500	25.7	1800	48.6
14	4.3	40	7.3	160	14.5	540	26.7	2200	53.8
16	4.6	42	7.4	180	15.4	580	27.6	2600	58.5
18	4.9	44	7.6	200	16.2	620	28.6	3000	62.8
20	5.1	46	7.8	220	17.0	660	29.4	3400	66.9
22	5.4	48	8.0	240	17.8	700	30.4	3800	70.7
24	5.6	50	8.1	260	18.5	740	31.1	4200	74.3
26	5.9	60	8.9	280	19.2	780	32.0	4600	77.7
28	6.1	70	9.6	300	19.9	820	32.8	5000	81.0

• Established 1951 •
Cape Cod's Sailing Headquarters
and Wooden Boat Center

CATBOATS

Catboats are distinctive craft with their single mast far forward, large and usually gaff-rigged sail, great beam, and gently curved upright stem.

The great beam brings stability and creates a large cockpit for family outings.

They are ideally suited for sailing in shallow, relatively sheltered waters.

There's something about a catboat that beckons the eye and makes one want to smile.

- •14' Cat
- •16' Lynx Cabin
- •16' Lynx Open
- •16' Launch
- •18' Daysailer
- •20' Cruising Cat
- •21' Launch

45 Arey's Lane • PO Box 222
S. Orleans, MA 02662
508-255-0994 • www.areyspondboatyard.com

ELDRIDGE STORY CONTEST for 2014

We are seeking true stories about **a memorable incident afloat.** The winning entry will be published in our 2014 edition, and the author will receive $200. Submitted material becomes the property of the Publishers and will not be returned. See 2013 winner on facing page.

Submit your entry by EMAIL to:
ebb2flood@gmail.com, subject: Story Contest 2014
or in printed form* by mail to:

Eldridge Tide and Pilot Book
Story Contest
P.O. Box 775
Medfield, MA 02052
Deadline: August 20, 2013
Winner Notification: October 1, 2013
Limit: 600 words

Authors must provide their name, address, daytime phone number and email address.

*Finalists may be asked to send an electronic version.

Strangers in the Night

Our club cruise last summer took us to various ports of call on Narragansett Bay. The two week cruise was characterized by light air and a memorable heat wave of several days. Although we usually opt for moorings or to anchor our Tartan 37 sloop HIGHLANDER, the club booked slips in Newport, and we enjoyed the flexibility and relative luxury to easily come and go as we pleased.

We retired that evening to a hot, muggy cabin, opening all the hatches and port lights, and running a small fan that only served to move the hot air around. Around midnight, I awoke to the clattering of dishware coming from the galley. We had left the washed dishes and glasses in the sink to air dry . . . and I was impressed by my wife's diligence to tidy up the galley so late at night. One small problem: she was asleep in the bunk beside me!

I got up and quietly walked aft in the darkness, only to see shadows in the galley area. I retreated to the forward cabin and murmured to my wife, "Get up; someone is in our boat." I flicked on a dome light to see two little raccoon kits sitting in the sink staring at me. Stunned, I hollered at them "Get out of my boat, now!" They nervously slinked onto the companionway ladder and out into the cockpit. I instructed my wife to close all the port lights and hatches while I retrieved the hatch boards for the companionway. As I was about to insert the drop boards, my two little visitors poked their heads into the cabin as if to say "Is it OK to come below now?"

We secured all the hatches and port lights and, for the next hour or so, we observed the mother raccoon and her four kits cavort all over our boat. The kits spent much of their time wrestling with each other, rolling about and squealing like puppies. Then they found our kayak, which became a veritable raccoon playground. (I think we have the makings of a new animated film!) Then, all of a sudden, mom announced that playtime was over and they lined up on the toe rail to depart the vessel. Mom, without hesitation leaped onto the dock. The kits were hilarious, rocking back and forth, wiggling their butts, eyeing each other and working up the courage to jump. Then, one by one, off they went. We observed them visiting nearby vessels as well, where they occasionally found a trash bag left in the cockpit where they helped themselves.

We had left no food or trash for our nocturnal visitors, but we learned that, when dockside, we should expect the unexpected. Varmints can get aboard your vessel by jumping or climbing dock lines. Restrict access to your cabin area and leave no tantalizing treats for night visitors. Remember that we are only one step removed from "camping out."

George Gillis

Drawing by Hesterly Black Buckley

See p. 220 for 2014 Story Contest rules.

LANDRIGAN
CORPORATION

- Avon Rafts & Boats
- Crewsaver Rafts*
- RPR Buoy Rafts*
- Revere Survival Rafts*
- RFD Beaufort Rafts*
- Viking Leisure Rafts
- DSB-Autoflug Rafts
- Viking Rafts*
- Zodiac Boats and Rafts
- RFD/Toyo

**Sales, Rentals and Service
for Inflatable Life Rafts
Sales & Service
for Inflatable Boats**

**Indicates U.S.C.G.
approved rafts*

Christopher M. Quill
General Manager

2-12 Jeffries St.
P. O. Box 444
Boston, MA 02128
www.landrigancorp.com

Telephone (617) 567-2182
(617) 567-2749
FAX: (617) 569-6627
email: landrigancorp@gmail.com

★NANTUCKET SOUNDER★

The NANTUCKET SOUNDER measures depths to 60' – without batteries! A memorable gift for a sailor or distinctive regatta prize.

The complete package includes:

✓ 3-lb. polished solid bronze weight, with traditional bottom cavity

✓ 60' braided line, knotted every fathom

✓ custom Sunbrella storage bag with drawstring closure

✓ brochure with history, lore, instructions for use

ROBERT E. WHITE INSTRUMENTS, INC.
www.robertwhite.com
1-617-482-8460

See "Heaving the Lead," p. 198

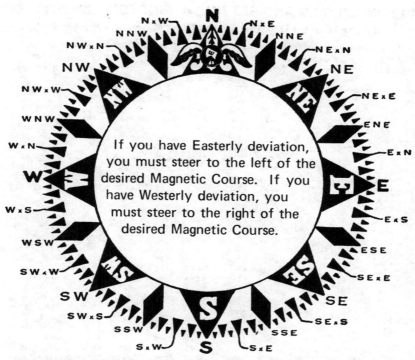

If you have Easterly deviation, you must steer to the left of the desired Magnetic Course. If you have Westerly deviation, you must steer to the right of the desired Magnetic Course.

Table for Turning Compass Points into Degrees, and the Contrary

MERCHANT MARINE PRACTICE

NORTH	**0**	**EAST**	**90**	**SOUTH**	**180**	**WEST**	**270**
N. 1/4E.	2 3/4	E. 1/4S.	92 3/4	S. 1/4W.	182 3/4	W. 1/4N.	272 3/4
N. 1/2E.	5 3/4	E. 1/2S.	95 3/4	S. 1/2W.	185 3/4	W. 1/2N.	275 3/4
N. 3/4E.	8 1/2	E. 3/4S.	98 1/2	S. 3/4W.	188 1/2	W. 3/4N.	278 1/2
N. by E.	11 1/4	E. by S.	101 1/4	S. by W.	191 1/4	W. by N.	281 1/4
N. by E. 1/4E.	14	E. by S. 1/4S.	104	S. by W. 1/4W.	194	W. by N. 1/4N.	284
N. by E. 1/2E.	17	E. by S. 1/2S.	107	S. by W. 1/2W.	197	W. by N. 1/2N.	287
N. by E. 3/4E.	19 3/4	E. by S. 3/4S.	109 3/4	S. by W. 3/4W.	199 3/4	W. by N. 3/4N.	289 3/4
N.N.E.	**22 1/2**	**E.S.E.**	**112 1/2**	**S.S.W.**	**202 1/2**	**W.N.W.**	**292 1/2**
N.E. by N. 3/4N.	25 1/4	S.E. by E. 3/4E.	115 1/4	S.W. by S. 3/4S.	205 1/4	N.W. by W. 3/4W.	295 1/4
N.E. by N. 1/2N.	28 1/4	S.E. by E. 1/2E.	118 1/4	S.W. by S. 1/2S.	208 1/4	N.W. by W. 1/2W.	298 1/4
N.E. by N. 1/4N.	31	S.E. by E. 1/4E.	121	S.W. by S. 1/4S.	211	N.W. by W. 1/4W.	301
N.E. by N.	33 3/4	S.E. by E.	123 3/4	S.W. by S.	213 3/4	N.W. by W.	303 3/4
N.E. 3/4N.	36 1/2	S.E. 3/4E.	126 1/2	S.W. 3/4S.	216 1/2	N.W. 3/4W.	306 1/2
N.E. 1/2N.	39 1/2	S.E. 1/2E.	129 1/2	S.W. 1/2S.	219 1/2	N.W. 1/2W.	309 1/2
N.E. 1/4N.	42 1/4	S.E. 1/4E.	132 1/4	S.W. 1/4S.	222 1/4	N.W. 1/4W.	312 1/4
N.E.	**45**	**S.E.**	**135**	**S.W.**	**225**	**N.W.**	**315**
N.E. 1/4E.	47 3/4	S.E. 1/4S.	137 3/4	S.W. 1/4W.	227 3/4	N.W. 1/4N.	317 3/4
N.E. 1/2E.	50 3/4	S.E. 1/2S.	140 3/4	S.W. 1/2W.	230 3/4	N.W. 1/2N.	320 3/4
N.E. 3/4E.	53 1/2	S.E. 3/4S.	143 1/2	S.W. 3/4W.	233 1/2	N.W. 3/4N.	323 1/2
N.E. by E.	56 1/4	S.E. by S.	146 1/4	S.W. by W.	236 1/4	N.W. by N.	326 1/4
N.E. by E. 1/4E.	59	S.E. by S. 1/4S.	149	S.W. by W. 1/4W.	239	N.W. by N. 1/4N.	329
N.E. by E. 1/2E.	62	S.E. by S. 1/2S.	152	S.W. by W. 1/2W.	242	N.W. by N. 1/2N.	332
N.E. by E. 3/4E.	64 3/4	S.E. by S. 3/4S.	154 3/4	S.W. by W. 3/4W.	244 3/4	N.W. by N. 3/4N.	334 3/4
E.N.E.	**67 1/2**	**S.S.E.**	**157 1/2**	**W.S.W.**	**247 1/2**	**N.N.W.**	**337 1/2**
E. by N. 3/4N.	70 1/4	S. by E. 3/4E.	160 1/4	W. by S. 3/4S.	250 1/4	N. by W. 3/4W.	340 1/4
E. by N. 1/2N.	73 1/4	S. by E. 1/2E.	163 1/4	W. by S. 1/2S.	253 1/4	N. by W. 1/2W.	343 1/4
E. by N. 1/4N.	76	S. by E. 1/4E.	166	W. by S. 1/4S.	256	N. by W. 1/4W.	346
E. by N.	78 3/4	S. by E.	168 3/4	W. by S.	258 3/4	N. by W.	348 3/4
E. 3/4N.	81 1/2	S. 3/4E.	171 1/2	W. 3/4S.	261 1/4	N. 3/4W.	351 1/2
E. 1/2N.	84 1/2	S. 1/2E.	174 1/2	W. 1/2S.	264 1/2	N. 1/2W.	354 1/2
E. 1/4N.	87 1/4	S. 1/4E.	177 1/4	W. 1/4S.	267 1/4	N. 1/4W.	357 1/4
EAST	**90**	**SOUTH**	**180**	**WEST**	**270**	**NORTH**	**0**

2013 SUN'S RISING AND SETTING AT BOSTON - 42° 20'N 71°W
Add one hour for Daylight Saving Time, March 10 - November 3
Times shown in table are first tip of Sun at Sunrise and last tip at Sunset.

Day	JANUARY Rise h m	JANUARY Set h m	FEBRUARY Rise h m	FEBRUARY Set h m	MARCH Rise h m	MARCH Set h m	APRIL Rise h m	APRIL Set h m	MAY Rise h m	MAY Set h m	JUNE Rise h m	JUNE Set h m	Day
1	0713	1622	0657	1658	0619	1734	0526	1810	0439	1844	0410	1914	1
2	0713	1623	0656	1700	0617	1735	0524	1811	0438	1845	0409	1915	2
3	0713	1624	0655	1701	0616	1737	0523	1812	0436	1846	0409	1916	3
4	0713	1625	0654	1702	0614	1738	0521	1813	0435	1847	0409	1916	4
5	0713	1626	0653	1704	0612	1739	0519	1815	0434	1848	0408	1917	5
6	0713	1627	0652	1705	0611	1740	0518	1816	0433	1849	0408	1918	6
7	0713	1628	0651	1706	0609	1741	0516	1817	0431	1850	0408	1918	7
8	0713	1629	0649	1708	0607	1743	0514	1818	0430	1851	0407	1919	8
9	0713	1630	0648	1709	0606	1744	0513	1819	0429	1853	0407	1920	9
10	0712	1631	0647	1710	0604	1745	0511	1820	0428	1854	0407	1920	10
11	0712	1633	0645	1712	0602	1746	0509	1821	0427	1855	0407	1921	11
12	0712	1634	0644	1713	0601	1747	0508	1822	0426	1856	0407	1921	12
13	0711	1635	0643	1714	0559	1748	0506	1824	0425	1857	0407	1922	13
14	0711	1636	0641	1715	0557	1750	0504	1825	0423	1858	0407	1922	14
15	0710	1637	0640	1717	0556	1751	0503	1826	0422	1859	0407	1923	15
16	0710	1638	0639	1718	0554	1752	0501	1827	0421	1900	0407	1923	16
17	0709	1639	0637	1719	0552	1753	0500	1828	0420	1901	0407	1923	17
18	0709	1641	0636	1721	0550	1754	0458	1829	0420	1902	0407	1924	18
19	0708	1642	0634	1722	0549	1755	0457	1830	0419	1903	0407	1924	19
20	0708	1643	0633	1723	0547	1757	0455	1831	0418	1904	0407	1924	20
21	0707	1644	0631	1724	0545	1758	0453	1833	0417	1905	0407	1924	21
22	0706	1646	0630	1726	0543	1759	0452	1834	0416	1906	0408	1924	22
23	0705	1647	0628	1727	0542	1800	0450	1835	0415	1907	0408	1925	23
24	0705	1648	0627	1728	0540	1801	0449	1836	0415	1908	0408	1925	24
25	0704	1649	0625	1729	0538	1802	0447	1837	0414	1908	0409	1925	25
26	0703	1651	0624	1730	0537	1803	0446	1838	0413	1909	0409	1925	26
27	0702	1652	0622	1732	0535	1804	0445	1839	0413	1910	0409	1925	27
28	0701	1653	0621	1733	0533	1806	0443	1840	0412	1911	0410	1925	28
29	0700	1655	....	....	0531	1807	0442	1842	0411	1912	0410	1925	29
30	0759	1656	....	....	0530	1808	0440	1843	0411	1913	0411	1925	30
31	0658	1657	....	....	0528	1809	....	....	0410	1914	....	....	31

Day	JULY Rise h m	JULY Set h m	AUGUST Rise h m	AUGUST Set h m	SEPTEMBER Rise h m	SEPTEMBER Set h m	OCTOBER Rise h m	OCTOBER Set h m	NOVEMBER Rise h m	NOVEMBER Set h m	DECEMBER Rise h m	DECEMBER Set h m	Day
1	0411	1924	0437	1903	0509	1818	0541	1725	0618	1637	0654	1612	1
2	0412	1924	0438	1902	0510	1816	0542	1723	0619	1636	0655	1612	2
3	0412	1924	0439	1901	0512	1814	0544	1722	0620	1635	0656	1612	3
4	0413	1924	0440	1900	0513	1812	0545	1720	0621	1633	0657	1612	4
5	0413	1923	0441	1858	0514	1811	0546	1718	0623	1632	0658	1612	5
6	0414	1923	0442	1857	0515	1809	0547	1717	0624	1631	0659	1611	6
7	0415	1923	0443	1856	0516	1807	0548	1715	0625	1630	0700	1611	7
8	0415	1922	0444	1854	0517	1806	0549	1713	0626	1629	0701	1611	8
9	0416	1922	0445	1853	0518	1804	0550	1711	0628	1628	0701	1611	9
10	0417	1922	0446	1852	0519	1802	0551	1710	0629	1627	0702	1611	10
11	0418	1921	0447	1850	0520	1800	0552	1708	0630	1626	0703	1612	11
12	0418	1920	0448	1849	0521	1759	0554	1707	0631	1625	0704	1612	12
13	0419	1920	0449	1848	0522	1757	0555	1705	0633	1624	0705	1612	13
14	0420	1919	0450	1846	0523	1755	0556	1703	0634	1623	0705	1612	14
15	0421	1919	0451	1845	0524	1753	0557	1702	0635	1622	0706	1612	15
16	0422	1918	0453	1843	0525	1751	0558	1700	0636	1621	0707	1613	16
17	0423	1917	0454	1842	0526	1750	0559	1659	0637	1620	0708	1613	17
18	0423	1917	0455	1840	0527	1748	0601	1657	0639	1619	0708	1613	18
19	0424	1916	0456	1839	0528	1746	0602	1655	0640	1619	0709	1614	19
20	0425	1915	0457	1837	0529	1744	0603	1654	0641	1618	0709	1614	20
21	0426	1914	0458	1836	0531	1743	0604	1652	0642	1617	0710	1615	21
22	0427	1913	0459	1834	0532	1741	0605	1651	0644	1617	0710	1615	22
23	0428	1912	0500	1832	0533	1739	0607	1649	0645	1616	0711	1616	23
24	0429	1911	0501	1831	0534	1737	0608	1648	0646	1615	0711	1616	24
25	0430	1911	0502	1829	0535	1736	0609	1647	0647	1615	0712	1617	25
26	0431	1910	0503	1828	0536	1734	0610	1645	0648	1614	0712	1618	26
27	0432	1909	0504	1826	0537	1732	0611	1644	0649	1614	0712	1618	27
28	0433	1908	0505	1824	0538	1730	0613	1642	0650	1613	0712	1619	28
29	0434	1906	0506	1823	0539	1729	0614	1641	0652	1613	0713	1620	29
30	0435	1905	0507	1821	0540	1727	0615	1640	0653	1613	0713	1621	30
31	0436	1904	0508	1819	....	....	0616	1638	....	....	0713	1621	31

2013 SUN'S RISING AND SETTING AT NEW YORK - 40° 42'N 74°W

Add one hour for Daylight Saving Time, March 10 - November 3

Times shown in table are first tip of Sun at Sunrise and last tip at Sunset.

Day	JANUARY Rise h m	Set h m	FEBRUARY Rise h m	Set h m	MARCH Rise h m	Set h m	APRIL Rise h m	Set h m	MAY Rise h m	Set h m	JUNE Rise h m	Set h m	Day
1	0720	1640	0706	1714	0630	1748	0539	1821	0454	1852	0427	1921	1
2	0720	1641	0705	1715	0628	1749	0538	1822	0453	1853	0427	1922	2
3	0720	1641	0704	1716	0626	1750	0536	1823	0452	1854	0426	1922	3
4	0720	1642	0703	1718	0625	1751	0534	1824	0451	1855	0426	1923	4
5	0720	1643	0702	1719	0623	1752	0533	1825	0449	1856	0426	1924	5
6	0720	1644	0700	1720	0622	1753	0531	1826	0448	1857	0425	1924	6
7	0720	1645	0659	1721	0620	1754	0529	1827	0447	1859	0425	1925	7
8	0720	1646	0658	1723	0619	1755	0528	1828	0446	1900	0425	1926	8
9	0720	1647	0657	1724	0617	1756	0526	1829	0445	1901	0425	1926	9
10	0719	1648	0656	1725	0615	1758	0525	1830	0444	1902	0425	1927	10
11	0719	1649	0655	1726	0614	1759	0523	1831	0443	1903	0424	1927	11
12	0719	1650	0653	1728	0612	1800	0522	1832	0442	1904	0424	1928	12
13	0719	1651	0652	1729	0611	1801	0520	1834	0441	1905	0424	1928	13
14	0718	1653	0651	1730	0609	1802	0518	1835	0440	1905	0424	1929	14
15	0718	1654	0650	1731	0607	1803	0517	1836	0439	1906	0424	1929	15
16	0717	1655	0648	1732	0606	1804	0515	1837	0438	1907	0424	1929	16
17	0717	1656	0647	1734	0604	1805	0514	1838	0437	1908	0424	1930	17
18	0716	1657	0646	1735	0602	1806	0512	1839	0436	1909	0425	1930	18
19	0716	1658	0644	1736	0601	1807	0511	1840	0435	1910	0425	1930	19
20	0715	1659	0643	1737	0559	1808	0509	1841	0434	1911	0425	1930	20
21	0715	1701	0641	1738	0557	1809	0508	1842	0434	1912	0425	1931	21
22	0714	1702	0640	1739	0556	1810	0507	1843	0433	1913	0425	1931	22
23	0713	1703	0639	1741	0554	1812	0505	1844	0432	1914	0426	1931	23
24	0713	1704	0637	1742	0552	1813	0504	1845	0431	1915	0426	1931	24
25	0712	1705	0636	1743	0551	1814	0502	1846	0431	1916	0426	1931	25
26	0711	1707	0634	1744	0549	1815	0501	1847	0430	1916	0427	1931	26
27	0710	1708	0633	1745	0547	1816	0500	1848	0430	1917	0427	1931	27
28	0709	1709	0631	1746	0546	1817	0458	1849	0429	1918	0427	1931	28
29	0708	1710	....	....	0544	1818	0457	1850	0428	1919	0428	1931	29
30	0708	1712	....	....	0543	1819	0456	1851	0428	1920	0428	1931	30
31	0707	1713			0541	1820	....	....	0427	1920	....	....	31

Day	JULY Rise h m	Set h m	AUGUST Rise h m	Set h m	SEPTEMBER Rise h m	Set h m	OCTOBER Rise h m	Set h m	NOVEMBER Rise h m	Set h m	DECEMBER Rise h m	Set h m	Day
1	0429	1931	0453	1911	0523	1828	0553	1738	0627	1652	0701	1629	1
2	0429	1931	0454	1910	0524	1826	0554	1736	0628	1651	0702	1629	2
3	0430	1931	0455	1909	0525	1825	0555	1734	0629	1650	0703	1629	3
4	0430	1930	0456	1908	0526	1823	0556	1733	0630	1649	0704	1629	4
5	0431	1930	0457	1906	0527	1821	0557	1731	0631	1647	0705	1629	5
6	0432	1930	0458	1905	0528	1820	0558	1730	0632	1646	0706	1629	6
7	0432	1929	0459	1904	0529	1818	0559	1728	0634	1645	0707	1628	7
8	0433	1929	0500	1903	0530	1816	0600	1726	0635	1644	0707	1628	8
9	0434	1929	0501	1902	0531	1815	0601	1725	0636	1643	0708	1629	9
10	0434	1928	0502	1900	0532	1813	0602	1723	0637	1642	0709	1629	10
11	0435	1928	0503	1859	0533	1811	0603	1722	0638	1641	0710	1629	11
12	0436	1927	0504	1858	0534	1810	0604	1720	0640	1640	0711	1629	12
13	0436	1927	0505	1856	0535	1808	0605	1718	0641	1640	0712	1629	13
14	0437	1926	0506	1855	0536	1806	0606	1717	0642	1639	0712	1629	14
15	0438	1926	0507	1854	0537	1805	0607	1715	0643	1638	0713	1630	15
16	0439	1925	0508	1852	0538	1803	0608	1714	0644	1637	0714	1630	16
17	0440	1924	0509	1851	0539	1801	0610	1712	0645	1636	0714	1630	17
18	0440	1924	0510	1849	0540	1800	0611	1711	0647	1636	0715	1631	18
19	0441	1923	0510	1848	0541	1758	0612	1709	0648	1635	0715	1631	19
20	0442	1922	0511	1846	0542	1756	0613	1708	0650	1634	0716	1631	20
21	0443	1921	0512	1845	0543	1754	0614	1707	0650	1634	0717	1632	21
22	0444	1921	0513	1843	0544	1753	0615	1705	0651	1633	0717	1632	22
23	0445	1920	0514	1842	0545	1751	0617	1704	0652	1632	0718	1633	23
24	0446	1919	0515	1840	0546	1749	0617	1702	0653	1632	0718	1634	24
25	0446	1918	0516	1839	0547	1748	0618	1701	0654	1631	0718	1634	25
26	0447	1917	0517	1837	0548	1746	0620	1700	0656	1631	0719	1635	26
27	0448	1916	0518	1836	0549	1744	0621	1658	0657	1631	0719	1636	27
28	0449	1915	0519	1834	0550	1743	0622	1657	0658	1630	0719	1636	28
29	0450	1914	0520	1833	0551	1741	0623	1656	0659	1630	0719	1637	29
30	0451	1913	0521	1831	0552	1739	0624	1655	0700	1630	0720	1638	30
31	0452	1912	0522	1829	....	....	0625	1653	....	....	0720	1639	31

2013 SUN'S RISING AND SETTING AT JACKSONVILLE - 30° 20'N   81° 37'W
Add one hour for Daylight Saving Time, March 10 - November 3
Times shown in table are first tip of Sun at Sunrise and last tip at Sunset.

Day	JANUARY Rise h m	JANUARY Set h m	FEBRUARY Rise h m	FEBRUARY Set h m	MARCH Rise h m	MARCH Set h m	APRIL Rise h m	APRIL Set h m	MAY Rise h m	MAY Set h m	JUNE Rise h m	JUNE Set h m	Day
1	0723	1737	0717	1803	0652	1826	0615	1846	0543	1905	0525	1924	1
2	0723	1738	0716	1804	0651	1826	0614	1846	0542	1905	0525	1924	2
3	0724	1739	0716	1805	0650	1827	0613	1847	0541	1906	0525	1925	3
4	0724	1740	0715	1806	0649	1828	0612	1847	0540	1906	0524	1925	4
5	0724	1740	0714	1807	0648	1828	0611	1848	0540	1907	0524	1926	5
6	0724	1741	0714	1808	0647	1829	0609	1849	0539	1908	0524	1926	6
7	0724	1742	0713	1809	0646	1830	0608	1849	0538	1908	0524	1927	7
8	0724	1743	0712	1809	0644	1830	0607	1850	0537	1909	0524	1927	8
9	0724	1744	0712	1810	0643	1831	0606	1850	0536	1910	0524	1928	9
10	0724	1744	0711	1811	0642	1832	0605	1851	0536	1910	0524	1928	10
11	0724	1745	0710	1812	0641	1832	0604	1852	0535	1911	0524	1929	11
12	0724	1746	0709	1813	0640	1833	0602	1852	0534	1912	0524	1929	12
13	0724	1747	0708	1813	0639	1834	0601	1853	0534	1912	0524	1929	13
14	0724	1748	0707	1814	0637	1834	0600	1854	0533	1913	0524	1930	14
15	0724	1749	0706	1815	0636	1835	0559	1854	0532	1914	0524	1930	15
16	0724	1749	0706	1816	0635	1836	0558	1855	0532	1914	0524	1930	16
17	0723	1750	0705	1817	0634	1836	0557	1855	0531	1915	0524	1931	17
18	0723	1751	0704	1817	0632	1837	0556	1856	0531	1916	0525	1931	18
19	0723	1752	0703	1818	0631	1837	0555	1857	0530	1916	0525	1931	19
20	0723	1753	0702	1819	0630	1838	0554	1857	0529	1917	0525	1931	20
21	0722	1754	0701	1820	0629	1839	0553	1858	0529	1917	0525	1931	21
22	0722	1755	0700	1820	0628	1839	0552	1859	0529	1918	0525	1932	22
23	0722	1756	0659	1821	0626	1840	0551	1859	0528	1919	0526	1932	23
24	0721	1756	0658	1822	0625	1841	0550	1900	0528	1919	0526	1932	24
25	0721	1757	0657	1823	0624	1841	0549	1901	0527	1920	0526	1932	25
26	0720	1758	0656	1823	0623	1842	0548	1901	0527	1921	0527	1932	26
27	0720	1759	0655	1824	0621	1842	0547	1902	0526	1921	0527	1932	27
28	0719	1800	0653	1825	0620	1843	0546	1903	0526	1922	0527	1932	28
29	0719	1801	....	....	0619	1844	0545	1903	0526	1922	0528	1932	29
30	0718	1802	....	....	0618	1844	0544	1904	0526	1923	0528	1932	30
31	0718	1803	....	....	0617	1845	....	....	0525	1923	....	....	31

Day	JULY Rise h m	JULY Set h m	AUGUST Rise h m	AUGUST Set h m	SEPTEMBER Rise h m	SEPTEMBER Set h m	OCTOBER Rise h m	OCTOBER Set h m	NOVEMBER Rise h m	NOVEMBER Set h m	DECEMBER Rise h m	DECEMBER Set h m	Day
1	0528	1932	0545	1920	0603	1849	0620	1811	0641	1739	0706	1726	1
2	0529	1932	0546	1919	0604	1848	0621	1810	0642	1738	0706	1726	2
3	0529	1932	0546	1919	0604	1846	0621	1809	0643	1737	0707	1726	3
4	0530	1932	0547	1918	0605	1845	0622	1808	0643	1736	0708	1726	4
5	0530	1932	0548	1917	0606	1844	0622	1807	0644	1736	0709	1726	5
6	0530	1932	0548	1916	0606	1843	0623	1805	0645	1735	0709	1726	6
7	0531	1932	0549	1915	0607	1842	0624	1804	0646	1734	0710	1726	7
8	0531	1932	0549	1914	0607	1840	0624	1803	0647	1734	0711	1726	8
9	0532	1931	0550	1913	0608	1839	0625	1802	0647	1733	0712	1726	9
10	0532	1931	0551	1913	0608	1838	0626	1801	0648	1732	0712	1726	10
11	0533	1931	0551	1912	0609	1837	0626	1800	0649	1732	0713	1727	11
12	0533	1931	0552	1911	0609	1835	0627	1758	0650	1731	0714	1727	12
13	0534	1930	0552	1910	0610	1834	0627	1757	0651	1731	0714	1727	13
14	0535	1930	0553	1909	0611	1833	0628	1756	0652	1730	0715	1728	14
15	0535	1930	0554	1908	0611	1832	0629	1755	0652	1730	0716	1728	15
16	0536	1929	0554	1907	0612	1830	0629	1754	0653	1729	0716	1728	16
17	0536	1929	0555	1906	0612	1829	0630	1753	0654	1729	0717	1729	17
18	0537	1928	0555	1905	0613	1828	0631	1752	0655	1728	0717	1729	18
19	0537	1928	0556	1904	0613	1826	0631	1751	0656	1728	0718	1729	19
20	0538	1928	0557	1903	0614	1825	0632	1750	0657	1728	0719	1730	20
21	0538	1927	0557	1901	0614	1824	0633	1749	0657	1727	0719	1730	21
22	0539	1927	0558	1900	0615	1823	0634	1748	0658	1727	0720	1731	22
23	0540	1926	0558	1859	0615	1821	0634	1747	0659	1727	0720	1731	23
24	0540	1925	0559	1858	0616	1820	0635	1746	0700	1726	0720	1732	24
25	0541	1925	0559	1857	0617	1819	0636	1745	0701	1726	0721	1733	25
26	0541	1924	0600	1856	0617	1818	0636	1744	0702	1726	0721	1733	26
27	0542	1924	0601	1855	0618	1816	0637	1743	0702	1726	0722	1734	27
28	0543	1923	0601	1854	0618	1815	0638	1742	0703	1726	0722	1734	28
29	0543	1922	0602	1852	0619	1814	0639	1741	0704	1726	0722	1735	29
30	0544	1922	0602	1851	0619	1813	0639	1740	0705	1726	0723	1736	30
31	0544	1921	0603	1850	....	....	0640	1740	....	....	0723	1737	31

2013 SUN'S SETTING AT OTHER LOCATIONS FOR FLAG USE
Add one hour for Daylight Saving Time, March 10 - November 3

Times shown in tables pp. 224-226 are first tip of Sun at Sunrise and last tip at Sunset.

Vernal Equinox: March 20th, 6:02 a.m. E.S.T.   Summer Solstice: June 21st, 12:04 a.m. E.S.T.
Autumnal Equinox: Sept. 22nd, 3:44 p.m. E.S.T.   Winter Solstice: Dec. 21st, 12:11 p.m. E.S.T.

Add to or subtract from the referenced table

	1/15	2/15	3/15	4/15	5/15	6/15	7/15	8/15	9/15	10/15	11/15	12/15
BOSTON p. 224												
New London, CT	+7	+6	+4	+2	0	-1	0	+1	+2	+5	+6	+7
Newport, RI	+4	+3	+1	-1	-2	-3	-2	-1	0	+2	+4	+5
New Bedford, MA	+3	+2	0	-1	-2	-3	-2	-1	0	+1	+2	+3
Vineyard Haven, MA	+1	-1	-2	-4	-5	-6	-5	-4	-3	-2	0	+1
Nantucket, MA	-1	-2	-4	-6	-7	-8	-7	-6	-5	-3	-2	-1
Portland, ME	-8	-6	-3	-1	+1	+2	+1	0	-2	-4	-6	-7
Rockland, ME	-14	-12	-8	-6	-4	-2	-4	-5	-7	-10	-12	-14
Bar Harbor, ME	-18	-15	-11	-8	-5	-3	-5	-7	-9	-13	-17	-18
NEW YORK p. 225												
Hampton Roads, VA	+18	+15	+9	+2	0	-1	-1	+2	+7	+13	+18	+20
Oxford, MD	+14	+12	+9	+5	+4	+3	+3	+5	+8	+11	+14	+15
Annapolis, MD	+14	+13	+10	+7	+6	+5	+5	+7	+9	+12	+14	+15
Cape May, NJ	+8	+7	+4	+1	0	-1	-1	+1	+3	+6	+8	+9
Atlantic City, NJ	+5	+4	+2	0	-1	-2	-2	0	+2	+4	+6	+6
Mannasquan, NJ	+2	+1	0	-1	-2	-2	-2	-1	0	+1	+2	+2
Port Jefferson, NY	-5	-4	-4	-3	-3	-3	-3	-3	-4	-4	-5	-5
Bridgeport, CT	-4	-4	-3	-2	-2	-1	-1	-2	-3	-4	-4	-5
New Haven, CT	-7	-6	-4	-3	-3	-3	-3	-3	-4	-5	-6	-7
JACKSONVILLE p. 226												
Morehead City, NC	-28	-24	-20	-14	-10	-7	-9	-13	-19	-24	-28	-29
Wilmington, NC	-22	-18	-14	-10	-5	-3	-5	-8	-14	-18	-22	-23
Myrtle Beach, SC	-16	-14	-10	-6	-3	-1	-3	-5	-7	-12	-17	-17
Charleston, SC	-11	-9	-6	-3	+1	0	-1	-3	-7	-9	-11	-12
Savannah. GA	-1	0	+2	+4	+6	+6	+5	+4	+3	0	-2	-2
Brunswick, GA	+1	-1	0	+1	+2	+2	+1	+1	-1	+1	+2	+2
Ponce Inlet, FL	+1	-1	-1	-2	-4	-5	-5	-4	-2	0	+1	+1
Melbourne, FL	+1	-2	-4	-5	-7	-9	-9	-8	-5	-1	0	+1
North Palm Beach, FL	+2	-2	-6	-8	-11	-14	-14	-11	-7	-4	0	+2
Miami, FL	+6	0	-3	-8	-13	-15	-15	-11	-7	-2	+3	+5
Key West, FL	+13	+7	+2	-3	-8	-12	-12	-6	-1	+6	+11	+14

Celestial Navigation
A Fascinating Tool to Find Our Way in the World

Every time we got a chance to sit back and look up at the star-filled sky, thoughts of "Big Bang Theory" and ancient mariners seemed to pass through our heads. Somehow "Big Bang Theory" and expanding universes quickly got put aside because of their associated thoughts of finality. But, the thoughts of the ancient mariners, Columbus, Lewis & Clark, Shackleton & Worsley and many others, who used these little white dots to achieve major feats of discovery, were really intriguing. How did they do it? How did people find out where they were before the advent of navigation satellites and mobile GPS receivers? We started to feel guilty for not seeking some answers to these questions. So one day we decided to delve into the subject of celestial navigation. Why not? Learning a little bit about star and planetary motion and getting intimate with the planets, stars and our good friends, sun and moon, certainly wouldn't hurt us.

Committed to our study, the first task we took up was to find and buy a good quality sextant. With the help of Bruce Bauer's "The Sextant Handbook," we were off and running. After teaching ourselves the techniques of sextant mirror adjustments and basic sight taking, we felt confident to tackle the theoretical side of the subject. However, after reading a few interesting basic texts, we quickly realized there was so much more to learn. At that point we turned to our local United States Power Squadron for some expertise. With their help we learned more about the celestial bodies and their relative motion to the observer on earth. After a few more classes where we studied the necessary mathematical corrections, tables in the Nautical Almanac, calculations and plotting methods for determining our position, we then felt like we understood the subject and had the last pieces of the navigation puzzle. The whole picture of terrestrial and celestial navigation was complete. However, our study of the subject wasn't fully complete because the practical and really interesting part of the subject was still to be done.

Learning the theoretical parts of the subject now gave us the incentive to get to the field work – taking real sights. We quickly learned and appreciated the problems encountered by Frank Worsley, Shackleton's captain and navigator aboard the Antarctic explorer ENDURANCE. The marine environment was not always the navigator's friend. But, life is full of challenges. So waiting for Jupiter to appear on a cold November evening was just taken in stride. Our approach to this final stage was like any artist who realizes that perfection is only accomplished by practice, practice and more practice. It wasn't long before we reached our goal of getting consistent sights within three nautical miles of our known position. Once there, we finally felt we were ready to step aboard the clipper ship FLYING CLOUD and help Eleanor Creesy on her record breaking trip around Cape Horn.

After our fun study of celestial navigation, practicing it aboard our sailboat DAWN TREADER and teaching the subject for a few years, we really knew we were better navigators. We had added celestial navigation to our bag of tricks, which we could use to travel the world.

John and Barbara Healy

TIME OF LOCAL APPARENT NOON (L.A.N.) 2013 FOR THE CENTRAL MERIDIAN OF ANY TIME ZONE

LOCAL APPARENT NOON, 2013

	JAN.	FEB.	MAR.	APR.	MAY	JUN.	JUL.	AUG.	SEP.	OCT.	NOV.	DEC.
	h:m:s	h:m:s	h:m:s	h:m:s	h:m:s	h:m:s	h:m:s	h:m:s	h:m:s	h:m:s	h:m:s	h:m:s
1	12:03:47	12:13:38	12:12:15	12:03:45	11:57:02	11:57:52	12:03:56	12:06:18	11:59:52	11:49:32	11:43:35	11:49:10
2	12:04:15	12:13:45	12:12:03	12:03:27	11:56:55	11:58:02	12:04:07	12:06:14	11:59:33	11:49:13	11:43:34	11:49:34
3	12:04:42	12:13:51	12:11:50	12:03:09	11:56:49	11:58:12	12:04:18	12:06:09	11:59:14	11:48:54	11:43:34	11:49:57
4	12:05:09	12:13:57	12:11:37	12:02:52	11:56:43	11:58:22	12:04:29	12:06:03	11:58:54	11:48:36	11:43:35	11:50:22
5	12:05:36	12:14:02	12:11:24	12:02:35	11:56:39	11:58:33	12:04:39	12:05:57	11:58:34	11:48:18	11:43:37	11:50:47
6	12:06:02	12:14:06	12:11:10	12:02:18	11:56:34	11:58:44	12:04:49	12:05:51	11:58:13	11:48:00	11:43:40	11:51:12
7	12:06:28	12:14:09	12:10:55	12:02:01	11:56:30	11:58:55	12:04:59	12:05:44	11:57:53	11:47:43	11:43:43	11:51:38
8	12:06:54	12:14:11	12:10:41	12:01:44	11:56:27	11:59:07	12:05:08	12:05:36	11:57:33	11:47:27	11:43:47	11:52:04
9	12:07:18	12:14:13	12:10:26	12:01:28	11:56:25	11:59:19	12:05:17	12:05:27	11:57:12	11:47:10	11:43:52	11:52:31
10	12:07:43	12:14:14	12:10:10	12:01:12	11:56:22	11:59:31	12:05:26	12:05:18	11:56:51	11:46:54	11:43:58	11:52:58
11	12:08:07	12:14:14	12:09:54	12:00:56	11:56:21	11:59:43	12:05:34	12:05:09	11:56:30	11:46:39	11:44:05	11:53:26
12	12:08:30	12:14:13	12:09:38	12:00:41	11:56:20	11:59:56	12:05:42	12:04:59	11:56:08	11:46:24	11:44:13	11:53:54
13	12:08:52	12:14:12	12:09:22	12:00:26	11:56:20	12:00:08	12:05:49	12:04:48	11:55:47	11:46:09	11:44:21	11:54:22
14	12:09:14	12:14:09	12:09:06	12:00:11	11:56:20	12:00:21	12:05:55	12:04:36	11:55:26	11:45:56	11:44:30	11:54:51
15	12:09:35	12:14:06	12:08:49	11:59:56	11:56:21	12:00:34	12:06:01	12:04:25	11:55:04	11:45:42	11:44:40	11:55:19
16	12:09:56	12:14:03	12:08:32	11:59:42	11:56:22	12:00:47	12:06:07	12:04:12	11:54:43	11:45:29	11:44:51	11:55:48
17	12:10:15	12:13:58	12:08:15	11:59:29	11:56:24	12:01:00	12:06:12	12:03:59	11:54:21	11:45:17	11:45:03	11:56:18
18	12:10:34	12:13:53	12:07:57	11:59:15	11:56:26	12:01:13	12:06:16	12:03:46	11:54:00	11:45:05	11:45:15	11:56:47
19	12:10:53	12:13:47	12:07:40	11:59:02	11:56:29	12:01:26	12:06:20	12:03:32	11:53:38	11:44:54	11:45:29	11:57:17
20	12:11:10	12:13:41	12:07:22	11:58:50	11:56:32	12:01:39	12:06:24	12:03:17	11:53:17	11:44:44	11:45:43	11:57:46
21	12:11:27	12:13:34	12:07:04	11:58:38	11:56:36	12:01:52	12:06:26	12:03:03	11:52:56	11:44:34	11:45:58	11:58:16
22	12:11:43	12:13:26	12:06:46	11:58:26	11:56:41	12:02:05	12:06:28	12:02:47	11:52:34	11:44:25	11:46:14	11:58:46
23	12:11:58	12:13:18	12:06:28	11:58:14	11:56:46	12:02:18	12:06:30	12:02:31	11:52:13	11:44:17	11:46:30	11:59:16
24	12:12:12	12:13:09	12:06:10	11:58:04	11:56:51	12:02:30	12:06:31	12:02:15	11:51:52	11:44:09	11:46:48	11:59:45
25	12:12:26	12:12:59	12:05:51	11:57:53	11:56:57	12:02:43	12:06:31	12:01:58	11:51:32	11:44:02	11:47:06	12:00:15
26	12:12:39	12:12:49	12:05:33	11:57:43	11:57:04	12:02:56	12:06:31	12:01:41	11:51:11	11:43:56	11:47:25	12:00:45
27	12:12:50	12:12:38	12:05:15	11:57:34	11:57:11	12:03:08	12:06:30	12:01:24	11:50:51	11:43:50	11:47:45	12:01:14
28	12:13:02	12:12:27	12:04:57	11:57:25	11:57:18	12:03:20	12:06:29	12:01:06	11:50:31	11:43:46	11:48:05	12:01:44
29	12:13:12		12:04:39	11:57:17	11:57:26	12:03:32	12:06:27	12:00:48	11:50:11	11:43:42	11:48:26	12:02:13
30	12:13:21		12:04:20	11:57:09	11:57:34	12:03:44	12:06:25	12:00:30	11:49:51	11:43:39	11:48:48	12:02:42
31	12:13:30		12:04:02		11:57:43		12:06:22	12:00:11		11:43:36		12:03:11

Explanatory Notes: The noon sight and the Sun's Declination (p. 231) result in the vessel's parallel of latitude. It is taken at the time of the sun's meridian passage, when the sun is at maximum altitude.

The moment of meridian passage is called Local Apparent noon (L.A.N.), and only rarely is it the same time as noon Standard Time or Local Mean Time. Instead, as this Table shows, the sun is either ahead of or behind its theoretical schedule.

Two corrections are involved. 1) To correct for your difference in longitude from the central meridian of your time zone (i.e. 75° for U.S. Atlantic Coast), either a) add 4 minutes of time for each degree West or b) subtract 4 minutes of time for each degree East. 2) If necessary, convert from Daylight Savings Time to Standard Time by subtracting 1 hour from your watch.

Thus for Boston, at 71° West longitude (or 4° East of 75°), L.A.N. occurs 16 minutes before the times listed in the Table.

For New York, at 74° West (1° East of 75°), L.A.N. occurs 4 minutes earlier than times shown.

Converting arc to time:

360° = 24 hours
15° = 1 hour
1° = 4 minutes
15' = 1 minute
1' = 4 seconds

SUN'S TRUE BEARING AT RISING AND SETTING

To find compass deviation using the Sun.
Figures are correct for all Longitudes

Latitudes

Sun's Decl.	38° N Rise	38° N Set	40° N Rise	40° N Set	42° N Rise	42° N Set	44° N Rise	44° N Set	Sun's Decl.
N 23°	60.3°	299.7°	59.3°	300.7°	58.3°	301.7°	57.1°	302.9°	N 23°
22	61.6	298.4	60.7	299.3	59.7	300.3	58.6	301.4	22
21	63.0	297.0	62.1	297.9	61.2	298.8	60.1	299.9	21
20	64.3	295.7	63.5	296.5	62.6	297.4	61.6	298.4	20
19	65.6	294.4	64.9	295.1	64.0	296.0	63.1	296.9	19
18	66.9	293.1	66.2	293.8	65.4	294.6	64.6	295.4	18
17	68.2	291.8	67.6	292.4	66.8	293.2	66.0	294.0	17
16	69.5	290.5	68.9	291.1	68.2	291.8	67.5	292.5	16
15	70.8	289.2	70.3	289.7	69.6	290.4	68.9	291.1	15
14	72.1	287.9	71.6	288.4	71.0	289.0	70.4	289.6	14
13	73.4	286.6	72.9	287.1	72.4	287.6	71.8	288.2	13
12	74.7	285.3	74.3	285.7	73.8	286.2	73.2	286.8	12
11	76.0	284.0	75.6	284.4	75.1	284.9	74.6	285.4	11
10	77.3	282.7	76.9	283.1	76.5	283.5	76.0	284.0	10
9	78.6	281.4	78.2	281.8	77.9	282.1	77.4	282.6	9
8	79.8	280.2	79.5	280.5	79.2	280.8	78.9	281.1	8
7	81.1	278.9	80.9	279.1	80.6	279.4	80.3	279.7	7
6	82.4	277.6	82.2	277.7	81.9	278.1	81.7	278.3	6
5	83.7	276.3	83.5	276.5	83.3	276.7	83.0	277.0	5
4	84.9	275.1	84.8	275.2	84.6	275.4	84.4	275.6	4
3	86.2	273.8	86.1	273.9	86.0	274.0	85.8	274.2	3
2	87.5	272.5	87.4	272.6	87.3	272.7	87.2	272.8	2
N 1°	88.7	271.3	88.7	271.3	88.7	271.3	88.6	271.4	N 1°
0	90.0	270.0	90.0	270.0	90.0	270.0	90.0	270.0	0
S 1°	91.3	268.7	91.3	268.7	91.3	268.7	91.4	268.6	S 1°
2	92.5	267.5	92.6	267.4	92.7	267.3	92.8	267.2	2
3	93.8	266.2	93.9	266.1	94.0	266.0	94.2	265.8	3
4	95.1	264.9	95.2	264.8	95.4	264.6	95.6	264.4	4
5	96.3	263.7	96.5	263.5	96.7	263.3	97.0	263.0	5
6	97.6	262.4	97.8	262.2	98.1	261.9	98.3	261.7	6
7	98.9	261.1	99.1	260.9	99.4	260.6	99.7	260.3	7
8	100.2	259.8	100.5	259.5	100.8	259.2	101.1	258.9	8
9	101.4	258.6	101.8	258.2	102.1	257.9	102.6	257.4	9
10	102.7	257.3	103.1	256.9	103.5	256.5	104.0	256.0	10
11	104.0	256.0	104.4	255.6	104.9	255.1	105.4	254.6	11
12	105.3	254.7	105.7	254.3	106.2	253.8	106.8	253.2	12
13	106.6	253.4	107.1	252.9	107.6	252.4	108.2	251.8	13
14	107.9	252.1	108.4	251.6	109.0	251.0	109.6	250.4	14
15	109.2	250.8	109.7	250.3	110.4	249.6	111.1	248.9	15
16	110.5	249.5	111.1	248.9	111.8	248.2	112.5	247.5	16
17	111.8	248.2	112.4	247.6	113.2	246.8	114.0	246.0	17
18	113.1	246.9	113.8	246.2	114.6	245.4	115.4	244.6	18
19	114.4	245.6	115.1	244.9	116.0	244.0	116.9	243.1	19
20	115.7	244.3	116.5	243.5	117.4	242.6	118.4	241.6	20
21	117.0	243.0	117.9	242.1	118.8	241.2	119.9	240.1	21
22	118.4	241.6	119.3	240.7	120.3	239.7	121.4	238.6	22
S 23°	119.7	240.3	120.7	239.3	121.7	238.3	122.9	237.1	S 23°

Instructions: (1) Knowing the date, find the Sun's Declination from the facing page. Find that Declination down the left column on this page. (2) Find the column with your Latitude, and choose either Rise or Set to determine the True Bearing. (3) Add the local Westerly Variation to the figure. (4) If you are a couple of minutes after sunrise or before sunset, the Sun's bearing changes about 1° each 6 minutes during the first hour after sunrise and before sunset. (5) The deviation found will be correct only for the heading you are on at that time.

THE SUN'S DECLINATION 2013

For celestial navigators, the "noon sight" reading of the Sun's height above the horizon, together with the Sun's Declination from this table, determines latitude.

THE SUN'S DECLINATION 2013

MEAN NOON – 75° MERIDIAN (1700 G.M.T.)

Day	JAN. South	FEB. South	MAR. South	APR. North	MAY North	JUN. North	JUL. North	AUG. North	SEPT. North	OCT. South	NOV. South	DEC. South
1	-22 57	-16 55	-7 20	+4 47	+15 16	+22 08	+23 03	+17 51	+8 02	-3 26	-14 38	-21 54
2	-22 51	-16 37	-6 57	+5 11	+15 34	+22 16	+22 59	+17 35	+7 40	-3 50	-14 57	-22 03
3	-22 45	-16 19	-6 34	+5 34	+15 52	+22 23	+22 54	+17 20	+7 18	-4 13	-15 16	-22 11
4	-22 39	-16 01	-6 11	+5 56	+16 09	+22 30	+22 49	+17 04	+6 56	-4 36	-15 34	-22 19
5	-22 31	-15 43	-5 48	+6 19	+16 26	+22 37	+22 43	+16 47	+6 34	-5 00	-15 52	-22 27
6	-22 25	-15 25	-5 25	+6 42	+16 43	+22 43	+22 37	+16 31	+6 12	-5 22	-16 10	-22 35
7	-22 17	-15 06	-5 01	+7 04	+17 00	+22 49	+22 30	+16 14	+5 49	-5 45	-16 28	-22 40
8	-22 09	-14 47	-4 38	+7 27	+17 16	+22 54	+22 24	+15 57	+5 27	-6 08	-16 45	-22 47
9	-22 00	-14 28	-4 14	+7 49	+17 32	+22 59	+22 16	+15 39	+5 04	-6 31	-17 02	-22 53
10	-21 51	-14 08	-3 51	+8 11	+17 47	+23 03	+22 09	+15 22	+4 41	-6 53	-17 19	-22 58
11	-21 42	-13 48	-3 27	+8 33	+18 03	+23 07	+22 01	+15 04	+4 18	-7 16	-17 36	-23 03
12	-21 32	-13 28	-3 04	+8 55	+18 18	+23 11	+21 52	+14 46	+3 55	-7 38	-17 52	-23 07
13	-21 22	-13 08	-2 40	+9 17	+18 33	+23 15	+21 44	+14 28	+3 32	-8 01	-18 08	-23 11
14	-21 11	-12 48	-2 16	+9 38	+18 47	+23 18	+21 34	+14 09	+3 09	-8 23	-18 23	-23 15
15	-21 00	-12 27	-1 53	+10 00	+19 01	+23 20	+21 25	+13 50	+2 46	-8 45	-18 39	-23 18
16	-20 48	-12 06	-1 29	+10 21	+19 15	+23 22	+21 15	+13 31	+2 23	-9 07	-18 54	-23 20
17	-20 36	-11 45	-1 05	+10 42	+19 28	+23 24	+21 05	+13 12	+2 00	-9 29	-19 08	-23 22
18	-20 24	-11 24	-0 42	+11 03	+19 41	+23 25	+20 54	+12 53	+1 37	-9 51	-19 22	-23 24
19	-20 11	-11 02	-0 18	+11 24	+19 54	+23 26	+20 43	+12 33	+1 14	-10 13	-19 36	-23 25
20	-19 58	-10 41	+0 06	+11 44	+20 07	+23 26	+20 32	+12 13	+0 50	-10 34	-19 50	-23 26
21	-19 45	-10 19	+0 30	+12 05	+20 19	+23 26	+20 20	+11 53	+0 27	-10 56	-20 03	-23 26
22	-19 31	-9 57	+0 53	+12 25	+20 31	+23 26	+20 08	+11 33	+0 04	-11 17	-20 16	-23 26
23	-19 17	-9 35	+1 17	+12 45	+20 42	+23 25	+19 56	+11 13	-0 20	-11 38	-20 28	-23 25
24	-19 03	-9 13	+1 41	+13 05	+20 53	+23 24	+19 43	+10 52	-0 43	-11 59	-20 40	-23 24
25	-18 48	-8 51	+2 04	+13 24	+21 04	+23 22	+19 30	+10 32	-1 06	-12 19	-20 52	-23 22
26	-18 33	-8 28	+2 28	+13 43	+21 14	+23 20	+19 17	+10 11	-1 30	-12 40	-21 03	-23 20
27	-18 17	-8 06	+2 51	+14 02	+21 24	+23 17	+19 03	+9 50	-1 53	-13 00	-21 14	-23 18
28	-18 01	-7 43	+3 14	+14 21	+21 34	+23 15	+18 50	+9 29	-2 17	-13 20	-21 25	-23 15
29	-17 45		+3 38	+14 40	+21 43	+23 11	+18 35	+9 07	-2 40	-13 40	-21 35	-23 11
30	-17 28		+4 01	+14 58	+21 52	+23 08	+18 21	+8 46	-3 03	-14 00	-21 45	-23 07
31	-17 12		+4 24		+22 00		+18 06	+8 24		-14 19		-23 03

Vernal Equinox: March 20th, 6:02 a.m. E.S.T.
Summer Solstice: June 21st, 12:04 a.m. E.S.T.

Autumnal Equinox: September 22nd, 3:44 a.m. E.S.T.
Winter Solstice: December 21st, 12:11 p.m. E.S.T.

To find Sun's Declination in the Atlantic Time Zone (1 hour earlier than E.S.T.), take 1/24 of the difference between Day 1 and Day 2. Add or subtract this figure from Day 2 to find the Declination for Day 2.

If Declination is increasing (N. or S.), *subtract*.   If Declination is decreasing (N. or S.), *add*.

231

2013 MOONRISE AND MOONSET
BOSTON, MA
Add one hour for Daylight Saving Time, March 10 - November 3

Day	JANUARY Rise	Set	FEBRUARY Rise	Set	MARCH Rise	Set	APRIL Rise	Set	MAY Rise	Set	JUNE Rise	Set	Day
1	2056	0919	2311	0921	2211	0759	....	0905	....	1014	0012	1233	1
2	2200	0948	....	0956	2319	0837	0018	1007	0032	1123	0041	1337	2
3	2305	1016	0019	1035	....	0921	0109	1114	0107	1230	0111	1439	3
4	....	1045	0128	1121	0026	1012	0153	1222	0138	1336	0141	1540	4
5	0012	1118	0234	1215	0127	1110	0231	1330	0208	1440	0214	1639	5
6	0121	1154	0335	1317	0223	1213	0304	1437	0237	1543	0250	1735	6
7	0231	1237	0429	1425	0311	1321	0335	1544	0307	1645	0330	1829	7
8	0342	1328	0517	1536	0353	1431	0405	1648	0338	1746	0414	1918	8
9	0448	1428	0558	1648	0430	1541	0435	1752	0412	1845	0502	2003	9
10	0549	1535	0634	1800	0504	1649	0505	1855	0450	1941	0554	2043	10
11	0641	1648	0706	1909	0535	1756	0538	1955	0531	2033	0650	2119	11
12	0726	1801	0736	2016	0605	1902	0613	2054	0617	2121	0747	2152	12
13	0805	1914	0806	2120	0635	2006	0652	2149	0707	2204	0845	2222	13
14	0838	2023	0836	2223	0706	2108	0736	2239	0800	2243	0945	2250	14
15	0909	2130	0908	2323	0740	2208	0823	2326	0856	2318	1046	2318	15
16	0938	2235	0942	....	0816	2305	0914	....	0954	2349	1148	2348	16
17	1007	2337	1019	0021	0857	2358	1009	0007	1054	....	1253	....	17
18	1036	....	1101	0116	0941	....	1106	0044	1155	0019	1400	0019	18
19	1108	0038	1148	0208	1030	0047	1205	0118	1258	0048	1510	0054	19
20	1143	0136	1239	0255	1123	0131	1307	0150	1403	0117	1621	0134	20
21	1222	0233	1334	0338	1220	0211	1410	0219	1511	0148	1730	0222	21
22	1305	0326	1432	0416	1319	0248	1516	0249	1622	0222	1835	0318	22
23	1354	0416	1533	0451	1420	0321	1624	0320	1734	0300	1932	0423	23
24	1447	0501	1636	0523	1524	0352	1735	0352	1846	0345	2022	0534	24
25	1544	0542	1741	0554	1629	0422	1847	0429	1953	0438	2104	0648	25
26	1644	0619	1846	0623	1737	0452	1959	0511	2053	0539	2141	0801	26
27	1746	0652	1954	0653	1846	0523	2107	0559	2146	0647	2213	0913	27
28	1849	0723	2102	0724	1957	0557	2210	0655	2230	0758	2244	1021	28
29	1952	0752	....	....	2107	0635	2305	0757	2308	0910	2314	1127	29
30	2057	0821	....	....	2216	0719	2352	0905	2341	1020	2345	1231	30
31	2203	0850	....	....	2321	0808	....	....	....	1128			31

Day	JULY Rise	Set	AUGUST Rise	Set	SEPTEMBER Rise	Set	OCTOBER Rise	Set	NOVEMBER Rise	Set	DECEMBER Rise	Set	Day
1	....	1333	0011	1511	0126	1556	0210	1530	0405	1530	0507	1521	1
2	0017	1433	0056	1559	0223	1629	0311	1559	0512	1606	0616	1613	2
3	0051	1530	0145	1642	0322	1701	0413	1629	0621	1647	0722	1713	3
4	0130	1625	0238	1721	0422	1730	0518	1700	0730	1735	0822	1820	4
5	0212	1715	0334	1757	0524	1759	0624	1734	0837	1829	0914	1931	5
6	0259	1802	0432	1829	0627	1829	0731	1811	0938	1931	0959	2043	6
7	0350	1844	0531	1859	0731	1900	0839	1854	1033	2037	1039	2154	7
8	0444	1921	0632	1928	0836	1934	0945	1943	1120	2146	1114	2303	8
9	0541	1955	0733	1956	0942	2012	1048	2038	1201	2256	1146	....	9
10	0639	2026	0835	2025	1048	2055	1145	2140	1238	....	1217	0010	10
11	0738	2055	0939	2056	1153	2146	1236	2246	1311	0004	1248	0116	11
12	0838	2123	1044	2131	1253	2243	1321	2354	1342	0112	1321	0219	12
13	0939	2151	1150	2210	1349	2346	1400	....	1413	0218	1355	0321	13
14	1042	2221	1256	2256	1438	....	1435	0104	1445	0323	1433	0421	14
15	1147	2253	1401	2350	1522	0054	1508	0213	1519	0426	1515	0518	15
16	1253	2330	1501	....	1601	0205	1540	0321	1555	0529	1601	0612	16
17	1401	....	1556	0051	1636	0316	1612	0428	1635	0628	1651	0700	17
18	1509	0012	1645	0159	1709	0427	1645	0534	1719	0725	1744	0744	18
19	1615	0103	1728	0311	1742	0537	1720	0638	1807	0817	1839	0824	19
20	1715	0201	1806	0424	1814	0644	1758	0740	1858	0904	1936	0859	20
21	1809	0308	1840	0537	1848	0751	1840	0839	1952	0946	2033	0931	21
22	1855	0421	1913	0648	1924	0854	1926	0934	2048	1024	2131	1000	22
23	1935	0535	1945	0758	2004	0955	2015	1024	2145	1058	2230	1029	23
24	2011	0650	2017	0904	2047	1052	2107	1109	2243	1129	2330	1057	24
25	2044	0801	2051	1009	2133	1144	2202	1149	2342	1158	....	1125	25
26	2115	0911	2128	1110	2223	1232	2258	1225	....	1226	0032	1156	26
27	2146	1017	2208	1208	2317	1315	2356	1258	0042	1255	0137	1230	27
28	2218	1121	2252	1303	....	1353	....	1329	0145	1326	0243	1310	28
29	2252	1223	2340	1353	0013	1428	0056	1358	0250	1359	0351	1357	29
30	2330	1322	....	1438	0110	1500	0157	1427	0358	1437	0458	1452	30
31	....	1418	0031	1519	....	....	0300	1457	....	....	0602	1555	31

Time meridian 75° W. 0000 is midnight. 1200 is noon. Standard Time.

2013 MOONRISE AND MOONSET
NEW YORK, NY
Add one hour for Daylight Saving Time, March 10 - November 3

Day	JAN Rise	JAN Set	FEB Rise	FEB Set	MAR Rise	MAR Set	APR Rise	APR Set	MAY Rise	MAY Set	JUN Rise	JUN Set	Day
	h m	h m	h m	h m	h m	h m	h m	h m	h m	h m	h m	h m	
1	2052	0915	2307	0917	2207	0754	....	0900	....	1009	0008	1229	1
2	2155	0943	....	0951	2316	0832	0015	1002	0028	1118	0037	1333	2
3	2301	1011	0016	1030	....	0916	0106	1109	0103	1226	0106	1435	3
4	....	1041	0124	1116	0022	1006	0149	1217	0134	1332	0136	1536	4
5	0008	1113	0230	1210	0124	1104	0227	1325	0204	1436	0209	1635	5
6	0117	1149	0331	1312	0219	1208	0300	1433	0233	1539	0245	1732	6
7	0228	1232	0426	1420	0308	1316	0331	1539	0302	1642	0324	1826	7
8	0338	1323	0513	1531	0350	1426	0401	1644	0334	1742	0408	1915	8
9	0445	1422	0554	1644	0427	1536	0430	1748	0407	1841	0457	2000	9
10	0546	1530	0630	1755	0500	1645	0501	1851	0445	1938	0549	2040	10
11	0638	1642	0702	1904	0531	1752	0533	1952	0526	2030	0644	2116	11
12	0723	1756	0732	2011	0600	1858	0608	2050	0612	2118	0742	2148	12
13	0801	1909	0802	2116	0630	2002	0647	2145	0702	2201	0840	2218	13
14	0834	2019	0831	2219	0701	2105	0730	2236	0755	2240	0940	2246	14
15	0905	2126	0903	2320	0735	2205	0818	2322	0851	2314	1041	2314	15
16	0933	2231	0937	....	0811	2302	0909	....	0949	2346	1144	2343	16
17	1002	2333	1014	0018	0851	2355	1004	0004	1049	....	1249	....	17
18	1031	....	1056	0113	0936	....	1101	0041	1150	0015	1356	0014	18
19	1103	0034	1142	0205	1025	0044	1201	0115	1253	0044	1506	0049	19
20	1138	0133	1233	0252	1118	0128	1302	0146	1359	0113	1617	0129	20
21	1217	0229	1329	0334	1215	0208	1406	0215	1507	0143	1727	0216	21
22	1300	0323	1427	0413	1314	0244	1512	0245	1618	0217	1832	0313	22
23	1349	0412	1528	0448	1416	0317	1620	0315	1731	0255	1929	0417	23
24	1442	0458	1632	0520	1519	0348	1731	0348	1842	0340	2018	0529	24
25	1539	0539	1736	0550	1625	0418	1843	0424	1950	0433	2100	0643	25
26	1639	0615	1842	0619	1733	0448	1955	0505	2050	0534	2137	0756	26
27	1741	0649	1949	0649	1842	0519	2104	0554	2142	0642	2209	0908	27
28	1844	0719	2058	0720	1953	0553	2207	0649	2226	0753	2240	1017	28
29	1948	0748	....	....	2104	0630	2301	0752	2304	0905	2310	1123	29
30	2053	0817	....	....	2213	0713	2348	0859	2337	1015	2340	1227	30
31	2200	0846	....	....	2317	0803			....	1123	....	....	31

Day	JUL Rise	JUL Set	AUG Rise	AUG Set	SEP Rise	SEP Set	OCT Rise	OCT Set	NOV Rise	NOV Set	DEC Rise	DEC Set	Day
	h m	h m	h m	h m	h m	h m	h m	h m	h m	h m	h m	h m	
1	....	1329	0005	1507	0121	1552	0205	1526	0401	1525	0503	1516	1
2	0012	1429	0051	1555	0218	1626	0306	1555	0509	1601	0613	1608	2
3	0046	1527	0140	1639	0317	1657	0409	1625	0618	1642	0718	1708	3
4	0124	1621	0233	1718	0418	1726	0514	1656	0727	1729	0818	1815	4
5	0207	1712	0329	1753	0520	1755	0620	1729	0833	1824	0911	1926	5
6	0253	1758	0427	1825	0623	1824	0727	1806	0935	1926	0956	2038	6
7	0344	1840	0527	1855	0727	1855	0835	1849	1029	2032	1035	2149	7
8	0439	1918	0627	1924	0832	1929	0942	1937	1116	2141	1110	2259	8
9	0536	1951	0729	1952	0939	2007	1044	2033	1157	2251	1142	....	9
10	0634	2022	0831	2021	1045	2050	1142	2135	1234	....	1213	0006	10
11	0733	2051	0935	2052	1149	2140	1232	2241	1307	0000	1244	0111	11
12	0834	2119	1040	2126	1250	2237	1317	2349	1338	0107	1316	0215	12
13	0935	2147	1146	2205	1346	2341	1356	....	1409	0214	1350	0317	13
14	1038	2216	1253	2251	1435	....	1431	0059	1440	0319	1428	0417	14
15	1143	2248	1357	2344	1518	0049	1504	0208	1514	0423	1510	0515	15
16	1250	2325	1458	....	1557	0200	1536	0316	1550	0525	1556	0608	16
17	1358	....	1553	0045	1632	0312	1607	0424	1630	0625	1646	0657	17
18	1506	0007	1642	0153	1705	0423	1640	0530	1714	0722	1739	0741	18
19	1612	0057	1724	0306	1737	0532	1715	0634	1801	0814	1834	0820	19
20	1712	0156	1802	0419	1810	0640	1753	0737	1853	0901	1931	0855	20
21	1805	0303	1836	0532	1843	0747	1835	0836	1947	0943	2028	0927	21
22	1852	0416	1908	0644	1919	0851	1920	0931	2043	1020	2127	0957	22
23	1932	0530	1940	0753	1958	0951	2009	1021	2140	1054	2226	1025	23
24	2007	0645	2012	0900	2041	1048	2102	1106	2238	1125	2326	1052	24
25	2039	0757	2046	1005	2128	1141	2157	1146	2337	1154	....	1121	25
26	2111	0906	2123	1107	2218	1228	2253	1222	....	1222	0028	1151	26
27	2141	1013	2203	1205	2312	1311	2351	1254	0038	1251	0133	1226	27
28	2213	1118	2247	1259	....	1349	....	1325	0141	1321	0239	1305	28
29	2247	1220	2335	1349	0008	1424	0051	1354	0246	1354	0347	1351	29
30	2324	1319	....	1435	0106	1456	0152	1423	0354	1432	0455	1446	30
31	....	1415	0026	1516	....	....	0255	1453	....	....	0558	1550	31

Time meridian 75° W.   0000 is midnight.   1200 is noon.   Standard Time.

PHASES OF THE MOON 2013 E.S.T.

● New Moon, ☽ 1st Quarter, ○ Full Moon, ☾ Last Quarter, A in Apogee

P in Perigee, N, S Moon farthest North or South of Equator, E on Equator

January			February			March			April			May			June		
E	3	1am	☽	3	9am	☽	4	5pm	S	1	7am	☽	2	6am	E	1	7am
☽	4	11pm	S	5	8pm	S	5	2am	☽	3	midn	E	5	1am	●	8	11am
S	9	11pm	P	7	7am	P	5	6pm	E	7	8pm	●	9	7pm	N	8	3pm
P	10	5am	●	10	2am	E	11	1pm	●	10	5am	N	12	8am	A	9	5pm
●	11	3pm	E	12	3am	●	11	3pm	N	15	1am	A	13	9am	E	16	2pm
E	15	6pm	☽	17	4pm	N	18	5pm	A	15	5pm	☽	18	midn	☽	16	noon
☽	18	7pm	A	19	2am	A	18	10pm	☽	18	8am	E	19	6pm	S	22	noon
A	22	6am	N	19	9am	☽	19	noon	E	22	9am	○	24	11pm	P	23	6am
N	23	1am	○	25	3pm	E	25	11pm	○	25	3pm	P	25	9pm	○	23	7am
○	27	midn	E	26	2pm	○	27	4am	P	27	3pm	S	26	midn	E	28	3pm
E	30	7am				P	30	11pm	S	28	2pm	☾	31	2pm	☾	30	midn

July			August			September			October			November			December		
N	5	10pm	N	2	5am	●	5	5am	E	3	6am	☽	3	8am			
A	6	8pm	A	3	4am	E	5	10pm	●	4	8pm	S	6	2am	●	2	7pm
●	8	2am	●	6	5pm	☽	12	noon	S	9	7pm	P	6	4am	S	3	noon
E	13	9am	E	9	4pm	S	12	2pm	P	10	6pm	☽	10	1am	P	4	5am
☽	15	10pm	☽	14	6am	P	15	noon	☽	11	6pm	E	12	11am	☽	9	10am
S	19	11pm	S	16	8am	E	18	9pm	E	16	5am	○	17	10am	E	9	5pm
P	21	3pm	P	18	8pm	○	19	6am	○	18	7pm	N	19	1pm	N	16	8pm
○	22	1pm	○	20	9pm	N	25	9pm	N	23	5am	A	22	5am	○	17	4am
E	26	1am	E	22	11am	☾	26	11pm	A	25	9am	☾	25	2pm	A	19	7pm
☾	29	1pm	☾	28	5am	A	27	1pm	☾	26	7pm	E	27	1am	E	24	10am
			N	29	1pm				E	30	3pm				☾	25	9am
			A	30	7pm										S	31	midn

Midnight is the *beginning* of the day.

see p. 235 for daily moon phases throughout the year

SEXTANTS

- New sextants by Cassens & Plath, Tamaya, Astra IIIB
- Repair and adjustment of sextants of all makes.
- Pre-owned sextants, fully refurbished, with a 60-day money-back guarantee. Save up to 50% over the cost of a new sextant.

See our website for current listings, or call for further details.

ROBERT E. WHITE INSTRUMENTS, INC.
www.robertwhite.com
1-617-482-8460

Daily Moon Phases 2013

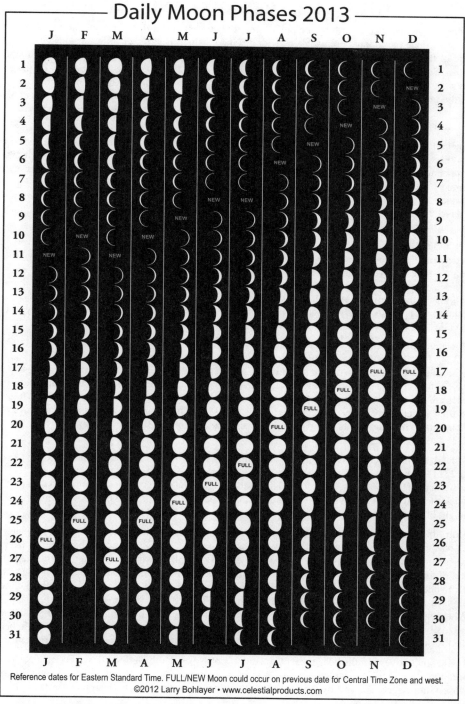

Reference dates for Eastern Standard Time. FULL/NEW Moon could occur on previous date for Central Time Zone and west.
©2012 Larry Bohlayer • www.celestialproducts.com

Catalog of other moon calendars, cards, imprints and astronomy items available from Celestial Products.

800-235-3783

CELESTIAL PRODUCTS ™

www.mooncalendar.com

THE TIDES, THE MOON, AND THE SUN

Tides are created on the earth by the pull of gravity between the earth and moon, and to a lesser extent the sun. Since the moon's pull weakens with distance, its pull is stronger on water located on the near side of the earth than it is on the earth's center. This creates a bulge of water on the side facing the moon. Similarly, the moon's pull on the earth's center is stronger than it is on the water on the earth's far side. This tends to pull the earth away from the water, creating another bulge of water of equal size on the far side of the earth. High tides are where the bulges are. The two bulges can also be explained as the moon's gravity being dominant on the earth's near side, and centrifugal force being dominant on the earth's far side.

The earth rotates in the same direction as the moon orbits, but much more rapidly, with a period of 24 hours vs. 27.3 days. The tidal bulges, or ocean tides, follow the slowly orbiting moon, which takes 24 hours and 50 minutes to reappear above the same part of the earth, so that each day the tides occur 50 minutes later than the previous day. As there are usually two highs and two lows per day, highs and lows average about 6 hours 12 1/2 minutes apart. A handy fact for coastwise planners: in the course of 7 days, the tides are about the *reverse* of the previous week: if on a Sunday it is *low* tide at about noon, the following Sunday it will be *high* at about noon.

The time of high tide usually does not usually coincide exactly with the time the moon is overhead or underneath. The largest astronomical reason for this is the effect of the sun, which has its own tidal effect on the earth. Although the sun has a mass 27 million times that of the moon, it is the moon which dominates by being on average 390 times closer to earth. Since the sun's effect on the tides is about one-half that of the moon, the sun can shift tidal times by up to one hour or more, depending on its position. Tidal times are also greatly affected by land masses that impede the current flows necessary to create the tides, the speeds of traveling ocean waves, and underwater topography.

How much the ocean tides rise and fall depends basically on three conditions. (See Phases of the Moon, p. 234.) First, when the sun and moon are in a line with the earth, their gravitational forces work together to produce a greater range of tide than usual. This occurs both at full moon, when the moon is opposite the earth from the sun, and at new moon, when the moon is between the earth and sun. These higher tides are called "spring tides." But when the moon and sun are at right angles to the earth (first and last quarter, or half moon), their forces are working against each other, and the result is a lower range of tide than usual. These are called "neap tides." As each year has about 13 "lunar" months, we have 26 spring tides and 26 neap tides in the year.

Second, the moon's orbit around the earth is elliptical, ranging from 252,000 miles at apogee (A) down to 221,000 miles at perigee (P), so the moon's effect on the earth is greater at "P" than at "A." Note again in the High and Low Water Tables how much higher the tide is when the Full Moon is at "P" than when the Full Moon is at "A." The position of the moon along its elliptical path is very important to the height of the tides.

Third, the plane of the moon's orbit about the earth is inclined to the plane of the earth's equator. The moon therefore travels above and below the earth's equator, and sits directly above the equator only twice a month. When it is over the equator, the day's two high tides will be about the same height. The rest of the time the moon is either above the northern hemisphere (northern declination) or the southern hemisphere (southern declination). When the moon is north of the equator (N) or south (S), the two high water marks on the same day will differ in height. This effect is known as "semidiurnal inequality." When the moon has northern declination and is over the U.S., this high tide will be the greater of our two daily highs. Our second high tide of the day, when the moon is over Asia, will be less high, because the far side tidal bulge will be greatest over South America, and less over us in the northern hemisphere.

The height of tides is influenced most by the moon's phase, with the highest tides at Full and New Moon; second by the moon's distance from earth in its elliptical orbit, tides being highest when the moon is closest, at perigee; and last by the moon's declination, north or south, which creates tides of different heights on the same day.

For a more complete discussion, see NOAA's website: http://tidesandcurrents.noaa.gov/restles1.html

The Publishers thank Nelson Caldwell, of the Smithsonian Astrophysical Observatory, Cambridge, MA, and Hale Bradt, Department of Physics, M.I.T., for their valuable contributions to this article.

Visibility of The Planets, 2013

MERCURY can only be seen low in the east before sunrise, or low in the west after sunset. It is visible in the mornings from January 1 to 2, March 11 to May 4, July 19 to August 16, and November 8 to December 12. It is brighter toward the end of each period. It is visible in the evenings from January 31 to February 26, May 19 to July 1, and September 4 to October 27, and it is brighter at the beginning of each period.

VENUS is a brilliant object in the morning sky from the beginning of the year until mid-February, when it becomes too close to the Sun for observation. From the end of the first week of May it reappears in the evening sky until the end of the year. Venus is in conjunction with Mercury on May 25 and June 20, with Jupiter on May 28 and with Saturn on September 20.

MARS can be seen in the evening sky in Capricornus and in Aquarius from late January, until in the second week of February it becomes too close to the Sun for observation. It reappears in the morning sky during the second half of June in Taurus and moves into Gemini in mid-July. It remains in the morning sky for the rest of the year, moving into Cancer from late August, Leo in late September, and Virgo from the end of November. Mars is in conjunction with Mercury on February 8 and with Jupiter on July 22.

JUPITER is in Taurus at the beginning of the year, and can be seen for more than half the night until late February, after which it can be seen only in the evening sky. In the first week of June it becomes too close to the Sun for observation. In reappears in the morning sky in early July in Gemini where it remains throughout the rest of the year. Jupiter is in conjunction with Mercury on May 27, with Venus on May 28, and with Mars on July 22.

SATURN rises shortly after midnight at the beginning of the year in Libra, passes into Virgo in mid-May, and once again into Libra in early September. It is at opposition on April 28, when it can be seen throughout the night. From late July until mid-October it is visible only in the evening sky. Then it becomes too close to the Sun for observation. In the second half of November it reappears and can be seen in the morning sky for the rest of the year. Saturn is in conjunction with Venus on September 20 and with Mercury on October 10 and November 26.

Conjunction occurs when a body has the same horizontal bearing from Earth as another. When Venus is in conjunction with Jupiter on May 28, they appear one over the other, in the same sector of the sky.

Opposition occurs when a body farther than Earth from the Sun appears opposite the Sun. On a line drawn from the Sun through the Earth and beyond, the body lies on that extension.

Elongation is apparent motion eastward or westward (relative to the Sun) across the sky. When a planet has 0° elongation, it lies on a line from Earth to the Sun, is in conjunction and not visible; when it has 90° elongation, it is in eastern quadrature; when it has 180° elongation, it is in opposition and has the best visibility; when it has 270° elongation, it is in western quadrature.

Visibility of Planets in Morning and Evening Twilight

	Morning		Evening	
VENUS	January 1 – February 16		May 7 – December 31	
MARS	---		January 1 – February 9	
	June 20 – December 31		---	
JUPITER	---		July 4 – December 31	
	January 1 – June 5		---	
SATURN	January 1 – April 28		April 28 – October 20	
	November 24 – December 31		---	

RADIO TELEPHONE INFORMATION – VHF SYSTEM

Calling Guidelines: Avoid excessive calling. Make calls as brief as possible. Give name of called vessel first, then "This is (name of your vessel)," your call sign (if you have a Station License), and the word "Over." If station does not answer, delay your repeat call for 2 minutes. At the end of your message, sign off with "This is (your vessel's name)," your call sign, and "Out."

Range and Power: Operation is essentially line-of-sight. Since the elevation of antennas at both communications points extends the "horizon," range may be 20 to 50 miles on a 24-hour basis between a boat and a land station. Effective range between boats will be less because of lower antenna heights. 25 watts is the maximum power permitted.

Interference factor: Most VHF-FM equipment has 6 or more channels, so it is possible to shift to a clear channel. Like the FM in your home radio, the system is practically immune to interference from ignition noise, static, etc., except under unusual conditions.

Channelization: A minimum of 3 channels is required by the FCC. Two are mandatory: Channel 16 (156.800 MHz), the International Distress frequency; and Channel 06 (156.300 MHz), the Intership Safety Frequency. The Coast Guard *strongly recommends* that you have Channel 22A as your third channel.

Channel	Purpose and Comments
16 156.800 MHz	**Distress and Safety**: Ship to Shore and Intership. Guarded 24 hours by the Coast Guard. No routine messages allowed other than to establish the use of a working channel. *See page 239* for Distress calling procedure. **Calling**: Ship to Shore and Intership. Use Channel 16 to establish contact, then switch to a working channel (see below). Calling Channel: New England waters. Commercial and pleasure.
09 156.450 MHz	**Boater Calling:** Commercial and Non-Commercial
06 156.300 MHz	**Intership Safety:** No routine messages allowed. 06 is limited to talking with the Coast Guard and others at the scene of an emergency, and to information on the movement of vessels.
22A 157.100 MHz (21 in Canada) 161.65 MHz	**Maritime Safety Information** channel. Not guarded by the CG, but after a vessel makes contact with the CG for non-distrress calls on Channel 16, they will tell you to switch to and use *only* 22A for communicating. Channel 22A is also used for CG weather advisories and Notices to Mariners. *Times* of these broadcasts given on Channel 16.
12, 14, 20A, 65A, 66A, 73, 74, 77	**Ship to Shore and Intership:** Port operations, harbormasters, etc. (Your electronics dealer should have local frequencies.)
08, 67, 88A	**Commercial (intership only):** For ocean vessels, dredges, tugs, etc.
07A, 10, 11, 18A, 19A, 79A, 80A	**Commercial only**
13 156.650 MHz	**Intership Navigation Safety:** (bridge to bridge). Ships > 20 m length maintain a listening watch on this channel in US waters.
68, 69, 71, 72, 78A	**Ship to Shore and Intership, Pleasure craft only:** Shore stations, marinas, etc. The best channels for general communication.
70 156.525 MHz	**Digital Selective Calling (DSC).** Special equipment required. See p. 241 Marine Communications.
81A 157.075 MHz 83A 157.175 MHz *for Keyed Fog Signals,* Check Notice to Mariners	If fog signal is radio activated. During times of reduced visibility, within ½ mile of the fog signal, turn VHF marine radio to channel 81A or 83A. Key microphone 5 – 10 times consecutively to activate fog signal for 45 minutes. The CG is currently using **83A, 81A** if interference.
AIS 1 161.975 MHz	Automatic Identification System (AIS)
AIS 2 162.025 MHz	Automatic Identification System (AIS)

238

MARINE EMERGENCY AND DISTRESS CALLS

See p. 241, Marine Communications, for information on why you should update your VHF Radio for Digital Selective Calling (DSC).

If you have DSC, have an MMSI number and your unit is properly installed with a GPS connection, follow your manufacturer's instructions.

If you do <u>not</u> have a DSC-equipped radio, use the following:

Speak slowly and clearly. Use: VHF Ch. 16 (156.800 MHz) or MF/HF 2182 kHz

I. DISTRESS SIGNAL (top priority)

If you are in distress (i.e. when threatened by grave and imminent danger) transmit the International distress call on either 2182 kHz or 156.800 MHz (Channel 16) — "MAYDAY MAYDAY MAYDAY, THIS IS (Your vessel's name and call sign repeated three times)"

IF CALLING FROM A VESSEL IN TROUBLE — give:

1. WHO you are (Your vessel's name, registration number or call sign).
2. WHERE you are (Your vessel's position in latitude/longitude or true bearing and distance in nautical miles from a known geographical point. Local names known only in the immediate vicinity are confusing).
3. WHAT is wrong (Nature of distress or difficulty, if not in distress).
4. Kind of assistance desired.
5. Number of persons aboard and condition of any injured.
6. Present seaworthiness of your vessel.
7. Description of your vessel (length, type cabin, masts, power, color of hull, superstructure and trim).
8. Your listening frequency and schedule.

IF CALLING WHILE OBSERVING ANOTHER VESSEL IN DIFFICULTY — give:

1. Your position and the bearing and distance of the vessel in difficulty.
2. Nature of distress or difficulty.
3. Description of the vessel in distress or difficulty, (see item 7 above).
4. Your intentions, course and speed, etc.
5. Your radio call sign, name of your vessel, listening frequency and schedule.

If there is no immediate response, repeat appropriate messages above; if still no response, you may send on any other available frequency until you make contact.

IF YOU HEAR A MAYDAY CALL — Immediately discontinue any transmission. Note details in your radio log right away. Do not make any transmission on this distress channel until MAYDAY condition is lifted by the Coast Guard, unless you are in a position to be of assistance.

II. URGENCY SIGNAL (second in priority)

If you have an urgent message to send (threat to a vessel's safety or to someone on board, overboard or within sight), use the same procedure as above but say the word "PAN" three times. "PAN" (pronounced "PAWN") is also used as a warning signal that a Distress Signal may be sent out at a later stage. Morse Code signal is – (T) – (T) – (T)

III. SAFETY SIGNAL (third priority)

If you wish to report navigation or weather warnings (ice, derelicts, tropical storms, etc.) use the same procedure as above but say the word "SECURITY" (pronounced SAY-CUR-I-TAY) three times. Morse Code signal is – • • – (X) – • • – (X) – • • – (X)

See p. 8 for a list of visual and audible distress signals

How to Contact the U.S. Coast Guard

U.S. Coast Guard Rescue Coordination Centers (RCCs)
24-hour Regional Contacts for Emergencies

RCC Boston, MA – 617-223-8555 New England south to northern New Jersey
RCC Norfolk, VA – 757-398-6231 New Jersey to border of N. Carolina and S. Carolina
RCC Miami, FL – 305-415-6800 S. Carolina to Key West including much of Caribbean

USCG Navigation Information Service (NIS). Watchstander, (24/7): 703-313-5900

USCG Suspected Terrorist Incidents Hotline, National Response Center (NRC): 800-424-8802

USCG Maritime Safety Line: 800-682-1796

INTERNET: USCG - www.navcen.uscg.gov/ Canada - www.notmar.gc.ca/

U.S. Coast Guard Stations – (monitoring VHF Ch. 16)

1st District – Boston – (800) 848-3942

Eastport, ME (207) 853-2845
Jonesport, ME (207) 497-2134
Southwest Harbor, ME (207) 244-4250
Rockland, ME (207) 596-6667
Boothbay Hbr., ME (207) 633-2661
S. Portland, ME (207) 767-0364
Sector Northern New England (207) 767-0302
Portsmouth, NH (603) 436-4415
Merrimac-Newburyport, MA (978) 465-0731
Gloucester, MA (978) 283-0705
Boston, MA (617) 223-3224
Point Allerton-Hull, MA (781) 925-0166
Scituate, MA (781) 545-3801
Cape Cod Canal-E. Entr. (508) 888-0020
Provincetown, MA (508) 487-0077
Chatham, MA (508) 945-3830
Brant Pt.-Nantucket, MA (508) 228-0388
Woods Hole, MA (508) 457-3219
Menemsha, MA (508) 645-2662
Castle Hill, Newport, RI (401) 846-3676
Point Judith, RI (401) 789-0444
New London, CT (860) 442-4471
New Haven, CT (203) 468-4498
Sector NY, NY (718) 354-4353
Fire Island, NY (631) 661-9101
New York Station, NY (718) 354-4099
Eatons Neck, NY (631) 261-6959
Kings Point, NY (516) 466-7135
Jones Beach, NY (516) 785-2995
Moriches, NY (631) 395-4400
Shinnecock, NY (631) 728-0078
Montauk, NY (631) 668-2773
Sandy Hook, NJ (732) 872-3429

5th District – Portsmouth, VA (757) 398-6486

Manasquan Inlet, NJ (732) 899-0887
Shark River, NJ (732) 776-6730
Barnegat, NJ (609) 494-2661
Atlantic City, NJ (609) 344-6594
Cape May, NJ (609) 898-6995
Great Egg, NJ (609) 399-0144
Indian River Inlet, DE (302) 227-2440
Ocean City, MD (410) 289-1905

5th District, cont.

St. Inigoes, MD (301) 872-4344
Crisfield, MD (410) 968-0323
Annapolis, MD (410) 267-8108
Oxford, MD (410) 226-0581
Curtis Bay-Baltimore, MD (410) 576-2625
Stillpond, MD (410) 778-2201
Chincoteague, VA (757) 336-2874
Little Creek-Norfolk, VA (757) 464-9371
Wachapreague, VA (757) 787-9526
Portsmouth, VA (757) 483-8527
Cape Charles, VA (757) 331-2000
Milford Haven, VA (804) 725-3732
Oregon Inlet, NC (252) 441-6260
Hatteras Inlet, NC (252) 986-2176
Hobucken, NC (252) 745-3131
Ocracoke, NC (252) 928-4731
Fort Macon, NC (252) 247-4581
Elizabeth City, NC (252) 335-6086
Wrightsville Beach, NC (910) 256-4224
Emerald Isle, NC (252) 354-2719
Oak Island, NC (910) 278-1133

7th District – Miami, FL (305) 415-6800

Georgetown, SC (843) 546-2052
Charleston, SC (843) 720-7727
Tybee, GA (912) 786-5440
Brunswick, GA (912) 267-7999
Mayport, FL (904) 564-7592
Ponce de Leon Inlet, FL (386) 428-9085
Cape Canaveral, FL (321) 853-7601
Fort Pierce Inlet, FL (772) 464-6100
Lake Worth Inlet, FL (561) 840-8503
Ft. Lauderdale, FL (954) 927-1611
Miami Beach, FL (305) 535-4368
Islamorada, FL (305) 664-4404
Marathon, FL (305) 743-1945
Key West, FL (305) 292-8856

Canada-Nova Scotia

**Canadian Coast Guard
Joint Rescue Coordination Center
Halifax, NS (902) 427-2110**

MARINE COMMUNICATIONS

Emergencies: The Coast Guard is required to monitor Channel 16; they are not required to answer the telephone. In an emergency, use your VHF radio to call the Coast Guard on Channel 16 (156.80 MHz). Digital Selective Calling (DSC) is on Channel 70 on your VHF. The Coast Guard urges, in the strongest terms possible, that you take the time to interconnect your GPS and DSC-equipped radio. Doing so may save your life in a distress situation!

DSC: As part of the Global Maritime Distress and Safety System (GMDSS), Rescue 21 is the Coast Guard system that provides the emergency response made possible by DSC-equipped VHF radios. It has been active for a while, and if you don't yet have a DSC-VHF radio, you need to know the significant advantages it offers.

Rescues initiated by DSC-equipped radios are far quicker and more successful. Why? With the push of one button, an automated digital distress alert is sent to other DSC-equipped vessels and rescue facilities. This transmission includes your vessel's unique, 9-digit MMSI (Marine Mobile Service Identity) number, which contains your vessel's description for easier identification by response teams. If connected to a compatible GPS, the signal will give your vessel's latitude and longitude for faster and more efficient assistance or rescue. For more information go to: www.navcen.uscg. gov/?pageName=mtDsc. Domestic users (non-commercial) who do not travel outside of the US can be issued an MMSI number without applying for an FCC Station License. You can register for an MMSI online at www.BoatUS.com, or www.seatow.com/boating_safety/.

Non-emergency: Near shore (range will vary) a cell phone can be used successfully for non-emergency calls. The usable distance assumes line-of-sight, so an antenna which is higher may help communicate farther. That distance may be less where there are fewer cell towers.

MARINE WEATHER FORECASTS

VHF-FM, NOAA All-Hazards Weather Radio - Continuous broadcasts 24 hours a day are provided by the National Weather Service with taped messages repeated every 4-6 minutes. These are updated every 3-6 hours and include weather and radar summaries, wind observations, visibility, sea conditions and detailed local forecasts. NOAA VHF-FM broadcasts can be received 20-40 miles from transmitting site.

	MHz			MHz
WX-1	162.550		WX-5	162.450
WX-2	162.400		WX-6	162.500
WX-3	162.475		WX-7	162.525
WX-4	162.425			

Jonesboro, ME (5)	Riverhead, NY (3)	Cape Hatteras, NC (3)	Melbourne, FL (1)
Ellsworth, ME (2)	Philadelphia, PA (3)	New Bern, NC (2)	Fort Pierce, FL (4)
Dresden, ME (3)	Atlantic City, NJ (2)	Georgetown, SC (6)	W. Palm Bch., FL (3)
Gloucester, MA (4)	Lewes, DE (1)	Charleston, SC (1)	Miami, FL (1)
Boston, MA (3)	Baltimore, MD (2)	Beaufort, SC (5)	Key West, FL (2)
Hyannis, MA (1)	Hagerstown, MD (3)	Brunswick, GA (4)	
Providence, RI (2)	Norfolk, VA (1)	Jacksonville, FL (1)	
New York, NY (1)	Mamie, NC (4)	Daytona Bch., FL (2)	

TIME SIGNALS

Bureau of Standards Time Signals: WWV, Ft. Collins, Col., every min. on 2500, 5000, 10000, 15000, 20000, 25000 kHz. **Canadian Time Signals:** CHU, (frequently easier to get than WWV) 45° 17' 47" N, 75° 45' 22" W. Continuous transmission on 3330 kHz, 7850 kHz and 14670 kHz. For more information on time visit the following websites. http://tf.nist. gov/timefreq/, http://nist.time.gov/

Omission of a tone indicates the 29th second of each minute. The new minute is marked by the full tone *immediately* following the voice announcement. Five sets of two short tones mark the first five seconds of the next minute. The hour is identified by a pulse of one full second followed by 12 seconds of silence.

Swimmers Beware:
Undertow, Alongshore Currents and Rip Currents

Understanding the behavior of ocean water near the shore can help bathers enjoy swimming with greater confidence. There are three types of water movement which swimmers should understand.

Undertow
When a large wave approaches a beach, it breaks, rides up the beach, and then retreats. The retreating water is **undertow**. The water motion is circular: water moves toward the beach at the top of the wave, and away from the beach beneath the wave. The force of undertow increases with wave size and angle of the ocean bottom. Swimmers knocked down either by a breaking wave or by the undertow will not be dragged far to sea by the undertow, as the next wave reverses the process.

Alongshore Current
Water motion parallel to the beach is called **alongshore current**. Swimmers, especially children, should choose landmarks before entering the water to find their way back if an alongshore current has moved them along the beach. In the highest surf conditions, these currents can be strong enough to make standing difficult.

Rip Current
A third type is **rip current**, occasionally mislabeled "rip tide." This dangerous phenomenon is water moving seaward, away from the beach. It results from water finding an exit in a depression in the bottom between shoal areas, or from being deflected from the shore by sandbars, piers, and shoreline anomalies. To avoid this danger, study the water surface before going into the water. Rip currents might appear as wide breaks in the wave crests, or smooth-looking low spots in the approaching waves. The boundaries of the rip current might appear as lines of foam, debris, or swirling eddies. Be aware that rip currents can change locations in short periods of time as they create new channels.

What to Do
When caught in a rip current and being carried to sea, a swimmer should avoid swimming directly against the current toward land. Instead, escape the rip current by swimming perpendicular to the current and parallel to the shoreline. Once out of the stream, head for land.

We thank Dr. Ben J. Korgen for his contribution to this article.

HYPOTHERMIA
and Cold Water Immersion
What You Need To Know

It is not uncommon for a boater to fall off a boat or dock. Most are rescued immediately. However, when rescue is delayed and conditions are present which threaten survival, all who go boating should know what to do.

Hypothermia is a state of low body core temperature - specifically below 95° F. This loss of body heat may be caused by exposure to cold air or cold water. Since water conducts heat away 25 times more quickly than air, time is critical for rescue. There are many variables beyond water temperature that combine to determine survival time: whether a life jacket is on, body size and composition, type of clothing, movement in the water, etc. Wearing a Personal Flotation Device (PFD) greatly extends survival time by keeping your head above water and by allowing you to float without expending energy.

What a person in the water should do:
1. If at all possible, get out of the water, or at least grab hold of anything floating. If the boat is swamped, stay with it and crawl as far out of the water as possible.
2. Do not try to swim, unless a boat or floating object is very nearby and you are certain you can get to it.
3. Control heat loss by keeping clothing on as partial insulation. In particular, keep the head out of water. To protect the groin, sides, and chest from heat loss, use the H.E.L.P. (heat escape lessening position), a fetal position with hands clasped around the legs, which extends survival time.
4. Conserve energy by remaining as still as possible. Physical effort promotes heat loss. Swimming, or even treading water, reduces survival time.

The states of hypothermia:
1. Mild: victim feels cold, exhibits violent shivering, lethargy, slurred speech
2. Medium: loss of some muscle control, incoherence or combativeness, stupor, and exhaustion
3. Severe: unconsciousness, respiratory distress, possible cardiac arrest

What a rescuer should do:
1. Move the victim to a warm place, position on his/her back, and check breathing and heartbeat.
2. Start CPR if necessary (see pp. 244-245).
3. Carefully remove wet clothing, cutting it away if necessary.
4. Take steps to raise the body temperature gradually: cover the victim with blankets or a sleeping bag, and apply warm moist towels to the neck, chest, and groin.
5. Provide warm oral fluids and sugar sources after uncontrolled shivering stops and the patient shows evidence of ability to swallow and of rewarming.

What NOT to do:
1. Do not give alcohol, coffee, tea, or nicotine. If the victim is not fully conscious, do not attempt to provide food or water.
2. Do not massage arms or legs or handle the patient roughly, as this could cause cold blood from the periphery to circulate to the body's core, which needs to be warm first.

See **Emergency First Aid, pp. 244-245.**

EMERGENCY FIRST AID

These are guidelines to be used only when professional help is not readily available.

Good Samaritan laws were enacted to encourage people to help others in emergency situations. Laws vary from state to state, but all require that the caregiver use common sense and a reasonable level of skill.

Before giving care to a conscious victim you must first get consent. If the victim does not give consent call 911. Consent may be implied if a victim is unconscious, confused, or seriously ill.

Prevent disease transmission by avoiding contact with bodily fluids, using protective equipment such as disposable gloves and thoroughly washing hands after giving care.

PRIMARY ASSESSMENT
Check for: 1. Unresponsiveness 2. Breathing - Look, listen and feel. 3. Pulse (any movement or sign of life) - If pulse and breathing are present, check for and control any severe bleeding.

* If no sign of life or breathing, call for help and then begin CPR. For children, do 2 minutes of CPR, then call for help while continuing CPR.

* If pulse is present but no breathing, begin Rescue Breathing.

* If airway is obstructed, do Heimlich to clear airway. Do not use Heimlich if drowning is suspected; go to Rescue Breathing.

CPR* - Use only when there is no sign of breathing and no sign of movement or life. Call or get someone to call for help. Roll victim onto back as a unit, being careful to keep spine in alignment, and open airway. Tilt head back and lift chin. Look, listen and feel for breath for 3-5 seconds. If no breath, keep head tilted back, pinch nose shut, seal your lips tight around victim's mouth, GIVE 2 FULL BREATHS for 1 to 1 ½ seconds each, checking for chest rise. Locate notch at lower end of breast bone at about the level of the nipple line, place heel of other hand on breastbone next to fingers, remove hand from notch and put it on top of other hand, keeping fingers off of chest. Position shoulders over hands and compress breastbone 1 ½ to 2 inches. GIVE 30 COMPRESSIONS in approx. 20 seconds. GIVE 2 FULL BREATHS. Do 4 cycles of 30 compressions and 2 breaths. Recheck pulse and breathing after 1 minute. If no pulse, give 2 full breaths and continue CPR.

** To perform CPR you should be trained. Courses are available through the American Red Cross and the American Heart Association. **If you are unable or uncomfortable doing Rescue Breathing, the American Heart Association states that performing Chest Compressions alone can be effective in helping to circulate oxygenated blood through the body. Follow these two important steps: 1) first call 911 and 2) using both hands pump on center of chest between the nipples hard, fast and continuously. For internet help for the traditional instruction of CPR, use www. heart.org and click on CPR. For the new hands only go to www.handsonlycpr.org.***

RESCUE BREATHING - no obstruction. Call or get someone to call for help. Pulse present, unresponsive, no breathing. Roll victim onto back and open airway. Tilt head back and lift chin. Look, listen and feel for breath for 3-5 seconds. If no breath, keep head tilted back, pinch nose shut, seal your lips tight around victim's mouth, GIVE 2 NORMAL FULL BREATHS for 1 to 1 ½ seconds each until chest rises. Feel for pulse at side of neck for 5-10 seconds. If pulse present, begin Rescue Breathing for 1 minute. Keep head tilted back, pinch nose. Give 1 breath every 5 seconds. Look, listen and feel for breath between breaths. RECHECK PULSE EVERY MINUTE. If victim has pulse but is not breathing, continue rescue breathing. If victim has no sign of life or breath, go to CPR.

OBSTRUCTED AIRWAY - If victim cannot cough, breathe, or speak, use HEIMLICH. If drowning suspected, use Rescue Breathing. Do not try to clear water from lungs. Roll to side if vomiting occurs so victim won't choke.

244

HEIMLICH - If victim is conscious, stand behind him. Wrap your arms around victim's waist. Place your fist (thumbside) against the victim's stomach in the midline, just above the navel and well below the rib margin. Grasp your fist with other hand. Press into stomach with a quick upward thrust. If victim is unconscious, lay victim on back, do finger sweep on adult (on child only if you can see object). Attempt rescue breathing. If airway remains blocked, give 6-10 abdominal thrusts and repeat as necessary.

BLEEDING - Apply pressure directly over wound with a dressing, until bleeding stops or until EMS rescuers arrive. If possible, press edges of a large wound together before using dressing and bandage. If bleeding continues, apply additional bandages and continue to maintain pressure. If possible, elevate wounded area, apply ice wrapped in cloth to wound and keep the patient warm.

SHOCK - Confused behavior, rapid pulse and breathing, cool moist skin, blue tinge to lips and nailbeds, weakness, nausea and vomiting, etc. Keep patient lying down with legs elevated. Remove wet clothing. Maintain normal body temperature. Do not give victim food or drink.

BURNS, SCALDS - No open blisters: Use cool water, then cover with a moist sterile dressing. Open blisters - Heat: Cover with dry sterile dressing. Do not put water on burn or remove clothing sticking to burn. Treat for shock. Open blisters - Chemical: Flush all chemical burns with water for 15 to 30 minutes. Remove all clothing on which chemical has spilled. Cover with dry sterile dressing and treat for shock. Eyes: Flush with cool water only for 15 minutes.

FRACTURES - Do not move victim or try to correct any deformity. Immobilize the area. If bone penetrates the skin use a sterile dressing and control bleeding before splinting. Splint a broken arm to the trunk or a broken leg to the other leg. A padded board or pole can be used along the side, front or back of a broken limb. A pillow or a rolled blanket can be used around the arm or leg. For an injured shoulder put a pillow between the arm and chest and bind arm to body. For an injured hip, place pillow between legs and bind legs together.

HEAD, NECK and **SPINE INJURIES** - Do not move victim or try to correct any deformity. Stabilize head and neck as you found them.

POISONING - Call for help immediately. Contact Poison Control Center 1-800-222-1222. Have poison container available. Keep syrup of ipecac and activated charcoal available, but do not administer unless advised to do so. Antidotes listed on label may be wrong.

HEAT PROSTRATION - Strip victim. Move to shaded area. Wrap in cool, wet sheet. Treat for shock.

EXPOSURE TO COLD - Provide a warm dry bunk and warm drink, not coffee, tea or alcohol. Frostbite: Rewarm slowly, beginning with the body core rather than the extremities. Elevate and protect affected area. Do not rub frozen area, break blisters or use dry heat to thaw. Treat for shock. **See Hypothermia and Cold Water Immersion article p. 243.**

SUNBURN – Treat heat prostration if present. Take the heat out of the skin by using a cool damp cloth laid over the area. Do not apply ice as this may damage the skin further. Painkillers like acetaminophen (Tylenol) or ibuprofen may be used for pain. Use topical lotions to keep the skin moist and reduce dehydration. Those containing Aloe work well. If the skin is blistering, prevent secondary infection by keeping the area clean and by applying an antibacterial cream. Rest, keep hydrated and seek medical help if area does not improve.

FORECASTING
with Wind Direction and Barometric Pressure

Wind Dir.	Pressure	Trend	Likely Forecast
SW to NW	30.1-30.2	Steady	Fair, little temp. change
	30.1-30.2	Rising rapidly	Fair, perhaps warmer with rain
	30.2+	Steady	Fair, no temp. change
	30.2+	Falling	Fair, gradual rise in temp.
S to SW	30.0	Rising slowly	Clearing, then fair
S to SE	30.2	Falling rapidly	Increasing wind, rain to follow
S to E	29.8	Falling rapidly	Severe NE gale, heavy rain/snow
SE to NE	30.1-30.2	Falling slowly	Rain
	30.1-30.2	Falling rapidly	Increasing wind and rain
	30.0	Falling slowly	Rain continuing
	30.0	Falling rapidly	Rain, high wind, then clearing and cooler
E to NE	30.0+	Falling slowly	Rain with light winds
	30.1	Falling rapidly	Rain or snow, increasing wind
Shifting W	29.8	Rising rapidly	Clearing and cooler

KEYS TO PREDICTING THE WEATHER

The most important point to remember about barometric pressure is that the **trend** (up, down, or steady) and the **rate of change** are far more predictive of coming weather than the position of the pointer at any one time. Tap your barometer periodically; the pointer's direction should indicate the pressure trend. Pay little attention to the words Stormy, Rain, Change, Fair, Very Dry; they are traditional, decorative, and often inaccurate.

In addition to changes in barometric pressure, the **state of the air** (cool, dry, warm, moist) and the appearance of the sky foretell coming weather. See Weather Signs on the next page.

Long foretold – long last; short notice – soon past. This handy saying has much truth in it. Slow changes last longer; sudden changes are quickly over. A steady barometer with dry air indicates continuing fine weather. A rapid rise or fall of barometric pressure indicates unsettled or stormy weather for a short period of time.

WEATHER SIGNS IN THE SKY

Signs of Good Weather

- A gray sky in the morning or a "low dawn" – when the day breaks near the horizon, with the first streaks of light low in the sky – brings fair weather.
- Light, delicate tints with soft, undefined clouds accompany fine weather.
- Seabirds flying out early and far to sea suggest moderate wind, fair weather.
- A rosy sky at sunset, clear or cloudy: "Red sky at night, sailor's delight."
- High, wispy cirrus clouds, or even high cumulus, indicate immediate fair weather, with a possible change from a front within 24 hours.
- High contrails disappearing quickly show dry air aloft.
- Steady mild-to-moderate winds from the same direction indicate continuing fair weather.
- A low dew point relative to temperature means dry air. (see p. 256)

Signs of Bad Weather

- "Red sky at morning, sailor take warning." Poor weather, wind, maybe rain.
- A "high dawn" – when the first streaks of daylight appear above a bank of clouds – often precedes a turn for worse weather.
- Light scud clouds driving across higher, heavy clouds show wind and rain.
- Hard-edged, inky clouds foretell rain and strong wind.
- Seabirds hanging over the land or headed inland suggest wind and rain.
- Remarkable clearness of atmosphere near the horizon, when distant hills or vessels are raised by refraction, are signs of an Easterly wind and indicate coming wet weather.
- Long-lasting contrails indicate humid air aloft.
- Low-level clouds, and clouds at several heights
- Rising humidity, dewpoint close to temperature
- Strong early-morning winds

Signs of Wind

- Soft-looking, delicate clouds indicate light to moderate wind.
- Stronger wind is suggested by hard-edged, oily-looking, ragged clouds, or a bright yellow sky at sunset.
- A change in wind is indicated by high clouds crossing the sky in a different direction from that of lower clouds.
- Increasing wind and possibly rain are preceded by greater than usual twinkling of stars, indistinctness of the moon's horns, "wind dogs" (fragments of rainbows) seen on detached clouds, and the rainbow.
- "First rise after very low, indicates a stronger blow."

How To Become Wind-Wise

Wind is the most dynamic of weather factors, and both power and sail boaters ignore it to their peril. A calm day can postpone or cancel a sailing outing, while powerboat skippers love it. A windy day can thrill a sailor but keep the power-boater at home.

Our suggestion: watch the wind <u>before</u> you get to the shore.

The **MAESTRO** gives you:

- current wind speed from 0-100 mph
- memory of the highest gust
- wind direction from 16 points
- choice of silver or black dial
- brass case (nickel or chrome extra)
- 60' wires, mounting hardware
- speed & direction sensors
- full 5-year warranty
- made in the USA
- *free shipping* in continental U.S.

The **MAESTRO** is handsome and practical – a great gift!
Become wind-wise and call us.

ROBERT E. WHITE INSTRUMENTS, INC.
www.robertwhite.com
617-482-8460

 # Wind Chill Chart

	Temperature (°F)																
Calm	**40**	**35**	**30**	**25**	**20**	**15**	**10**	**5**	**0**	**-5**	**-10**	**-15**	**-20**	**-25**	**-30**	**-35**	**-40**	**-45**
5	36	31	25	19	13	7	1	-5	-11	-16	-22	-28	-34	-40	-46	-52	-57	-63
10	34	27	21	15	9	3	-4	-10	-16	-22	-28	-35	-41	-47	-53	-59	-66	-72
15	32	25	19	13	6	0	-7	-13	-19	-26	-32	-39	-45	-51	-58	-64	-71	-77
20	30	24	17	11	4	-2	-9	-15	-22	-29	-35	-42	-48	-55	-61	-68	-74	-81
25	29	23	16	9	3	-4	-11	-17	-24	-31	-37	-44	-51	-58	-64	-71	-78	-84
30	28	22	15	8	1	-5	-12	-19	-26	-33	-39	-46	-53	-60	-67	-73	-80	-87
35	28	21	14	7	0	-7	-14	-21	-27	-34	-41	-48	-55	-62	-69	-76	-82	-89
40	27	20	13	6	-1	-8	-15	-22	-29	-36	-43	-50	-57	-64	-71	-78	-84	-91
45	26	19	12	5	-2	-9	-16	-23	-30	-37	-44	-51	-58	-65	-72	-79	-86	-93
50	26	19	12	4	-3	-10	-17	-24	-31	-38	-45	-52	-60	-67	-74	-81	-88	-95
55	25	18	11	4	-3	-11	-18	-25	-32	-39	-46	-54	-61	-68	-75	-82	-89	-97
60	25	17	10	3	-4	-11	-19	-26	-33	-40	-48	-55	-62	-69	-76	-84	-91	-98

Wind (mph)

Frostbite Times: 30 minutes | 10 minutes | 5 minutes

BEAUFORT SCALE

Beaufort Force	Knots	Wind Condition	Conditions at Sea	Conditions Ashore
0	0-1	**Calm**	Smooth, mirror-like sea	Calm, smoke rises vertically
1	1-3	**Light Air**	Scaly ripples, no foam crests	Smoke drifts at an angle, leaves move
2	4-6	**Light Breeze**	Small wavelets, crests glassy, not breaking	Leaves rustle, flags begin to move
3	7-10	**Gentle Breeze**	Large wavelets, some crests break, scattered whitecaps	Small branches move, light flags extended
4	11-16	**Moderate Breeze**	Small waves 1-4 ft. getting longer, numerous whitecaps	Leaves, loose paper lifted, larger flags flapping
5	17-21	**Fresh Breeze**	Moderate waves 4-8 ft., many whitecaps	Small trees in leaf begin to sway, flags extended
6	22-27	**Strong Breeze**	Larger waves 8-13 ft., more whitecaps, spray	Larger tree branches and small trees in motion
7	28-33	**Near Gale**	Sea heaps up, waves 13-20 ft., white foam streaks	Whole trees moving, resistance in walking
8	34-40	**Gale**	Waves 13-20 ft. of greater length, crests break, spindrift	Large trees in motion, small branches break
9	41-47	**Strong Gale**	High waves, 20+ ft., dense streaks of foam, spray reduces visibility	Slight structural damage, roof shingles may blow off, signs in motion
10	48-55	**Storm**	Very high waves, 20-30 ft., overhanging crests, lowered visibility, sea white with densely blown foam	Trees broken or uprooted, considerable structural damage, very high tides
11	56-63	**Violent Storm**	Exceptionally high waves, 30-45 ft., foam patches cover sea, visibility limited	Widespread damage, light structures in peril, coastal flooding
12	64+	**Hurricane**	Air filled with foam, waves 45+ ft., wind shrieks, sea white with spray, visibility poor	Storm surge at coast, serious beach erosion, extensive flooding, trees and wires down

NOTES:
- When the wind speed doubles, the pressure of the wind on an object *quadruples*. Example: the wind pressure at 40 kts. is *four times* what it is at 20 kts.
- In many tidal waters wave heights are apt to increase considerably in a very short time, and conditions can be more dangerous near land than in the open sea.

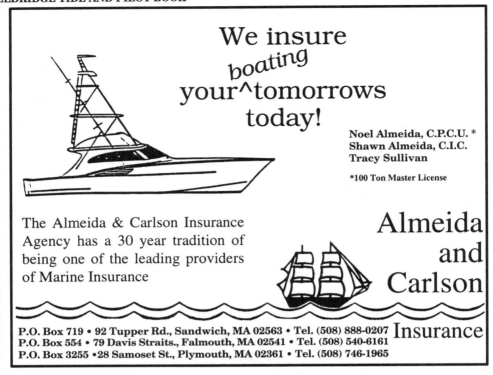

We insure
your^tomorrows today!
boating

Noel Almeida, C.P.C.U. *
Shawn Almeida, C.I.C.
Tracy Sullivan

*100 Ton Master License

The Almeida & Carlson Insurance Agency has a 30 year tradition of being one of the leading providers of Marine Insurance

Almeida and Carlson Insurance

P.O. Box 719 • 92 Tupper Rd., Sandwich, MA 02563 • Tel. (508) 888-0207
P.O. Box 554 • 79 Davis Straits., Falmouth, MA 02541 • Tel. (508) 540-6161
P.O. Box 3255 •28 Samoset St., Plymouth, MA 02361 • Tel. (508) 746-1965

Hurricane CAROL – August 1954

Like some tropical storms, the tropical depression that became Hurricane Carol developed not west of Africa, but much closer to the U.S. mainland, in the Bahamas. It was to be the most destructive hurricane to strike southern New England since the Great New England Hurricane of 1938.

It began on August 25, growing stronger as it moved northwest. Although it weakened briefly, it finally intensified, reaching hurricane status while east of Cape Canaveral, FL. During the evening of August 30, off Cape Hatteras, Carol rapidly accelerated, making landfall on eastern Long Island and Old Saybrook, CT about 12 hours later. The storm, now moving at a very brisk 35 m.p.h., slammed into the coast near the time of high tide. Coastal areas to the east of these points experienced winds which were the sum of the rotational winds (80-100 m.p.h.) and the speed of forward motion (35 m.p.h.). Over Block Island, RI, gusts reached 135 m.p.h., the highest winds recorded there. The barometer plummeted to 28.36 inHg on the south shore of Long Island.

The wind and the storm surge, coming close to high tide, created massive flooding, with surges of 10 to 15 feet east of New London, CT. Narragansett Bay, RI and New Bedford, MA recorded heights of over 14 feet. Downtown Providence, RI was under 12 feet of water. To add to the misery, rainfall amounts ranged from 2 to 6 inches. Trees and power lines were down almost everywhere, with all of Rhode Island, much of eastern Connecticut and eastern Massachusetts losing electrical power and telephone service. As roofs were ripped off buildings, 4000 homes were destroyed, along with 3500 automobiles and over 3000 boats. Sixty-five people died.

A very strong Category 3 hurricane, Carol was the third-costliest hurricane in the United States at the time, causing an estimated $450 million in damage, equivalent to almost $4 billion today. *Adapted from a NOAA article at www.nhc.noaa.gov / HAW2 /*

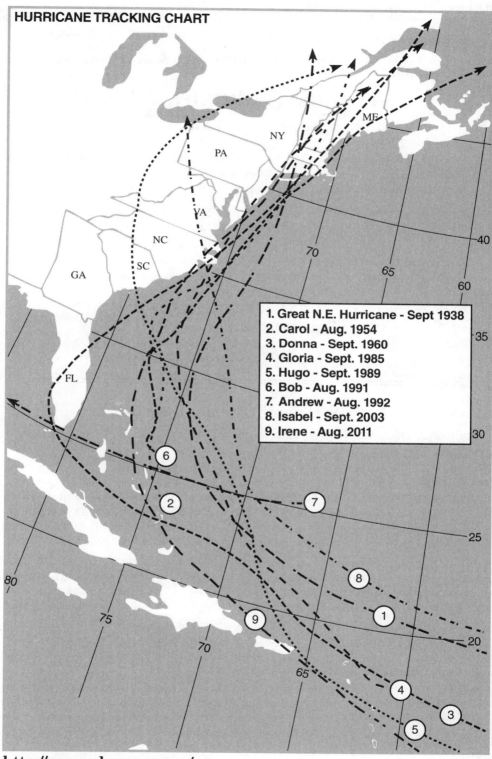

HURRICANE TRACKING CHART

1. Great N.E. Hurricane - Sept 1938
2. Carol - Aug. 1954
3. Donna - Sept. 1960
4. Gloria - Sept. 1985
5. Hugo - Sept. 1989
6. Bob - Aug. 1991
7. Andrew - Aug. 1992
8. Isabel - Sept. 2003
9. Irene - Aug. 2011

Admiralty & Maritime Law

Thomas F. Murphy, Jr.
Attorney at Law

- Master, U.S. Merchant Marine, Oceans, steam, motor, sail & gas turbine, and Marine Engineering; sailed foreign & U.S. coastwise
- Member, Boston Area Maritime Security Committee (CG)

Experience, at sea & at law:
- U.S. Coast Guard, Deck Watch Officer (EAGLE, et al.) and JAG
- U.S. Dept. of Justice, Admiralty and Shipping Section, NYC, Trial Counsel
- Special Assistant Attorney General, Comm. of Massachusetts
- National Sealift Training Program, U.S. Merchant Marine Academy

781-864-1605
ships3408@yahoo.com

25 Garden Road, Wellesley Hills, MA 02481-3018

The Saffir-Simpson Hurricane Wind Scale

CATEGORY ONE: Winds 74-95 mph: Very dangerous winds will produce some damage. Falling or flying debris. Damage primarily to power lines, mobile homes, shopping center roofs, shrubbery, and trees. Also, some coastal road flooding and minor pier damage.

CATEGORY TWO: Winds 96-110 mph: Extremely dangerous winds will cause extensive damage. Some roofing material, door, and window damage to buildings. Considerable damage to vegetation, mobile homes, and piers. Small craft in unprotected areas break moorings. Near-total power outages. Some water systems fail.

CATEGORY THREE: Winds 111-130 mph: Devastating damage will occur. Some structural damage to small residences. Mobile homes destroyed. Many trees snapped or uprooted. Coastal flooding may extend inland, destroying smaller structures, damaging larger structures. Electricity and water may be unavailable for days or weeks.

CATEGORY FOUR: Winds 131-155 mph: Catastrophic damage will occur. More extensive failures including roofs on small residences. Major erosion of beach areas. Major damage to lower floors of structures near the shore. Power poles down. Terrain may be flooded well inland. Long-term water shortages.

CATEGORY FIVE: Winds greater than 155 mph: Catastrophic damage will occur. Complete roof failure on many residences and industrial buildings. Some complete building failures with small utility buildings destroyed. Major damage to most structures located near the shoreline. Massive evacuation of residential areas may be required. Most of the area will be uninhabitable for weeks or months.

HURRICANES

For their awesome power to wreak havoc by wind and water, hurricanes have always been fascinating. Early warnings have all but eliminated surprise, yet these storms often defy attempts to prepare. Always vulnerable, we must know what to expect.

Hurricanes affecting the East Coast are born as tropical depressions in the Atlantic west of Africa, move westward through the eastern Caribbean, and eventually veer northwest and then north and northeast up our coast (see p. 251). Counter-clockwise winds spiral inward and accelerate toward the eye, the center of lowest pressure. The sharper the drop in pressure, the more violent the winds. Hurricanes lose power as they move north out of the tropics because warm ocean water, the energy source which helped create them, turns cooler.

A hurricane's forward motion, which can vary from 5 to 50+ knots, means that the winds are stronger on the right side. Winds of 100 knots spiraling around the eye, when you add a forward speed of 25 knots, create a speed of 125 knots on the right side, but only 75 knots on the left side, a dramatic difference. Note: a doubling of wind speed means the force on an object is increased four times, so that a wind of 100 knots has four times the power it does at 50 knots.

If the eye is moving directly toward you, the wind direction will remain fairly constant and the velocity will increase until the eye arrives. When the eye passes, the velocity will suddenly increase, rather stronger than before, from the opposite direction. These factors make the vicinity of the eye most dangerous.

In our diagram the hurricane is approaching, and vessels A, B, and C are at positions A1, B1, and C1 relative to the storm. When the storm passes, these vessels will be at positions A2, B2, and C2. Each will have experienced very different wind speeds and directions:

Vessel A, in the least dangerous semi-circle, will experience winds from the NE (at A1), backing to N (least velocity), NW, and finally W (at A2) as the storm passes.

Vessel B (at B1) will have ENE winds, increasing until the eye arrives. After the deceptive calm of the eye passes, the wind will rise, stronger than before, from the WSW (at B2), gradually decreasing.

Vessel C, in the most dangerous semi-circle, has the strongest winds, beginning (at C1) from the E, veering to SE, S (greatest velocity), and finally to SW (at C2).

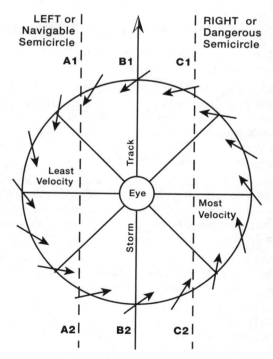

If space and time permit, try to reduce your vulnerability by proceeding at right angles to the storm track. Which way to go depends on a number of factors, including how far away the storm is, its speed, the speed of the vessel, and sea conditions or sea room on either side of the expected storm path.

Hurricane Precautions Alongshore

Extremely high tides accompany hurricanes. If the storm arrives anywhere near the usual time of high water, low-lying areas will be flooded. Especially high tides will occur in all bays or V-mouth harbors if they are facing the wind direction. High water in all storm areas will remain a much longer time.

At or near the coastline, pull small craft well above the high water mark, dismast sailboats, remove outboard motors, and remove or lash down loose objects.

Seek the most protected anchorage possible, considering possible wind direction reversals, extreme tides, and other vessels. If on a mooring or at anchor, use maximum scope, allowing for room to swing clear of other boats. In a real blow it is easy to slack off, but not to shorten scope. Use as much chain in your anchor rode as possible. Another piece of chain or a weight, attached halfway along your mooring or anchor line, will help absorb sudden strains. Use chafing gear liberally at bits and bow chocks to minimize fraying of lines. Rig fenders to minimize damage from/to other boats.

Shut off gas, stove tanks, etc. Douse any fires in heating stoves. Secure all portholes, skylights, ventilators, hatch covers, companionways, etc. Pump the boat dry.

At a wharf or pier, use fenders liberally. If possible, rig one or more anchors abreast of the boat in the event the tide rises above pilings.

Boats are replaceable: don't wait for the last moment to get ashore!

Hurricane Precautions Offshore

Monitor storm reports on your radio. The U.S. Coast Guard warns all vessels offshore to seek shelter at least 72 hours ahead of a hurricane.

But, if caught offshore with no chance to reach shelter, watch the wind most carefully. First, note that if you face the wind, the eye is about 10 points or 112° to your right. If the wind "backs" (moves counter-clockwise), you are already on the less dangerous side of the storm track. If the wind "veers" (moves clockwise), you are on the right or more dangerous side. If the wind direction is constant, the hurricane's eye is headed directly at you, so make haste to get to the left side of the track.

Use your radiotelephone to advise the Coast Guard and other vessels of your position. Have a liferaft and safety equipment (flares, flashlights, EPIRB, etc.) ready. Put on life jackets. If it is impossible to hold your intended course, head your powerboat directly into the wind and sea, using only enough power to maintain steerageway. If power fails, rig a sea anchor or drogue to keep the bow to the wind.

Sailing vessels heaving to should consider doing so on the starboard tack (boom to port) in the more dangerous semicircle, or on the port tack (boom to starboard) in the less dangerous semicircle, to keep the wind drawing aft.

NOTE: This information is necessarily very general, the diagram (p. 253) is over-simplified, and the suggestions assume a straight storm track. If the storm track curves to the right, vessels A and B will have an easier time of it, but C may wind up on the track. The best advice: monitor weather reports continuously and seek shelter well ahead of time.

National Weather Service – www.nws.noaa.gov
National Hurricane Center – www.nhc.noaa.gov
NOAA Hurricane Research – www.aoml.noaa.gov/hrd

WEATHER NOTES
From Maine to the Chesapeake

Sea Fog

There is always invisible moisture in the air, and the warmer the air, the more moisture it can contain invisibly. But when such a mass of moist air is cooled off, as it does when passing over a body of cooler water, the moisture often condenses into visible vapor, or fog. The fog clears when the air temperature rises, from the sun or a warm land mass, or by a warm, dry wind.

To predict fog accurately, you can use a "sling psychrometer." This instrument uses two thermometers side by side, one of which has a wick fastened to the bulb end. After wetting the wick on the "wet bulb" thermometer, the user swings the instrument in a circle for 60-90 seconds. This causes water to evaporate from the wet bulb thermometer, lowering its reading. The dry bulb thermometer simply tells air temperature. The difference in readings between the dry bulb and wet bulb thermometers determines the relative humidity of the air, and - especially valuable for determining the likelihood of fog - the dew point. The dew point is the (lower) temperature to which air must be cooled for condensation, or fog, to occur. (see Dew Point Table, p. 256)

Eastport, Maine to Cape Cod

Cold water (48°-55°) off the northern New England coast often causes heavy fog conditions in the spring and summer, when a warm moist southwesterly flow of air passes over it. East of Portland to the Bay of Fundy, fog is not apt to occur when the dew point is under 55°, unless there is a very warm moist wind. The effect of the cold water on the warm air is reduced if the winds become brisk, as they are apt to do in the afternoon. Visibility should then improve.

Long Island Sound and the New Jersey Coast

Summertime warm water (in the 70s) in this area rarely cools down any warm air mass enough to produce fog. This is not the case farther offshore, where cooler water temperatures (in the 50s) can produce fog.

On the south coast of Long Island, when the southwest wind blows toward the shore at the same time as the ebb tide, inlets can become dangerous with short, steep seas. Also, offshore swells can become very high near the mouths of inlets.

On the New Jersey shore, prevailing winds in summer are southerly, increasing in mid-morning to rarely more than 20 knots and usually dying down at dusk. Occasional summer thunderstorms can be expected. Any brisk winds from the east, northeast, or southeast can produce dangerous conditions along this lee shore and at the mouths of inlets. When the wind is from offshore like this, inlets should be entered on a flood tide.

At the mouth of Delaware Bay, seas can build up to a hazardous degree when there is a southeast wind at the same time as an ebb current at the mouth of the Bay.

Chesapeake Bay

There is little chance of fog in this region because of the warmth of the water. The Bay has quirks of its own in weather and sea conditions. It is a narrow and fairly shallow body of water, and winds tend to blow up or down it. Sharp seas can result, depending on the direction of the current and the wind. Opposing forces make for rough water.

Prevailing winds in spring and summer are southerly, freshening in the afternoon after a morning of calm. Summer thunderstorms occur frequently in afternoon and early evening, usually from the west. In the fall, after a cold front passes through, the winds will shift into the north or northeast, usually for three days, and increase in velocity, causing seas to build up. Calm follows for a day or so until the wind shifts to the southwest.

Dew Point and Humidity Afloat

Relative humidity (RH) is the measure of the air's capacity to hold water vapor at a certain temperature. At higher temperatures the air can hold more moisture: a 50%RH at 60°F is pleasant, but 50%RH at 80°F is unpleasant because the air is holding far more moisture. High humidity makes fog more likely and tends to make everyone uncomfortable.

Dew point is slightly different. It is the temperature to which air must be cooled for suspended (invisible) water vapor to condense into (visible) water. Fog and rain are examples. Dew on the deck in the morning means the night temperatures were low enough that the air could no longer hold all its daytime moisture. If the dew point and air temperature are quite close, then fog is more likely, and you might wait before heading to your next destination. Dew points under 55°F are comfortable, but those above 64°F are sticky to oppressive.

Marine weather forecasts often give dew point readings. If we want to measure dew point, there are some handheld digital instruments for under $100 which measure temperature, humidity, and dew point. If the outside temperature is 75°F and the dew point is in the 50s, go boating. If there's little spread between air temperature and dew point, you might want to postpone your voyage.

The table below is for those who have a sling psychrometer to measure dry-bulb and wet-bulb temperatures. A dry bulb reading of 70°F and a wet-bulb reading that is 4°F lower yields a dew point of 64°F, which means uncomfortably damp with possible fog. Periodic measurements which show an increase in the difference between dry- and wet-bulb readings mean fog should dissipate and visibility increase.

Sling Psychrometers and Hygrometers are available at www.robertwhite.com.

DEW POINT

Dry-bulb temp. F	Difference between dry-bulb and wet-bulb temperatures														Dry-bulb temp. F
	1°	2°	3°	4°	5°	6°	7°	8°	9°	10°	11°	12°	13°	14°	
+50	+48	+46	+44	+42	+40	+37	+35	+32	+29	+25	+21	+17	+12	+5	+50
52	50	48	46	44	42	40	37	35	32	29	25	21	17	11	52
54	52	50	49	47	44	42	40	37	35	32	28	25	21	16	54
56	54	53	51	49	47	45	42	40	37	35	32	28	25	21	56
58	56	55	53	51	49	47	45	43	40	38	35	32	28	25	58
+60	+58	+57	+55	+53	+51	+49	+47	+45	+43	+40	+38	+35	+32	+28	+60
62	60	59	57	55	54	52	50	48	45	43	41	38	35	32	62
64	62	61	59	57	56	54	52	50	48	46	43	41	38	35	64
66	64	63	61	60	58	56	54	52	50	48	46	44	41	39	66
68	67	65	63	62	60	58	57	55	53	51	49	46	44	42	68
+70	+69	+67	+66	+64	+62	+61	+59	+57	+55	+53	+51	+49	+47	+45	+70
72	71	69	68	66	64	63	61	59	58	56	54	52	50	47	72
74	73	71	70	68	67	65	63	62	60	58	56	54	52	50	74
76	75	73	72	70	69	67	66	64	62	61	59	57	55	53	76
78	77	75	74	72	71	69	68	66	65	63	61	59	57	55	78
+80	+79	+77	+76	+74	+73	+72	+70	+68	+67	+65	+64	+62	+60	+58	+80
82	81	79	78	77	75	74	72	71	69	67	66	64	62	61	82
84	83	81	80	79	77	76	74	73	71	70	68	67	65	63	84
86	85	83	82	81	79	78	76	75	74	72	70	69	67	66	86
88	87	85	84	83	81	80	79	77	76	74	73	71	70	68	88
+90	+89	+87	+86	+85	+84	+82	+81	+79	+78	+76	+75	+73	+72	+70	+90
92	91	89	88	87	86	84	83	82	80	79	77	76	74	73	92
94	93	92	90	89	88	86	85	84	82	81	79	78	76	75	94
96	95	94	92	91	90	88	87	86	84	83	82	80	79	77	96
98	97	96	94	93	92	91	89	88	87	85	84	82	81	80	98
+100	+99	+98	+96	+95	+94	+93	+91	+90	+89	+87	+86	+85	+83	+82	+100

Bullseye Banzai

by Peter H. Spectre

Back in the days when lightships marked important positions off the coast, sailors didn't have radar, Loran, Decca, Omega, Satnav, RDF, UHF, VHF, GPS, or anything else to tell them where they were. The lightship told them.

It was a good thing, too, because before the introduction of electronics, making a landfall at the end of a long ocean passage was often a dicey affair. You could come on soundings after days without a reliable fix and find yourself navigationally stumped. Are you coming on to the coast of Maine, or will that be New Hampshire or Massachusetts over the horizon? If you're reasonably certain it is Maine, what part will it be? Penobscot Bay? Muscongus Bay? Casco Bay?

And then there's a hail from the lookout — "Lightship ahead!... there's writing on the side..." — it's a billboard floating out there on the ocean, a big sign with bold white letters six feet tall. Not only does it tell you that you are here, it tells you where here is. Going to Boston? Turn left. Down east? Turn right. To Portland? Take the channel between Portland Head and Cushing Island; at the Bug Light, hang a left.

The arrangement was convenient for the sailor, but not necessarily for the lightship crew. There must have been times when they thought that something else besides white letters was painted on the side of the hull. A bullseye, perhaps.

Think about it. Lightships marked shipping routes. CAPE ELIZABETH, off Portland. AMBROSE, off New York. The legendary NANTUCKET, off Nantucket Island. DIAMOND SHOALS, off Cape Hatteras. VINEYARD, in Vineyard Sound. In a fog, before radar, anchored on station — in other words, invisible and motionless — a lightship was an easy target. Collisions were frequent; being run down and sunk was not unheard of.

Plenty of lightships had brushes with disaster, but the Nantucket lightship took the cake. In January 1934 it was struck by the transatlantic liner WASHINGTON and survived. A few months later, in May, in a thick dungeon of fog, it was run down by another liner, the high-speed OLYMPIC, and that's all she wrote. The NANTUCKET sank; seven of the crew were lost.

There was also a bullseye for what we now euphemistically call "weather events." Anchored in the open, unprotected, lightships took every storm as it came. Once again the NANTUCKET suffered the worst. In 1878 the mooring cables parted in a gale and it was forced 800 miles offshore, almost to Bermuda. In 1905, during a winter storm, it sank. In the winter of 1959 it was driven off station all the way to Montauk Point, Long Island, New York.

And then there was a bullseye in the conventional sense. As far as we know few lightships were ever fired upon, but we do know that the DIAMOND SHOALS off Cape Hatteras was. In August 1918, utterly defenseless, it was sunk by gunfire from a German submarine.

Yes, in the good old days the surfmen of the lifesaving service had courage, and the keepers of the lighthouses had fortitude, but the crews of the lightships, sitting ducks on the ocean, had guts.

Peter H. Spectre of Spruce Head, Maine, is a freelance writer and editor. This article originally appeared in Maine Boats, Homes & Harbors magazine and appears here with the author's permission.

What Time Is It?

by Jan Adkins

THIS VENERABLE BOOK has a heritage of practical value to mariners. In its yearly incarnations it has hurried commerce, kept sailors safe, and has offered assurance to those in little boats on the large ocean.

It seems like a book of technical certainties, scientific data, and mathematical inevitability. In great part this is true. But anyone exploring the science of time and tides must acknowledge that time is a fuzzy concept, and that tides move in strange ways.

All the tables in this book deal with time that was originally measured by three oscillators – separate clocks: the earth's daily spin, the earth's journey around the sun, and the phases of the moon. None of these oscillators pays a bit of attention to the other two.

We say our day is 24 hours. We call this a *solar day*. But earth revolves once every 23 hours 56 minutes and 4.091 seconds in relation to distant stars (a *sidereal day*). Our planetary orbit changes our angle to the sun about 1° every day, and this shift accounts for our noon-to-noon measure of 24 hours. Tell your paymaster that you're putting in an extra 3 minutes and 55 seconds.

But even this is not completely accurate, because the earth's orbit around the sun isn't a circle, but an ellipse with a difference of 3,107,000 miles (5,000,000 km) between *perhelion* (our closest approach to the sun) and *aphelion* (farthest). Newtonian mechanics insists that a planet describing an ellipse goes faster on the tighter curves, slower on the broad curves, and there goes accuracy. More bad news: the shape of the ellipse itself rotates around the sun. Add – or subtract – *precession* from the accuracy: the earth wobbles just a bit like a top. The length of our apparent days is the result of a jolt given to the earth long ago, knocking its *spin axis* 23.4° out of the *ecliptic* (the plane of our ellipse around the sun). In the summer the north pole points toward the sun, in the winter it points away, and our time in the sun is subject to the season and to our latitude. Disgusting.

What we blithely assume is a 24-hour day is actually an approximation, an average.

In the last century science determined that the big oscillators were simply too ragged for close work. In the 1930's careful astronomical observatories shifted from pendulum clocks to quartz crystal clocks with a frequency of 100,000 Hz. This improved accuracy to about .005 second a day. Most contemporary quartz wristwatches are set to 32,768 Hz and are accurate to about half a second a day.

Still not good enough. The measure of time has been determined by the frequency of Cesium 133 at 9,192,631,770 pulses a second. At this rate the Cesium atomic clock might lose or gain a second in 1,400,000 years.

This is a new age of time. High frequency oscillators and the electronic ability to count the pulses gives us the accuracy to measure the passage of radio waves between our GPS satellites and our position, to calculate the solid geometry, and to place ourselves within a meter or two on the heaving sea.

Although the *Eldridge Tide and Pilot Book* is conveniently notated yearly in months and even in Daylight Savings Time (a New Deal innovation of the 30's), science long ago gave up on months and even years. Scientific time is measured in (average, theoretical) days beginning at a relatively arbitrary point. The first day of 2015 will be TJD 17,023 (*Truncated Julian Day*, the updated, shorter version used by NASA).

But even with precise time, tide is a challenge of fantastic complexity. It's affected by so many elements! The main factors are the sun and the moon. The moon is close, about 270,000 miles away. The sun is 93,000,000 miles away (give or take, see above) but enormously larger. The tidal influence of the moon is slightly more than twice that of the sun. These forces have their own positional geometry, however: they can multiply effects for a *spring tide* or nearly cancel effects for a *neap tide*. These gravitational forces also cause a "land tide" – the earth's exterior shell buckles up and down about 12 inches twice a day. But the ocean is a fluid, at the whim of hydrography, shore geography, ocean currents, the Coriolis force due to Earth's spin, the constrictions of shores and rivers, and even wind. A reliable tide chart can't be generated by a simple formula. The tables in this small book are miracles of long empirical observation, intelligent estimation, and mathematical calculation. Over many years we've achieved a remarkable accuracy.

Professor Einstein established the curious fact that time for objects traveling near the speed of light is elastic. But we're simple mariners moving at antique speeds. We keep our time as well as we can, we reckon currents and wind and a bit of intuition in our courses. We're closer to Captain Eldridge than to Captain Kirk.

A version of this article, which the author adapted for Eldridge, first appeared in Maine Boats, Homes & Harbors.

Jan Adkins, author of many articles and books, is a frequent contributer to Eldridge, with hand-drawn graphics and entertaining articles.

COAST GUARD POLLUTION REGULATIONS

The Damage Caused by Pollution

Sewage is not just a repulsive visual pollutant. The microorganisms in sewage, including pathogens and bacteria, degrade water quality by introducing diseases like hepatitis, cholera, typhoid fever and gastroenteritis, which can contaminate shellfish beds. Shellfish are filter feeders that eat tiny food particles filtered through their gills into their stomachs, along with bacteria from sewage. Nearly all waterborne pathogens can be conveyed by shellfish to humans. Stormwater runoff and drainage from fertilized lawns contain chemical products and nutrients. Although nutrients are necessary for waterborne plants, when too abundant they can stimulate algae blooms. This process leads to oxygen depletion, which can harm and kill aquatic life.

Federal Regulations for Waste Disposal

<u>Prohibited in all waters</u>: The discharge of plastic or garbage mixed with plastic, including synthetic ropes, fishing nets and plastic bags.

<u>Prohibited within 25 n.m. of land</u>. The discharge of dunning, lining, and packing materials that float.

<u>Prohibited within 12 n.m. of land</u>: The discharge of unground garbage larger than 1 inch, including food waste, paper, rags, glass, metal, bottles, crockery and similar refuse.

<u>Prohibited within 3 n.m. of land</u>: The discharge of any garbage, including ground food waste, paper, rags, glass, etc.

Marine Sanitation Devices (MSD)

Vessels under 65' may install type I, II or III MSD. Vessels over 65' must install a type II or III MSD. All installed MSD's must be U. S. Coast Guard certified.

- **Type I** MSDs are allowed only on vessels under 65'. They treat sewage with disinfectant chemicals before discharge. The discharge must not show any visible floating solids, and must have a fecal coliform bacterial count not greater than 1000 per 100 milliliters of water.

- **Type II** MSDs provide a higher level of treatment than Type I, using greater levels of chemicals to create effuent having less than 200 per 100 milliliters and suspended solids not greater than 150 milligrams per liter.

- **Type III** MSDs do not allow discharge of sewage, except through a Y-valve to discharge at a pumpout facility, or overboard when outside the 3 nautical miles. They include holding tanks, recirculating and incinerating units.

- **Portable toilets** or "porta-potties" are not considered installed toilets and are not subject to MSD regulations. They are, however, subject to the disposal regulations which prohibit the disposal of raw sewage within the three-mile limit or territorial waters of the U.S.

No Discharge Areas (NDAs) are water bodies where the Environmental Protection Agency (EPA) and local communities prohibit the discharge of all vessel sewage. Chesapeake Bay and Narragansett Bay, among others, have been designated as NDAs. Many States are adding NDAs. **It is the boater's responsibility to be aware of where those NDAs are.** See p. 261 for State contact information.

When operating vessel in NDAs, the operator must secure each Type I or Type II MSD in a manner which prevents discharge of treated or untreated sewage. Acceptable methods of securing the MSD include: closing the seacock and removing the handle, padlocking the seacock in the closed position, using a non-releasable wire-tie to hold the seacock in the closed position, or locking the door to the space enclosing the toilets with a padlock or door handle key lock.

Type III MSDs, or holding tanks, must also be secured in a manner that prevents discharge of sewage. Acceptable methods of securing the device include: closing each valve leading to an overboard discharge and removing the handle, padlocking each valve leading to an overboard discharge in the closed position, or using a non-reusable wire-tie to hold each valve leading to an overboard discharge in a closed position. Sewage held in Type III MSDs can be removed by making arrangements with landside pumpout stations or pumpout boats. Call Harbormaster for details.

Pumpout Information - State Sources

Please be sure to call or radio in advance for rates and availability. While we have taken all possible care in compiling this list, changes may have occurred and we cannot guarantee accuracy. For more current information check the state website or call the agency listed. See p. 260 for No Discharge Areas (NDAs) information.

Look for ⊑⊑⊑ Clean Vessel Act (CVA):
http://wsfrprograms.fws.gov/Subpages/GrantPrograms/CVA/CVA.htm

Most major harbors now have a pumpout boat.
Contact the local Harbormaster. Many monitor VHF channel 09.

MAINE: ME Dept. of Environ. Protection, 207-287-7905
http://www.maine.gov/dep/water/wd/vessel/pumpout/

NEW HAMPSHIRE: NH Environ. Serv., 603-271-8803
http://des.nh.gov/organization/divisions/water/wmb/cva/dir_map.htm

MASSACHUSETTS: MA Coastal Zone Mgmt., 617-626-1200
www.mass.gov/czm/nda/pumpouts/index.htm

RHODE ISLAND: RI Environmental Mgmt., 401-222-6800
www.dem.ri.gov/programs/benviron/water/shellfsh/pump/index.htm

CONNECTICUT: CT Environ. Protection, 860-424-3034, 860-424-3652
www.ct.gov/dep/cwp/view.asp?A=2705&Q=323708

NEW YORK: NY State Environmental Facilities Corp., 800-200-2200
www.efc.ny.gov/cvap

NEW JERSEY: NJ Fish & Wildlife, 856-785-2711
http://njfishandwildlife.org/cvahome.htm, NJBoating.org

DELAWARE: DE Fish & Wildlife, 302-739-9915
http://www.dnrec.delaware.gov/p2/Pages/PumpoutStations.aspx

MARYLAND: MD Natural Resources, 410-260-8772
dnr.maryland.gov/boating/pumpout/locations.asp

VIRGINIA: VA Dept. of Health, 804-864-7468
http://www.vdh.virginia.gov/EnvironmentalHealth/Onsite/MARINA/

NORTH CAROLINA: NC Div. of Coastal Management, 888-472-6278
www.nccoastalmanagement.net/marinas/pumplist.htm

SOUTH CAROLINA: SC Dept. of Health & Env. Control, 843-953-9062
http://www.dnr.sc.gov/marine/vessel/index.html

GEORGIA: contact local marinas

FLORIDA: FL Dept. of Environmental Protection, 850-245-2100
www.dep.state.fl.us/cleanmarina/CVA/default.htm

Got a Minute?
Angular and Linear Equivalents

Whether you are navigating purely by GPS or using a paper chart, it can be helpful to know how degrees, minutes, and seconds – or tenths or hundredths of a minute – translate into linear distance on the water. Knowing both is important because your GPS can display part of a coordinate as 41° 23' 25", or as 41° 23.42', where each is correct, but one is more accurate.

First, the basics. Latitude is the angular distance north or south of the Equator, and the parallels are equidistant. The latitude scale appears on the vertical edges of your chart. (Longitude, measured east and west of Greenwich and appearing along the top and bottom edges of your chart, is never used for distance measurement.) For practical purposes, the distance between parallels of latitude which are one degree (1°) apart is 60 nautical miles (n.m.).

- 1° (degree) = 60 nautical miles (Ex: from 42° North to 43° North is 60 n.m.)
- 1' (minute, or 1/60th of a degree) = 1 n.m., or 6076 feet)
- 1" (second, or 1/60th of a minute) = 101.3 feet (acceptable for general purposes)

The U.S. Coast Guard gives positions of buoys, lights, and lighthouses in degrees, minutes, and seconds, or within roughly 100 feet. (See pp. 166-197).

Sometimes minutes are divided into tenths or hundredths instead of seconds.

- 1' (minute) = 1 n.m., or 6076 feet
- 0.1' (1/10th of a minute) = 608 feet (acceptable tolerance at sea; not so near shore)
- 0.01' (1/100th of a minute) = 61 feet (acceptable for almost any purpose)

Use the Table below to convert seconds to tenths or hundredths of a minute.

Table for Converting Seconds to Decimals of a Minute

From many sources, including charts, Light Lists, and Notices to Mariners, positions are in degrees, minutes, and seconds. These are written either 34° 54' 24" or 34-54-24

However, for navigating with GPS, Loran, chart plotters, and celestial calculators, it can be useful to convert the last increment – seconds – to either tenths or hundredths of a minute. The numbers above become 34° 54.40' or 34-54.4'

Secs.	Tenths	Hundredths	Secs.	Tenths	Hundredths	Secs.	Tenths	Hundredths
1	.0	.02	21	.4	.35	41	.7	.68
2	.0	.03	22	.4	.37	42	.7	.70
3	.1	.05	23	.4	.38	43	.7	.72
4	.1	.07	24	.4	.40	44	.7	.73
5	.1	.08	25	.4	.42	45	.8	.75
6	.1	.10	26	.4	.43	46	.8	.77
7	.1	.12	27	.5	.45	47	.8	.78
8	.1	.13	28	.5	.47	48	.8	.80
9	.2	.15	29	.5	.48	49	.8	.82
10	.2	.17	30	.5	.50	50	.8	.83
11	.2	.18	31	.5	.52	51	.9	.85
12	.2	.20	32	.5	.53	52	.9	.87
13	.2	.22	33	.6	.55	53	.9	.88
14	.2	.23	34	.6	.57	54	.9	.90
15	.3	.25	35	.6	.58	55	.9	.92
16	.3	.27	36	.6	.60	56	.9	.93
17	.3	.28	37	.6	.62	57	1.0	.95
18	.3	.30	38	.6	.63	58	1.0	.97
19	.3	.32	39	.7	.65	59	1.0	.98
20	.3	.33	40	.7	.67	60	1.0	1.00

TABLE OF EQUIVALENTS
and other useful information

Length

English | Metric
English	Metric
1 inch	2.54 centimeters
1 foot	.30 meters
1 fathom	1.61 meters
1 statute mile	1.61 kilometers
1 nautical mile	1.85 kilometers

Metric	English
1 meter	39.37 inches
"	3.28 feet
"	.55 fathoms
1 kilometer	.62 statute miles
"	.54 nautical miles

Nautical	Terrestrial
1 fathom	6 feet
1 cable	608 feet
1 nautical mile	6076 feet
"	1.15 statute miles
1 knot	1.15 mph
7 knots	8 mph approx.

Capacity

English	Metric
1 quart	.95 liters
1 gallon	3.78 liters

Metric	English
1 liter	1.06 quarts
"	.26 US gallons

Weight

English	Metric
1 ounce	28.35 grams
1 pound	.45 kilograms
1 US ton	.907 metric tons
"	.893 long tons

Metric	English
1 gram	.035 ounces
1 kilogram	2.20 pounds
1 metric ton	2204.6 pounds

Weight of 1 US Gallon
Gasoline	6 pounds
Diesel fuel	7 pounds
Fresh water	8.3 pounds
Salt water	8.5 pounds

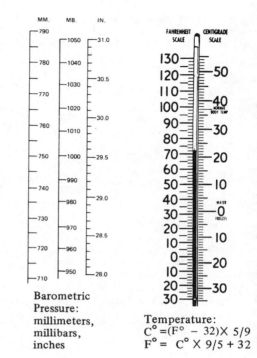

Barometric Pressure: millimeters, millibars, inches

Temperature:
$$C° = (F° - 32) \times 5/9$$
$$F° = C° \times 9/5 + 32$$

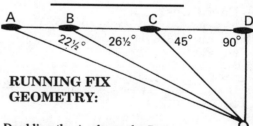

RUNNING FIX GEOMETRY:

Doubling the Angle on the Bow
1. Angle DCO = 45°; Angle CDO = 90°; True distance run (CD) = distance DO.
2. Angle DAO = 22½°; Angle DCO = 45°; True distance run (AC) = Distance CO.

Other Useful Bow Bearings
3. Angle DBO = 26½°; Angle DCO = 45°; True distance run (BC) = distance DO.
4. Example 3 also works with angles of 25° and 41°; 32° and 59°; 35° and 67°; 37° and 72° when distance run will be distance DO.

CRUISING CHARTS

DESIRABLE CRUISING CHARTS FROM CAPE BRETON I. TO KEY WEST, FL.

Numbers listed to the left are general coastal charts. Indented numbers refer to harbor charts. For USCG Local Notices to Mariners for Critical Chart updates: www.nauticalcharts.noaa.gov/mcd/updates/LNM_NM.html; for Canadian Notices to Mariners: www.notmar.gc.ca/

1:80(000), 1:40(000), etc. indicates scale

Canada
4013   Halifax to Sydney 1:350
4279   Bras d'Or Lake 1:60
4447   Pomquet and Tracadie Harbours 1:25
4385   Chebucto Hd. to Betty Is. 1:39
4321   Cape Canso to Liscomb Is. 1:108.8
4227   Country Hbr. to Ship Hbr. 1:50
4320   Egg Is. to W. Ironbound Is. 1:145
4012   Yarmouth to Halifax 1:300
4386   St. Margaret's Bay 1:39.4
4381   Mahone Bay 1:38.9
4384   Pearl Is. to Cape LaHave 1:39
4211   Cape LaHave to Liverpool Bay 1:37.5
4230   Little Hope Is. to Cape St. Mary's 1:50
4240   Liverpool Hbr. to Lockeport Hbr. 1:60
4241   Lockeport to Cape Sable 1:60
4242   Cape Sable to Tusket Is. 1:60
4243   Tusket Is. to Cape St. Mary's 1:60
4010   Bay of Fundy (inner portion) 1:200
4011   Appr. to Bay of Fundy 1:300
4118   St. Mary's Bay 1:60
4396   Annapolis Basin 1:24
4116   Appr. to St. John 1:60
4340   Grand Manan 1:60

U.S. East Coast
13325   Quoddy Narrows to Petit Manan Is. 1:80
13312   Frenchman & Blue Hill Bays & apprs. 1:80
13302   Penobscot Bay and apprs. 1:80
    13315 Deer Is. Thoro. and Casco Pass. 1:20
    13308 Fox Islands Thorofare 1:15
13288   Monhegan Is. to Cape Elizabeth 1:80
    13290 Casco Bay 1:40
13286   Cape Elizabeth to Portsmouth 1:80
    13283 Cape Neddick Hbr. to Isles of Shoals 1:20, Portsmouth Hbr. 1:10
13278   Portsmouth to Cape Ann 1:80, Hampton Harbor 1:30
    13281 Gloucester Hbr. and Annisquam R. 1:10
13267   Massachusetts Bay 1:80
    13275 Salem and Lynn Harbors 1:25, Manchester Harbor 1:10
    13276 Salem, Marblehead & Beverly Hbrs. 1:10
    13270 Boston Harbor 1:25
13246   Cape Cod Bay 1:80
    13253 Plymouth, Kingston and Duxbury Hbrs. 1:20, Greens Hbr. 1:10
    13236 Cape Cod Canal and approaches 1:20

13237   Nantucket Sound and approaches 1:80
    13241 Nantucket Island 1:40
    13242 Nantucket Harbor 1:10
13218   Martha's Vineyard to Block Island 1:80
    13230 Buzzards Bay 1:40, Quicks Hole 1:20
    13233 Martha's Vineyard 1:40, Menemsha Pond 1:20
    13221 Narragansett Bay 1:40
13205   Block Island Sound and apprs. 1:80
    13214 Fishers Island Sound 1:20
    13212 Approaches to New London Hbr. 1:20
    13219 Point Judith Harbor 1:15
    13217 Block Island 1:15
    13211 North Shore of Long Is. Sd.-Niantic Bay & Vicinity 1:20
    13213 New London Harbor and Vicinity 1:10, Bailey Point to Smith Cove 1:5
    13209 Block Is. Sd. & Gardiners Bay, Long Is., 1:40
12354   Long Island Sound - eastern part 1:80
    12375 Connecticut R. -Long Is. Sd. to Deep R. 1:20
    12374 Duck Island to Madison Reef 1:20
    12373 Guilford Hbr to Farm R. 1:20
    12371 New Haven Harbor 1:20
    12370 Housatonic R. and Milford Hbr. 1:20
    12362 Port Jefferson & Mt. Sinai Hbrs. 1:10
12363   Long Island Sound - western part 1:80
    12369 Stratford to Sherwood Pt. 1:20
    12368 Sherwood Pt. to Stamford Hbr. 1:20
    12367 Greenwich Pt. to New Rochelle 1:20
    12366 L.I. Sd. and East R., Hempstead Hbr. to Tallman Is. 1:20
    12365 L.I. Sd. S. Shore, Oyster and Huntington Bays 1:20
12353   Shinnecock Light to Fire Island Light 1:80
    12352 Shinnecock B. to E. Rockaway In. 1:20; 1:40
    12339 East R. - Tallman I. to Queensboro Br. 1:10
    12331 Raritan Bay and Southern Part of Arthur Kill 1:15
    12327 New York Harbor 1:40

12335 Hudson & E. Rs. - Governors I. to 67 St. 1:10

12326 Appr. to N.Y., Fire I. to Sea Girt 1:80

12350 Jamaica Bay and Rockaway In. 1:20

12323 Sea Girt to Little Egg In. 1:80

12324 Sandy Hook to Little Egg Harbor 1:40

12318 Little Egg In. to Hereford In. 1:80, Absecon In. 1:20

12316 Little Egg Harbor to Cape May 1:40

12304 Delaware Bay 1:80

12311 Delaware R.- Smyrna R. to Wilmington 1:40

12312 Wilmington to Philadelphia 1:40

12277 Chesapeake and Delaware Canal, Salem R. Ext. 1:20

12214 Cape May to Fenwick I. 1:80

12211 Fenwick I. to Chincoteague In.1:80, Ocean City In. 1:20

12210 Chincoteague In. to Great Machipongo In. 1:80, Chincoteague In. 1:20

12221 Chesapeake Bay Entrance 1:80

12222 Cape Charles to Norfolk Hbr. 1:40

12224 Cape Charles to Wolf Trap 1:40

12228 Pocomoke and Tangier Sds. 1:40

12231 Tangier Sd.-northern part 1:40

12225 Wolf Trap to Smith Point 1:80

12230 Smith Point to Cove Point 1:80

12263 Cove Point to Sandy Point 1:80

12273 Sandy Point to Susquehanna River 1:80

12233 Chesapeake Bay to Piney Pt. 1:40

12274 Head of Chesapeake Bay 1:40

12278 Appr. to Baltimore Harbor 1:40

12286 Piney Pt. to Lower Cedar Pt. 1:40

12288 Lower Cedar Pt. to Mattawoman Cr. 1:40

12289 Mattawoman Cr. to Georgetown 1:40; Washington Hbr. 1:20

12282 Severn and Magothy Rs. 1:25

12253 Norfolk Hbr. and Elizabeth R. 1:20

12254 Cape Henry to Thimble Shoal Lt. 1:20

12256 Chesapeake Bay-Thimble Shoal Channel 1:20

12245 Hampton Roads 1:20

12207 Cape Henry to Currituck Bch. Lt. 1:80

12205 Cape Henry to Pamlico Sd. incl. Albemarle Sd. 1:40; 1:80

12204 Currituck Beach Lt. to Wimble Shoals 1:80

11555 Cape Hatteras-Wimble Shoals to Ocracoke In. 1:80

11548 Pamlico Sd.-western part 1:80

11550 Ocracoke In. and N. Core Sd. 1:40

11545 Beaufort In. and S. Core Sd. 1:40, Lookout Bight 1:20

11544 Portsmouth I. to Beaufort incl. Cape Lookout Shoals 1:80

11543 Cape Lookout to New R. 1:80

11539 New R. In. to Cape Fear 1:80

11536 Appr. to Cape Fear R. 1:80

11535 Little R. In. to Winyah Bay Entr.1:80

11531 Winyah Bay to Bulls Bay 1:80

11532 Winyah Bay 1:40

11521 Charleston Hbr. & Appr. 1:80

11513 St. Helena Sd. to Savanna R. 1:80

11509 Tybee I. to Doboy Sd. 1:80

11502 Doboy Sd. to Fernandina 1:80

11488 Amelia I. to St. Augustine 1:80

11486 St. Augustine Lt. to Ponce de Leon In. 1:80

11484 Ponce de Leon In. to Cape Canaveral 1:80

11476 Cape Canaveral to Bethel Shoal 1:80

11474 Bethel Shoal to Jupiter In. 1:80

11466 Jupiter In. to Fowey Rocks 1:80, Lake Worth In. 1:10

11469 Straits of FL.Fowey Rks., Hillsboro Inlet to Bimini Is. Bahamas 1:100

11462 Fowey Rocks to Alligator Reef 1:80

11452 Alligator Reef to Sombrero Key 1:80

11442 Sombrero Key to Sand Key 1:80

11439 Sand Key to Rebecca Shoal 1:80

11438 Dry Tortugas 1:30

To find your nearest NOAA Chart Agent: http://aeronav.faa.gov/agents.asp

Print-on-Demand Nautical Charts for up to date NOAA charts: www.OceanGrafix.com

NOAA has posted all 1000+ of its US Nautical charts on the internet. The charts can be viewed using any internet browser. Each chart is up-to-date with the most recent Notices to Mariners. Use these online charts as a ready reference or planning tool, not for actual navigation. Online charts can be viewed at: www.nauticalcharts.noaa.gov/mcd/OnLineViewer.html

Ferry Service Information

🚗 Vehicle reservations may be required

CANADA

Bay ferries 🚗, between St. John, NB and Digby, NS, (877) 762-7245. www.nfl-bay.com/

MAINE

-- For all Maine Ferry Service information: www.exploremaine.org/ferry/

Maine State Ferry Service, Rockland ME, (207) 596-5400. General Schedule Information
www.maine.gov/mdot/msfs/

    Frenchboro Ferry 🚗 between Frenchboro and Bass Harbor, Bass Harbor (207) 244-3254

    Islesboro Ferry 🚗 between Islesboro (207) 734-6935 and Lincolnville (207) 789-5611

    Matinicus Island Ferry 🚗 between Matinicus Island and Rockland (207) 596-5400

    North Haven Ferry 🚗 between North Haven (207) 867-4441 and Rockland (207) 596-5400

    Vinalhaven Ferry 🚗 between Vinalhaven (207) 596-5450 and Rockland (207) 596-5400

Monhegan Island Ferry between Monhegan Island and Port Clyde (207) 372-8848. www.monheganboat.com

MASSACHUSETTS

Steamship Authority 🚗 www.steamshipauthority.com/ssa/

    Between Woods Hole, MA (508) 548-3788 (information), (508) 477-8600 (car reservation) and Martha's
    Vineyard (508) 693-9130

    Between Hyannis and Nantucket. Hyannis (508) 771-4000, Fast Ferry (508) 495-3278 (passenger
    reservation), Nantucket (508) 228-0262

Island Queen Ferry between Falmouth and Oak Bluffs, M.V. (508) 548-4800. www.islandqueen.com

SeaStreak between New Bedford and Martha's Vineyard (866) 683-3779. www.mvexpressferry.com/

Hy-Line Cruises, Nantucket, Martha's Vineyard, Hyannis loop (800) 492-8082. www.hy-linecruises.com/

-- For more Martha's Vineyard ferry information: www.mvol.com/directory/transportation/Ferries/

Freedom Cruise Line between Harwichport and Nantucket (508) 432-8999. www.nantucketislandferry.com

Cuttyhunk Is. Ferry between Cuttyhunk and New Bedford (508) 992-0200. www.cuttyhunkferryco.com/

RHODE ISLAND

Vineyard Fast Ferry between Quonsett, RI and M.V. (401) 295-4040. www.vineyardfastferry.com

Block Island Ferry 🚗 and High Speed Ferry between Block Island and Jerusalem (Pt. Judith)
    (866) 783-7996. www.blockislandferry.com/

Jamestown-Newport Ferry (401) 423-9900. www.jamestownnewportferry.com/

CONNECTICUT

Cross Sound Ferry 🚗 between New London, CT (860) 443-5281, Orient Pt., L.I., NY (631) 323-2525.
    www.longislandferry.com

Block Is. Express Ferry between New London (860) 444-4624 and Block Is. (401) 466-2212.
    www.goblockisland.com

Fishers Island Ferry 🚗 between Fishers Island, NY (631) 788-7744 and New London, CT (860) 442-
    0165. Car reservations must be made online only: www.fiferry.com

Bridgeport-Port Jefferson Ferry 🚗 between Port Jefferson, NY (631) 473-0286 and Bridgeport, CT
    (888) 443-3779. www.88844ferry.com

NEW YORK

Long Island *is served by two year-round ferry lines that cross Long Island Sound connecting Port Jefferson
to Bridgeport, CT and Orient Point to New London, CT. For more information for ferries in Long Island
Sound (Fire Island, Shelter Island, etc.):* www.webscope.com/li/ferries.html

Seastreak serving NY, NJ, Martha's Vineyard, MA. (800) 262-8743. http://seastreak.com/

NEW JERSEY

Cape May-Lewes Ferry 🚗 between Cape May, NJ (800) 643-3779 and Lewes, DE.,
    www.capemaylewesferry.com

NORTH CAROLINA

-- To request all NC ferry routes and schedules (800) 293-3779 or download at www.ncferry.org,
    including **Hatteras Inlet Ferry** 🚗 between Hatteras and Ocracoke; **Cedar Island and Swan
    Quarter Ferry** between Cedar Island and Swan Quarter

Where To Buy The Eldridge Tide and Pilot Book

CANADA

NOVA SCOTIA

Halifax
Binnacle Yachting Equip.

ONTARIO

Toronto
Nautical Mind Bookstore

UNITED STATES

MAINE

Bar Harbor
Sherman's Book Store
Bath
Bath Bookshop
Maine Maritime Museum
Blue Hill
Blue Hill Books
Boothbay
Sherman's Book Store
Brooksville
Buck's Harbor Marine
Camden
Owl and Turtle Bookshop
Sherman's of Camden
Damariscotta
Maine Coast Book Shop
Freeport
Sherman's Book Store
Kittery
Jackson Hardware
Northeast Harbor
F.T. Brown Co.
Portland
Chase Leavitt
Hamilton Marine
West Marine
Rockland
Reading Corner
Searsport
Hamilton Marine
South Freeport
Brewer's Yacht Yard
Stonington
Billings Diesel & Marine
Yarmouth
Landing Boat Supply

NEW HAMPSHIRE

Keene
Toadstool Bookshop
Portsmouth
West Marine
Seabrook
West Marine

MASSACHUSETTS

Beverly Farms
The Bookshop

Boston
Boston Hbr. Sailing Club
Boston Sailing Center
Boxell's Chandlery
Braintree
West Marine
Buzzards Bay
Red Top Sporting Goods
Cataumet
Kingman Yachting Center **
Parker's Boat Yard **
Chatham
Mayflower Shop
Stage Harbor Marine
Yellow Umbrella Books
Cohasset
Buttonwood Books
Concord
Concord Book Shop
Cotuit
Peck's Boats
Cuttyhunk
Island Market
Danvers
West Marine
Dedham
West Marine
Duxbury
Bayside Marine Corp.
East Sandwich
Titcomb's Bookshop
Edgartown
Edgartown Books
Edgartown Marine
Fairhaven
West Marine
Falmouth
Booksmith-Falmouth Plaza
Eastman's Sport & Tackle
MacDougalls **
West Marine
Gloucester
The Bookstore
Building Center of Gloucester
Harwichport
Allen Harbor Marine Serv.
Hingham
RNR Marine
Hyannis
Sea Sports
Sports Port
West Marine
Marblehead
The Forepeak
F. L. Woods
Lynn Marine Supply Co.
Marblehead Outfitters
Marblehead
Spirit of '76 Bookstore
West Marine
Marion
Book Stall
Burr Bros. Boats **
Mashpee
Bosun's Marine
Market Street Bookshop

Nantucket
Mitchell's Book Corner
Nantucket Ship Chandlery
New Bedford
Bay Fuels, Inc.
C.E. Beckman Co.
CMS Enterprises Inc.
Hercules SLR
Lighthouse Marine Supply
Luzo Fishing Gear
New Bedford Ship Supply
West Marine
Newton
Charles River Canoe & Kayak
North Dartmouth
Baker Books
North Falmouth
N. Fal. Hardware & Marine
Oak Bluffs
Dick's Bait and Tackle
Orleans
Booksmith/Musicsmith
Goose Hummock Shop
Nauset Marine
Peabody
West Marine
Plymouth
West Marine
Provincetown
Land's End Mar. Supply
Quincy
Marina Bay **
Raynham
Slip's Capeway Marine
Rockport
Toad Hall Bookstore
Sandwich
Sandwich Ship Supply
Scituate
Front St. Bookshop
Front St. Marine
Seekonk
West Marine
South Dartmouth
Cape Yachts
Concordia Co. **
South Yarmouth
Riverview Bait & Tackle
Swansea
Newsbreak, Inc.
Vineyard Haven
Bunch of Grapes Book Store
Gannon & Benjamin Marine
Martha's Vineyard Fuel & Ice
Martha's Vineyard Shipyard **
West Marine
Wakefield
Boats and Motors
West Dennis
Sportsman's Landing
Westport
Partners Village Store
Weymouth
Monahan's Marine
Winthrop
Woodside Hardware
Woburn
West Marine

RHODE ISLAND

Barrington
Barrington Books
Brewer Cove Haven Marina **
Bristol
Herreshoff Museum
Jamestown Distributors
East Greenwich
West Marine
Jamestown
Conanicut Marine **
Jamestown Boat Yard
Narragansett
R.I. Engine Co.
West Marine
Newport
Newport Nautical Supply
NV.Charts
West Marine
Portsmouth
Ship's Store & Rigging
Providence
New England Marine Supply
Warren
West Marine
Wakefield
Ram Point Marina
Snug Harbor Marina
Westerly
Other Tiger

CONNECTICUT

Branford
Birbarie Marine Sales
West Marine
Clinton
Riverside Basin Marina
West Marine
Deep River
Brewer Deep River Marina
Essex
Boatique
Fairfield
West Marine
Guilford
Breakwater Books
Madison
R. J. Julia Booksellers
Milford
Ship's Store@MilfordBoat-
Works
Mystic
Bank Square Books
Brewer Yacht Yard
Mystic Seaport Stores
West Marine
New London
West Marine
Noank
Spicer's Marinas
Norwalk
West Marine
Old Lyme
Kellog Marine Supply

Old Saybrook
Emerson & Cook Book Co.
North Cove Outfitters, Inc.
River's End Tackle
West Marine
Portland
William J. Petzold Inc.
Portland Boat Works
South Norwalk
Rex Marine Center
Stamford
Brewer Yacht Haven
Hathaway Reiser & Raymond
Landfall Navigation **
West Marine
Stonington
Wilcox Marine Supply
Union Beach
J. T.'s Fly Shop
Waterford
Defender Industries
Hillyer's Tackle Shop

NEW YORK

Babylon
West Marine
Brooklyn
Bernie's Fishing Tackle
City Island, Bronx
Bridge Marine Supply
Cold Spring
Hudson Valley Outfitters
Connelly
Rondout Yacht Basin
East Hampton
Seacoast Enterprises
Three Mile Harbor Boat Yard
Fisher's Island
Pirate's Cove Marine
Freeport
Fred Chall Marine
Freeport Marine Supply
Garden City
West Marine
Glen Cove
Brewer Glen Cove Marina
Greenport
Brewer Stirling Hbr.
Marina
S.T. Preston **
White's Hardware
Huntington
Book Revue
Coney's Marine
West Shore Marina
Island Park
West Marine
Latham
West Marine
Montauk
Montauk Marine Basin
New Rochelle
Post Marine Supply
West Harbor Yacht Service
New York City
New York Kayak Co.
New York Nautical **
West Marine

Northport
Tidewater Marine
Oyster Bay
Nobman's Marine Hdwre.
Oyster Bay Marine Supply
Seawanhaka Boat Yard
Patchoque
West Marine
Port Jefferson
West Marine
Port Washington
Brewer Capri Marina
West Marine
Riverhead
West Marine
Sag Harbor
Emporium Hardware
Henry Persan & Sons
Sag Harbor Yacht Yard
Saugerties
Atlantic Kayak Tours
Shelter Island
Coecles Harbor Marina
Southold
Wego Bait and Tackle
Staten Island
Nautical Chart Supply
Upper Nyack
Julius Peterson
Westhampton Beach
Chesterfield Assoc.
West Haverstraw
West Marine
West Islip
West Marine

NEW JERSEY

Atlantic Highlands
West Marine
Bayonne
Ken's Marina Services
Belford
Mariner's Mart
Brick
West Marine
Cape May
South Jersey Marina
West Marine
Cherry Hill
West Marine
Eatontown
West Marine
Lodi
West Marine
Mt. Laurel
West Marine
Paramus
Ramsey Outdoor
Perth Amboy
West Marine
Somers Point
West Marine
South Amboy
Lockwood Boat Works
West Marine
Toms River
West Marine

PENNSYLVANIA

Bensalem
West Marine
Philadelphia
Pilot House Nautical Books
Pittsburgh
West Marine

DELAWARE

Bear
West Marine
New Castle
West Marine
Rehoboth Beach
West Marine

MARYLAND

Annapolis
Fawcett Boat Supplies
West Marine
Baltimore
Maryland Nautical Sales
West Marine
Chester
West Marine
Easton
West Marine
Edgewater
West Marine
Georgetown
Georgetown Yacht Basin
Glen Burnie
West Marine
Havre de Grace
West Marine
Middle River
West Marine
Ocean City
West Marine
Pasadena
West Marine
Rock Hall
West Marine
Solomons
West Marine
Tracey's Landing
West Marine

VIRGINIA

Alexandria
West Marine
Deltaville
West Marine
Glen Allen
West Marine
Gloucester Point
West Marine
Hampton
West Marine
Norfolk
W.T. Brownley
West Marine
Portsmouth
Tidewater Yacht Agency

Virginia Beach
West Marine
Woodbridge
West Marine

NORTH CAROLINA

Beaufort
N.C. Maritime Museum
Scuttlebutt
Charlotte
West Marine
Cornelius
West Marine
Morehead City
DeeGee's
West Marine
Nags Head
West Marine
New Bern
West Marine
Oriental
West Marine
Raleigh
US Power Squadron
West Marine
Washington
West Marine
Wilmington
West Marine

SOUTH CAROLINA

Charleston
West Marine
Cherry Grove
West Marine
Hilton Head
West Marine

GEORGIA

Brunswick
West Marine
Savannah
West Marine

FLORIDA

Daytona
West Marine
Delray
West Marine
Ft. Lauderdale
Bluewater Books & Charts
West Marine
Fort Pierce
West Marine
Hollywood
West Marine
Jacksonville
West Marine
Key Largo
West Marine
Lake Park
West Marine
Marathon
West Marine

Miami
West Marine
North Palm Beach
West Marine
Port Charlotte
West Marine
St. Augustine
West Marine
Stuart
West Marine
Tequesta
West Marine
Titusville
West Marine
Vero Beach
West Marine
West Palm Beach
West Marine

ILLINOIS

Momence
Baker & Taylor

COLORADO

Fort Collins
Geomart

ELDRIDGE 2013

can be purchased from the following on line:

Amazon.com

US Power Squadron members can purchase on line at:
www.shopusps.org/books.html

Available at most East Coast West Marine. For store locations in each state see website:
WestMarine.com

www.robertwhite.com
www.eldridgetide.com

For a current list of
ELDRIDGE dealers please visit:

Robert E. White Instruments **
www.eldridgetide.com
www.robertwhite.com

** *Advertisers in book. Refer to page 271.*

Twenty Questions for a Rainy Day
(Answers on pages indicated)

1. What does MMSI stand for, and why do you need one? (p. 241)
2. T/F: At the peak of high or low tide, the current begins to reverse direction. (p. 6)
3. T/F: The Summer Solstice marks the longest day of the year. (general knowledge)
4. Your ship's bell clock strikes 1 bell. What 3 times could it be? (p. 204)
5. T/F: A sailing vessel has more right-of-way than a vessel fishing with nets. (p. 7)
6. T/F: Neap tides occur about twice a month. (p. 199)
7. Hurricane Carol was a Category 3 storm in 1954. How many categories are there on the Saffir-Simpson scale? (p. 252)
8. Why did the leadsman "arm" the hollow bottom of the sounding lead with tallow before heaving it? (p. 198)
9. T/F: An overtaking vessel is to sound one short blast if it intends to pass on the other vessel's starboard side. (p. 7)
10. T/F: Long contrails indicate dry weather aloft. (p. 247)
11. T/F: Perigee indicates the closest point of orbit, and apogee the farthest. (p. 236)
12. Your height of eye is 6 ft. Can you see a 70' headland from 10 n.m. away? (p. 219)
13. Why do you suppose that mariners began to use compass cards graduated in degrees after centuries of using traditional points? (see p. 223; answer is for you to deduce)
14. One degree of latitude equals 60 n.m. Is the same true for longitude? (p. 262)
15. A sling psychrometer shows a wet bulb reading 14° below the dry bulb reading of 60°F. What is the dew point? Are you likely to experience fog? (p. 256)
16. T/F: A yacht club burgee can be flown while racing. (p. 216)
17. T/F: A red and white buoy marks safe water, a fairway or mid-channel. (p. 213)
18. T/F: Because portable toilets are not subject to MSD regulations, you can dump their contents anywhere. (p. 260)
19. T/F: VHF Channel 16 is for initiating a call, but only to establish a different working channel. (p. 238)
20. International signal flag "R" has what meaning? (p. 218)

It helps to say, "I saw it in the **ELDRIDGE TIDE & PILOT BOOK.**"

INDEX TO ADVERTISERS

For more information about **ELDRIDGE** advertisers and links to their websites visit:
www.eldridgetide.com

BEAUTIFUL FUN ACCESSIBLE
FRIENDLY TASTY CLOSE TO YOU
KINGMAN YACHT CENTER
.com

Summer is here-
Where are you?

- Overnight Guest Slips & Moorings
- Complimentary Launch Service
- Mile-long Beach and Hiking Trails
- A Beautiful, Natural Harbor Off Buzzards Bay
- Shops, Galleries and Provisions On-site
- World Famous Chart Room Restaurant
- Reciprocity at the Kingman Yacht Club
- Events Every Weekend All Summer Long
- Saturday Nite Boat-in Movies
- Immaculate Showers and Laundry
- Competitively Priced Gas and Diesel Fuel
- Complete Marine Repair Facility
- Yacht Brokerage and SeaTow on Site
- *Brand New Every Day!*

Shipyard Lane
Cataumet (Cape Cod) MA 02534
Tel: 508 / 563-7136
Fax: 508 / 563-6493
KingmanYachtCenter.com